# SYMBOLIC LOGIC

# SYMBOLIC LOGIC

BY

CLARENCE IRVING LEWIS

AND

COOPER HAROLD LANGFORD

Second Edition

DOVER PUBLICATIONS, INC.

Published simultaneously in Canada by McClelland and Stewart Limited.

This new Dover edition, first published in 1959, is a corrected and unabridged republication of the First Edition, to which Clarence Irving Lewis has added Appendix III.

Manufactured in the United States of America

Dover Publications, Inc.
180 Varick Street
New York 14, New York

# PREFACE

Symbolic logic does not presuppose either logic or mathematics. Since it is itself logic in an exact form, and since it constitutes the theoretical foundation of mathematics in general, it is capable of being understood without previous training in either of these branches. The purpose of this book is that of providing an introduction to the subject in a form which is consonant with this priority of symbolic logic and which makes minimum demands on the reader in the way of previous technical training. However, discussion is not confined to the elements. The first five chapters cover those topics which lend themselves most easily to beginning study, and certain later portions are so written that a general view of the topic in question may be gained without technical difficulties. Chapters I–V follow the same general plan of development as Lewis's *Survey of Symbolic Logic* (now out of print); but the subject-matter is here somewhat more condensed, and certain parts which are mathematically but not logically important have been omitted. An attempt has been made to keep the exposition as simple and clear as possible, and the extreme of rigor has sometimes been sacrificed to this consideration.

The remainder of the book is independent of Chapters I–V, and these may well be omitted by readers who already have an elementary knowledge of symbolic logic. Chapter VI provides a new foundation for the subject, by the more rigorous 'logistic' method, an understanding of which is essential for those who wish to go on to the study of *Principia Mathematica* and similar contemporary treatises. Chapters VII and VIII presuppose this preceding development, but are not themselves essential to the understanding of anything further in the book. These chapters touch upon some of the most difficult and abstract questions connected with the subject, but they are also of the first importance for the nature and purport of symbolic logic. Chapter IX contains a general development of the theory of propositions, and it, together with VI, provides a foundation for the subsequent discussion. In XI and XII, application is made of the logic of propositions to the theory of sets of postulates, the first of these chapters giving a general and elementary treatment, and the second dealing with a special topic not appropriate to an introductory discussion. Postulational technique is important at many points in mathematics; but the fundamental conceptions that occur are logical rather than mathematical in a strict sense, and we have confined the discussion very largely to developing and illustrating these conceptions. In Chapter XIII we endeavor to give some account of the paradoxes that have arisen in logic and of the bearing of these paradoxes on logical theory.

The choice of characters for symbolic logic continues to be a problem, since no set of universally accepted conventions has as yet emerged. In this book we have adopted the symbols used by Whitehead and Russell in *Principia Mathematica* wherever the idea to be symbolized coincides precisely with one which occurs in that work. For the rest, we have been guided partly by historical precedents and partly by considerations of convenience and clarity.

Chapters I–VIII and Appendix II have been written by Mr. Lewis; Chapters IX–XIII and Appendix I, by Mr. Langford. Each of us has given the other such assistance as he might; but final responsibility for the contents of the chapters is as indicated.

Important assistance in the writing of the book has been received from many sources. Our indebtedness to the publications of Professors Lukasiewicz and Tarski, as well as to Ludwig Wittgenstein's *Tractatus Logico-philosophicus*, will be evident in Chapters VII and VIII; and we have drawn freely upon the writings of Professor E. V. Huntington for materials used in Chapters XI and XII. We are also indebted, especially in Chapters IX, XI, and XII, to the published and unpublished views of Professor H. M. Sheffer, with whom both of us have been associated. Dr. William T. Parry of Harvard University has made extensive and important contributions to the development of Chapter VI. Our indebtedness to him for work contained in Appendix II, and also to Dr. M. Wajsberg of the University of Warsaw, to Mr. Paul Henle of Harvard University, and to the published monograph of Professor Oskar Becker, is more specifically acknowledged in that place. Proof of one critical theorem in Chapter VI was provided by Professor S. L. Quimby, of Columbia University. Dr. David Wilson has read Chapters VII and VIII in manuscript, correcting several mistakes; and Dr. Kurt E. Rosinger has read the whole of Chapters I–VIII, verifying the proofs and eliminating numerous errors.

C. I. Lewis.
C. H. Langford.

## EDITOR'S INTRODUCTION

The present volume is a most unusual one and meets a long-felt and important need. Recent years have witnessed a considerable growth of interest in symbolic logic in the United States. Americans have made important contributions to the subject, but these contributions have usually been in detached articles in the journals. Professor Lewis's *A Survey of Symbolic Logic* in 1918 traced the history of the most important developments of symbolic logic from Leibniz to the twentieth century and discussed the relation of a "system of strict implication" to systems of material implication and to the classic algebra of logic. But there has been no authoritative treatment of the field of symbolic logic in the light of developments of the last fifteen years, a treatment which would present constructively the achievements in symbolic logic by one who had taken part in making the achievements possible and believed heartily in the importance of this branch of philosophic thought. This present volume is just such a treatment. Its two authors have had wide experience both as teachers of symbolic logic in the classroom and as writers on important problems in the field. Their experience is adequate guarantee that the book will prove useful and stimulating to many readers.

The book is suited to two classes of readers. On the one hand it offers, especially in Chapters I to V, an introduction to symbolic logic for elementary students. It here presents the material in a form available for classroom use as well as for private study; and it orients the reader by furnishing a discussion of the connection between symbolic logic and traditional non-symbolic logic. On the other hand, it contains sections that develop original material or bring together important material by other authors which has not previously been assembled and has not appeared except in technical articles. These sections concern the specialist; but as they raise problems of general and often controversial nature, they will also appeal to many others who have philosophical interests. A complete list of the topics of these sections is not needed here and can easily be derived from table of contents and index. But it should be noted that the distinction between the logic of intensions and the logic of extensions, presented earlier by Professor Lewis in his *Survey*, is carried out with new force and is made basic to the discussion of the entire volume. The conception of consistency between propositions, which, it is contended, is incapable of definition in terms of material implication, is thus brought into harmony with the current mathematical conception. A new operation, converse substitution, is presented that makes possible the proof of existence propositions. The matrix method is developed further than ever before and is employed to defend the idea of plurality of logical truth; that is, it is so handled as to free the question of mathematical validity from ordinary logical intuitions and thus supports the supposition of a variety of non-Aristotelian logics akin to the variety of non-Euclidean geometries. The issues here raised and argued lead on to problems concerning the nature of logic and truth and other fundamental philosophical ideas.

The present volume is therefore fitted to introduce the elementary student to the field of symbolic logic and to interest the specialist. And its bearings on broader problems of logic make it a challenge to serious students of philosophy.

STERLING P. LAMPRECHT,
*General Editor*.

AMHERST COLLEGE.

# CONTENTS

# SYMBOLIC LOGIC

# CHAPTER I

## INTRODUCTION

The study with which we are concerned in this book has not yet acquired any single and well-understood name. It is called 'mathematical logic' as often as 'symbolic logic,' and the designations 'exact logic,' 'formal logic,' and 'logistic' are also used. None of these is completely satisfactory; all of them attempt to convey a certain difference of this subject from the logic which comes down to us from Aristotle and was given its traditional form by the medieval scholastics. This difference, however, is not one of intent: so far as it exists, it is accidental or is due to the relative incompleteness and inexactness of the Aristotelian logic. The use of symbols has characterized logic from the beginning—for example, in the use of letters to represent the terms of the syllogism. Symbolic logic merely extends this use in ways which are required by, or conducive to, clarity and precision. Thus the subject matter of symbolic logic is merely *logic*—the principles which govern the validity of inference.

It is true, however, that the extended use of symbolic procedures opens up so much which is both new and important that symbolic logic becomes an immensely deeper and wider study than the logic of tradition. New implications of accepted logical principles come to light; subtle ambiguities and errors which have previously passed unnoticed are now detected and removed; new generalizations can be made which would be impossible of clear statement without a compact and precise symbolism: the subject of logic becomes broader in its scope, and enters into new relationships with other exact sciences, such as mathematics.

That such changes should come about as a result of a more auspicious mode of representation, will not be surprising if we consider a little the parallel case of mathematics. Arithmetic, at first, lacked any more appropriate medium than that of ordinary language. Ancient Greek mathematicians had no symbol for zero, and used letters of the alphabet for other numbers.

As a result, it was impossible to state any general rule for division —to give only one example. Operations which any fourth-grade child can accomplish in the modern notation, taxed the finest mathematical minds of the Age of Pericles. Had it not been for the adoption of the new and more versatile ideographic symbols, many branches of mathematics could never have been developed, because no human mind could grasp the essence of their operations in terms of the phonograms of ordinary language.

Thus while the subject-matter which symbolic logic studies is merely that of logic in any form, it does not follow that there will be no important results of it which are not possible in the older terms. Quite the contrary. As a result of improved methods of notation, we find ourselves in a lively period of new discoveries: an old subject, which has been comparatively stagnant for centuries, has taken on new life. We stand to-day, with respect to logic, where the age of Leibnitz and Newton stood with respect to what can be accomplished in terms of number; or where Riemann and Lobatchevsky stood with respect to geometry. A wealth of new facts dawn upon us, the significance of which we are only beginning to explore. The manner in which the forms and principles characterizing inference admit of extension and generalization, and the connection between such general principles and the more special procedures of other exact sciences —these are matters concerning which the last four decades have produced more light than any preceding four centuries since Aristotle. It is probable that the near future will see further results of equal or greater importance.

As might be expected, it is difficult to mark any historical beginning of the distinctively symbolic method in logic. It is of the essence of the subject that its laws hold for all terms—or all propositions, or all syllogisms, or all conditional arguments, and so on. Thus it is natural that, in the expression of its laws, some indifferent terms or 'variables' should be used to designate those elements of any piece of reasoning which are irrelevant to the validity of it. Even the traditional logic, recognizing that only the *form* of the syllogism (its mood and figure) need be considered in determining its validity, most frequently used letters—*A*, *B*, *C*, or *S*, *M*, and *P*—for the terms of the propositions composing the syllogistic argument. Frequently, also, it was recognized that, in a hypothetical argument, validity did not depend upon the particularity or content of the statements connected by the 'if-then' relation. This recognition was exhibited by throwing the argument into such form as,

If *A*, then *B*.
But *A* is true.
Hence *B* is true.

Here symbols are used for propositions, which is a step beyond the use of them for substantive terms.

However, the advances which the symbolic procedure makes upon traditional methods hardly begin to appear until symbols are used not only for terms, or for propositions, but for the relations between them. Here and there, through the history of logic in the middle ages, one finds such symbols for the logical relations, used as a kind of shorthand. But it is not until the time of Leibnitz that this use of symbolism begins to be studied with a view to the correction and extension of traditional logic.

Leibnitz may be said to be the first serious student of symbolic logic, though he recognized the *Ars Magna* of Raymond Lull and certain other studies as preceding him in the field. Leibnitz projected an extended and Utopian scheme for the reform of all science by the use of two instruments, a universal scientific language (*characteristica universalis*) and a calculus of reasoning (*calculus ratiocinator*) for the manipulation of it. The universal language was to achieve two ends; first, by being common to all workers in the sciences, it was to break down the barriers of alien speech, achieving community of thought and accelerating the circulation of new scientific ideas. Second, and more important, it was to facilitate the process of logical analysis and synthesis by the substitution of compact and appropriate ideograms for the phonograms of ordinary language.

In part, this second point of Leibnitz's scheme was thoroughly sound: the superiority of ideograms to phonograms in mathematics is an example; and science since Leibnitz's time has made continuously increasing use of ideograms devised for its particular purposes. But in part his program was based upon more dubious conceptions. He believed that all scientific concepts were capable of analysis into a relatively few, so that with a small number of original or undefined ideas, all the concepts that figure in science could be defined. The manner of such definition would, then, exhibit the component simple ideas used in framing a complex notion, somewhat as the algebraic symbolization of a product may exhibit its factors, or the formula of a chemical substance will exhibit its component elements and their relation. Finally, he conceived that the reasoning of science could then be carried out simply by that analysis and synthesis of concepts to which such ideographic symbolisms would supply the clue.

To criticize and evaluate these conceptions of Leibnitz would be a complicated business which is impossible here. Briefly, we may note that the kind of development which he here envisages for science in general coincides to a remarkable extent with the logistic analysis now achieved in mathematics and beginning to be made in other exact sciences. On the other hand, the notion that such development is the major business of science reflects that exaggeration of the rôle of deduction, as against induction, which is characteristic of Leibnitz's rationalistic point of view. And the conception that the primitive or simple concepts which would be disclosed by a just analysis of scientific ideas are uniquely determinable is not supported by developments since his time. Instead, we find that a plurality of possible analyses, and of primitive concepts, is the rule.

Leibnitz himself is more important for his prophetic insight, and for his stimulation of interest in the possibilities of logistic, than for any positive contribution. Though the projects above referred to were formulated before he was twenty years old,[1] and though he made innumerable studies looking toward the furtherance of them, the results are, without exception, fragmentary. The reformation of all science was, as he well understood, an affair which no man could accomplish single-handed. Through-

[1] They constitute the subject of his first published work, the intent of which is set forth on the title page as follows: "Dissertatio de Arte Combinatoria; In qua ex Arithmeticæ fundamentis Complicationum ac Transpositionum Doctrina novis præceptis exstruitur, & usus ambarum per universum scientiarum orbem ostenditur; nova etiam Artis Meditandi, seu Logicæ Inventionis semina sparguntur." This book was published in Leipzig, in 1666.

out his life he besought the coöperation of learned societies to this end, but of course without success.

The *calculus ratiocinator* was a more restricted project. If this had been accomplished, it would have coincided with what we now know as symbolic logic. That is, it would have been an organon of reasoning in general, developed in ideographic symbols and enabling the logical operations to be performed according to precise rules. Here Leibnitz achieved some degree of success; and it would be interesting to examine some of his results if space permitted. He did not, however, lay a foundation which could be later built upon, because he was never able to free himself from certain traditional prepossessions or to resolve the difficulties which arose from them.[2]

Other scholars on the Continent were stimulated by these studies of Leibnitz to attempt a calculus of logic. The best of such attempts are those of Lambert and Holland.[3] But all of them are inferior to Leibnitz's own work.

The foundations from which symbolic logic has had continuous development were laid in Great Britain between 1825 and 1850. The signally important contribution was that of the mathematician George Boole; but this was preceded by, and in part resulted from, a renewed interest in logic the main instigators of which were Sir William Hamilton and Augustus De Morgan. Hamilton's "quantification of the predicate" is familiar to most students of logic. "All *A* is *B*" may mean "All *A* is *all B*" or "All *A* is *some B*." The other traditional forms of propositions may be similarly dealt with so as to render the 'quantity' of the predicate term unambiguous. The idea is a simple one, and really of little importance for exact logic: no use has been made of it in recent studies. It was not even new: Leibnitz, Holland, and others had previously quantified the predicate. But often the historical importance of an idea depends less upon its intrinsic merit than upon the stimulus exercised upon other minds; and this is a case in point. The sole significance of quantification of

[2] For example, the conception that every universal proposition implies the corresponding particular; and the conception that the relations of terms in extension are always inversely parallel to their relations in intension.

[3] See Bibliography at the end of the chapter.

the predicate for exact logic is that it suggests a manner in which propositions can be treated as equations of terms; and the mere representation of propositions as equations keeps the thought of an analogy between logic and mathematics before the mind. This single fact, together with Hamilton's confident assumption that now at last logic was entering upon a new period of development, seems to have been a considerable factor in the renewal of logical studies in Great Britain.

Augustus De Morgan brought to the subject of logic a more versatile mind than Hamilton's, and one trained in mathematics. He, too, quantified the predicate, and he gives an elaborate table of the thirty-two different forms of propositions which then arise, with rules of transformation and statement of equivalents. His contributions are, in fact, literally too numerous to mention: one can only select the most important for brief notice. One of the most prophetic is his observation that the traditional restriction to propositions in which the terms are related by some form of the verb 'to be,' is artificial and is not dictated by any logical consideration. He wrote, "The copula performs certain functions; it is competent to those functions . . . because it has certain properties which validate its use. . . . Every transitive and convertible relation is as fit to validate the syllogism as the copula '*is*,' and by the same proof in every case. Some forms are valid when the relation is only transitive and not convertible; as in 'give.' Thus if $X — Y$ represent $X$ and $Y$ connected by a transitive copula, *Camestres* in the second figure is valid, as in

'Every $Z — Y$, No $X — Y$, therefore No $X — Z$.'"[4]

He also investigated many other non-traditional modes of inference, suggested new classifications, and indicated novel principles which govern these. In so doing, he provided the first clear demonstration that logical validity is not confined to the traditional modes and traditional principles.

De Morgan also made numerous and extended studies of the hitherto neglected logic of relations and relative terms. These investigations dropped from sight in the next twenty-five years—that is, until they were renewed by Charles S. Peirce. But as

[4] *Transactions of the Cambridge Philosophical Society*, X, 177.

we now know, this study of relations in general is that extension of logic which is most important for the analysis of mathematics. De Morgan was first in this field, and he correctly judged the significance of it. In the concluding paper of one series of studies, he remarks:

"And here the general idea of relation emerges, and for the first time in the history of knowledge, the notion of relation and *relation of relation* are symbolized. And here again is seen the scale of graduation of forms, the manner in which what is difference of form at one step of the ascent is difference of *matter* at the next. But the relation of algebra to the higher developments of logic is a subject of far too great extent to be treated here. It will hereafter be acknowledged that, though the geometer did not think it necessary to throw his ever-recurring *principium et exemplum* into imitation of *Omnis homo est animal, Sortes est homo*, etc., yet the algebraist was living in the higher atmosphere of syllogism, the unceasing composition of relation, before it was admitted that such an atmosphere existed." [5]

To-day we can observe how accurately this trenchant prophecy has been fulfilled.

George Boole was really the second founder of symbolic logic. His algebra, first presented in 1847, is the basis of the whole development since. Intrinsically it may be of no greater importance than the work of De Morgan; and Leibnitz's studies exhibit at least an equal grasp of the logical problems to be met. But it is here for the first time that a complete and workable calculus is achieved, and that operations of the mathematical type are systematically and successfully applied to logic.

Three fundamental ideas govern the structure of Boole's system: (1) the conception of the operation of "election" and of "elective symbols"; (2) the "laws of thought" expressible as rules of operation upon these symbols; and (3) the observation that these rules of operation are the same which would hold in an algebra of the numbers 0 and 1.

The elective symbol $x$ represents the result of electing all the $x$'s in the universe: that is, $x$, $y$, $z$, etc., are symbols for classes, conceived as resulting from an operation of selection.

This operation of electing can be treated as analogous to algebraic multiplication. If we first select (from the world of

[5] *Loc. cit.*, p. 358.

existing things) the $x$'s, and then from the result of that select the $y$'s, the result of these two operations in succession, represented by $x \times y$, or $x\,y$, will be the class of things which are both $x$'s and $y$'s.

It is obvious that the order of operations of election does not affect the result: whether we first select the $x$'s and then from the result of that select the $y$'s; or first select the $y$'s and from the result of that select the $x$'s; in either case we have the class 'both $x$ and $y$.' That is, 'both $x$ and $y$' is the same as 'both $y$ and $x$':

$$x\,y = y\,x.$$

The law that if $x = y$, then $z\,x = z\,y$, will also hold: if $x$ and $y$ are identical classes, or consist of the same members, then 'both $z$ and $x$' will be the same class as 'both $z$ and $y$.'

Repetition of the same operation of election does not alter the result: selecting the $x$'s and then from the result of that selecting again all the $x$'s merely gives the class of $x$'s. Thus

$$x\,x = x, \qquad \text{or} \qquad x^2 = x.$$

This is the one fundamental law peculiar to this algebra, which distinguishes it from the usual numerical algebra.

Boole uses the symbol $+$ as the sign of the operation of aggregation, expressible in language by "Either . . . or . . . ." The class of things which are either $x$'s or $y$'s (but not both) is represented by $x + y$. This operation is commutative:

$$x + y = y + x.$$

The class of things which are either $x$ or $y$ coincides with the class which are either $y$ or $x$.

The operation of election, or 'multiplication,' is distributive with respect to aggregation, or 'addition':

$$z(x + y) = z\,x + z\,y.$$

That is, if we select from the class $z$ those things which are either $x$ or $y$, the result is the same as if we select what is 'either both $z$ and $x$ or both $z$ and $y$.'

The operation of 'exception' is represented by the sign of subtraction: if $x$ is 'men' and $y$ is 'Asiatics,' $x - y$ will be 'all men except Asiatics' or 'all men not Asiatics.'

Multiplication is associative with respect to subtraction: that is,

$$z(x - y) = z\,x - z\,y.$$

'White (men not Asiatics)' are the class 'white men except white Asiatics.'

Boole accepts the general algebraic principle that

$$-y + x = x - y,$$

regarding it as a convention that these two are to be equivalent in meaning.

The number 1 is taken to represent 'the universe' or 'everything,' and 0 to represent 'nothing,' or the class which has no members. These interpretations accord with the behavior of 0 and 1 in the algebra:

$$1 \cdot x = x.$$

Selecting the $x$'s from the universe gives the class $x$.

$$0 \cdot x = 0.$$

Selecting the $x$'s from the class 'nothing' gives 'nothing.'

The negative of any class $x$ is expressible as $1 - x$; the 'not-$x$'s' are 'everything except the $x$'s.' Thus what is '$x$ but not $y$' is $x(1 - y)$. And the law holds that

$$x(1 - y) = x \cdot 1 - x\,y = x - x\,y.$$

What is '$x$ but not $y$' coincides with the class '$x$ excepting what is both $x$ and $y$.'

The aggregate or sum of any class and its negative is 'everything':

$$x + (1 - x) = x + 1 - x = 1.$$

Everything is either $x$ or not-$x$. The product of a class and its negative is 'nothing':

$$x(1 - x) = x - x^2 = x - x = 0.$$

Nothing is both $x$ and not-$x$. This equation holds because of the previous law, $x^2 = x$.

An important consequence of the law, $x + (1 - x) = 1$, is that, for any class $z$,

$$z = z \cdot 1 = z[x + (1 - x)] = z\,x + z(1 - x).$$

That is, the class $z$ coincides with 'either both $z$ and $x$ or both $z$ and not-$x$.' This law allows any class-symbol $x$ to be introduced into any expression which does not originally contain it—a procedure of great importance in manipulating this algebra, and one which accords with a fundamental logical fact.

It will be evident from the foregoing that at least a considerable number of the operations of ordinary algebra will be valid in this system. The results will be logically interpretable and logically valid. Leibnitz and his Continental successors had all of them tried to make use of the mathematical operations of addition and subtraction; and most of them had tried to use multiplication and division. Always they ran into insuperable difficulties—though they did not always recognize that fact. Boole's better success rests upon four features of his procedure: (1) he thinks of logical relations in extension exclusively, paying no regard to relations of intension; (2) he restricts 'sums,' $x + y$, to the adjunction of classes *having no members in common;* (3) in the law $x\,x = x$, he finds, at one and the same time, the distinctive principle of his algebra and the representation of a fundamental law of logic; (4) in hitting on the analogy of 1 to 'everything' and 0 to 'nothing,' he is able to express such basic logical principles as the laws of Contradiction and of the Excluded Middle Term in terms of the algebra.

The second of these features was later eliminated from his system—to its advantage—but for the time being it contributed to his success by avoiding certain difficulties which otherwise arise with respect to addition. These difficulties had been the principal reason for the failure of previous attempts at a mathematical calculus of logic. In good part, Boole's better success is due to superior ingenuity rather than greater logical acumen. This ingenuity is particularly evident in his meeting of certain difficulties which have, perhaps, already occurred to the reader:

(1) What will be the meaning of an expression such as $1 + x$? Recognizing that terms of a sum must represent classes having no members in common, and that no class $x$ can be related in that manner to the class 'everything' except the class 0, we might say that $1 + x$ has no meaning unless $x = 0$. But in the

manipulation of equations, expressions of this form can occur where $x = 0$ is false.

(2) What about $x + x$? Since the terms of this sum violate the requirement that they have no common members, such an expression will not be logically interpretable. But expressions of this form are bound to occur in the algebra. How are they to be dealt with?

(3) If the operations of ordinary algebra are to be used, then division will appear, as the inverse of multiplication. But if $x\,y = z$, and hence $x = z/y$, can the 'fraction' $z/y$ be interpreted; and is the operation logically valid?

Boole surmounts these difficulties, and many others which are similar, by clever devices which depend upon recognizing that his system is completely interpretable as an algebra in which the "elective symbols" are restricted to the numbers 0 and 1. The distinctive law of the system is $x\,x = x$. This holds of 0 and 1, and of no other numbers. Suppose, then, we forget about the logical interpretation of the system, and treat it simply as a numerical algebra in which the variables, or literal symbols, are restricted to 0 or 1. All the ordinary laws and operations of algebra may then be allowed. As Boole says,

> " But as the formal processes of reasoning depend only upon the laws of the symbols, and not upon the nature of their interpretation, we are permitted to treat the above symbols, $x$, $y$, $z$, as if they were quantitative symbols of the kind described. We may in fact lay aside the logical interpretation of the symbols in the given equation; convert them into quantitative symbols, susceptible only of the values 0 and 1; perform upon them as such all the requisite processes of solution; and finally restore them to their logical interpretation. . . .
>
> "Now the above system of processes would conduct us to no intelligible result, unless the final equations resulting therefrom were in a form which should render their interpretation, after restoring to the symbols their logical significance, possible. There exists, however, a general method of reducing equations to such a form." [6]

With the devices which make up this general method we need not trouble ourselves. It is, as a matter of fact, always possible to secure a finally interpretable result, even though the intermediate stages of manipulation involve expressions which are

[6] *Laws of Thought*, pp. 69–70.

not interpretable; and such results are always in accord with the logical significance of the original data, representing a valid inference. It is not, of course, satisfactory that a logical calculus should involve expressions and operations which are not logically interpretable; and all such features of Boole's Algebra were eventually eliminated by his successors. But even in its original form, it is an entirely workable calculus.

The main steps of the transition from Boole's own system to the current form of Boolean Algebra may be briefly summarized.

W. S. Jevons did not make use of the algebraic methods, but formulated a procedure for solving logical problems by manipulations of the "logical alphabet," which represents what we shall later come to know as 'the expansion of 1'; that is, all possible combinations of the terms involved in any problem. Since this method of Jevons's, though entirely workable and valid, is less simple than the algebraic, and is no longer in use, our chief interest is in two differences of Jevons from Boole which were adopted later as modifications of Boole's algebra.

Jevons interprets $a + b$ to mean 'either $a$ or $b$ *or both.*' Logically it is merely a matter of convention whether we choose to symbolize by $a + b$ Boole's meaning of 'either-or' as mutually exclusive, or this non-exclusive meaning of Jevons. But adoption of the wider, non-exclusive meaning has three important consequences which are advantageous: it removes any difficulty about expressions of the form $a + a$; it leads to the law $a + a = a$, and it introduces the possibility of a very interesting symmetry between the relation of logical product, $a\,b$, and the logical sum, $a + b$. As we have seen, Boole's interpretation of the relation $+$ has the consequence that $a + a$ is logically uninterpretable. When such expressions occur in his system, they are treated by ordinary algebraic laws, which means that $a + a = 2a$; and such numerical coefficients must be got rid of by devices. If the other meaning be chosen, $a + a$ has meaning, and $a + a = a$ states an obvious principle. With this principle in the system, numerical coefficients do not occur. Thus the two laws, $a\,a = a$ and $a + a = a$, together result in the elimination of all notion of number or quantity from the algebra. Also, when $a + b$ means 'either $a$ or $b$ or both,' the negative of $a\,b$, 'both $a$ and $b$,' is 'either not-$a$

or not-$b$,' $(1 - a) + (1 - b)$, or as it would be written in the current notation, $-a + -b$. This law had already been stated by De Morgan, and, as we shall see, is a very important principle of the revised Boolean algebra.

John Venn and Charles S. Peirce both followed the practice of Jevons in this matter; and no important contributor since that time has returned to Boole's narrower meaning of $a + b$, or failed to recognize the law $a + a = a$.

Also, Boole's system was modified by eliminating the operations of subtraction and division. Peirce included these in certain of his early papers, but distinguished a relation of "logical subtraction" and "logical division" from "arithmetical subtraction" and "arithmetical division" (within a Boolean system). Later he discarded these operations altogether, and they have not been made use of since. As Peirce points out, $a/b$ is uninterpretable unless the class $a$ is contained in the class $b$. Even when this is the case, $a/b$ is an ambiguous function of $a$ and $b$, which can have any value between the 'limits' $a\,b$ and $a + (1 - b)$, or $a + -b$. When $a + b$ is given the wider meaning 'either $a$ or $b$ or both,' $a - b$, defined as the value of $x$ such that $a = b + x$, is also an ambiguous function. Nothing is lost in the discarding of these two operations: anything expressible by means of them can likewise be expressed—and better expressed—in terms of the relations of logical product and logical sum alone. The only remaining use of either is in the function 'negative of.' The negative of $a$, which Boole expressed by $1 - a$, is now written $-a$; and it does not behave, in the algebra, like a minus quantity.

Peirce added a new relation, the inclusion of one class in another; "All $a$ is $b$," now symbolized by $a \subset b$. This is not a mathematical alteration of the algebra, since the same relation is expressible in Boole's terms as $a(1 - b) = 0$. But it is an obvious advantage that this simplest and most frequent of logical relations should be simply represented.

These changes, then, mark the development from Boole's own system to the algebra of logic as we now know it: (1) substitution of the meaning 'either $a$ or $b$ or both' for 'either $a$ or $b$ but not both' as the relation symbolized by $a + b$; (2) addition of the law, $a + a = a$, eliminating numerical coefficients; (3) as a result of the two preceding, the systematic connection of sums and products, according to De Morgan's Theorem; (4) elimination of the operations of subtraction and division; (5) addition of Peirce's relation, $a \subset b$. The changes (1), (2), and (4) together result in the disappearance from the algebra of all expressions and operations which are not logically interpretable. Other and less fundamental changes, consisting mostly of further developments which do not affect the mathematical character of the system, had also been introduced, principally by Peirce and Schröder. The resulting system, given its definitive form by Schröder, in 1890, is the subject of the next chapter.

The next stage in the development of the subject is the bringing together of symbolic logic and the methodology of rigorous deduction, as exhibited in pure mathematics. This turns principally upon development of the logic of propositions and propositional functions, and the logic of relations. Two lines of research, more or less independent, lead up to this. Starting from beginnings made by Boole himself, Peirce and Schröder developed the logic of propositions, propositional functions, and relations, up to the point where these approximate to a calculus which is adequate to the actual deductive procedures exemplified by mathematics. Peano and his collaborators, in the *Formulaire de mathématiques*, began at the other end. They took mathematics in its ordinary deductive form and rigorously analyzed the processes of proof which they found in such deductions. By symbolizing the logical relations upon which proof depends, they gave mathematics the 'logistic' form, in which the principles of logic actually become the vehicles of the demonstration. These general logical principles, set forth in the earlier sections of the *Formulaire*, coincide, to a degree, with the logical formulæ resulting from the work of Peirce and Schröder; but it was found necessary to make certain important additions. (Frege also had developed arithmetic in the logistic form, at an earlier date, and had made most penetrating analyses of the logic of mathematics. But Frege's work passed unnoticed until 1901, when attention was called to it by Mr. Bertrand Russell.)

Boole had indicated a second interpretation of his algebra. In this second interpretation, any term $a$ is taken to represent the times when (or cases in which) the proposition $a$ is true. The negative $1 - a$ or $-a$, will then represent the times, or cases, when the proposition $a$ is false; $a \times b$, or $a\,b$, will represent the cases in which $a$ and $b$ are both true; and $a + b$, the cases in which one of the two, $a$ and $b$, is true. The entire algebra will then hold for the logical relations of propositions. This will be true whether we take the system in its original form, or as modified by Schröder; with the sole fundamental difference that, in the former case, $a + b$ must be interpreted as the times when $a$ or $b$ *but not* both are true, whereas in the latter case it represents the times when $a$ or $b$ *or* both are true.

However, we should recognize to-day that a statement which is sometimes true and sometimes false is not a proposition but a 'propositional function.' Thus the interpretation of the algebra made by Boole is in reality for propositional functions rather than propositions; or more accurately, Boole makes both applications, not distinguishing them, but providing a discussion which strictly applies only to functions. Peirce and Schröder distinguished these two. The entire algebra applies to *both*. But it is a distinguishing feature of a proposition, as against a propositional function, that if it is ever true, it is always true, and if it is ever false, then it is always false. In other words, a proposition is either definitely true or definitely false; while a propositional function may be sometimes true and sometimes false. Since in the algebra, $a = 1$ will mean "The class of cases in which $a$ is true is *all* cases" and $a = 0$ will mean "$a$ is true in *no* case," $a = 1$ represents "$a$ is true," and $a = 0$ represents "$a$ is false." Thus when the distinction is made between propositions and propositional functions, the whole of the algebra holds of both, but there is an *additional* law holding of propositions, but not of propositional functions: "If $a \neq 0$, then $a = 1$."

Peirce and Schröder made the distinction in question. They developed the calculus of propositions, incorporating this additional principle. And they developed the calculus of propositional functions, incorporating the ideas "$a$ is sometimes true," "$a$ is always true," "$a$ is sometimes false," and "$a$ is always false." The result of symbolizing these conceptions, and developing the laws which hold of them, is a considerable expansion of the calculus of propositional functions beyond what can be symbolized in terms of the Boolean algebra. These matters are to be discussed in Chapters IV and V. Though the calculuses there given are not precisely those of Peirce and Schröder, and though the method is not quite the same, these differences are not fundamental. We shall, therefore, omit further discussion of the subject here. What is important for understanding the development of symbolic logic is to remember that substantially such calculuses as are given in Chapters IV and V were at hand in the period when Peano and his collaborators began their work.

The aim of the *Formulaire de mathématiques* is stated in the opening sentence of the Preface: "Le Formulaire de Mathématiques a pour but de publier les propositions connues sur plusiers sujets des sciences mathématiques. Ces propositions sont exprimées en formules par les notation de la Logique mathématique, expliquées dans l'Introduction au Formulaire."

The authors had before them, on the one hand, mathematics in the ordinary but non-logistic deductive form. It was by this time (1895) generally recognized as the ideal of mathematical form that each branch of the subject should be derived from a small number of assumptions, by a rigorous deduction. It was also recognized that pure mathematics is abstract; that is, that its development is independent of the nature of any concrete empirical things to which it may apply. If, for example, Euclidean geometry is true of our space, and Riemannian geometry is false of space, this fact of material truth or falsity is irrelevant to the mathematical development of Euclid's system or of Riemann's. As it became customary to say, the only truth with which pure mathematics is concerned is the truth that certain postulates imply certain theorems. The emphasis which this conception throws upon the *logic* of mathematics, is obvious: the logic of it is the *truth* of it; no other kind of truth is claimed for pure mathematics.

On the other hand, Peano and his collaborators had before them the developed logic of Peirce and Schröder, which had now become a sufficiently flexible and extended system to be capable (almost) of representing all those relations which hold amongst the assumed entities of mathematical systems, by virtue of which postulates deductively give rise to theorems. It becomes, therefore, an obvious step to use the notations of symbolic logic for representing those relations, and those steps of reasoning, which, in the usual deductive but non-logistic form, are expressed in ordinary language.

Let us take a sample of mathematics as exhibited in the *Formulaire.*[7] For the development of arithmetic, the following undefined ideas are assumed:

"No signifies 'number,' and is the common name of 0, 1, 2, etc.

"0 signifies 'zero.'

"+ signifies 'plus.' If $a$ is a number, $a+$ signifies 'the number succeeding $a$.'"

In terms of these ideas, the following postulates are assumed:

"1·0 $\text{No} \in \text{Cls}$

"1·1 $0 \in \text{No}$

"1·2 $a \in \text{No} \,.\supset.\, a+ \in \text{No}$

"1·3 $s \in \text{Cls} \,.\, 0 \in s : a \in s \,.\supset_a.\, a+ \in s : \supset .\, \text{No} \in s$

"1·4 $a, b \in \text{No} \,.\, a+ = b+ :\supset.\, a = b$

"1·5 $a \in \text{No} \,.\supset.\, a+ -= 0$"

Let us translate these into English, thus giving the meaning of the symbolism:

1·0 No is a class, or 'number' is a common name.

1·1 0 is a number.

1·2 If $a$ is a number, then the successor of $a$ is a number; that is, every number has a next successor.

1·3 If $s$ is a class, and 0 is a member of $s$; and if, for all values of $a$, "$a$ is an $s$" implies "The successor of $a$ is an $s$," then 'number' belongs to the class $s$. In other words, every class $s$ which is such that 0 belongs to it, and that if $a$ belongs to it, the successor of $a$ belongs to it, is such that every number belongs to it.

1·4 If $a$ and $b$ are numbers, and the successor of $a$ is identical with the successor of $b$, then $a$ is identical with $b$. That is, no two distinct numbers have the same successor.

[7] See V, 27–32. The successive volumes of this work do not represent a continuous development but are, to an extent, different redactions or editions.

1·5 If $a$ is a number, then the successor of $a$ is not identical with 0.

The ideas of 'zero,' 0, and 'successor of $a$,' $a+$, being assumed, the other numbers are defined in the obvious way: $1 = 0+$, $2 = 1+$, etc.

Further ideas which are necessary to arithmetic are defined as they are introduced. Sometimes such definitions take a form in which they are distinguished from postulates only by convention. For example, the sum of two numbers, represented by the relation $+$ (which must be distinguished from the idea "successor of $a$,' $a+$) is defined by the two assumptions:

$$a \in \text{No} \,.\supset.\, a + 0 = a$$
$$a, b \in \text{No} \,.\supset.\, a + (b+) = (a + b)+$$

These are read: (1) If $a$ is a number, then $a + 0 = a$. (2) If $a$ and $b$ are numbers, then $a$ plus the successor of $b$, is the successor of ($a$ plus $b$).

The product of two numbers is defined by:

$$a, b \in \text{No} \,.\supset.\, a \times 0 = 0$$
$$a \times (b + 1) = (a \times b) + a$$

It will be fairly obvious how, from these assumptions, the laws governing the sums and products of numbers in general may be deduced.

With the detail of this first development of mathematics in the logistic form we cannot deal here. But several important facts which stand out may be noted. First, in translating the logical relations and operations actually exhibited in mathematical deductions from ordinary language to precise symbols, the authors of the *Formulaire* were obliged to note logical relations and to make distinctions which had previously passed unnoticed. One example of this occurs in the above: they had to distinguish the relation of a member of a class to the class itself (symbolized by $\epsilon$) from the relation of a subclass to the class including it—the relation of $a$ to $b$ when all $a$ is $b$. Another example is the fact that they had very frequently to make use of the idea of a singular subject, '*the* so-and-so,' distinguishing statements about such a subject from those about '*some* so-and-so' or about '*every* so-and-so.' The greater precision of the logistic method revealed the necessity for such distinctions, and for such additions to logical principles, through the fact that, in the absence of them, fallacious mathematical consequences would follow from perfectly good assumptions, or valid mathematical consequences, which should be capable of being proved, could not actually be deduced. Thus, starting with the aim to take mathematics as already developed, and to express the logical relations and operations of proof in an exact and terse symbolism, the authors found that they must first expand logic beyond any previously developed form. The head and front of mathematical logic is found in the calculus of propositional functions, as developed by Peirce and Schröder; but even this logic is not completely adequate to the task in hand.

A second result which stands out in the *Formulaire* is one which was already implicit in the recognition of pure mathematics as abstract and independent of any concrete subject-matter tc which it may apply. One of two things must be true of mathematics: either (1) it will be impossible to express the logic of it completely in terms of principles which are universally true—laws of logic which are true of every subject-matter, and not simply of deductions in geometry or in arithmetic—or (2) mathematics must consist of purely analytic statements. If the essential truth asserted by mathematics is that certain assumptions imply certain theorems, and if every such implication in mathematics is an instance of some universally valid principle of deduction (principle of logic), then there can be no step in a proof in mathematics which depends, for example, upon the particular character of our space, or the empirical properties of countable collections. That is to say, Kant's famous dictum that mathematical judgments are *synthetic a priori* truths, must be false. Such mathematical truths will be *a priori*, since they can be certified by logic alone. But they will be *a priori* precisely because they are *not synthetic*, but are merely instances of general logical principles.

As has been said, this is implicit in the previously recognized ideal of mathematics as at once deductive and abstract; for example, in the recognition that non-Euclidean geometry has the same mathematical validity as Euclid. The importance of the logistic development, in this connection, is that the possibility of achieving the logistic form depends upon the elimination from mathematics of any deductive step which is not simply an instance of some universal logical principle; and that symbolic representation is a very reliable check upon this purely analytic character of the demonstration. Thus the actual achievement of the logistic form is a concrete demonstration that it *is a priori* and that it is *not*, in any least detail, *synthetic*. Since this result is of immense importance for our understanding of mathematics, it constitutes one significant consequence of modern logistic.

This bearing of their work is one with which the authors of the *Formulaire* are not explicitly concerned. It had, however, been noted by Frege as a central point of his logistic development of arithmetic, and it was again recognized by the authors of *Principia Mathematica* as an essential bearing of their work.

The *Principia* may, in good part, be taken as identical in its aim with the *Formulaire*. So far as this is the case, the difference between the two works is much as might be expected between a first attempt at the realization of certain aims and a later work having the advantage of the earlier results. Peano had taken mathematics as he found it and translated it completely into precise symbols, and in so doing achieved a degree of explicit analysis and explicit formulation of principles which was not attained in the non-logistic form. The *Principia* goes further in the same direction: the analysis of mathematics is here more extended and more meticulous; the logical connections are more firmly made; the demonstrations achieve rigor in a higher degree.

However, there is also a shift of emphasis. The purpose is no longer that of a compendious presentation of mathematics in the neatest form; it is, rather, the demonstration of the nature of mathematics and its relation to logic. On this point, moreover, the authors of the *Principia* found it possible to go far beyond Peano in the derivation of mathematical truth from logical truth. In the *Formulaire*, as we have seen, the development of arithmetic requires, in addition to the general principles of logic, (1) the undefined ideas, 'number,' 'zero,' and 'the successor of (any given number)'; (2) five postulates in terms of these; (3) definitions of arithmetical relations or operations, such as + and ×, in a fashion which is hardly distinguishable from additional postulates. By contrast, in the *Principia*, the development of arithmetic is achieved in a fashion such that: (1) *All* ideas of arithmetic are defined; the only undefined ideas in the whole work being those of logic itself. 'Number,' 'zero,' 'the successor of,' the relations + and ×, and all other ideas of arithmetic are defined in terms of the *logical* ideas assumed, such as 'proposition,' 'negation,' and 'either-or.' This achievement is so extraordinary that one hardly credits it without examining the actual development in the *Principia* itself. (2) *Postulates of arithmetic are eliminated.* There are some exceptions to this, but exceptions which affect only a certain class of theorems concerning transfinite numbers. These exceptions are made explicit by stating the assumption made (there are two such) as an hypothesis to the theorem in question. With these somewhat esoteric exceptions, the propositions of mathematics are proved to be merely *logical consequences of the truths of logic itself.* When mathematical ideas have been defined—defined in terms of logical ideas—the postulates previously thought necessary for mathematics, such as Peano's postulates for arithmetic, which we have given, can all be *deduced.*[8]

Logic itself, in a form sufficient for all further demonstrations, is developed in the early sections. And it is developed in the same deductive fashion, from a small number of undefined ideas and a few postulates in terms of these. Thus it is proved that these primitive ideas and postulates for logic are the only assumptions required for the whole of mathematics.[9]

It is difficult or impossible to convey briefly the significance of this achievement. It will be increasingly appreciated, as time goes on, that the publication of *Principia Mathematica* is a

[8] The steps by which all Peano's five postulates are rendered unnecessary is clearly and interestingly explained in the first three chapters of Russell's *Introduction to Mathematical Philosophy*. This book is written without symbols, and is intelligible to any reader having an elementary knowledge of mathematics.

[9] Various fundamental ideas of geometry are developed in the later portion of Volume III of the *Principia;* but Volume IV, intended to complete that subject, has not appeared.

landmark in the history of mathematics and of philosophy, if not of human thought in general. Speculation and plausible theories of the nature and basis of mathematical knowledge have been put forward time out of mind, and have been confronted by opposed conceptions, equally plausible. Here, in a manner peculiarly final, the nature and basis of mathematical truth is definitely determined, and demonstrated *in extenso.* It follows logically from the truths of logic alone, and has whatever characters belong to logic itself.

Although contributions to logic and to mathematics in the logistic form have been more numerous in the period since *Principia Mathematica* than in any other equal period of time, it is hardly possible as yet to have perspective upon these. Three outstanding items may be mentioned. First, by the work of Sheffer and Nicod, considerably greater economy of assumption for any such development as that of the *Principia* has been achieved: two undefined ideas and five symbolic postulates of logic (as in the first edition of the *Principia*) have been replaced by one undefined idea and a single postulate. Second, the nature of logical truth itself has become more definitely understood, largely through the discussions of Wittgenstein. It is 'tautological'—such that any law of logic is equivalent to some statement which exhausts the possibilities; whatever is affirmed in logic is a truth to which no alternative is conceivable. From the relation of mathematics to logic, it follows that mathematical truth is similarly tautological.[10] Third, we are just beginning to see that logical truth has a variety and a multiform character hardly to be suspected from the restricted conceptions in terms of which, up till now, it has always been discussed. The work of Lukasiewicz, Tarski, and their school demonstrates that an unlimited variety of systems share that same tautological and undeniable character which we recognize in the logic of our familiar deductions. The logic which we readily recognize as such has been restricted to those forms which we have found useful in application—somewhat as geometry was restricted up to the time of Riemann and Lobatchevsky. The field of logical

[10] With the further detail of Wittgenstein's conceptions the present authors would not completely agree.

truth, we begin to understand, is as much wider than its previously recognized forms as modern geometry is wider than the system of Euclid.

The second and third of these recent developments will be considered in Chapters VII and VIII.

The relation of logic to other sciences than mathematics is an obvious subject for future investigation. The extent to which, and the sense in which, other sciences are, or may be, deductive, is a complex question. That as they become exact, they may also achieve deductive form, is rendered plausible by recent developments in physics, and by the studies of Carnap. Whether if they can thus become deductive, their basic ideas and principles can be analytically derived from logic, like those of mathematics, is a further and even more doubtful question. But we may be sure that the not too distant future will see developments bearing upon these questions.

## BIBLIOGRAPHY

(Works referred to in the preceding chapter)

Leibnitz, G. W., *Philosophische Schriften* (hrsg. v. C. I. Gerhardt, Berlin, 1887), Bd. VII; see esp. fragments XX and XXI.

Couturat, L., *La logique de Leibniz, d'après des documents inédits* (Paris, 1901).

Lambert, J. H., *Deutscher Gelehrter Briefwechsel*, 4 vols. (hrsg. v. Bernouilli, Berlin, 1781–1784).

——————, *Logische und philosophische Abhandlungen*, 2 vols. (hrsg. v. Bernouilli, Berlin, 1872–1887).

Hamilton, Sir W., *Lectures on Logic* (Edinburgh, 1860).

De Morgan, A., *Formal Logic; or, the Calculus of Inference, Necessary and Probable* (London, 1847).

——————, "On the Syllogism," etc., five papers, *Transactions of the Cambridge Philosophical Society*, Vols. VIII, IX, X (1846–1863).

——————, *Syllabus of a Proposed System of Logic* (London, 1860).

Boole, G., *The Mathematical Analysis of Logic* (Cambridge, 1847).

——————, *An Investigation of the Laws of Thought* (London, 1854; reprinted, Chicago, 1916).

Jevons, W. S., *Pure Logic, or the Logic of Quality Apart from Quantity* (London, 1864).

Venn, J., "Boole's Logical System," *Mind*, I (1876), 479–491.

——————, *Symbolic Logic*, 2d ed. (London, 1894).

PEIRCE, C. S., "Description of a Notation for the Logic of Relatives," *Memoirs of the American Academy of Arts and Sciences*, IX (1870), 317–378.

———, "On the Algebra of Logic," *American Journal of Mathematics*, III (1880), 15–57.

———, "On the Logic of Relatives," in *Studies in Logic by Members of Johns Hopkins University* (Boston, 1883).

———, "On the Algebra of Logic; a Contribution to the Philosophy of Notation," *American Journal of Mathematics*, VII (1885), 180–202.

FREGE, G., *Begriffschrift, eine der arithmetischen nachgebildete Formelsprache des reinen Denkens* (Halle, 1879).

———, *Die Grundlagen der Arithmetik* (Breslau, 1884).

———, *Grundgesetze der Arithmetik*, 2 vols. (Jena, 1893–1903).

SCHRÖDER, E., *Vorlesungen über die Algebra der Logik*, 3 vols. (Leipzig, 1890–1905).

———, *Abriss der Algebra der Logik*, in parts (hrsg. E. Müller, Leipzig, 1909).

PEANO, G., *Formulaire de mathématiques*, 5 vols. (Turin, 1895–1908).

RUSSELL, B. A. W., *Principles of Mathematics*, Vol. I (Cambridge, 1903).

WHITEHEAD, A. N., and RUSSELL, B. A. W., *Principia Mathematica*, 3 vols. (Cambridge, 1910–1913; 2d ed., 1925–1927).

SHEFFER, H. M., "A Set of Five Independent Postulates for Boolean Algebras," etc., *Transactions of the American Mathematical Society*, XIV (1913), 481–488.

NICOD, J., "A Reduction in the Number of the Primitive Propositions of Logic," *Proceedings of the Cambridge Philosophical Society*, XIX (1916), 32–42.

WITTGENSTEIN, L., *Tractatus Logico-philosophicus* (New York, 1922).

LUKASIEWICZ, J., "Philosophische Bemerkungen zu mehrwertigen Systemen des Aussagenkalküls," *Comptes Rendus des séances de la Société des Sciences et des Lettres de Varsovie*, XXIII (1930), Classe III, 51–77.

———, and TARSKI, A., "Untersuchungen über den Aussagenkalkül," *ibid.*, 1–21.

CARNAP, R., *Der logische Aufbau der Welt* (Berlin, 1928).

## CHAPTER II

### THE BOOLE–SCHRÖDER ALGEBRA

As we have seen in the preceding chapter, the algebra of logic founded by Boole was modified in important respects by his successors and given its definitive form by Schröder. This modified system is commonly called the Boolean Algebra, but the name Boole-Schröder Algebra is more appropriate in the circumstances. Not only is this algebra the historical basis of other developments in symbolic logic, but it forms the simplest and best introduction to the whole subject. Its laws are, for the most part, analogous to the simpler portions of ordinary algebra.

This system has many possible interpretations or applications, four of them being within the field of exact logic. For the sake of clarity, we shall regard it, in this chapter, as a calculus of classes. Its other interpretations will be explained in the chapters to follow.

In dealing with the logic of terms in propositions, either of two interpretations may frequently be chosen: the proposition may be taken as asserting a relation between the concepts which the terms connote, or between the classes which the terms denote. Thus "All men are mortal" may be taken to mean "The concept 'man' includes or implies the concept 'mortal,'" or it may be taken to mean "The class of men is contained in the class of mortals." The laws governing the relations of concepts constitute the logic of the *connotation* or *intension* of terms; those governing the relations of classes constitute the logic of the *denotation* or *extension* of terms. The laws of intension are, for the most part, parallel to those of extension; but the relations of given terms in intension are not, to the same extent, parallel to the relations of those same terms in extension. To avoid confusion, then, it will be important to remember that the logic which the algebra is here taken to represent is that of classes, or of terms in extension.

The ideas assumed are as follows:

(1) Any term of the system, $a$, $b$, $c$, etc., will represent some class of things, named by some logical term.

(2) $a \times b$ represents what is common to $a$ and $b$; the class composed of those things which are members of $a$ and members of $b$, both. For brevity, we shall ordinarily write $a \cdot b$ or $a\,b$ instead of $a \times b$. This relation may be read as '$a$ and $b$' or 'both $a$ and $b$.'

(3) The negative of $a$ will be written $-a$. This represents the class of all things which are not members of the class $a$; and may be read as 'not-$a$.'

(4) The unique class 'nothing' will be represented by 0. This is called the 'null class.'

The logic of the null class is one of those points concerning which it is important to remember that we are here dealing with the extension of terms. The term 'unicorn' and the term 'centaur' have very different connotations; they are not equivalent in intension. But the *class* of things denoted by 'unicorn' is the same as the *class* denoted by 'centaur'; namely, the class of nothing existent. Thus the extension of the two terms is identical: there is only one class 'nothing,' and all terms which name no existent thing denote this same class, 0.

(5) $a = b$ means "The terms $a$ and $b$ have the same extension; the class $a$ and the class $b$ have identically the same members."

Here again, we should remember that we are dealing with the extension of terms. 'Man' = 'featherless biped,' because although the two terms have different connotations, they denote precisely the same class of objects (barring the plucked chicken).

Other ideas to be introduced can be defined in terms of the above. Laws of the algebra will be numbered, in the decimal system. The definitions immediately following are the first such laws.

*1·01* $1 = -0$ Def.

That is, 1 represents the class of all things which are not members of the null class; thus 1 represents 'everything' or 'everything being considered' or 'the universe of discourse.'

*1·02* $a + b = -(-a \times -b)$ Def. $a \vee b \leftrightarrow \sim(\sim a \cdot \sim b)$

That is, $a + b$ represents the class of things which are either members of $a$ or members of $b$ (or members of both). Since $-a \times -b$ is the class of what is both not-$a$ and not-$b$ (neither $a$ nor $b$), the negative of this, $-(-a \times -b)$, will be what is either $a$ or $b$ or both.

*1·03* $a \subset b$ is equivalent to $a \times b = a$ Def.

This is the relation of class-inclusion: $a \subset b$ represents "$a$ is contained in $b$" or "Every $a$ is also a $b$." The class 'both men and mortals' is identical with the class 'men' if and only if all men are mortals.

It is important to note that $a \subset b$ will hold whenever $a = b$, This is consonant with usual modes of predication: for example. the class 'men' is identical with the class 'animals that laugh'; and "All men are animals that laugh" holds true. The relation $a \subset b$ is *not* analogous to $a < b$, but to $a \leqq b$.

The following laws are assumed to hold for all terms of the system:

*1·1* $a \times a = a$.

What is both $a$ and $a$, is identical with $a$. Since this law holds, there are no exponents in this algebra.

*1·2* $a \times b = b \times a$.

What is both $a$ and $b$ is the same as what is both $b$ and $a$.

*1·3* $a \times (b \times c) = (a \times b) \times c$.

Since this law holds, parentheses in 'products' can be omitted.

*1·4* $a \times 0 = 0$.

What is both $a$ and nothing, is nothing.

*1·5* If $a \times -b = 0$, then $a \subset b$.

If nothing is both $a$ and not-$b$, then all $a$ is $b$.

*1·6* If $a \subset b$ and $a \subset -b$, then $a = 0$.

If all $a$ is $b$ and all $a$ is not-$b$, then $a$ is a class which has no members.

All the laws of the algebra can be rigorously deduced from these three definitions and six postulates, given above. However, proofs will frequently be omitted here, or indicated only. A sufficient number will be given in full to make clear the manner of such derivation.

*2·1* If $a = b$, then $a\,c = b\,c$ and $c\,a = c\,b$.

*2·12* If $a = b$, then $a + c = b + c$ and $c + a = c + b$.

These two laws follow immediately from the meaning of the relation $=$.

*2·2* $a = b$ is equivalent to the pair, $a \subset b$ and $b \subset a$.

If $a = b$, then by 1·1, $a\,b = a\,a = a$; and $b\,a = b\,b = b$.
But by def. 1·03, $a\,b = a$ is $a \subset b$; and $b\,a = b$ is $b \subset a$.
Conversely, if $a\,b = a$ and $b\,a = b$, then [1·2]

$$a = a\,b = b\,a = b.$$

If two classes are identical, then each is contained in the other; and classes such that each is contained in the other are identical.

*2·3* $a \subset a$.

This follows from 2·2, since $a = a$. Every class is contained in itself: "All $a$ is $a$" holds for every $a$.

*2·4* $a\,b \subset a$ and $a\,b \subset b$.

By 1·1, 1·2, and 1·3, $(a\,b)a = a(a\,b) = (a\,a)b = a\,b$.
And by 1·03, $(a\,b)a = a\,b$ is $a\,b \subset a$.

What is both $a$ and $b$, is contained in $a$, and is contained in $b$.

*2·5* $a\,{-a} = 0 = {-a}\,a$.

By 2·4, $a\,{-a} \subset a$, and $a\,{-a} \subset {-a}$.
Hence by 1·6, $a\,{-a} = 0$.

This theorem states the Law of Contradiction: Nothing is both $a$ and not-$a$.

*2·6* $0 \subset a$.

By 1·2 and 1·4, $0 \cdot a = a \cdot 0 = 0$.
But [1·03] $0 \cdot a = 0$ is $0 \subset a$.

Theorem 2·6 states the principle that the null class is contained in every class. This follows from the law, $a \times 0 = 0$, together with the definition of the relation $a \subset b$. If we read this relation as "All $a$ is $b$," it is important to remember that we here deal with the extension of terms. If no $a$'s exist, then all the $a$'s there *are* will be anything you please. It is true in extension that "All centaurs are rational," "All centaurs are elephants," etc. This law, $0 \subset a$, is one of those which gives trouble if we attempt to apply the algebra to the logic of terms without making the distinction of extensional relations from intensional. In intension, "All centaurs are elephants" would mean "The connotation of 'centaur' includes or implies the connotation of 'elephant' "—and this would be false.

***2·7*** If $a \subset 0$, then $a = 0$.

[1·03] $a \subset 0$ is $a \cdot 0 = a$. But [1·4] $a \cdot 0 = 0$.

A class which is contained in the null class is itself null.

***2·8*** $a - b = 0$ is equivalent to $a\,b = a$, and to $a \subset b$.

If $a - b = 0$, then [1·5] $a \subset b$, and [1·03] $a\,b = a$.

And if $a\,b = a$, then $a - b = (a\,b) - b = a(b - b) = a \cdot 0 = 0$.

That is, "Nothing is $a$ but not $b$" is equivalent to "All $a$ is $b$." Postulate 1·5 assumes that $a - b = 0$ implies $a \subset b$. Theorem 2·8 proves that these two expressions are equivalent.

***2·81*** If $a \subset b$, then $a\,c \subset b\,c$, and $c\,a \subset c\,b$.

If $a \subset b$, or $a\,b = a$, then [2·1]

$$(a\,c)(b\,c) = (a\,b)(c\,c) = a(c\,c) = a\,c.$$

But [1·03] $(a\,c)(b\,c) = a\,c$ is $a\,c \subset b\,c$.

***2·9*** $-(-a) = a$.

[2·5] $-(-a) \cdot -a = 0$. Hence [2·8] $-(-a) \subset a$. (1)

[2·5] $-[-(-a)] \cdot -(-a) = 0$. Hence [2·8] $-[-(-a)] \subset -a$.

Hence [2·81] $a \cdot -[-(-a)] \subset a\, -a$.

But [2·5] $a - a = 0$. Hence [2·7] $a \cdot -[-(-a)] = 0$, and

[2·8] $a \subset -(-a)$. (2)

By 2·2, (1) and (2) together are equivalent to $-(-a) = a$.

"A double negative is equivalent to an affirmative": not-not-$a$ is $a$.

***2·91*** $a = -b$ is equivalent to $-a = b$.

If $a = -b$, then [2·9] $-a = -(-b) = b$.

And if $b = -a$, then $-b = -(-a) = a$.

*2·92* $a = b$ is equivalent to $-a = -b$.

The last three laws prove that $-a$ must be an unambiguous function of $a$: that is, a class can have only one negative, or the negatives of equals are equals.

The principle by which we have defined $a + b$,

$$a + b = -(-a -b),$$

is one form of De Morgan's Theorem, so called because the mathematician and logician, Augustus De Morgan, was the first to call attention to it. Other forms of this principle follow from the above definition, by 2·9, 2·91, and 2·92:

*3·1* $-(-a + -b) = a\ b$.

'Not-(either not-*a* or not-*b*)' is the same as 'both *a* and *b*.'

*3·11* $-(a + b) = -a -b$.

'Not-(either *a* or *b*)' is the same as 'not-*a* and not-*b*.'

*3·12* $-(a\ b) = -a + -b$.

'Not-(both *a* and *b*)' is the same as 'either not-*a* or not-*b*.'

*3·13* $-(a + -b) = -a\ b$.

*3·14* $-(-a\ b) = a + -b$.

*3·15* $-(-a + b) = a -b$.

*3·16* $-(a -b) = -a + b$.

In general terms, De Morgan's Theorem may be stated as follows: The negative of a product is the sum of the negatives of its terms; and the negative of a sum is the product of the negatives of its terms.

As a consequence of this principle, for every law of the algebra in terms of the relation of product, there is a corresponding law in terms of the relation of sum. For example, if as a special case of 1·1 we write,

$$-a -a = -a,$$

we shall have, by applying the principle [2·91] that the negatives of equals are equal,

$$-(-a -a) = -(-a).$$

Hence by De Morgan's Theorem, and 2·9, we shall have,

$$a + a = a.$$

This is the correlate of postulate 1·1, from which it is here derived. This correspondence, in the algebra, between principles in terms of $\times$ and principles in terms of $+$, is called the Law of Duality.

From the definition of 1, it follows that 0 and 1 are mutually negative terms:

*3·19* $0 = -1.$

From 3·19, it follows that if one of two principles which are related by the Law of Duality should involve the term 0, this will be replaced by 1 in the correlated principle; and if one of the two involves the term 1, this will be replaced by 0 in its correlate. For example, 2·5,

$$a - a = 0,$$

gives

$$-(a - a) = -0,$$

which is equivalent to

$$-a + a = 1.$$

We give, below, the correlates according to the Law of Duality of those principles which have already been stated in terms of the relation $\times$. Since these always follow from their correlates by some use of De Morgan's Theorem, together with the equivalences, $1 = -0$ and $0 = -1$, proofs may be omitted. The correlate from which the theorem is thus derived will be indicated, in square brackets, following it.

*3·2* $a + a = a.$ [1·1]

What is either *a* or *a*, is identical with *a*.

*3·3* $a + b = b + a.$ [1·2]

"Either *a* or *b*" is equivalent to "either *b* or *a*."

*3·31* $a + (b + c) = (a + b) + c.$ [1·3]

*3·4* $a + 1 = 1.$ [1·4]

What belongs either to the class *a* or to the class 'everything,' is identical with the class 'everything.'

***3·5*** $a + -a = 1.$ [2·5]

This is the Law of the Excluded Middle Term: Everything is either $a$ or not-$a$.

***3·6*** $-a + b = 1$ is equivalent to $a \subset b$. [2·8]

"Everything is either not-$a$ or $b$" is equivalent to "All $a$ is $b$."

The next two principles, concerning the relation $\subset$, are of fundamental importance:

***3·7*** If $a \subset b$ and $b \subset c$, then $a \subset c$.

[1·03] If $a \subset b$ and $b \subset c$, then $a\, b = a$ and $b\, c = b$.
Hence $a\, c = (a\, b)c = a(b\, c) = a\, b = a$.
But [1·03] $a\, c = a$ is $a \subset c$.

If all $a$ is $b$ and all $b$ is $c$, then all $a$ is $c$: the relation $\subset$ is transitive.

***3·8*** $a \subset b$ is equivalent to $-b \subset -a$.

[2·8] $a \subset b$ is equivalent to $a\, -b = 0$.
[2·9] $a\, -b = -(-a) \cdot -b = -b \cdot -(-a)$.
And [2·8] $-b \cdot -(-a) = 0$ is equivalent to $-b \subset -a$.

"All $a$ is $b$" is equivalent to "All not-$b$ is not-$a$." The terms of any relation $\subset$ may be transposed by negating both. This is called the Law of Transposition.

These last two laws are the fundamental principles underlying the validity of the syllogism. The logical copula 'is' may be replaced by *any* relation which is transitive and obeys the Law of Transposition: the validity of syllogistic reasoning will be unaffected by such substitution. As a matter of fact, the word 'is' in ordinary use expresses any one of a variety of logical relations, but only such as obey these two laws. Thus these principles might be said to define the logical meaning of the copula.

Other forms of the Law of Transposition are:

***3·81*** $a \subset -b$ is equivalent to $b \subset -a$.

***3·82*** $-a \subset b$ is equivalent to $-b \subset a$.

In terms of the relation $+$, there is another equivalent of $a \subset b$:

*3·83* $a + b = b$ is equivalent to $a \subset b$.

[3·8] $a \subset b$ is equivalent to $-b \subset -a$.

Hence [1·03] to $-a\, -b = -b$, and [2·92] to $-(-a\, -b) = b$.

And hence [1·02] $a \subset b$ is equivalent to $a + b = b$.

The next two theorems follow from previous principles by the Law of Transposition:

*3·9* $a \subset a + b$ and $b \subset a + b$.

[2·4] $-a\, -b \subset -a$ and $-a\, -b \subset -b$.

Hence [3·81] $a \subset -(-a\, -b)$ and $b \subset -(-a\, -b)$.

But [1·03] $-(-a\, -b) = a + b$.

*4·1* $a \subset 1$.

[2·6] $0 \subset -a$. Hence [3·8] $a \subset 1$.

It is well to note that this obvious principle, "Any class $a$ is contained in the class of 'everything,'" is equivalent to $0 \subset a$, "The null class is contained in every class"; and hence that the admission of either of these laws requires the other also.

*4·11* $a \cdot 1 = a$.

[4·1] $a \subset 1$, and [1·03] this is equivalent to $a \cdot 1 = a$.

What is common to $a$ and the class 'everything,' is $a$. The correlate of this by the Law of Duality is:

*4·12* $a + 0 = a$.

[4·11] $-a \cdot 1 = -a$. Hence [2·91] $a = -(-a \cdot 1) = a + 0$.

What is either $a$ or nothing, is $a$.

*4·13* $1 \subset a$ is equivalent to $a = 1$.

[1·03] $1 \subset a$ is $1 \cdot a = 1$. But [4·11] $1 \cdot a = a$.

Two further laws of the relation $\subset$ are frequently of use:

*4·2* If $a \subset b$ and $c \subset d$, then $a\,c \subset b\,d$.

[1·03] If $a \subset b$ and $c \subset d$, then $a\,b = a$ and $c\,d = c$.

Hence $a\,c \cdot b\,d = a\,b \cdot c\,d = a\,c$, or $a\,c \subset b\,d$.

*4·21* If $a \subset b$ and $c \subset d$, then $a + c \subset b + d$.

If $a \subset b$ and $c \subset d$, then [3·8] $-b \subset -a$ and $-d \subset -c$.

Hence [4·2] $-b\, -d \subset -a\, -c$, and [3·8] $-(-a\, -c) \subset -(-b\, -d)$.

But [1·03] $-(-a\, -c) = a + c$, and $-(-b\, -d) = b + d$.

If $a$ is contained in $b$ and $c$ is contained in $d$, then 'both $a$ and $c$' is contained in 'both $b$ and $d$,' and 'either $a$ or $c$' is contained in 'either $b$ or $d$.'

Since $a \cdot a = a$ and $a + a = a$, 4·2 and 4·21 have the corollaries:

*4·22* If $a \subset c$ and $b \subset c$, then $a + b \subset c$.

*4·23* If $a \subset b$ and $a \subset c$, then $a \subset b\, c$.

*4·24* If $a \subset b$, then $a\, c \subset b\, c$.

*4·25* If $a \subset b$, then $a + c \subset b + c$.

A principle which we shall find to be of importance later is the law that the product of any set of terms is always contained in their sum:

*4·3* $a\, b \subset a + b$.

[2·4] $a\, b \subset a$, and [3·9] $a \subset a + b$.

Hence [3·7] $a\, b \subset a + b$.

We turn now to laws which are of special importance in manipulating the algebra. The first of these is a general algebraic principle:

*4·4* $a(b + c) = a\, b + a\, c$.

What is '$a$, and either $b$ or $c$,' is the same as 'either $a$ and $b$ or $a$ and $c$.' This principle can be proved from previous theorems, but the proof is long and complex, and is omitted for that reason. This law, together with 1·2, has the consequence that all the laws of multiplication which hold of ordinary algebras hold also of this one, with the exception already noted that here $a \times a = a$. A corollary of 4·4 is:

*4·41* $(a + b)(c + d) = a\, c + b\, c + a\, d + b\, d$.

The next principle, called the Law of Absorption, is constantly of use for the purpose of simplifying expressions:

*4·5* $a + a\, b = a$.

[3·9] $a \subset a + a\, b$. (1)

[2·3] $a \subset a$, and [2·4] $a\, b \subset a$.

Hence [4·22] $a + a\, b \subset a$. (2)

[2·2] (1) and (2) are together equivalent to $a + a\, b = a$.

This law obviously extends to sums of any number of terms, if $a$ is a factor of each.

It is an extremely important property of this algebra that if a given expression does not involve a particular term or element, there is always an equivalent expression which does. That is, we can always introduce any element we please into any given expression. The principle which makes this possible is called the Law of Expansion:

***4·6*** $a = a(b + -b) = a\,b + a\,-b.$

$[3\cdot 5]\ b + -b = 1.$ And $[4\cdot 11]\ a\cdot 1 = a.$

As a consequence of this law, the universal class, 1, can always be expressed in whatever terms we choose. This is spoken of as 'expanding 1 for the elements $a, b, c, \ldots$':

***4·61*** $1 = (a + -a)(b + -b)(c + -c) \cdots$

$[3\cdot 5]\ 1 = a + -a.$

$[4\cdot 6]\ a + -a = (a + -a)(b + -b).$

And $(a + -a)(b + -b) = (a + -a)(b + -b)(c + -c).$

Etc., etc.

If 'the universe' be divided with respect to one element $a$, we have two divisions or subclasses:

$$1 = a + -a.$$

If it be divided with respect to two elements, we have four subclasses:

$$1 = (a + -a)(b + -b) = a\,b + a\,-b + -a\,b + -a\,-b.$$

For each added element introduced, the number of subclasses is multiplied by 2: thus division with respect to three elements gives eight subclasses; with respect to $n$ elements, $2^n$ subclasses.

Those who wish to use the algebra with facility should learn to write out such expansions readily, for any number of terms up at least to four.

There is an important point about the negative of given expressions, which has to do with this expansion of 1. Let us call an expression 'fully expanded' when every element which appears in the expression, or the negative of that element, appears in every term. Thus

$$a\, -b + -a\, b + -a\, -b$$

is fully expanded; $a$ or $-a$, and $b$ or $-b$, appears in every term. But

$$a + -a\, b$$

is not fully expanded; neither $b$ nor $-b$ appears in the first term. Thus the fully expanded expression which is equivalent to $a + -a\, b$ will be found by expanding the first term so as to introduce $b$:

$$a + -a\, b = a(b + -b) + -a\, b = a\, b + a\, -b + -a\, b.$$

And in general: To produce a fully expanded equivalent of any given expression, expand each term of that expression with respect to any element, or elements, not appearing in that term. The only short way of finding the negative of a complex expression requires that we should first give it this fully expanded form. The negative can then be found by the simple rule: The negative of any fully expanded expression is the remainder of the expansion of 1. For example, since

$$1 = a\, b + a\, -b + -a\, b + -a\, -b,$$

the negative of $a\, -b + -a\, b$ is $a\, b + -a\, -b$. The negative of $-a\, b$ is

$$a\, b + a\, -b + -a\, -b;$$

and so forth. If the given expression involves three elements, $a$, $b$, and $c$, then we make use of the expansion of 1 for these three terms:

$$1 = a\, b\, c + a\, b\, -c + a\, -b\, c + -a\, b\, c + a\, -b\, -c + -a\, b\, -c + -a\, -b\, c + -a\, -b\, -c.$$

Then if, for example, we wish to find the negative of

$$a\, b\, -c + a\, -b\, c + -a\, -b\, c,$$

this will be, in accordance with our rule,

$$a\, b\, c + -a\, b\, c + a\, -b\, -c + -a\, b\, -c + -a\, -b\, -c.$$

We shall make use of this rule later in the chapter.

Another corollary of 4·6 is:

**4·62** $a + b = a + -a\,b$.

[4·6] $a + b = a + (a\,b + -a\,b)$.

And [4·5] $a + (a\,b + -a\,b) = (a + a\,b) + -a\,b = a + -a\,b$.

In applying the algebra to the representation of logical inferences, the following law is frequently used:

**4·7** If $a + b = x$ and $a = 0$, then $b = x$.

If $a = 0$, then [4·12] $a + b = 0 + b = b$.

This law holds because negative terms in this algebra do not behave like minus quantities ( + and − are not inverses): $a + (-b)$ and $a\,-b$ are of quite different meaning, and $a + (-a)$ is not 0 but 1. For the same reason, we have also:

**4·71** $a + b = 0$ is equivalent to the pair, $a = 0$ and $b = 0$.

If $a + b = 0$, then $-a\,-b = 1$.

Hence $a = a \cdot 1 = a(-a\,-b) = (a\,-a)-b = 0 \cdot -b = 0$.

And $b = 1 \cdot b = (-a\,-b)b = -a(-b\,b) = -a \cdot 0 = 0$.

And if $a = 0$ and $b = 0$, $a + b = 0 + 0 = 0$.

In any algebra, if $a = 0$ and $b = 0$, then $a + b = 0$; but in this algebra the converse also holds: if a sum is null, each of its terms is null.

Corresponding to the last two, by the Law of Duality, we have the two following:

**4·8** If $a\,b = x$ and $a = 1$, then $b = x$.

**4·81** $a\,b = 1$ is equivalent to the pair, $a = 1$ and $b = 1$.

We turn now to the subject of equivalent equations of different forms:

**4·9** $a = b$ is equivalent to $a\,-b + -a\,b = 0$, and to $a\,b + -a\,-b = 1$.

[2·2] $a = b$ is equivalent to the pair, $a \subset b$ and $b \subset a$.

[2·8] $a \subset b$ is $a\,-b = 0$, and $b \subset a$ is $-a\,b = 0$.

[4·71] The pair, $a\,-b = 0$ and $-a\,b = 0$, are together equivalent to $a\,-b + -a\,b = 0$.

And [2·92] $a\,-b + -a\,b = 0$ is equivalent to

$$-(a\,-b + -a\,b) = 1 = a\,b + -a\,-b.$$

Equations in which one member is 0 are particularly convenient; hence it is well to remember the rule, according to 4·9, by which any equation may be given this form: Multiply each side of the equation by the negative of the other; add these two products, and equate to 0.

The next theorem is called Poretsky's Law of Forms or, briefly, Poretsky's Law.[1]

*4·92* $a = 0$ is equivalent to $t = a\,{-t} + {-a}\,t$.

$$[4\cdot 9]\ t = a\,{-t} + {-a}\,t \text{ is equivalent to}$$
$$\begin{aligned} 0 &= t\cdot{-(a\,{-t} + {-a}\,t)} + {-t}(a\,{-t} + {-a}\,t) \\ &= t(a\,t + {-a}\,{-t}) + a\,{-t} + {-a}\cdot 0 \\ &= a\,t + 0 + a\,{-t} + 0 = a(t + {-t}) = a. \end{aligned}$$

In this theorem, it is to be noted that, since $t$ does not appear in the given equation, $a = 0$, it represents a term which can be chosen at will, or in mathematical language 'is arbitrary.' Also, we have seen, in 4·9, that any equation may be given the form in which one member is 0. Hence, for any given equation whatever, there are as many equivalents as there are expressions, $t$, which can be chosen—that is, an unlimited number.

The more general form of Poretsky's Law is:

*4·93* $a = b$ is equivalent to $t = (a\,{-b} + {-a}\,b){-t} + (a\,b + {-a}\,{-b})t$.

$$[1\cdot 4,\ 4\cdot 11]\ 0\cdot{-t} + 1\cdot t = 0 + t = t.$$

Hence the theorem follows from 4·9.

For the solution of equations, and for various other purposes of the algebra, it is useful to consider expressions with which we may be dealing as functions of a certain element or elements. In this algebra, it does not require that an expression should have any particular relation to the elements in question in order that it may be taken as a function of them. Even if an element does not appear in the given expression, it may be introduced, by the Law of Expansion. Expressions which are assertable—that is, those which involve the relation $=$, or the relation $\subset$—are not ordinarily considered to be functions; but any expression whatever, which involves only the relations $+$ and $\times$, may be taken as a function of any element, or elements, we choose.

It is further useful to arrange functions in what is called the 'normal form.' The normal form of a function of one element,

[1] After the Russian logician, Platon Poretsky, who was the first to state it.

$x$, is

$$Ax + B -x.$$

Any function can be given this normal form. Suppose, for example, that we wish to treat

$$a\,x + b + -x\,c$$

as a function of $x$.

$$a\,x + b + -x\,c = a\,x + b(x + -x) + -x\,c = a\,x + b\,x + b\,-x + -x\,c$$
$$= (a + b)x + (b + c)-x.$$

That is, we proceed by the following rule: (1) If there is any term of the function (e.g., the term $b$ in the above) in which neither $x$ nor $-x$ appears, expand that term, or terms, with respect to $x$, by the law, $a = a\,x + a\,-x$. (2) Collect the coefficients of $x$, and of $-x$.

This reduction to the normal form can, with a little practice, be carried out by inspection: one has only to remember that any term (like $b$ in the above) in which neither $x$ nor $-x$ appears, will be a term in the coefficient of $x$ and of $-x$ both.

For convenience, let us use $f(x)$ to represent a function of $x$; and let us use capital letters for coefficients in functions which are in the normal form.

One advantage of giving expressions this form is that the various operations of the algebra can then be performed simply by operating on the coefficients: two functions of the same element can be added by adding the coefficients; can be multiplied by multiplying the coefficients; and the negative of a function can be obtained by negating each coefficient:

*5·1* $(A\,x + B\,-x) + (C\,x + D\,-x) = (A + C)x + (B + D)-x.$

The theorem follows from 4·4.

*5·2* $(A\,x + B\,-x) \times (C\,x + D\,-x) = A\,C\,x + B\,D\,-x.$

$$(A\,x + B\,-x) \times (C\,x + D\,-x)$$
$$= A\,C\,x + A\,D\,x\,-x + B\,C\,-x\,x + B\,D\,-x$$
$$= A\,C\,x + 0 + 0 + B\,D\,-x = A\,C\,x + B\,D\,-x.$$

That the product of two functions in the normal form is obtained merely by multiplying together the *corresponding* terms (which is the same as multiplying their coefficients) will be evident if we note, in the above proof, that every *cross*-product will involve a factor of the form $x\,{-x}$, and hence will be null.

**5·3** $-(A\,x + B\,{-x}) = -A\,x + -B\,{-x}$.

$$[3\cdot 11]\ -(A\,x + B\,{-x}) = -(A\,x) \times -(B\,{-x})$$
$$= (-A + -x)(-B + x)$$
$$= -A\,{-B} + -A\,x + -B\,{-x} + 0$$
$$= (-A\,{-B} + -A)x + (-A\,{-B} + -B){-x}.$$

But $[4\cdot 5]\ -A\,{-B} + -A = -A$, and $-A\,{-B} + -B = -B$.

Boole stated certain mathematically interesting laws concerning functions:

**5·4** If $f(x) = A\,x + B\,{-x}$, then $f(1) = A$, $f(0) = B$, and hence
$$f(x) = f(1)\cdot x + f(0)\cdot{-x}.$$

If $f(x) = A\,x + B\,{-x}$,
$$f(1) = A\cdot 1 + B\cdot{-1} = A\cdot 1 + B\cdot 0 = A$$
and
$$f(0) = A\cdot 0 + B\cdot{-0} = A\cdot 0 + B\cdot 1 = B.$$

Other laws of this type, which are mathematically but not logically important, are: If $f(x) = A\,x + B\,{-x}$, then

**5·41** $f(1) = f(A + B) = f(-A + -B)$.

**5·42** $f(0) = f(A\,B) = f(-A\,{-B})$.

**5·43** $f(A) = A + B = f(-B) = f(A\,{-B}) = f(A + -B)$
$= f(1) + f(0) = f(x) + f(-x)$.

**5·44** $f(B) = A\,B = f(-A) = f(-A\,B) = f(-A + B)$
$= f(1) \times f(0) = f(x) \times f(-x)$.

The normal form of a function of two variables, $x$ and $y$, will be
$$A\,x\,y + B\,{-x}\,y + C\,x\,{-y} + D\,{-x}\,{-y};$$
the normal form of a function of three variables will be found, similarly, by giving a coefficient to each term in the expansion of 1 for $x$, $y$, and $z$; and so on, for any number of elements.

Laws similar to 5·4 hold for functions of any number of elements. For example,
$$f(x, y) = f(1, 1)x\,y + f(0, 1){-x}\,y + f(1, 0)x\,{-y} + f(0, 0){-x}\,{-y}.$$

And in general, the coefficient of any term in a function of any number of elements, $f(x, y, z, \ldots)$, is $f(n_1, n_2, n_3, \ldots)$, where $n_1$ is 1 if $x$ is positive in the term in question, and 0 if $x$ is negative; $n_2$ is 1 if $y$ is positive, and 0 if $y$ is negative; $n_3$ is 1 if $z$ is positive, and 0 if $z$ is negative; and so on.

There is seldom any advantage, from the logical point of view, in considering functions of more than one element. Further laws governing these will, therefore, be omitted.

Of much more importance are laws concerning the limits of functions:

*5·5* $A\,B \subset A\,x + B\,{-x} \subset A + B.$

$$(A\,B)(A\,x + B\,{-x}) = A\,B\,x + A\,B\,{-x} = A\,B(x + {-x})$$
$$= A\,B.$$

Hence [1·03] $A\,B \subset A\,x + B\,{-x}$.

And $(A\,x + B\,{-x}) \times -(A + B) = (A\,x + B\,{-x})(-A\,{-B})$
$$= 0 + 0 = 0.$$

Hence [2·8] $A\,x + B\,{-x} \subset A + B$.

Thus the lower limit of a function is the product of the coefficients; and the upper limit is the sum of the coefficients. There are two corollaries of this law:

*5·51* If $A\,x + B\,{-x} = 0$, then $A\,B = 0$.

This follows from 5·5, by 2·7.

*5·52* If $A\,x + B\,{-x} = 1$, then $A + B = 1$.

This follows from 5·5, by 4·13.

The last two theorems serve as the formulæ for the elimination of any element $x$ from an equation. Since every equation can be given the form in which one member is 0, 5·51 can always be applied and is the principle most frequently used.

As we shall see in the next chapter, elimination of terms is one of the most important operations of the algebra, from the logical point of view. For example, syllogistic reasoning always proceeds by elimination of the middle term.

Another operation of the algebra which is applicable to processes of logical inference, is the solution of equations. In general, an equation in $x$ determines the value of $x$ only between limits:

*5·6* $A\,x + B\,-x = 0$ is equivalent to $B \subset x \subset -A$.

[4·71] $A\,x + B\,-x$ is equivalent to the pair, $A\,x = 0$ and $B\,-x = 0$.

But [2·8] $A\,x = 0$ is $x \subset -A$, and $B\,-x = 0$ is $B \subset x$.

Obviously, this solution will be unique when and only when these two limits of $x$ coincide:

*5·61* $-A\,x + A\,-x = 0$ is equivalent to $x = A$.

For equations with one member 1, the solution formula will be:

*5·62* $A\,x + B\,-x = 1$ is equivalent to $-B \subset x \subset A$.

[2·92] $A\,x + B\,-x = 1$ is equivalent to $-(A\,x + B\,-x) = 0$.

And [5·3] $-(A\,x + B\,-x) = -A\,x + -B\,-x$.

Hence the theorem follows from 5·6.

The most general solution formula, applicable to any equation, is:

*5·63* $A\,x + B\,-x = C\,x + D\,-x$ is equivalent to $(B\,-D + -B\,D) \subset x \subset (A\,C + -A\,-C)$.

[4·9] $A\,x + B\,-x = C\,x + D\,-x$ is equivalent to

$$(A\,x + B\,-x) \times -(C\,x + D\,-x) + -(A\,x + B\,-x) \times (C\,x + D\,-x) = 0.$$

But [5·3] $-(C\,x + D\,-x) = -C\,x + -D\,-x$, and $-(A\,x + B\,-x) = -A\,x + -B\,-x$.

And [5·2] $(A\,x + B\,-x)(-C\,x + -D\,-x) + (-A\,x + -B\,-x)(C\,x + D\,-x)$

$$= A\,-C\,x + B\,-D\,-x + -A\,C\,x + -B\,D\,-x$$

$$= (A\,-C + -A\,C)x + (B\,-D + -B\,D)-x.$$

[5·6] $(A\,-C + -A\,C)x + (B\,-D + -B\,D)-x = 0$ is equivalent to $(B\,-D + -B\,D) \subset x \subset -(A\,-C + -A\,C)$.

And $-(A\,-C + -A\,C) = A\,C + -A\,-C$.

In other algebras, the solution of an equation is itself in the form of an equation. Solutions in this algebra may also be given that form. But this more mathematical form of the solution is logically not important except when the determination of $x$ is unique, as in 5·61; and it depends upon slightly complicated considerations. We give this solution for equations with one member 0, as an example:

*5·7* If $A\,x + B\,{-x} = 0$, then for some (undetermined) value of $u$,
$x = B\,{-u} + {-A}\,u = B + u\,{-A}$.

Substituting the value, $B\,{-u} + {-A}\,u$, for $x$, in $A\,x + B\,{-x}$, we have

$$A(B\,{-u} + {-A}\,u) + B\cdot{-(B\,{-u} + {-A}\,u)}.$$

Since [5·3] $-(B\,{-u} + {-A}\,u) = {-B}\,{-u} + A\,u$, this is equivalent to $A(B\,{-u} + {-A}\,u) + B({-B}\,{-u} + A\,u)$.

Hence to $A\,B\,{-u} + 0 + 0 + A\,B\,u$, which is $A\,B({-u} + u)$ or $A\,B$.

But [5·51] if $A\,x + B\,{-x} = 0$, then $A\,B = 0$.

Hence if $A\,B = 0$, as the given equation requires, then the equation is satisfied by $x = B\,{-u} + {-A}\,u$.

Also if $A\,B = 0$, then $A\,B\,u = 0$, and

| | | |
|---|---|---|
| [4·12] | $B\,{-u} + {-A}\,u$ | $= B\,{-u} + {-A}\,u + A\,B\,u$ |
| [4·6] | | $= B\,{-u} + {-A}(B + {-B})u + A\,B\,u$ |
| | | $= B\,{-u} + {-A}\,B\,u + {-A}\,{-B}\,u + A\,B\,u$ |
| | | $= B\,{-u} + (A + {-A})B\,u + {-A}\,{-B}\,u$ |
| [4·6] | | $= B\,{-u} + B\,u + {-A}\,{-B}\,u$ |
| | | $= B + {-A}\,{-B}\,u.$ |

But [4·62] $B + {-A}\,{-B}\,u = B + {-B}\cdot u\,{-A} = B + u\,{-A}$.

Hence if $A\,B = 0$, as the given equation requires, then $B\,{-u} + {-A}\,u = B + u\,{-A}$.

It is to be observed that if $u = 0$, in the above, then

$$B\,{-u} + {-A}\,u = B.$$

And if $u = 1$, then

$$B\,{-u} + {-A}\,u = {-A}.$$

Thus since 0 and 1 are the limiting values of $u$, in

$$x = B\,{-u} + {-A}\,u,$$

this form of the solution expresses the same fact as $B \subset x \subset {-A}$.

As an example of the manner in which the process of solving equations may apply to logical inference, let

$$x = \text{mortals},$$
$$A = \text{perfect beings},$$
and
$$B = \text{men}.$$

Then the equation $A\,x + B\,{-x} = 0$ would mean "The class of those who are either perfect mortals or men who are not mortal, is an empty class." And the solution $B \subset x \subset -A$ would read "The class 'men' is contained in the class 'mortals,' which is contained in the class 'imperfect beings.'" And the other form of solution, $x = B + u\,{-A}$, would read "The class of mortals is the class of men together with some (undetermined) portion of the class 'imperfect beings.'"

In applying this algebra to the process of reasoning, it is important to be able to deal with inequations ($a \neq b$) as well as with equations. As we shall find in the next chapter, any universal proposition is expressible by some equation. A particular proposition, being the contradictory of some universal, is most simply expressed as an inequation. For example, since "All $a$ is $b$" is represented by $a\,{-b} = 0$, the contradictory particular, "Some $a$ is not $b$," is expressed by $a\,{-b} \neq 0$. Thus the principles of inequations are required for application to inference in which particular premises or conclusions are involved.

The laws governing inequations follow immediately from corresponding laws of equations, by general rules of reasoning such as every mathematical deduction presumes. Let $P$ and $Q$ be any propositions whatever; the following principles then hold:

(1) "If $P$, then $Q$" gives "If $Q$ is false, then $P$ is false." Thus, "If $a = b$, then $c = d$" gives "If $c \neq d$, then $a \neq b$."

(2) "$P$ is equivalent to $Q$" gives "'$P$ is false' is equivalent to '$Q$ is false'." Thus "$a = b$ is equivalent to $c = d$" gives "$a \neq b$ is equivalent to $c \neq d$."

(3) "If $P$ and $Q$, then $R$" gives "If $P$ holds but $R$ is false, then $Q$ is false" and "If $Q$ holds but $R$ is false, then $P$ is false." Thus "If $a = b$ and $c = d$, then $e = f$" gives "If $a = b$ but $e \neq f$, then $c \neq d$" and "If $c = d$ but $e \neq f$, then $a \neq b$."

We give below those theorems concerning inequations which are needed, indicating after each, in brackets, the previous theorem from which it follows by one or another of the above three principles:

***6·1*** If $a\,c \neq b\,c$, then $a \neq b$. [2·1]

***6·12*** If $a + c \neq b + c$, then $a \neq b$. [2·12]

***6·2*** $a\,b \neq a$, $a\,-b \neq 0$, $-a + b \neq 1$, and $a + b \neq b$ are all equivalent, and any one of these is equivalent to "It is false that $a \subset b$." [1·03, 2·8, 3·6, 3·83]

***6·3*** If $a + b = x$ and $b \neq x$, then $a \neq 0$. [4·7]

***6·31*** If $a = 0$ and $b \neq x$, then $a + b \neq x$. [4·7]

***6·32*** If $a + b \neq 0$ and $a = 0$, then $b \neq 0$. [4·71]

***6·4*** If $a \neq 0$, then $a + b \neq 0$. [4·71]

***6·41*** If $a\,b \neq 0$, then $a \neq 0$. [1·4]

***6·42*** If $a + b \neq 1$, then $a \neq 1$. [3·4]

***6·5*** If $a\,b \neq x$ and $a = x$, then $b \neq x$. [1·1]

***6·6*** If $a \neq 0$ and $a \subset b$, then $b \neq 0$.

[1·03] $a \subset b$ is equivalent to $a\,b = a$.

Hence if $a \neq 0$ and $a \subset b$, then $a\,b \neq 0$.

And [6·41] if $a\,b \neq 0$, then $b \neq 0$.

***6·7*** $a \neq b$ is equivalent to $a\,-b + -a\,b \neq 0$. [4.9]

***6·72*** $a \neq 0$ is equivalent to $t \neq a\,-t + -a\,t$. [4·92]

***6·73*** $a \neq b$ is equivalent to

$$t \neq (a\,-b + -a\,b)-t + (a\,b + -a\,-b)t. \quad [4·93]$$

***6·8*** If $A\,x + B\,-x \neq 0$, then $A + B \neq 0$.

[5·5] $(A\,x + B\,-x) \subset (A + B)$.

Hence the theorem follows from 6·6.

Laws such as 6·3, 6·31, and 6·32, according to which an equation and an inequation, combined, give an inequation, are particularly important: they apply to cases in which a universal premise (an equation) and a particular premise (an inequation) together give a particular conclusion. Examples will be given in the next chapter.

A great many laws of the algebra which have been proved for sums and products of two terms extend to sums and products of any number of terms. We have not thought it necessary to give the demonstration that such principles extend to sums and products of a larger number of terms, because such extension is a familiar principle of algebra in general, and is, for the most part, obvious in any case. Theoretically, such principles in the general form (for any finite number of terms) require proof that if they hold for $n$ terms, they will hold for $n + 1$ terms. That being established, it follows from the fact that they hold for two terms, that they will hold for any larger number (by the principle of mathematical induction).

Let us illustrate the general method by which such extension of a law from two terms to any larger number could be made. We choose an example in which the possibility of this is less obvious than in other cases: De Morgan's Theorem. In its general form, this law will be:

$$-(a + b + c + \ldots) = -a -b -c \ldots$$

Proof: By 3·11, the theorem holds for two terms,

$$-(a + b) = -a -b.$$

And if the theorem hold for $n$ terms, it will hold for $n + 1$ terms, because, by 3·11,

$$-[(a_1 + a_2 + \ldots + a_n) + a_{n+1}] = -(a_1 + a_2 + \ldots + a_n) \times -a_{n+1}.$$

Hence if the theorem holds for sums and products of $n$ terms, so that

$$-(a_1 + a_2 + a_3 + \ldots + a_n) = -a_1 \cdot -a_2 \cdot -a_3 \cdot \ldots \cdot -a_n,$$

then

$$-[(a_1 + a_2 + a_3 + \ldots + a_n) + a_{n+1}] = (-a_1 \cdot -a_2 \cdot -a_3 \cdot \ldots \cdot -a_n) \cdot -a_{n+1}.$$

Thus, since the theorem holds for two terms, and is such that if it hold for $n$ terms, it will hold for $n + 1$ terms, it will, therefore, hold for any finite number of terms.

In later chapters, we shall frequently make use of the theorems of the algebra in their general form, i.e., for any finite number of terms. The validity of this procedure depends upon such extension of the laws of the system, as given above, by use of the principle of mathematical induction.

# CHAPTER III

## THE LOGIC OF TERMS

Traditional logic is primarily a logic of terms. The laws of identity, contradiction, and the excluded middle, the *dictum de omni et nullo*, and the rules of the syllogism all tell us what must be or what cannot be true of the relations of terms. But terms have both intension and extension; they connote concepts or essential attributes, and they denote things or classes. The laws of intension and those of extension are analogous, but they do not apply to the same terms in the same way: the relations of a given set of terms in intension may not be parallel to their relations in extension. For example, "No trespassers are arrested" might be true in extension, meaning that the class of actually arrested trespassers has no members; but false in intension, meaning that the concepts 'trespassing' and 'being arrested' are mutually incompatible. Again, "Some illegal acts are moral" might be true in intension, meaning that, as the law stands, it is conceivable that a moral person might find himself in a situation requiring him to break it; but it might be false if it meant, in extension, that certain deeds actually done are at once moral and illegal.

In the light of such ambiguities, which affect inference, it has sometimes been argued that, in logic, all propositions should be interpreted in intension; or that all should be interpreted in extension. But a very little thought suffices to dispose of any such iron-clad rule. Propositions are not strings of marks, or series of sounds, except incidentally; in essence, a proposition expresses an asserted meaning. If the same form of words is sometimes meant to convey a certain relation of intension, and sometimes a relation of extension, the only valid rule of interpretation is that this form of words should be taken in the way it is meant, on each separate occasion. And a logic which is adequate to all propositions must, therefore, cover both intension and extension. The traditional logic is unsatisfactory on this point. The majority of its rules are valid both of intension and of extension. But some of them are ambiguous and are such that, whichever interpretation is chosen, they are partly incorrect. For example, the rules of the syllogism sanction *E A O* in the third figure. But the argument,

> No absentees are failed;
> All absentees receive a grade of zero;
> Therefore, some who receive a grade of zero do not fail;

is fallacious. It breaks down no matter how we attempt to interpret it. But the fallacy commonly escapes detection because if it be interpreted in intension and objection is raised, the objection can be answered by switching to an extensional interpretation; and if it be interpreted in extension and the mistake in it pointed out, the objection can be answered by switching to an intensional interpretation. This can happen because, if it be interpreted in intension, the mistake is in one place; and for the extensional interpretation, it is in another. But there is a mistake somewhere in any case. Thus no satisfactory logic of terms is possible so long as such ambiguities are allowed.

The Boole-Schröder Algebra unambiguously applies to the relations of terms in extension. When so applied, it is not a complete logic of terms (though it is at least as adequate as traditional principles), but it is precise and completely accurate. Moreover, when a universal proposition is true in intension, the corresponding relation in extension also holds: if the essence of *A* contains or implies the attribute *B*, then the class of actual *A*'s will be contained in the class of *B*'s; and if the essence of *C* is incompatible with the attribute *D*, then the classes of actual *C*'s and *D*'s can have no common members. For this and certain other reasons, the logic of terms in extension is applicable to a much wider range of actual inference than is the logic of intension. Hence the Boole-Schröder Algebra affords not only an exact logic but one having as wide a sphere of application as is possible without greater complexity.

Let us attend, then, to the precise significance of this interpretation of the algebra. The symbols, *a*, *b*, *c*, etc., are to signify classes—the aggregate of actual things denoted by some term or other. The 'product,' $a \times b$, or $a\,b$, represents the actual common members of the classes $a$ and $b$. If in a particular case no common members exist, $a\,b$ will coincide with the null class, 0. The negative of $a$, $-a$, will represent the class of things not members of $a$; $a + b$, the class of things which are members of $a$ or members of $b$ or members of both; and 1, the negative of 0, will be the class of which everything is a member, or from which nothing is excluded.

It is to be noted that 0 and 1 are unique classes, because we are dealing with the extension of terms. The term 'sea-serpent' and the term 'unicorn' are quite different in connotation, but the class of actual objects denoted by one is identical with the class denoted by the other. 'Nothing' and 'everything' are unique classes, no matter how various the terms denoting them.

The assertable relation $a \subset b$ will signify that every member of $a$ is also a member of $b$; that there is no actual $a$ outside the class $b$. For example, "All unicorns have curly tails," is an ambiguous statement: it may mean that the connotation of 'unicorn' implies having a curly tail, or it may mean only that there is no unicorn without a curly tail. But "unicorn $\subset$ animal with a curly tail" means unambiguously the latter. And it is true, regardless of connotations, because, since no unicorn exists, there are none outside the class of animals with curly tails. The class 0 is contained in every class.

The relation $a = b$ signifies that the extensions or classes, $a$ and $b$, are identical or comprise exactly the same actual objects. For example, "featherless biped = animal that laughs" is true because both of these terms denote precisely the class of men, though their connotations are not equivalent.

Various paradoxes and little puzzles about the logic of classes may be resolved by attention to these precise meanings.

Taking propositions to assert relations of extensions or classes, the four typical propositions may be represented as follows:

(1) All $a$ is $b$: $a \subset b$; $a\,b = a$; $a\,{-b} = 0$.

(2) No $a$ is $b$: $a \subset -b$; $a\,{-b} = a$; $a\,b = 0$.

(3) Some $a$ is $b$: $a\,{-b} \neq a$; $a\,b \neq 0$.

(4) Some $a$ is not $b$: $a\,b \neq a$; $a\,{-b} \neq 0$.

The alternative representations are, of course, equivalent in each case (see 1·03 and 2·8).[1] The following facts may be noted: The last expression given in each case is an equation or an inequation with one member 0, making them easily comparable. The universal affirmative, (1), and the particular negative, (4), are exact contradictories, as they should be. Similarly, the universal negative, (2), and the particular affirmative, (3), are contradictories. The two universals each affirm that something is $= 0$; the two particulars, that something is $\neq 0$. That is, a universal proposition in extension asserts a non-existence: "All *a* is *b*," that *a*'s which are not *b*'s do not exist; "No *a* is *b*," that *a*'s which are *b*'s do not exist. And a particular proposition in extension asserts an existence: "Some *a* is *b*," that *a*'s which are *b*'s exist; and "Some *a* is not *b*," that *a*'s which are not *b*'s exist.

In the solution of problems by means of the algebra, the following general rules ('rules of thumb,' not laws) will be of service: (1) Always express the data as equations, or inequations, with one member 0. This can always be done because

[4·9] $a = b$ is equivalent to $a\, -b + -a\, b = 0$,
[6·7] $a \neq b$ is equivalent to $a\, -b + -a\, b \neq 0$.

(2) In combining two equations, with one member 0, always add them; for the reason that

[4·71] $a + b = 0$ is equivalent to the pair, $a = 0$ and $b = 0$.

That is, if we combine two equations, $a = 0$ and $b = 0$, by addition, we lose nothing of the force of the equations combined. But if we should combine them by multiplication, the result, $a\, b = 0$, would be valid but would not be equivalent to the separate equations combined.

A very useful device for checking the work of the algebra is the so-called 'Venn diagram,' in which equations or inequations with one member 0 can always be represented.[2] In this type of diagram, classes are represented by circles or other areas, and the diagram is so drawn as always to represent 'the universe,' or

[1] References are, of course, to the numbered theorems of the preceding chapter.

[2] This style of diagram was originated by John Venn; see Bibliography, end of Ch. I.

1, for whatever terms may be in question. Thus for two terms, $a$ and $b$, one always draws overlapping circles, as in Figure 1.

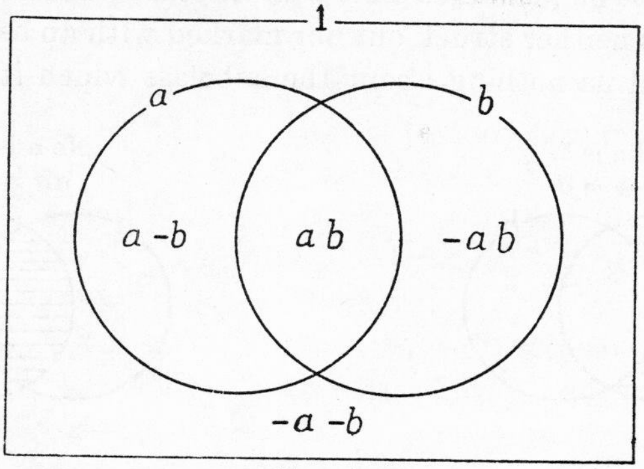


FIG. 1.

Here the left-hand circle is $a$; the right-hand circle is $b$. For two terms, $a$ and $b$,

$$[4\cdot 61]\quad 1 = a\,b + a\,{-b} + {-a}\,b + {-a}\,{-b},$$

and these divisions are labeled in this diagram, though ordinarily such subclasses will not be labeled. The area common to the two circles is $a\,b$; that which is in $a$ but outside $b$ is $a\,{-b}$; that which is in $b$ but outside $a$ is ${-a}\,b$; and that part of the rectangle, 1, which is outside both circles is ${-a}\,{-b}$. The general principle that, for any term $x$,

$$[3\cdot 5]\quad x + {-x} = 1,$$

enables us to identify the area representing the negative of any term: the negative of $x$ is the rest of the diagram, outside $x$. The area $a + b$ is, of course, that which is in either circle or both —that is, the area comprising $a\,b$, $a\,{-b}$, and ${-a}\,b$.

Having drawn the diagram in this way, we can then represent any given data by striking out any area which is $= 0$, and putting an asterisk, to indicate existence, in any area which is $\neq 0$. Thus the four typical propositions would be represented as in Figure 2. The rectangle for 'the universe' may be omitted if we remember that the area outside both circles is still a part of the diagram, representing the subclass ${-a}\,{-b}$.

It is a principle of this style of diagram that an unmarked area cannot be presumed to represent something which exists, and it cannot be presumed that what it represents does not exist. If an area is neither struck out nor marked with an asterisk, then the data tell us nothing about the subclass which it represents.

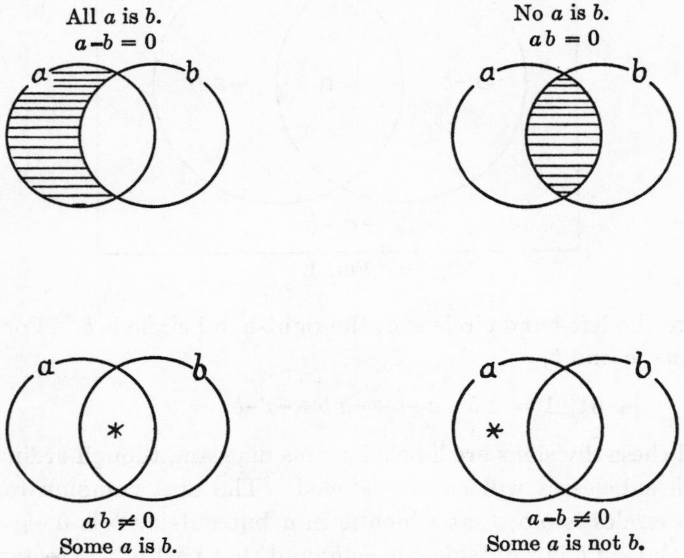


FIG. 2.

Thus in the representation of "Some *a* is *b*," for example, the area $a - b$ is unmarked, and the area $-a\, b$ is unmarked. Correspondingly, "Some *a* is *b*" does not tell us that $a - b$ (what is *a* but not *b*) exists or that it does not exist; and similarly tells us nothing about $-a\, b$.

This type of diagram can be extended to three terms by drawing three circles, each overlapping each. Four circles cannot be so drawn that each will intersect with every other in the fashion required, but four ellipses can. We give, in Figure 3, the representation of the universe for three and for four classes.[3]

[3] The ellipses are slightly deformed, for convenience. To make this diagram for four terms, draw first the upright ellipse, *a*, and mark the two points on it. Next, draw the horizontal ellipse, *d*, *from one of these points to the other*. Then draw ellipse *b*, from and returning to the lower marked point, and ellipse *c*, from and returning to the upper marked point.

The subdivisions are not marked in the diagram for four terms, the areas not being large enough to permit it. But each area can be named by observing whether it is in or out of $a$, in or out of $b$, etc. Similarly, in this or any other diagram, we can identify such an area as $a\,b$ by the fact that it is all that is common to $a$ and $b$; $a\,{-b}\,c$, by the fact that it is the whole area in $a$ and in $c$ but not in $b$; and so on.

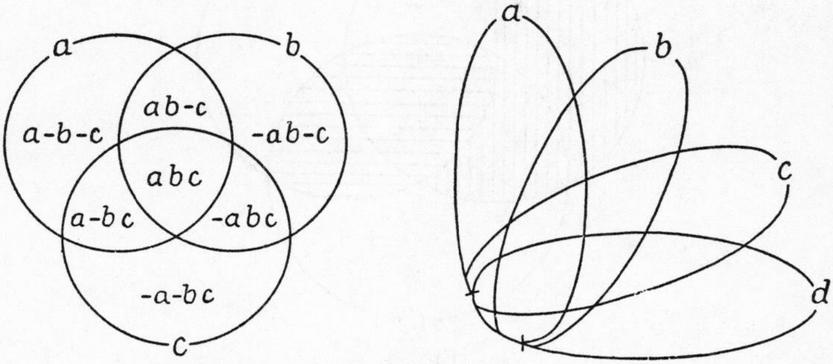


Fig. 3.

Let us now see how inference such as that of the syllogism would be represented, both by the algebra and in the diagram. Suppose we have given the syllogistic premises:

$$\text{All } a \text{ is } b\text{:}\quad a\,{-b} = 0. \qquad (1)$$

$$\text{No } b \text{ is } c\text{:}\quad b\,c = 0. \qquad (2)$$

Combining these by addition, we have,

$$a\,{-b} + b\,c = 0. \qquad (3)$$

The middle term, common to the two premises, is $b$; to get the syllogistic conclusion, we eliminate this middle term by the elimination formula [5·51],

$$\text{If } A\,x + B\,{-x} = 0, \text{ then } A\,B = 0.$$

In equation (3), $b$ corresponds to the $x$ of this formula; that is, (3) can be written

$$c\,b + a\,{-b} = 0.$$

Hence the result of the elimination is

$$a\,c = 0,$$

which is the syllogistic conclusion "No $a$ is $c$."

In Figure 4, premise (1) is represented by vertical strokes; (2), by horizontal strokes. As a result of these two together, the whole of the area $a\,c$ is struck out. Thus the conclusion can be read from this diagram representing the premises.

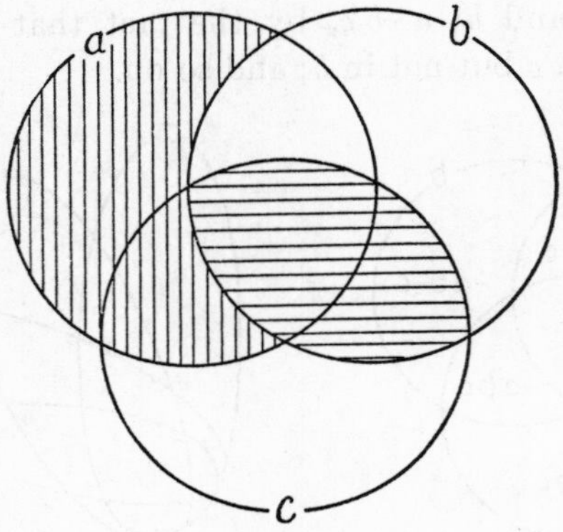


FIG. 4.

If both of the premises of a syllogism are universal, the conclusion is always reached in precisely this way, by the algebraic elimination of the middle term, according to formula 5·51. The reader may satisfy himself of this, and gain practice in using the algebra and the diagram, by carrying out this elimination for the premises (1) "All *a* is *b*, and all *b* is *c*," and (2) "All *a* is *b*, and no *c* is *b*," and so on.

A valid syllogism requires that one premise be universal. When one premise is universal and one particular, the algebraic operation is different from the preceding. Suppose we are given:

$$\text{All } a \text{ is } b\text{:} \quad a\,{-b} = 0. \qquad (1)$$

$$\text{Some } a \text{ is } c\text{:} \quad a\,c \neq 0. \qquad (2)$$

The result to be obtained is in terms of *b* and *c* alone, since *a* is common to the premises. The derivation of such a result, where an equation and an inequation are given, is as follows: First expand both premises to contain all three terms. By 4·6, (1) is equivalent to

$$a\,{-b}(c + {-c}) = a\,{-b}\,c + a\,{-b}\,{-c} = 0. \qquad (3)$$

Similarly, since $a\,c = a\,c(b + -b) = a\,b\,c + a\,-b\,c$, (2) is equivalent to

$$a\,b\,c + a\,-b\,c \neq 0. \tag{4}$$

In (3) and (4), we now have an equation and an inequation with one term, $a\,-b\,c$, in common; and by 4·71 it follows from (3) that this term is null:

$$a\,-b\,c = 0. \tag{5}$$

By 6·32, "If $a + b \neq 0$ and $a = 0$, then $b \neq 0$," it follows from (4) and (5) together that

$$a\,b\,c \neq 0. \tag{6}$$

And by 6·41, if $a\,b\,c \neq 0$, then $b\,c \neq 0$. This last is the syllogistic conclusion "Some $b$ is $c$."

In the diagram for one universal and one particular premise, it is always necessary to put in the universal premise first. For example, if we should attempt to represent the particular premise, $a\,c \neq 0$, first in Figure 5, we should not know whether to place

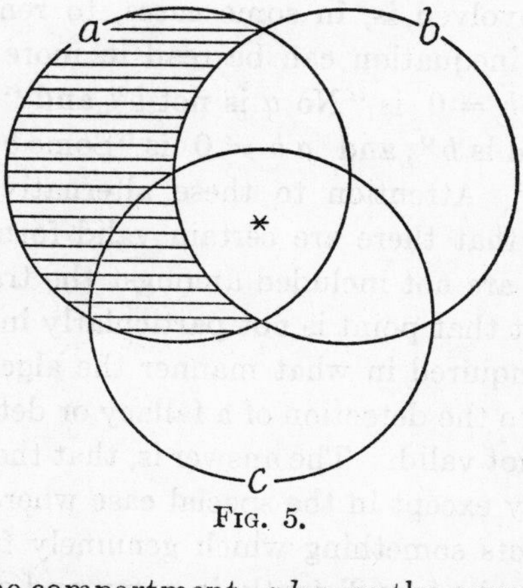


FIG. 5.

the asterisk in the compartment $a\,b\,c$ or the compartment $a\,-b\,c$. If we know only that something is both $a$ and $c$, we know that something is either (1) $a$ and $b$ and $c$ or (2) $a$ and not-$b$ and $c$ (or both), but we do not know which of these alternatives is the true one. (We might put an asterisk in both these compartments of the diagram, connecting the two by a dotted line, to indicate the tentative character of this placing.) However, when the universal premise, $a -b = 0$, has been represented in the diagram, this doubt is resolved; there is only one compartment within the area $a\,c$ left undeleted, in which to place the asterisk.

This asterisk in the compartment $a\,b\,c$ could be read "Some $a$ is $b$" or "Some $a$ is $c$" or "Some things are $a$, $b$, and $c$, all three," as well as "Some $b$ is $c$." All of these conclusions, as a fact, follow from the given premises. The syllogistic conclusion, like every syllogistic conclusion, is simply *one* of the conclusions which the premises give; namely, that one which meets two extra-logical requirements: (1) it follows from neither premise alone, and (2) it does not involve the middle term, common to the two premises.

This last example may serve as a paradigm for every valid syllogism with one particular premise. Just as the procedure of the previous illustration covers every case in which both premises are universal, so here, the process exemplified is the same as it would be for any syllogism with a particular premise. The only further point involved is, in some cases, to remember that an equation or an inequation can be read in more than one way: for example, $a -b = 0$ is "No $a$ is not-$b$" and "No not-$b$ is $a$," as well as "All $a$ is $b$"; and $a\,b \neq 0$ is "Some $b$ is $a$" as well as "Some $a$ is $b$." Attention to these alternative readings will reveal the fact that there are certain valid forms of syllogistic inference which are not included amongst the traditional moods and figures—but that point is not particularly important.

It may be inquired in what manner the algebra, or the diagram, can lead to the detection of a fallacy or determination that an inference is not valid. The answer is, that there is no decisive test of invalidity except in the special case where the conclusion drawn contradicts something which genuinely follows from the premises. One who is sufficiently in command of the operations of the algebra to be clear that a certain conclusion cannot be derived from what is given, may detect a fallacy through that fact; but there is no other general method. In the diagram, the matter is somewhat simpler, since if one merely represents the premises correctly, any conclusion which cannot be read from this representation does not follow. An example or two may be worth while. Let us take the familiar fallacy of the undistributed middle term. Suppose we are given:

All $a$ is $b$: $a -b = 0$.
All $c$ is $b$: $c -b = 0$.

A conclusion which commits the fallacy will be:

All $a$ is $c$: $a -c = 0$.

Here if we combine the premises, we have,

$$a -b + c -b = 0.$$

We know that, since this is a case of two universal premises, if there is a syllogistic conclusion it must follow from this last equation by the elimination formula, 5·51. But that formula will not apply here, because there is no element corresponding to the $x$ of the formula, which is positive in one term of the sum and negative in the other. Nor will any other algebraic operation give $a -c = 0$. If the reader will make the diagram for these premises, striking out the areas $a -b$ and $c -b$, he will discover that the result does not delete the whole of $a -c$ but only $a -b -c$.

Again, suppose we should be given the premises:

All $a$ is $b$: $a -b = 0$.
Some $b$ is not $c$: $b -c \neq 0$.

And suppose the suggested conclusion be:

Some $a$ is not $c$: $a -c \neq 0$.

Here we proceed as in the valid example above, for one particular premise. Expanding each of the premises for all three elements, we have,

$$a -b(c + -c) = a -b\,c + a -b -c = 0$$
and $$a\,b -c + -a\,b -c \neq 0.$$

But the equation and the inequation here have no term in common, and therefore cannot be combined in the manner of the previous example.

In this case, the diagram will exhibit the fact that no syllogistic conclusion is possible, by the failure to determine that the asterisk, representing the inequation, belongs unambiguously in any single compartment.

There is another and a simpler general method which applies to all syllogistic reasoning, though the basis of it in the algebra is not so immediately evident. This procedure is that of Mrs. Ladd-Franklin's "antilogism," or as we shall call it, the 'inconsistent triad.' If we take any valid syllogism and replace the conclusion by its contradictory, the result is a set of three propositions any two of which determine the third to be false. For example, given "All men are mortal" and "All Greeks are men," the conclusion is "All Greeks are mortal." Replacing this by its contradictory, "Some Greeks are not mortal," we have the inconsistent triad:

(1) All men are mortal.
(2) All Greeks are men.
(3) Some Greeks are not mortal.

Taking any two of these as premises gives the contradictory of the third as a valid syllogistic conclusion:

(1) All men are mortal.
(2) All Greeks are men.
Hence, all Greeks are mortal.

(1) All men are mortal.
(3) Some Greeks are not mortal.
Hence, some Greeks are not men.

(2) All Greeks are men.
(3) Some Greeks are not mortal.
Hence, some men are not mortal.

The principle upon which this character of the inconsistent triad turns has been recognized ever since the time of Aristotle. It may be stated thus: If two premises give a conclusion, then if one of these premises be true but the conclusion false, the other premise must be false. If the reader will compare this principle with the above example, its validity will be apparent.

The use of this method for testing syllogistic inference depends upon the fact that *in symbols* every inconsistent triad has the same pattern. The rule is as follows: Express each of the three propositions of the syllogism in question as an equation, or an inequation, with one member 0. Replace the *conclusion* by its contradictory; i.e., change $= 0$ to $\neq 0$, or $\neq 0$ to $= 0$. This gives the inconsistent triad. Every genuine inconsistent triad meets the following requirements: (1) It contains two universal propositions and one particular—two equations and one inequation. (2) The two equations ($= 0$) will have one element in common, which will be positive in one and negative in the other. (3) The inequation ($\neq 0$) will combine the other two elements appearing in the equations, with whatever sign they there have. For example, the inconsistent triad above is,

(1) All $b$ (men) is $c$ (mortal): $b\,\text{-}c = 0$.
(2) All $a$ (Greeks) is $b$ (men): $a\,\text{-}b = 0$.
(3) Some $a$ is not $c$: $a\,\text{-}c \neq 0$.

Comparison of this with the rule will show that it meets all the requirements.

As a further illustration, let us test a syllogism with a particular premise:

No $a$ is $b$: $a\,b = 0$.
Some $b$ is $c$: $b\,c \neq 0$.
Hence, some $a$ is not $c$: $a\,\text{-}c \neq 0$.

Replacing the conclusion by its contradictory, we have the triad

$$a\,b = 0,$$
$$b\,c \neq 0,$$
$$a\,\text{-}c = 0.$$

This does not conform to the rule: it has two equations and one inequation; but the term which is common to the equations, $a$, is not once positive and once negative; and $c$, in the inequation, is positive when, by the rule, it should be negative. Our conclusion, above, is therefore fallacious, as may easily be verified by other tests. The *valid* conclusion from the given premises would be

Some $c$ is not $a$: $c\,\text{-}a \neq 0$.

This would give the triad

$$a\,b = 0,$$
$$b\,c \neq 0,$$
$$c\,-a = 0.$$

This conforms to the rule in all particulars.

It may have occurred to the reader that this method of the inconsistent triad will fail in the case of syllogisms with two universal premises and a particular conclusion—*E A O* and *A A I* in the third and fourth figures, and the moods with a 'weakened conclusion.' Such syllogisms will violate the rule for the reason that both premises are universals (equations), and the conclusion being particular, its contradictory will be another universal, giving a triad with three equations, instead of two equations and an inequation.

The reason for this failure is a very simple one: these moods are not valid, but represent an error of traditional logic. The illustration about absentees on page 50 is a case in point, being an example of *E A O* in the third figure.

A particular conclusion cannot validly be drawn from a universal premise, or from any number of universal premises. This is borne out not only by the method of the inconsistent triad but by the algebra or the diagram as well, as the reader may discover by experiment. The simplest case in point is the traditional inference of "Some $a$ is $b$" from "All $a$ is $b$." This fails, as a fact, whenever no $a$ exists. If $a$ is an empty class ($a = 0$), then "All $a$ is $b$" ($a\,-b = 0$) is true, but "Some $a$ is $b$" ($a\,b \neq 0$) is false. If there are no centaurs, then "All centaurs are Greek" is true, but "Some centaurs are Greek" is false. In fact, if $a$ is an empty class, every universal proposition with $a$ as subject is true, but every particular proposition with $a$ as subject is false. If there are no centaurs, then "All centaurs are $x$" will be true, no matter what $x$ is: all the centaurs there *are*, will be anything you please. Also, "No centaur is $y$" will be true, whatever $y$ may be. But "Some centaur is $z$" and "Some centaur is not $w$" will be false, for every $z$ and $w$.

The principles of the algebra require this. If $a = 0$, then by 2·6, $a \subset b$ and $a \subset -b$: if $a = 0$, then $a\,-b = 0$ and $a\,b = 0$, by 1·4. Also, if $a = 0$, then $a\,b \neq 0$ and $a\,\text{-}b \neq 0$ must be false, since when $a = 0$,

$$a\,b = 0 \cdot b = 0, \quad \text{and} \quad a\,\text{-}b = 0 \cdot \text{-}b = 0.$$

These facts point to the invalidity of certain other traditionally sanctioned modes of immediate inference also; for example, the inference "Some *b* is *a*" from "All *a* is *b*"; and the inferences "Some *a* is not *b*" and "Some *b* is not *a*" from "No *a* is *b*." All of these are invalid, committing the same fallacy of inferring an existence from a non-existence. Sometimes this fallacy is a bit concealed, as when "Some *b* is not *a*" is inferred from "No *a* is *b*" by way of the intermediate step "No *b* is *a*." Consider the following:

(1) No artist is perfect.
Hence (2) No perfect being is an artist.
Hence (3) Some perfect beings are not artists.

If (3) follows from (2), it likewise follows from (1), but the inference of (3) from (1) is obviously unsound. The point worth noting here is that the reasoning breaks down, not because there are no artists, but because there may be no perfect beings. Thus we cannot say, "The inference from universal to particular will hold provided that the subject of the universal denotes a class having members": the trouble here is that the predicate "perfect" may denote an empty class.

Since inference from universal to particular is invalid, the only genuinely valid immediate inferences are those in which the given proposition and the proposition inferred are equivalent. For example, "Some *a* is *b*" and "Some *b* is *a*" are equivalent: they would have the same equation and be represented by the same diagram. Similarly, "All *a* is *b*," "No *a* is not-*b*," "No not-*b* is *a*," and "All not-*b* is not-*a*" are equivalent. Also "No *a* is *b*" and "No *b* is *a*" are equivalent, and either of them is equivalent to "All *a* is not-*b*," and to "All *b* is not-*a*."

The same fallacy affects the traditional doctrine of the 'square of opposition,' according to which *A* and *E*, contraries, are supposed to be such that both may be false but both cannot be true; *I* and *O*, subcontraries, such that both may be true but both cannot be false; *A* and *O*, *E* and *I*, contradictories, such that both cannot be true and both cannot be false. $I$ is supposed to follow from $A$, and $O$ from $E$. None of these relations really holds except that of contradiction between $A$ and $O$, $E$ and $I$. When $x = 0$, $A$ and $E$ are both true, $I$ and $O$ both false; the supposed relations of contraries, subcontraries, and subalterns all break down. If $y = 0$, or if $-y = 0$, *some* of them break down. Since a general principle of inference which sometimes fails is never really valid, this entire traditional doctrine—except for contradictories—must be abandoned.

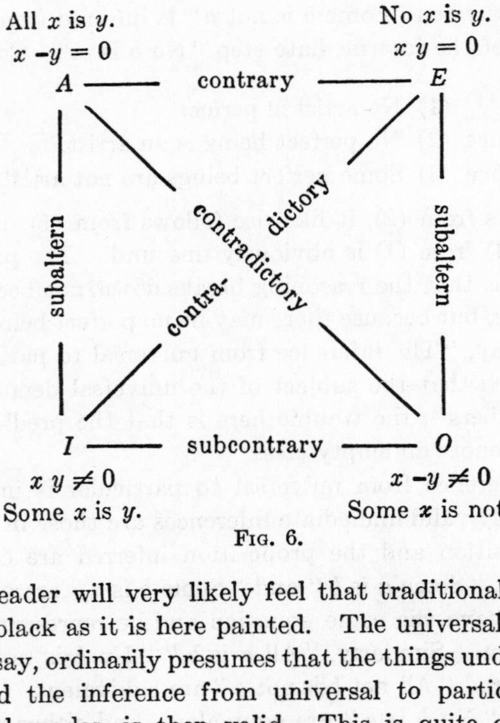


FIG. 6.

The reader will very likely feel that traditional logic is not quite so black as it is here painted. The universal proposition, one may say, ordinarily presumes that the things under discussion exist; and the inference from universal to particular, in the traditional modes, is then valid. This is quite correct. But since it is not always true that such existence is assumed—and plenty of examples can be given of that—a correct logic will require that this assumption be explicit when it is actually made. And if it is an explicit premise, then the inference follows according to the algebra. Only, the so-called immediate inferences are then not immediate, and the so-called syllogisms are not syllogisms. Thus the apparent simplicity and generality of traditional principles cover a real ambiguity, and when this ambiguity is dispelled they must be replaced by somewhat more complex laws of more restricted application.

Suppose we are given:

$$\text{All } a\text{'s are } b\text{'s: } a\,{-b} = 0.$$
$$\text{And } a\text{'s exist: } a \neq 0.$$

We may then infer, by the algebra:

$$a = a\,b + a\,{-b}. \quad \text{Hence } a\,b + a\,{-b} \neq 0.$$

But [6·32] if $a\,b + a\,{-b} \neq 0$ and $a\,{-b} = 0$, then $a\,b \neq 0$: Some $a$ is $b$.

Similarly for 'syllogisms' such as *E A O*. Suppose we are given:

$$\text{No } b \text{ is } c\text{: } b\,c = 0.$$
$$\text{All } b \text{ is } a\text{: } b\,{-a} = 0.$$
$$\text{And } b \text{ exists: } b \neq 0.$$

We may then proceed:

$b = a\,b + {-a}\,b$. Hence $a\,b + {-a}\,b \neq 0$.

But ${-a}\,b = 0$. Hence [6·32] $a\,b \neq 0$.

But $ab = a\,b\,c + a\,b\,{-c}$. Hence $a\,b\,c + a\,b\,{-c} \neq 0$.

Also, since $b\,c = 0$, $a\,b\,c + {-a}\,b\,c = 0$. Hence [4·71] $a\,b\,c = 0$.

[6·32] Since $a\,b\,c + a\,b\,{-c} \neq 0$ and $a\,b\,c = 0$, $a\,b\,{-c} \neq 0$.

And [6·41] since $a\,b\,{-c} \neq 0$, $a\,{-c} \neq 0$: Some $a$ is not $c$.

If this seems complex, as compared with *E A O*, we should remember that when the assumption of existence, which is essential to validity, is added to the 'syllogism,' it also will become complex; in fact, it must have precisely the complexity represented by this train of algebraic deduction.

Somewhat similarly for the relations of the 'square of opposition': "There are *a*'s, and all *a* is *b*" is genuinely contrary to "There are *a*'s, and no *a* is *b*"; these can both be false, but they cannot both be true. The subcontraries, however, "Some *a* is *b*" and "Some *a* is not *b*," are not genuinely such that both may be true but both cannot be false; and no explicit statement of assumed existence can make them so. If they are to be taken in extension, they already assert existence, and it is by virtue of that fact that they can both be false. The propositions truly having this subcontrary relation would be the true contradictories of the above 'amended' universals; that is, the traditional *I* would have to be replaced by "Either there are no *a*'s or some *a* is *b*"; the traditional *O*, by "Either there are no *a*'s or some *a* is not *b*."

It may also be thought that something of importance for the validity of traditional logic is to be found in the logic of intension, omitted from consideration when the algebra is interpreted as a logic of classes. As a matter of fact, interpreting the traditional modes in intension does not help them a bit. If the interpretation is completely and consistently intensional, precisely the same forms of inference which are fallacious in extension will be found to be fallacious in intension also. The logic of the intension of terms is a slightly complicated matter, and perhaps of no great importance. We shall include here a statement of the basic facts, for the reason that this topic is so seldom discussed. But any reader who chooses may well omit the next few pages.

Let us first see what the typical propositions will mean when interpreted in intension. "All *a* is *b*," as a statement about connotations, means "The concept *a* contains or requires *b*; whatever would fall under the meaning of *a* must necessarily have the character *b*; all possible or logically conceivable *a*'s must be *b*'s." Similarly, "No *a* is *b*" in intension means "The concept *a* excludes *b*; nothing which could fall under the meaning of *a* could have the character *b*; no possible or logically conceivable *a* could be a *b*." 'Some,' in a proposition concerning intensions, means 'A definable species of' or 'Some logically conceivable.' Thus, in intension, "Some *a* is *b*" means "A conceivable species of *a* is *b*"; and "Some *a* is not *b*" means "A conceivable species of *a* is not *b*."

The Boole-Schröder Algebra can be applied, completely and with accuracy, to such relations of intension. But it must, of course, be reinterpreted. Let *a*, *b*, *c*, etc., represent the conceptual meanings or connotations of terms. Let $a \times b$ be the qualification or limitation of concept *a* by concept *b*; or the qualification of $b$ by $a$. Let $-a$ be 'not-$a$.' Let 0 mean 'logically inconceivable or self-contradictory.' Since when $a = 0$, $-a = 1$, 1 will represent that whose negative is inconceivable; that is, a concept such that everything conceivable falls under it. Consonantly, $a \neq 0$ will mean "$a$ is not self-contradictory; $a$ is conceivable or possible." And $a \neq 1$ will mean, "$a$ is not such that everything which is conceivable or possible falls under it." Since the relation $a \subset b$ is equivalent to $a\,b = a$ and to $a\,-b = 0$, it will mean "What is $a$ but not $b$, is logically inconceivable," or "All possible $a$'s are $b$'s." With these interpretations, all the laws of the algebra will hold.

In the logic of extension, we have met with the paradox that when $a = 0$, $a \subset b$ will hold, whatever $b$ may represent. The precisely similar paradox recurs in the logic of intension. The question arises what is true of the logically inconceivable. For example, are the propositions "All round squares are round" and "All round squares are square" both true, or both false, or what? According to the above interpretation, since $a\,b \subset a$ is a general law of the algebra, we shall have "round square $\subset$ round" and "round square $\subset$ square." Also, $a \subset b$ is equivalent to $a\,-b = 0$. Thus, since it is true that a round square which is not round is inconceivable, and a round square which is not square is not conceivable, we shall have to admit that "round square $\subset$ round" and "round square $\subset$ square" both hold. Again, a round square which is triangular is inconceivable; in fact, a round square which is $x$ is inconceivable, whatever $x$ may be. Thus "All round squares are triangles" will be true in intension: since 'round square' = 0, anything may be truly predicated of it in intension.

With respect to concepts which have possible though no actual denotation, the case is different. In intension, "All unicorns have a single horn" is true: it follows from the concept of this animal that it must have a single horn. But "All unicorns have two horns" is false. That is, there is a definite intensional truth and falsity about non-existent but conceivable things like unicorns; and it is not the case that concerning the merely non-existent anything one may please is true. But the self-contradictory or inconceivable occupies, in intension, the same position that the non-existent does in extension: anything whatever may be truly predicated of it. Perhaps it would still be plausible to maintain that "All round squares are round" is false; but whoever takes that position will get into worse trouble than he gets out of. For example, he must either deny this form of words to be a meaningful assertion, or he must deny the generality of the law $a\,b \subset a$ in intension. But if he assert that meaningful statements cannot be made about the inconceivable, he seems to be making one himself: if he say that the inconceivable has no predicates, he appears to give it the predicate 'having no predicates.' On the other hand, it seems absurd to deny that the complex concept $a\,b$ contains or requires $a$. Even if he avoid these difficulties, we shall have others ready for him.

From the fact that the algebra can be thus interpreted for intensional relations, it should follow that the traditional modes which are not in accord with the algebra, when the extensional interpretation is assigned, will likewise fail to be truly valid in intension. This is the fact. For example, if the general principle "'All $a$ is $b$' implies 'Some $a$ is $b$'" be announced for intension, it is invalidated by those exceptions, like 'round square,' in which the term $a$ represents something inconceivable. The additional premise, 'and $a$ is conceivable' ($a \neq 0$), if assumed, must be made explicit. With this added premise, the inference is valid, but is not what the announced principle asserts, and is not immediate. Entirely similar considerations apply to all the other traditional modes whose fallacious character, when interpreted in extension, has been pointed out. They are equally invalid in intension. It is a usual, though not universally safe, presumption that terms meant in extension denote something which *exists*. And likewise, it is a usual but not universally safe presumption that terms meant in intension name something logically conceivable. In both cases, however, precision requires that this presumption, if made, should be explicit. Without that, the inference is not in valid form; and a logic which validates the form in which it is not explicit, is incorrect.

Furthermore, we must not confuse the fact that for every law of extension there is an analogous law of intension, with the notion that the relations of terms in intension are parallel to their relations in extension. If we have any set of concrete terms—'men,' 'mortals,' 'featherless bipeds'—their relations in extension constitute one set of facts, and their relations in intension another set of facts which may not be parallel. For example, the class 'men' is contained in the class 'mortals' (extension); also the connotation of 'man' includes the connotation of 'mortal' (parallel relation of intension). But the class 'featherless bipeds' is contained in the class 'men,' although the parallel relation of intension does not hold; it is not true that the connotation of 'featherless biped' contains or implies the attribute 'human.'

Thus a logic which should be adequate to deal with all the relations of terms which figure in and affect inference, would have to represent their relations of intension differently from their relations of extension; and such a logic must include not only the laws of intension and the laws of extension but also laws connecting the two. For example, it must include the law that if the connotation of *a* includes that of *b*, then the class *a* is contained in *b* (but the reverse does not always hold). The Boole-Schröder Algebra is inadequate to such complete representation of the logic of terms, though it is completely applicable to the relations of extension, and likewise completely applicable to the relations of intension.

We have made this somewhat long digression concerning intension, extension, and the algebra, for two reasons: In the first place, because the impression prevails in some quarters that the algebra, as a logic of classes, is not only free from the errors of tradition but is adequate where Aristotelian logic is not. As a fact, neither of them is adequate: a complete and accurate logic of terms has never been developed by anybody. It is not a difficult matter, and awaits only the attention of some student who will bring to bear upon the subject the exact methods now available. In the second place, we think that the bearing of exact methods upon the simple problems of logic is a more pressing matter, at the present juncture, than the mere manipulation of the mathematical machinery. At the moment, the elaboration of the formulæ has been somewhat more adequately attended to than the simpler business of assessing their precise significance for logic.

Let us now return to topics more strictly related to the algebra. There is one point of considerable theoretical importance concerning which the algebra leaves no possible doubt: there is no such thing as *the* conclusion from any premise or any set of premises; given any premises whatever, there are an infinite number of conclusions which may validly be drawn. This is an unavoidable consequence of Poretsky's Law of Forms:

[4·92] $a = 0$ is equivalent to $t = a\, -t + -a\, t$.

[4·93] $a = b$ is equivalent to $t = (a\, -b + -a\, b)\, -t + (a\, b + -a\, -b)t$.

[6·72] $a \neq 0$ is equivalent to $t \neq a\, -t + -a\, t$.

[6·73] $a \neq b$ is equivalent to $t \neq (a\, -b + -a\, b)\, -t + (a\, b + -a\, -b)t$.

This law, in its various forms, tells us that, given any data expressible as an equation or as an inequation, there is a consequence in terms of any $t$ we choose, whether $t$ appears in the given data or not. As an illustration, let us observe something of the variety of conclusions which can be drawn from the premises

All men ($a$) are mortal ($b$): $a\, -b = 0$.

All men ($a$) are fallible ($c$): $a\, -c = 0$.

The combined premises, $a\, -b + a\, -c = 0$, are equivalent to

$$t = (a\, -b + a\, -c)\, -t + -(a\, -b + a\, -c)t.$$

In this result, let us first choose $b$ for $t$:

$$\begin{aligned} b &= (a\, -b + a\, -c)\, -b + -(a\, -b + a\, -c)b \\ &= a\, -b + a\, -b\, -c + (-a + b)(-a + c)b \\ &= a\, -b + (-a + -a\, b + -a\, c + b\, c)b \\ &= a\, -b + -a\, b + b\, c. \end{aligned}$$

That is, the premises give the conclusion "The mortal beings are those who are men but not mortal, or mortal but not men, or fallible mortals." There may be 'objections' to this conclusion. In the first place, one may say "That part of the statement about mortal beings and those who are men but not mortal is false." But this is a mistake. The premises require that the class 'immortal men' should be an empty class. To adjoin this class to others is to add nothing. Hence if the mortal beings are those who are either mortal but not men or fallible mortals (as the premises require), then the addition "men but not mortal" leaves the conclusion still correct. Adding such empty classes may be a 'joke,' but some jokes are logical and some not. This one is perfectly logical, and the conclusion follows from the premises given.

One may also object that, however valid, this conclusion is of no use. Very likely this is the case. But what has logical validity to do with usefulness? One who supposes that to be logical is *ipso facto* to be of use, has not observed the logical pedant at his best. Even though *illogical* inference is *never* useful, it does not follow that *all* truly logical inference is of use. That is precisely one point which needs emphasis: useful trains of reasoning must be logical; but they also need to be guided by other considerations which are quite apart from logic.

Let us make another choice, substituting $b\,c$ for $t$:

$$
\begin{aligned}
b\,c &= (a\,{-b} + a\,{-c})\,{-(b\,c)} + {-(a\,{-b} + a\,{-c})}b\,c \\
&= (a\,{-b} + a\,{-c})({-b} + {-c}) + ({-a} + b)({-a} + c)b\,c \\
&= a\,{-b} + a\,{-c} + ({-a} + b\,c)b\,c \\
&= a\,{-b} + a\,{-c} + b\,c.
\end{aligned}
$$

But, by 3·83, $a\,{-b} + a\,{-c} + b\,c = b\,c$ is equivalent to

$$(a\,{-b} + a\,{-c}) \subset b\,c.$$

Thus this conclusion can be read "All those who are either men but not mortal or men but not fallible are fallible mortals." This time the whole conclusion seems to be a joke. But if we remember that a conclusion drawn by Poretsky's law is equivalent to the data (so that, turn about, the premises given are inferrable from the conclusion), it is rather interesting, because it gives us the following little problem: "If all those who are either men but not fallible or men but not mortal, are fallible mortals, what follows about the class of men?" The answer is "That all men are fallible and all men are mortal"; the longer statement is just another way of saying that.

Let us make one further such substitution; of $a$ for $t$:

$$a = (a\,{-b} + a\,{-c})\,{-a} + -(a\,{-b} + a\,{-c})a$$
$$= 0 + (-a + b\,c)a = a\,b\,c.$$

But [1·03] $a = a\,b\,c$ is $a \subset b\,c$.

This is the obvious conclusion, "All men are fallible mortals." If we seem not to have had much luck in drawing from our premises conclusions which are both important and other than obvious, it may be well to point out that the premises in this case are traditionally supposed to give *no* mediate inferences whatever.

We could exhaust the possible substitutions for $t$ above, and resulting conclusions, which should be restricted to the terms $a$, $b$, and $c$, which appear in the premises (there are 256 of these), but of course the law holds also where $t$ is anything we please. An infinite number of conclusions follow from the given premises. This fact is quite interesting in view of conceptions which are cultivated, if not enforced, by traditional doctrines—that all valid inference, except immediate, is fundamentally syllogistic; that given two premises, the syllogistic conclusion, if any, is determined; and that, therefore, the inferences to be drawn from given premises are dictated by logic. As a fact, and as the above considerations prove beyond a doubt, logic cannot be thus prescriptive. Given premises *and* conclusion, logic can determine whether this conclusion follows; or given the premises, it can, in terms of general formulæ, divide all possible propositions into two classes, those which can be inferred from these premises and those which cannot. (Traditional logic does not provide any method of doing this last, but symbolic logic does.) But it is completely impossible that any logic should dictate *the* conclusion from given premises, or even *a* conclusion; precisely because the number of inferences which can validly be drawn is always infinite.

It is an obvious corollary that the direction which a process of inference is to take must be determined by non-logical considerations such as usefulness and pertinence to the problem in hand. For some centuries logicians debated whether logic is a science or an art, because they mistakenly supposed that it could prescribe the course of sound thinking. Logic is a science, but reasoning is an art. Logic may be taught; but reasoning to valuable results requires also other characteristics which are difficult or impossible to impart—imagination, ingenuity, a sense for the relevant, and persistence.

Aside from the errors of traditional logic, its principles also impose non-logical and unwarranted restrictions upon valid inference. But in part, these restrictions are dictated by general considerations of practice, calculated to satisfy the extra-logical considerations to which useful thinking must give heed. If we were set the problem of formulating such modes of inference as will meet, in maximum degree, the criteria (1) simplicity and ease of understanding, (2) wide range of application, (3) accord with the most frequently desirable direction of thinking, we should be hard put to it to do better than the syllogism. This fact does not necessarily reflect any peculiar cleverness on the part of Aristotle and the other founders of logic. They looked back to those types of inference, previously uncodified, which successful human thinking most frequently exemplified, or to which cogent examples of reasoning might be reduced. Naturally such exemplified modes of inference reflect the pragmatic determinants of good reasoning as well as the consideration of validity.

It remains to illustrate briefly the application of the algebra to problems which are outside the scope of traditional modes. The examples chosen are from historical sources.

*Example 1.*[4]

The members of a certain collection are classified in three ways: as $a$'s or not, as $b$'s or not, and as $c$'s or not. It is then found that the class $b$ is made up precisely of the $a$'s which are not $c$'s and the $c$'s which are not $a$'s. How is the class $a$ constituted?

Given: $b = a\,{-c} + {-a}\,c$. To solve for $a$.

By 4·9, the given equation is equivalent to

$$b\,{-(a\,{-c} + {-a}\,c)} + {-b}(a\,{-c} + {-a}\,c) = 0.$$

Hence $b(a\,c + {-a}\,{-c}) + {-b}(a\,{-c} + {-a}\,c) = 0.$

$$a\,b\,c + {-a}\,b\,{-c} + a\,{-b}\,{-c} + {-a}\,{-b}\,c = 0.$$ (See Figure 7.)

[4] See Venn, "Boole's System of Logic," in *Mind*, I (1876), 487.

Collecting the coefficients of $a$ and $-a$:

$$(b\,c + -b\,-c)a + (b\,-c + -b\,c)\,-a = 0.$$

Hence [5·6] $(b\,-c + -b\,c) \subset a \subset -(b\,c + -b\,-c)$.

But $-(b\,c + -b\,-c) = b\,-c + -b\,c$.

Hence [2·2] $a = b\,-c + -b\,c$.

The class $a$ is composed of the $b$'s which are not $c$'s together with the $c$'s which are not $b$'s. This conclusion may be read from the diagram (Figure 7) of the given data. It is interesting to note, from this diagram, that the given equation sets up a

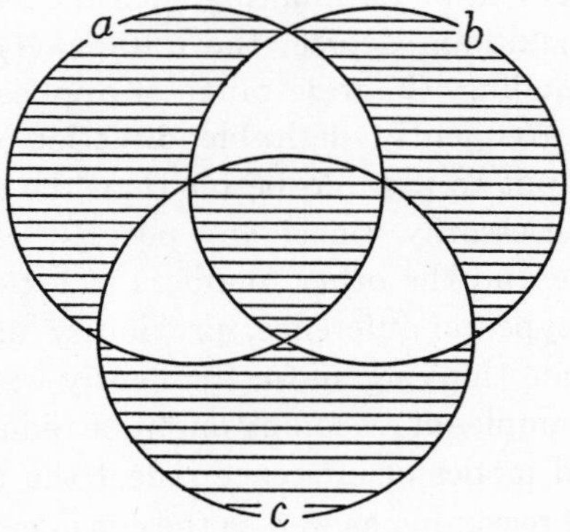


FIG. 7.

relation which is symmetrical with respect to all three classes, $a$, $b$, and $c$. The conclusion accords with this, being of the same form as the data, with $a$ and $b$ interchanged.

*Example 2.*[5]

A certain club has the following rules: (1) The financial committee shall be chosen from among the general committee. (2) No one shall be a member both of the general and library committees unless he be also on the financial committee. (3) No member of the library committee shall be on the financial committee. Simplify these rules.

Let $f$ = member of the financial committee,
$g$ = member of the general committee,
$l$ = member of the library committee.

[5] See Venn, *Symbolic Logic*, 2d ed., p. 331.

Given: (1) $f \subset g$; $f -g = 0$.
(2) $(g\, l) \subset f$; $-f\, g\, l = 0$.
(3) $f\, l = 0$.

To combine and simplify.

By 4·71, the premises are together equivalent to $f -g + -f\, g\, l + f\, l = 0$.

Hence, $f -g + -f\, g\, l + f\, l(g + -g) = 0 = f -g + -f\, g\, l + f\, g\, l + f -g\, l = (f -g + f -g\, l) + g\, l(-f + f)$.

But [4·5] $f -g + f -g\, l = f -g$.

And [4·6] $g\, l(-f + f) = g\, l$.

Hence the data are equivalent to $f -g + g\, l = 0$, and [4·71] to $f -g = 0$ and $g\, l = 0$.

And [2·8] $f -g = 0$ is $f \subset g$.

Thus the rules may be simplified as follows: (1) The financial committee shall be chosen from among the general committee. (2) No member of the general committee shall be on the library committee.

*Example 3.*[6]

Demonstrate that from the premises "All *a* is either *b* or *c*" and "All *c* is *a*" no conclusion can be drawn which involves only two of the classes, *a*, *b*, and *c*.

Given: (1) $a \subset (b + c)$.
(2) $c \subset a$.

To prove that elimination of any one element will give no conclusion, or a conclusion which follows from one or other of the premises alone. (De Morgan does not mean to include immediate inferences.)

By 2·8, (1) is equivalent to $a -(b + c) = 0 = a -b -c$.

And (2) is equivalent to $-a\, c = 0$.

Combining these: $a -b -c + -a\, c = 0$.

Eliminating *a*, [5·51] $(-b -c)c = 0$; which is the identity, $0 = 0$.

Eliminating *c*, $-a(a -b) = 0$; which is the identity, $0 = 0$.

[6] See De Morgan, *Formal Logic*, p. 123.

To eliminate $b$, expand the equation as a normal-form function of $b$:

$$a -b -c + -a\, c(b + -b) = 0 = (-a\, c)b + (a -c + -a\, c) -b.$$

Hence, $(-a\, c)(a -c + -a\, c) = 0 = -a\, c$; which is identical with (2).

Thus the result of elimination of any one of the terms, $a$, $b$, and $c$, is either indeterminate or identical with a premise.

*Example 4.*[7]

Suppose that the analysis of the properties of a particular class of substances has led to the following general conclusions:

(1) That wherever the properties $a$ and $b$ are combined, either the property $c$, or the property $d$, is present also; but they are not jointly present.

(2) That wherever the properties $b$ and $c$ are combined, the properties $a$ and $d$ are either both present with them, or both absent.

(3) That wherever the properties $a$ and $b$ are both absent, the properties $c$ and $d$ are both absent also; and *vice versa*, where the properties $c$ and $d$ are both absent, $a$ and $b$ are both absent also.

Let it then be required from the above to determine what may be concluded in any particular instance from the presence of the property $a$ with respect to the presence or absence of the properties $b$ and $c$, paying no regard to the property $d$.

Given: (1) $(a\, b) \subset (c -d + -c\, d)$.

(2) $(b\, c) \subset (a\, d + -a -d)$.

(3) $(-a -b) \subset (-c -d)$, and $(-c -d) \subset (-a -b)$:

$$-a -b = -c -d.$$

To eliminate $d$ and solve for $a$.

By 2·8, (1) is equivalent to

$$a\, b -(c -d + -c\, d) = 0 = a\, b\, (c\, d + -c -d)$$
$$0 = a\, b\, c\, d + a\, b -c -d. \qquad (4)$$

Similarly, (2) is equivalent to

$$b\, c -(a\, d + -a -d) = 0 = b\, c\, (a -d + -a\, d)$$
$$0 = a\, b\, c -d + -a\, b\, c\, d. \qquad (5)$$

[7] Boole, *Laws of Thought*, pp. 118–120.

By 4·9, (3) is equivalent to

$$-a\,-b\,-(-c\,-d) + -(-a\,-b)\,-c\,-d = 0,$$

Or [3·12] $-a\,-b\,(c + d) + (a + b)\,-c\,-d = 0 =$

$$-a\,-b\,c + -a\,-b\,d + a\,-c\,-d + b\,-c\,-d. \qquad (6)$$

Combining (4), (5), and (6),

$$a\,b\,c\,d + a\,b\,-c\,-d + a\,b\,c\,-d + -a\,b\,c\,d + -a\,-b\,c + -a\,-b\,d + a\,-c\,-d + b\,-c\,-d = 0. \qquad (7)$$

Collecting the coefficients of $d$, (7) is,

$$(a\,b\,c + -a\,b\,c + -a\,-b\,c + -a\,-b)\,d + (a\,b\,-c + a\,b\,c + -a\,-b\,c + a\,-c + b\,-c)\,-d = 0.$$

Simplifying these coefficients, by 4·5 and 4·6,

$$(b\,c + -a\,-b)\,d + (a\,b + -a\,-b\,c + a\,-c + b\,-c)\,-d = 0.$$

Eliminating $d$, by 5·51,

$$(b\,c + -a\,-b)(a\,b + -a\,-b\,c + a\,-c + b\,-c) = 0 = a\,b\,c + -a\,-b\,c.$$

By 5·6, the equation $a\,b\,c + -a\,-b\,c = 0$, gives the solution for $a$, $(-b\,c) \subset a \subset (-b + -c)$.

Wherever the property $c$ is present but $b$ is absent, property $a$ is present; and wherever $a$ is present, either $b$ is absent or $c$ is absent. This conclusion can be read from the diagram (Figure 8), which represents equation (7), in which the premises are combined.

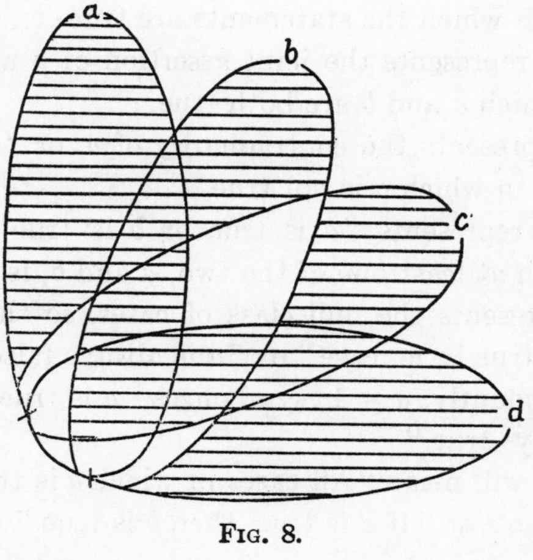


FIG. 8.

## CHAPTER IV

### THE TWO-VALUED ALGEBRA

The Boole-Schröder Algebra applies to assertable statements as well as to classes. Perhaps this may be made clear by the device which traditional logic has sometimes used to make the transition from the syllogism proper to the 'hypothetical syllogism.' The conditional argument "If *A* is *B*, *C* is *D*; but *A* is *B*: therefore *C* is *D*" may be translated:

> All cases in which *A* is *B* are cases in which *C* is *D*.
> This case is a case in which *A* is *B*.
> Hence, this case is a case in which *C* is *D*.

That is to say, a logic of classes can be extended to assertable statements by applying it to the classes of cases in which such statements are true. Such a class of cases constitutes the extension of the statement. Thus a logic of classes in extension likewise applies to the logic of statements in extension. The algebra, therefore, admits of such application, when the following interpretations are assigned:

(1) $a$, $b$, $c$, etc., represent statements in extension: the classes of instances in which the statements are true.

(2) $a \times b$ represents the joint assertion of $a$ and $b$; the class of cases in which $a$ and $b$ are both true.

(3) $-a$ represents the contradictory of $a$, or "$a$ is false"; the class of cases in which $a$ is not true.

(4) $a + b$ represents "$a$ is true or $b$ is true"; the class of cases in which at least one of the two, $a$ and $b$, is true.

(5) 0 represents the null class of cases, so that $a = 0$ symbolizes "$a$ is true in no case" or "$a$ is always false."

(6) Consonantly, $a = 1$ symbolizes "$a$ is true in every case" or "$a$ is always true."

(7) $a \subset b$ will mean "All cases in which $a$ is true are cases in which $b$ is true" or "If $a$ is true, then $b$ is true."

(8) $a = b$ will mean "The cases in which $a$ is true are identically the cases in which $b$ is true" or "$a$ is true when $b$ is true, and false when $b$ is false."
All the laws of the algebra will hold for this interpretation.

However, statements are of two general types. (1) There are those which cover, or assert, ambiguously, any one of a multiplicity of instances. Such statements contain some term (or terms) which, implicitly or explicitly, is variable in denotation. For example, "All *A* is *B*" contains the variable terms *A* and *B*. It is true in some instances—for some meanings of *A* and *B*—and false for others: the statement itself cannot properly be said to be either true or false. (2) There are statements which contain no such variable term, but are unambiguous and either definitely true or definitely false. Statements of the first type are now called 'propositional functions'; and the name 'proposition' is restricted to the second type. Thus a proposition, in contrast to a propositional function, will contain no variable or ambiguous term: it cannot be true in some instances and false in others; if it is ever true it is always true, and if it is ever false it is always false.

The Boole-Schröder Algebra applies both to propositions and to propositional functions. The application to propositional functions is more closely related to its interpretation for classes than is the application to propositions. Thus if our principal interest were in the algebra, we should take up propositional functions next. But in order to understand current developments in symbolic logic, it is better to reverse this order: we shall consider propositions in this chapter, propositional functions in the next.

As we have just seen, there is no difference, for propositions, between being true and being always true; between being false and being always false. Thus there is one further principle, which does not hold for classes or for propositional functions, which is required in order to restrict the terms of the algebra to statements which are propositions: namely, "For every element $a$, either $a = 0$ or $a = 1$." If we add this assumption, and its consequences, to the Boole-Schröder Algebra, we have what is called the Two-valued Algebra. This is a calculus of propositions in extension.

The Two-valued Algebra, then, as a mathematical system, consists of all the laws of the Boole-Schröder Algebra, as set forth in Chapter II, together with the additional laws which result when we add the postulate which restricts the elements of the algebra to one or other of the two values, 0 and 1. Thus there is no need to prove over again those laws of the Two-valued Algebra which are already established in Chapter II. But for completeness, we shall repeat here those which are important for the logic of propositions.

In thus repeating them, however, we shall transcribe these laws into a somewhat different symbolism. This translation will serve two purposes: first, it will set off the propositional interpretation of principles which are common to the two systems from their interpretation for classes. And second, it will introduce the reader to the symbolism most used to-day for the calculus of propositions. These changes of symbolism include the following:

(1) Instead of $a, b, c$, etc., we shall use $p, q, r$, etc., for propositions.

(2) Instead of $-p$, we shall write $\sim p$ for the contradictory of $p$, or "$p$ is false."

(3) Instead of $p \subset q$, we shall write $p \supset q$ for "If $p$ is true, then $q$ is true" or "$p$ implies $q$."

(4) Instead of $p + q$, we shall write $p \vee q$ for "At least one of the two, $p$ and $q$, is true" or "Either $p$ or $q$."

(5) Instead of $p = q$, we shall write $p \equiv q$ for "$p$ and $q$ are both true or both false" or "$p$ is equivalent to $q$." However, we shall continue to use the symbol $=$ for purely notational equivalences, such as $p = 1$, and for indicating that two expressions are to have the same meaning, by definition.

Let us now see what some of our theorems, in Chapter II, will look like, and will mean, as laws of the Two-valued Algebra. For example, 3·7 will be,

$$\text{If } p \supset q \text{ and } q \supset r, \text{ then } p \supset r,$$

and will be read "If $p$ implies $q$ and $q$ implies $r$, then $p$ implies $r$." And 2·92 will be

$$p \equiv q \text{ is equivalent to } \sim p \equiv \sim q,$$

which may be read "'$p$ is equivalent to $q$' is equivalent to '($p$ is false) is equivalent to ($q$ is false.)'"

At once the reader will observe that we are here writing the same relations in two different ways. In 2·92, the phrase "is equivalent to" connecting $p \equiv q$ and $\sim p \equiv \sim q$ supposedly represents the same relation as the symbol $\equiv$; that is, the relation of being equivalent propositions. To write this same relation sometimes in English, sometimes in symbols, is awkward and possibly confusing. The theorem would be read in the same way if written completely in symbols:

$$(p \equiv q) \equiv (\sim p \equiv \sim q).$$

Similarly in 3·7, "If . . ., then . . ." supposedly represents the same relation of implication which is symbolized by $\supset$. The theorem would be read in the same way if written

$$(p \supset q \text{ and } q \supset r) \supset (p \supset r).$$

Further, the relation represented here by "and" is that of joint-assertion, or 'both true,' which is the same which would be symbolized, between $p$ and $q$, by $p \times q$ or $p\,q$. The meaning would, therefore, be unchanged if we should write the theorem completely in symbols, thus:

$$[(p \supset q)(q \supset r)] \supset (p \supset r).$$

This is true, of course, only because the elements of the system now represent propositions. For the *class*-interpretation of the algebra, the relation symbolized by $\subset$ in the theorem

If $a \subset b$ and $b \subset c$, then $a \subset c$,

is *not* the relation meant by the English "If . . ., then . . .": and the relation "and" between $a \subset b$ and $b \subset c$ is *not* the relation of classes symbolized by $\times$.

The question as to what right we have to translate the English part of our theorems into symbols, in the case of the propositional interpretation, is a separate question, which we shall have to deal with later. But at least one sees that the reading of the theorems is not affected if we represent them in this more compact and less awkward form. This is the practice we shall adopt here in repeating, as laws of the propositional calculus, the theorems proved in Chapter II.

One more change of notation is required if we are to bring our symbolism completely into accord with current practice: the substitution of bold-faced dots, as punctuation, for the use of parentheses and brackets in formulæ. For example, we have written above

$$[(p \supset q)(q \supset r)] \supset (p \supset r).$$

Hereafter, this will be written,

$$p \supset q \,.\, q \supset r \,:\, \supset \,.\, p \supset r.$$

The general principle of such punctuation is simple: a double dot or colon (:) is a stronger mark of punctuation than a single dot (.); three dots is a stronger mark than two; four is stronger than three, etc. For example, the formula above is read "If $p$ implies $q$ and $q$ implies $r$, then $p$ implies $r$." If we had written instead

$$p \supset q : q \supset r \,.\supset .\, p \supset r,$$

it would have meant the same as

$$(p \supset q)[(q \supset r) \supset (p \supset r)],$$

that is, "$p$ implies $q$; and if $q$ implies $r$, then $p$ implies $r$." However, parentheses are still used where it is necessary to indicate the negative of a complex expression: the negative of $p\,q$ is written $\sim(p\,q)$; the negative of $p \vee \sim q$, $\sim(p \vee \sim q)$.

With a little practice, the reader will have no trouble in interpreting the significance of this style of punctuating the symbolism; especially since the meaning of the first few theorems to be cited will be given. A complete and careful account of the matter is contained in the Appendix on "The Use of Dots as Brackets."

One further point, and we shall have done with these preliminary matters: A proposition $p$ is either always true or always false; either $p = 1$ or $p = 0$. The symbolism $\sim p$ means "$p$ is false"; so does $p = 0$. Hence these two are here interchangeable. Similarly $p$ and $p = 1$ are different ways of expressing "$p$ is true," and are interchangeable. We can, then, wherever we choose, write $\sim p$ for $p = 0$, in a theorem, and $p$ for $p = 1$; the meaning of the theorem will be unaffected. Thus the expressions $p = 0$ and $p = 1$ can be eliminated. However, we shall sometimes write a principle in both ways, in order that the derivation of the simpler form may be clear. The first few laws will be given both in symbols and in English; and occasionally later theorems also will be translated.

The additional postulate of the Two-valued Algebra may be expressed as follows:

*7·1* $(p = 0) \equiv \sim p$

This leads immediately to the consequence:

*7·11* $p \equiv (p = 1)$

[2·9] $\sim(\sim p) \equiv p$. Hence [7·1] $(\sim p = 0) \equiv p$.

And [2·91, 1·01] $\sim p = 0$ is equivalent to $p = 1$.

Although we give the theorems, below, the same number which they had in Chapter II, it should be remembered that whenever they are simplified in form by substituting $\sim p$ for $p = 0$, or $p$ for $p = 1$, this procedure depends upon 7·1 or 7·11.

The theorems of Chapter II which are most important as laws of the propositional calculus are the following:

*1·02* $p \vee q \,.\equiv.\, \sim(\sim p \sim q)$

"Either $p$ is true or $q$ is true" is equivalent to "It is false that '$p$ is false and $q$ is false.'"

*1·1* $p\,p \,.\equiv.\, p$

"$p$ and $p$ are both true" is equivalent to "$p$ is true."

*1·2* $p\,q \,.\equiv.\, q\,p$

"$p$ and $q$ are both true" is equivalent to "$q$ and $p$ are both true."

*2·2* $p \equiv q \,.\equiv:\, p \supset q \,.\, q \supset p$

"$p$ is equivalent to $q$" is equivalent to "$p$ implies $q$, and $q$ implies $p$."

*2·3* $p \supset p$

Any proposition $p$ implies itself.

*2·4* $p\,q . \supset . p \qquad p\,q . \supset . q$

If $p$ and $q$ are both true, then $p$ is true: and if $p$ and $q$ are both true, then $q$ is true.

*2·5* $\sim(p \sim p) \qquad p \sim p . = . 0$

It is false that "$p$ is both true and false"; or, no proposition $p$ is both true and false.

*2·8* $\sim(p \sim q) . \equiv . p \supset q \qquad p \sim q . = . 0$ is equivalent to $p \supset q$.

"It is false that '$p$ is true and $q$ false'" is equivalent to "$p$ implies $q$." This theorem will be of particular importance later, in discussing the meaning of 'implies.'

*2·81* $p \supset q . \supset : p\,r . \supset . q\,r$ If $p \supset q$, then $p\,r \supset q\,r$.

*2·9* $\sim(\sim p) \equiv p$

"It is false that $p$ is false" is equivalent to "$p$ is true."

*2·91* $p \equiv \sim q . \equiv . \sim p \equiv q$

*3·1* $\sim(\sim p \vee \sim q) . \equiv . p\,q$

"It is false that 'either $p$ is false or $q$ is false'" is equivalent to "$p$ and $q$ are both true."

*3·12* $\sim(p\,q) . \equiv . \sim p \vee \sim q$

*3·2* $p \vee p . \equiv . p$

*3·3* $p \vee q . \equiv . q \vee p$

*3·5* $p \vee \sim p \qquad p \vee \sim p . = . 1$

*3·6* $\sim p \vee q . \equiv . p \supset q \qquad \sim p \vee q . = . 1$ is equivalent to $p \supset q$.

*3·7* $p \supset q . q \supset r : \supset . p \supset r$

The relation of implication is transitive.

*3·8* $p \supset q . \equiv . \sim q \supset \sim p$

"$p$ implies $q$" is equivalent to "If $q$ is false, then $p$ is false."

*3·81* $p \supset \sim q . \equiv . q \supset \sim p$

*3·82* $\sim p \supset q . \equiv . \sim q \supset p$

*3·9* $p . \supset . p \vee q$

If $p$ is true, then either $p$ is true or $q$ is true.

*4·2* $p \supset r . q \supset s : \supset : p q . \supset . r s$

*4·21* $p \supset r . q \supset s : \supset : p \vee q . \supset . r \vee s$

*4·22* $p \supset r . q \supset r : \supset : p \vee q . \supset . r$

*4·23* $p \supset q . p \supset r : \supset : p . \supset . q r$

*4·4* $p . q \vee r : \equiv : p q . \vee . p r$

*4·6* $p . \equiv : p q . \vee . p \sim q$

*4·62* $p \vee q . \equiv : p . \vee . \sim p q$

The further theorems below, which were not proved in Chapter II, are also of importance in the calculus of propositions. Most of them involve some use of 7·1 or 7·11, and thus do not belong to the calculus of classes.

*7·2* $p q . \supset . r : \equiv : p . \supset . q \supset r : \equiv : q . \supset . p \supset r$

[3·6] $p q . \supset . r : \equiv : \sim(p q) . \vee . r$

[3·12] $\equiv : \sim p \vee \sim q . \vee . r$

[3·31] $\equiv : \sim p . \vee . \sim q \vee r$

[3·6] $\equiv : \sim p . \vee . q \supset r$

[3·6] $\equiv : p . \supset . q \supset r$

Since, by 2·2, equivalence is a reciprocal implication, 7·2 implies two corollaries:

*7·21* $p q . \supset . r : \supset : p . \supset . q \supset r$

*7·22* $p . \supset . q \supset r : \supset : p q . \supset . r$

The law upon which Mrs. Ladd-Franklin's 'antilogism,' discussed in Chapter III, depends is the following:

*7·3* $p q . \supset . r : \equiv : p \sim r . \supset . \sim q : \equiv : q \sim r . \supset . \sim p$

[3·6] $p q . \supset r : \equiv : \sim(p q) . \vee . r$

[3·12] $\equiv : \sim p \vee \sim q . \vee . r$

[3·31] $\equiv : \sim p \vee r . \vee . \sim q$

[3·12] $\equiv : \sim(p \sim r) . \vee . \sim q$

[3·6] $\equiv : p \sim r . \supset . \sim q$

The relation $p \supset q$ in this calculus has not quite the usual meaning of "$p$ implies $q$," due to the fact that relations of the system are those of extension. For this reason, the relation here symbolized by $\supset$ is commonly called 'material implication.' Theorems which exhibit the peculiar properties of this relation are the following:

***7·4*** $p . \supset . q \supset p$

[4·1] If $p = 1$, then $q \supset p$; $(p = 1) . \supset . q \supset p$

[7·11] $p \equiv (p = 1)$

If $p$ is true, then any proposition $q$ implies $p$; or, a true proposition is implied by any proposition.

***7·41*** $\sim p . \supset . p \supset q$

[2·6] If $p = 0$, then $p \supset q$; $(p = 0) . \supset . p \supset q$

If $p$ is false, then $p$ implies any proposition $q$; or, a false proposition implies any proposition.

***7·5*** $p\, q . \supset . p \supset q$ $\qquad$ $p\, q . \supset . q \supset p$

[2·4] $p\, q . \supset . q$ and $p\, q . \supset . p$

[7·4] $q . \supset . p \supset q$ and $p . \supset . q \supset p$

Hence [3·7] the theorem follows.

If $p$ and $q$ are both true, then each implies the other.

***7·51*** $\sim p \sim q . \supset . p \supset q$ $\qquad$ $\sim p \sim q . \supset . q \supset p$

[2·4] $\sim p \sim q . \supset . \sim p$ and $\sim p \sim q . \supset . \sim q$

[7.41] $\sim p . \supset . p \supset q$ and $\sim q . \supset . q \supset p$

Hence [3·7] the theorem follows.

If $p$ and $q$ are both false, then each implies the other.

***7·52*** $\sim p\, q . \supset . p \supset q$

[2·4] $\sim p\, q . \supset . q$

[7·4] $q . \supset . p \supset q$

Hence [3·7] the theorem follows.

If $p$ is false and $q$ true, then $p$ implies $q$.

***7·6*** $\sim(p \supset q) \supset p$

[3·8] 7·41 is equivalent to the theorem.

If $p$ does not imply some given proposition $q$, then $p$ is true.

***7·61*** $\sim(p \supset q) \supset \sim q$

[7·4] $q . \supset . p \supset q$; which [3·81] is equivalent to the theorem.

If $q$ is not implied by some given proposition $p$, then $q$ is false.

**7·62** $\sim(p \supset q) \,.\supset.\, p \supset \sim q$

[7·61] $\sim(p \supset q) \supset \sim q$

[7·4] $\sim q \,.\supset.\, p \supset \sim q$

Hence [3·7] the theorem follows.

If $p$ does not imply $q$, then $p$ implies the denial of $q$.

**7·63** $\sim(p \supset q) \,.\supset.\, \sim p \supset q$

[2·9] $\sim(p \supset q) \supset \sim(\sim p)$

[7·41] $\sim(\sim p) \,.\supset.\, \sim p \supset q$

Hence [3·7] the theorem follows.

If $p$ does not imply $q$, then the denial of $p$ implies $q$.

**7·64** $\sim(p \supset q) \,.\supset.\, \sim p \supset \sim q$

[7·61] $\sim(p \supset q) \supset \sim q$

[7·4] $\sim q \,.\supset.\, \sim p \supset \sim q$

Hence [3·7] the theorem follows.

If $p$ does not imply $q$, then the denial of $p$ implies the denial of $q$.

**7·65** $\sim(p \supset q) \,.\supset.\, q \supset p$

[7·61] $\sim(p \supset q) \supset p$

[7·4] $p \,.\supset.\, q \supset p$

Hence [3·7] the theorem follows.

If $p$ does not imply $q$, then $q$ implies $p$.

All of these peculiar properties of material implication are simple consequences of the four principles:

(1) $p \equiv (p = 1)$
(2) $\sim p \equiv (p = 0)$
(3) $0 \supset p$
(4) $p \supset 1$

These four laws confine the calculus to relations of extension—on the interpretation of 0 as the null class of cases, or falsity, and 1 as the universal class of cases, or truth. When $\sim p$, "$p$ is false," is equivalent to $p = 0$; and $p$, or "$p$ is true," is equivalent to $p = 1$, the elements of the system, $p$, $q$, $r$, etc., do not really represent propositions—that is, different meaningful assertions—but only the truth or falsity of these, the class of cases (1 or 0) in which they are true. Any two elements which have the value

1 are identical so far as their properties in this calculus are concerned; and any two elements having the value 0 are identical. Thus, in strict accuracy, it should be said that there are only two elements in this Two-valued Algebra; the two truth-values or extensions of propositions, 0 and 1. Every element $p$ simply represents, ambiguously, one or other of these. That the extension 1—the extension of any true proposition—contains every extension, is the real meaning of 7·4,

$$p \,.\supset.\, q \supset p, \qquad\qquad (p = 1) \,.\supset.\, q \supset p.$$

"A true proposition is implied by any proposition $q$." And that the extension 0—the extension of any false proposition—is contained in every extension, is the real meaning of 7·41,

$$\sim p \,.\supset.\, p \supset q, \qquad\qquad (p = 0) \,.\supset.\, p \supset q.$$

"A false proposition implies any proposition $q$."

The remainder of these paradoxical laws of material implication result simply from the fact that, for any pair of propositions, $p$ and $q$, there are only four possibilities as to truth-value:

(1) $p = 1, q = 1$: $\quad p \supset q, \quad q \supset p, \quad \sim p \supset q, \quad \sim q \supset p.$
(2) $p = 0, q = 1$: $\quad p \supset q, \quad \sim(q \supset p), \quad \sim p \supset q, \quad \sim q \supset p.$
(3) $p = 1, q = 0$: $\quad \sim(p \supset q), \quad q \supset p, \quad \sim p \supset q, \quad \sim q \supset p.$
(4) $p = 0, q = 0$: $\quad p \supset q, \quad q \supset p, \quad \sim(\sim p \supset q), \quad \sim(\sim q \supset p).$

The material implication, $p \supset q$, *always* holds unless $p = 1$ and $q = 0$—case (3): thus its exact meaning is given by 2·8,

$$p \supset q \,.\equiv.\, \sim(p \sim q),$$

$p \supset q$ is equivalent to "It is false that '$p$ is true and $q$ false.'"

Since the relation $p \equiv q$ is a reciprocal implication, it shares the peculiarities of material implication, and is called 'material equivalence.' It does not represent equivalence of logical force or meaning, but only equivalence of truth-value. It holds whenever $p$ and $q$ are both true or both false; and fails to hold only when one of two propositions is true and the other false:

*7·7* $\quad p\, q \,.\supset.\, p \equiv q$

*7·71* $\quad \sim p \sim q \,.\supset.\, p \equiv q$

*7·72* $\quad p \sim q \,.\supset.\, \sim(p \equiv q)$

The fact that almost all developments of symbolic logic are based upon this relation of extensional or material implication—a relation of truth-values, not of content or logical significance—is due to their having been built up, gradually, on the foundation laid by Boole; that is, upon a calculus originally devised to deal with the relations of classes. There is nothing more esoteric, behind these peculiar properties of material implication, than this somewhat unfortunate historical accident.

We shall have occasion in Chapter VI to develop a calculus of propositions which is not restricted to such material or extensional relations, and is based upon an implication-relation not having these peculiar properties.

# CHAPTER V

## EXTENSION OF THE TWO-VALUED ALGEBRA TO PROPOSITIONAL FUNCTIONS

As we have seen, a propositional function is a statement involving some term or terms whose meaning is ambiguous or variable. "All *A* is *B*," "If *A* is *B*, *C* is *D*," "*A* is mortal," etc., are propositional functions, in which *A*, *B*, etc., are the variable elements. If in "*A* is mortal" we substitute 'Socrates' for *A*, the statement becomes true. If we substitute 'Sirius,' it becomes false. If we substitute '7,' it becomes nonsense. Thus any variable in any propositional function has a definite range of meaning—a range of specific terms which it ambiguously represents. The variable *A*, in "*A* is mortal," includes in its range of meaning the specific term 'Socrates,' for which the propositional function is true, and the term 'Sirius,' for which the function is false; but the number '7,' which makes the function nonsense, is excluded from this range. Specific terms within the range of meaning of a variable in a function are called 'values' of that variable. What is and what is not included among the values of a variable are determined by the rest of the statement—the invariant part of the function: the range of values which 'make sense' when substituted for *A* in "*A* is mortal," is fixed, not by *A*, but by "is mortal." When, for each variable in a propositional function, a value of that variable is substituted, the expression becomes a proposition which is either definitely true or definitely false. The prevailing definitions are the following: A proposition is any expression which is either true or false. A propositional function is an expression containing a variable or variables, and such that when for each variable a value of that variable is substituted, it becomes a proposition. It should be remembered that the values of a variable include terms which make the function false, as well as those which make it true.

It is customary to represent the invariant part of any propositional function by $\varphi$, $\psi$, etc., or by $f$, $f'$, $F$, etc. We shall use the Greek letters here. (Propositional functions in general should not be confused with the functions of the Boole-Schröder Algebra discussed in Chapter II. These latter are expressions *in the algebra*: when the algebra is interpreted as a propositional calculus, they are propositional functions, but of a very special kind; when the algebra is given the class-interpretation, they are not propositional functions at all.) The variables in any propositional function are represented by $x$, $y$, $z$, etc. Thus the whole propositional function is symbolized by $\varphi(x)$, $\psi(x, y)$, etc. When there is only one variable, the parentheses can be omitted, and the function written as $\varphi x$, $\psi x$, etc.

Let us begin with the simplest case—functions of one variable. $\varphi x$ represents any statement such as "$x$ is mortal," "$x$ runs fast," "The successor of $x$ is an odd number." Let us represent the different values of $x$, in $\varphi x$, by $a$, $b$, $c$, etc. Then $\varphi a$, $\varphi b$, $\varphi c$, etc., are *propositions*. Since this is the case, the Two-valued Algebra applies to them: they represent, in special form, precisely the same thing which is symbolized by $p$, $q$, $r$, etc., in the preceding chapter; and all the laws of that system will hold of such propositions.

Suppose now we are given an expression such as

$$\varphi a \times \varphi b \times \varphi c \times \ldots,$$

or

$$\varphi a \cdot \varphi b \cdot \varphi c \cdot \ldots,$$

Since $\varphi a$, $\varphi b$, $\varphi c$, etc., are propositions, this is simply an expression of the form, $p \cdot q \cdot r \cdot \ldots$, in the Two-valued Algebra. It means "$\varphi a$ is true and $\varphi b$ is true and $\varphi c$ is true, and so on": that is, "$\varphi x$ is true for all values of $x$," or loosely, "$\varphi x$ is always true." Similarly, the expression

$$\varphi a \vee \varphi b \vee \varphi c \vee \ldots$$

means "Either $\varphi a$ is true or $\varphi b$ is true or $\varphi c$ is true, and so on": that is, "$\varphi x$ is true for some (at least one) value of $x$," or loosely, "$\varphi x$ is sometimes true."

These are important new ideas of the calculus of propositional functions. We shall use the current symbolism for them: $(x) \cdot \varphi x$ for "$\varphi x$ is true for all values of $x$"; and $(\exists x) \cdot \varphi x$ for "$\varphi x$ is true for some value, or values, of $x$." The symbolism

$(\exists x)$ here suggests "There exists an $x$ such that ..." These conventions can be expressed as definitions:

***8·01*** $(x) . \varphi x . = : \varphi a . \varphi b . \varphi c . \ldots$

***8·02*** $(\exists x) . \varphi x . = : \varphi a \vee \varphi b \vee \varphi c \vee \ldots$

These definitions are not, in reality, theoretically adequate. They presume that we could, if we chose and had the time, extend the expression on the right-hand side so as to exhaust the values of $x$ in $\varphi x$. But this would be possible only in case the number of such distinct values of $x$ should be finite. As a matter of fact, the number of values of a variable, in a propositional function, is often infinite—for example, when the variables represent numbers and the function is a formula of arithmetic. However, the procedure here set forth is so convenient, and so well exemplifies the connection between the calculus of propositions and the calculus of propositional functions, that we shall adopt it, in spite of this theoretical inadequacy. So long as no other relations are introduced than those with which we have here to deal, all theorems which hold for any finite number of values of a variable, hold generally. So that the theorems which are proved, on the basis of the definitions given above, are without exception valid theorems and perfectly general in their application.

It is to be observed that $(x) . \varphi x$ and $(\exists x) . \varphi x$ are propositions—compound propositions, whose constituents, connected by 'and' or 'or,' are the propositions $\varphi a$, $\varphi b$, etc. Also, since $p \supset q$ and $p \equiv q$ are propositions when $p$ and $q$ are propositions, $\varphi a \supset \psi a$ and $\varphi a \equiv \psi a$ are propositions. Hence, since $\varphi x \supset \psi x$ has as its values the propositions $\varphi a \supset \psi a$, $\varphi b \supset \psi b$, etc., $\varphi x \supset \psi x$ is a propositional function of the single variable $x$. Likewise, $\varphi x \equiv \psi x$ is a propositional function of one variable.

By applying the laws of the Two-valued Algebra to such propositions as $\varphi a$, $\psi a$, $\varphi b$, $\psi b$, etc., to propositions such as $\varphi a \supset \psi a$ and $\varphi a \equiv \psi a$, and to compound propositions of the forms

$$(x) . \varphi x, \quad (\exists x) . \varphi x, \quad (x) . \varphi x \supset \psi x, \quad (\exists x) . \varphi x \equiv \psi x,$$

etc., the calculus of propositional functions of one variable can be derived from the calculus of propositions. The principal theorems will be given below, and the manner of their derivation, when not obvious, will be indicated.

To avoid unnecessary parentheses, we adopt the following mode of writing negatives:

***8·03*** $\sim(x) \,.\, \varphi x \,.\, = \,.\, \sim[(x) \,.\, \varphi x]$

***8·04*** $\sim(\exists x) \,.\, \varphi x \,.\, = \,.\, \sim[(\exists x) \,.\, \varphi x]$

The first two theorems represent the extension of De Morgan's Theorem to propositional functions:

***8·1*** $(x) \,.\, \varphi x \,.\, \equiv \,.\, \sim(\exists x) \,.\, \sim\varphi x$

$$[3\cdot1] \quad \varphi a \,.\, \varphi b \,.\, \varphi c \,.\, \ldots : \equiv \,.\, \sim(\sim\varphi a \vee \sim\varphi b \vee \sim\varphi c \vee \ldots)$$

"$\varphi x$ is true for all values of $x$" is equivalent to "It is false that '$\varphi x$ is false for some values of $x$.'"

***8·11*** $(\exists x) \,.\, \varphi x \,.\, \equiv \,.\, \sim(x) \,.\, \sim\varphi x$

$$[1\cdot02] \quad \varphi a \vee \varphi b \vee \varphi c \vee \ldots : \equiv \,.\, \sim(\sim\varphi a \,.\, \sim\varphi b \,.\, \sim\varphi c \,.\, \ldots)$$

"$\varphi x$ is sometimes true" is the negative of "$\varphi x$ is always false."

It is understood, of course, that principles referred to in proof are the laws of the Two-valued Algebra, as given in the preceding chapter.

***8·2*** $(x) \,.\, \varphi x \,.\supset.\, \varphi n$

$$[2\cdot4] \quad \varphi a \,.\, \varphi b \,.\, \varphi c \,.\, \ldots : \supset \,.\, \varphi a,$$

And $\varphi a \,.\, \varphi b \,.\, \varphi c \,.\, \ldots : \supset \,.\, \varphi b$, etc.

Or, whatever value of $x$, in $\varphi x$, $n$ may be,

$$\varphi a \,.\, \varphi b \,.\, \varphi c \,.\, \ldots : \supset \,.\, \varphi n.$$

The theorem reads "If $\varphi x$ is always true, then $\varphi n$ is true" or "What is true of all is true of any." In writing this theorem, we use $n$ to represent 'any given one of the values of $x$, whether $a$ or $b$ or $c$, etc.' This convention will be continued.[1]

Notice the dots in 8·2. If the theorem had been written without the dot preceding the implication-sign,

$$(x) \,.\, \varphi x \supset \varphi n,$$

[1] The symbol $n$, with this meaning, is what the authors of *Principia Mathematica* call a "real variable," in contrast to $x$, in $(x) \,.\, \varphi x$ and $(\exists x) \,.\, \varphi x$, which they call an "apparent variable." The proposition-signs $p$, $q$, etc., and the class-symbols $a$, $b$, etc., are special cases of such real variables, as are also the letters in any mathematical formula, whether representing 'unknowns' or 'constants.' Such symbols represent ambiguously any one of the class of propositions, or the class of numbers, etc.

it would have meant $(x) . (\varphi x \supset \varphi n)$ instead of $[(x) . \varphi x] \supset \varphi n$. The principle of such punctuation is this: $(x)$ and $(\exists x)$ are called 'operators.' The 'scope' of such an operator, or that part of the expression which 'For every $x$' or 'For some $x$' qualifies, extends from the dot (or dots) following the operator until we come to an equal or larger number of dots. Thus if we write

$$(x) : \varphi x . \varphi x \supset \psi x : \supset . (x) . \psi x,$$

it means "If for every $x$ ($\varphi x$ is true, and $\varphi x$ implies $\psi x$), then $\psi x$ is true for every $x$." But if we should write

$$(x) . \varphi x : \varphi x \supset \psi x : \supset . (x) . \psi x,$$

it would mean "If ($\varphi x$ is true for every $x$) and $\varphi x$ implies $\psi x$, then $\psi x$ is true for every $x$." [2]

*8·21* $\varphi n . \supset . (\exists x) . \varphi x$

[3·9] $\varphi a . \supset . \varphi a \vee \varphi b \vee \varphi c \vee \ldots$

$\varphi b . \supset . \varphi a \vee \varphi b \vee \varphi c \vee \ldots$

If $\varphi$ is true of a given value of $x$, then it is true for some value of $x$; or, what is true of one is true of some.

*8·22* $(x) . \varphi x . \supset . (\exists x) . \varphi x$

[4·3] $\varphi a . \varphi b . \varphi c . \ldots : \supset . \varphi a \vee \varphi b \vee \varphi c \vee \ldots$

What is true for every $x$, is true for some $x$.

It is interesting to note the manner in which a proposition of the form $(x) . \varphi x$, or $(\exists x) . \varphi x$, may be related to an 'unanalyzed' proposition, $p$:

*8·3* $(x) . \varphi x : p : \equiv : (x) : \varphi x . p$

$(x) . \varphi x : p : \equiv : (\varphi a . \varphi b . \varphi c . \ldots) p$

$(x) : \varphi x . p : \equiv : (\varphi a . p)(\varphi b . p)(\varphi c . p) \ldots$

[1·1] $(\varphi a . \varphi b . \varphi c . \ldots) p : \equiv : (\varphi a . p)(\varphi b . p)(\varphi c . p) \ldots$

The different meaning of $(x) . \varphi x : p$ and $(x) : \varphi x . p$ follows the rule stated above. This difference will probably be more easily appreciated if one observes the extended expression of the two in the first two lines of the proof. The theorem states that "($\varphi x$ is true for every $x$) and $p$ is true" is equivalent to "For

[2] This use of dots is explained in Appendix I.

every $x$, ($\varphi x$ and $p$) is true." For example, let

$\varphi x$ = Either $x$ is not Sunday or $x$ is a holiday,
and $p$ = Lincoln's Birthday is on Sunday.

Then, "It is always true that $x$ is not Sunday or $x$ is a holiday; and Lincoln's Birthday is on Sunday" is equivalent to "It is true for every $x$ that ($x$ is not Sunday or $x$ is a holiday, and Lincoln's Birthday is on Sunday)." This may seem to the reader like making a distinction between Tweedledum and Tweedledee, and then equating them. But if so, he will see shortly that the point has some importance.

As in 8·3, so in general, when a proposition involving a function $\varphi x$ is related to an unanalyzed proposition $p$, the scope of the operator for $\varphi x$ can be extended to include $p$, *when the relation between the two propositions is that of sum or that of product:*

***8·31*** $(x) . \varphi x . \vee . p : \equiv . (x) . \varphi x \vee p$

$[4 \cdot 4]\ (\varphi a . \varphi b . \varphi c . \ldots) \vee p :$
$\equiv : (\varphi a \vee p)(\varphi b \vee p)(\varphi c \vee p) \ldots$

For example, "Either (it is always true that $x$ has color) or something is not red" is equivalent to "($x$ has color or something is not red) is always true."

***8·32*** $(\exists x) . \varphi x : p : \equiv : (\exists x) : \varphi x . p$

$[1 \cdot 1,\ 4 \cdot 41]\ (\varphi a \vee \varphi b \vee \varphi c \vee \ldots) p :$
$\equiv : (\varphi a . p) \vee (\varphi b . p) \vee (\varphi c . p) \vee \ldots$

For example, "(It is true for some $x$ that $x$ is odd) and 0 is a number" is equivalent to "It is true for some $x$ that ($x$ is odd, and 0 is a number)."

***8·33*** $(\exists x) . \varphi x . \vee . p : \equiv : (\exists x) : \varphi x \vee p$

$[3 \cdot 2]\ (\varphi a \vee \varphi b \vee \varphi c \vee \ldots) \vee p :$
$\equiv : (\varphi a \vee p) \vee (\varphi b \vee p) \vee (\varphi c \vee p) \vee \ldots$

Exactly similar theorems hold when the unanalyzed proposition $p$ is the first member in the relation instead of the second:

***8·34*** $p : (x) . \varphi x : \equiv : (x) : p . \varphi x$

***8·35*** $p . \vee . (x) . \varphi x : \equiv : (x) . p \vee \varphi x$

***8·36*** $p : (\exists x) . \varphi x : \equiv : (\exists x) : p . \varphi x$

***8·37*** $p . \vee . (\exists x) . \varphi x : \equiv : (\exists x) . p \vee \varphi x$

We have also the corollaries:

**8·38** $(x) : \varphi x \,.\, p : \equiv : (x) : p \,.\, \varphi x$

**8·381** $(x) \,.\, \varphi x \vee p : \equiv : (x) \,.\, p \vee \varphi x$

**8·39** $(\exists x) : \varphi x \,.\, p : \equiv : (\exists x) : p \,.\, \varphi x$

**8·391** $(\exists x) \,.\, \varphi x \vee p : \equiv : (\exists x) : p \vee \varphi x$

However, when the relation between $(x) \,.\, \varphi x$, or $(\exists x) \,.\, \varphi x$, and the unanalyzed proposition $p$ is that of implication, the matter is not quite so simple:

**8·4** $(x) \,.\, \varphi x \,.\!\supset\!.\, p : \equiv : (\exists x) \,.\, \varphi x \supset p$

[3·6] $(x) \,.\, \varphi x \,.\!\supset\!.\, p : \equiv : \sim(x) \,.\, \varphi x \,.\!\vee\!.\, p$

[8·11] $\equiv : (\exists x) \,.\, \sim\varphi x \,.\!\vee\!.\, p$

[8·33] $\equiv : (\exists x) \,.\, \sim\varphi x \vee p$

[8·02] $(\exists x) \,.\, \sim\varphi x \vee p : \equiv : (\sim\varphi a \vee p) \vee (\sim\varphi b \vee p) \vee \ldots$

[3·6] $\equiv : (\varphi a \supset p) \vee (\varphi b \supset p) \vee \ldots$

[8·02] $\equiv : (\exists x) \,.\, \varphi x \supset p$

That is, "($\varphi x$ is true for all values of $x$) implies that $p$ is true" is equivalent to "There is some value of $x$ such that ($\varphi x$ implies $p$)."

**8·41** $(\exists x) \,.\, \varphi x \,.\!\supset\!.\, p : \equiv : (x) \,.\, \varphi x \supset p$

[3·6] $(\exists x) \,.\, \varphi x \,.\!\supset\!.\, p : \equiv : \sim(\exists x) \,.\, \varphi x \,.\!\vee\!.\, p$

[8·1] $\equiv : (x) \,.\, \sim\varphi x \,.\!\vee\!.\, p$

[8·31] $\equiv : (x) \,.\, \sim\varphi x \vee p$

[8·01] $(x) \,.\, \sim\varphi x \vee p : \equiv \,.\, (\sim\varphi a \vee p)(\sim\varphi b \vee p) \ldots$

[3·6] $\equiv \,.\, (\varphi a \supset p)(\varphi b \supset p) \ldots$

[8·01] $\equiv : (x) \,.\, \varphi x \supset p$

That is, "($\varphi x$ is true for some $x$) implies that $p$ is true" is equivalent to "For all values of $x$, it is true that ($\varphi x$ implies $p$)."

These last two theorems are a bit difficult. Let us take 8·41 first, and choose an example from logic itself:

Let $\varphi x$ = All Greeks are $x$'s, and all $x$'s are mortal.
Let $p$ = All Greeks are mortal.

Here $\varphi x$ is false for many values of $x$—for $x$ = 'house,' or $x$ = 'angel,' etc. But if there is some (any) value of $x$—e.g., $x$ = 'human'—such that $\varphi x$ is true, then $p$ is true. That is, it holds true for this example that

$$(\exists x) \,.\, \varphi x \,.\!\supset\!.\, p.$$

And here it is easy to see that this is equivalent to "It is true for every $x$ that ('All Greeks are $x$'s and all $x$'s are mortal' implies 'All Greeks are mortal')." That is, it is equivalent to

$$(x) \,.\, \varphi x \supset p.$$

Now let us take 8·4. This is more difficult unless we remember that $\varphi a \supset p$ is a material implication, meaning precisely "It is not the case that $\varphi a$ is true and $p$ false." With this in mind, we shall see that $(\exists x) \,.\, \varphi x \supset p$, which is

$$(\varphi a \supset p) \vee (\varphi b \supset p) \vee (\varphi c \supset p) \vee \ldots,$$

is equivalent to $\sim(\varphi a \,.\, \sim p) \vee \sim(\varphi b \,.\, \sim p) \vee \sim(\varphi c \,.\, \sim p) \vee \ldots$. Now $p$ is a proposition, and hence always true or always false. If (1) $p$ is true, then $\sim(\varphi a \,.\, \sim p)$ holds, and hence $(\exists x) \,.\, \varphi x \supset p$ holds. If (2) $p$ is false, then the truth of

$$\sim(\varphi a \,.\, \sim p) \vee \sim(\varphi b \,.\, \sim p) \vee \sim(\varphi c \,.\, \sim p) \vee \ldots$$

depends upon the truth of $\varphi a$, $\varphi b$, etc. It will be true if, and only if, at least one of $\varphi a$, $\varphi b$, etc., is false. That is, it will hold if, and only if, $(\exists x) \,.\, \sim\varphi x$ holds. Thus, putting together cases (1) and (2), we see that $(\exists x) \,.\, \varphi x \supset p$ will hold if, and only if, either $p$ is true or $(\exists x) \,.\, \sim\varphi x$ is true. That is, it is equivalent to

$$(\exists x) \,.\, \sim\varphi x \,.\!\vee\!.\, p.$$

But $(\exists x) \,.\, \sim\varphi x : \equiv : \sim(x) \,.\, \varphi x$.
And $\sim(x) \,.\, \varphi x \,.\!\vee\!.\, p : \equiv : (x) \,.\, \varphi x \,.\!\supset\!.\, p$.

It might be expected that the equivalences would be similar when the implication-relation between $p$ and the proposition involving $\varphi x$ runs the other way. But that is not the case:

*8·42* $p \,.\!\supset\!.\, (x) \,.\, \varphi x : \equiv : (x) \,.\, p \supset \varphi x$

[3·6] $p \,.\!\supset\!.\, (x) \,.\, \varphi x : \equiv : \sim p \,.\!\vee\!.\, (\varphi a \,.\, \varphi b \,.\, \varphi c \,.\, \ldots)$

[1·1, 4·4] $\equiv : (\sim p \vee \varphi a)(\sim p \vee \varphi b) \ldots$

[3·6] $\equiv : (p \supset \varphi a)(p \supset \varphi b) \ldots$

[8·01] $\equiv : (x) \,.\, p \supset \varphi x$

The equivalence holds between "$p$ implies that $\varphi x$ is always true" and "It is always true that $p$ implies $\varphi x$."

***8·43*** $p\,.\supset.\,(\exists x)\,.\,\varphi x :\equiv: (\exists x)\,.\,p \supset \varphi x$

$$\begin{aligned} &[3{\cdot}6]\ p\,.\supset.\,(\exists x)\,.\,\varphi x :\equiv: {\sim}p\,.\vee.\,(\varphi a \vee \varphi b \vee \ldots) \\ &[3{\cdot}2] \qquad\qquad \equiv: ({\sim}p \vee \varphi a) \vee ({\sim}p \vee \varphi b) \vee \ldots \\ &[3{\cdot}6] \qquad\qquad \equiv: (p \supset \varphi a) \vee (p \supset \varphi b) \vee \ldots \\ &[8{\cdot}02] \qquad\qquad \equiv: (\exists x)\,.\,p \supset \varphi x \end{aligned}$$

That is, "$p$ implies that $\varphi x$ is sometimes true" is equivalent to "For some values of $x$, it is true that $p$ implies $\varphi x$."

We turn next to relations between propositions both of which involve functions.

***8·5*** $(x)\,.\,\varphi x : (x)\,.\,\psi x :\equiv: (x) : \varphi x\,.\,\psi x$

$$\begin{aligned} &(x)\,.\,\varphi x : (x)\,.\,\psi x :\equiv: (\varphi a\,.\,\varphi b\,.\ldots)(\psi a\,.\,\psi b\,.\ldots) \\ &[1{\cdot}2, 1{\cdot}3] \qquad \equiv: (\varphi a\,.\,\psi a\,.\ldots)(\varphi b\,.\,\psi b\,.\ldots) \\ &\qquad\qquad\qquad \equiv: (x) : \varphi x\,.\,\psi x \end{aligned}$$

That "$\varphi x$ is always true and $\psi x$ is always true" is equivalent to "It is always true that $\varphi x$ and $\psi x$ both hold."

***8·51*** $(\exists x)\,.\,\varphi x\,.\vee.\,(\exists x)\,.\,\psi x :\equiv: (\exists x)\,.\,\varphi x \vee \psi x$

$$\begin{aligned} &[3{\cdot}3, 3{\cdot}31]\ (\varphi a \vee \varphi b \vee \ldots) \vee.(\psi a \vee \psi b \vee \ldots): \\ &\qquad\qquad \equiv: (\varphi a \vee \psi a) \vee (\varphi b \vee \psi b) \vee \ldots \end{aligned}$$

"Either $\varphi x$ is sometimes true or $\psi x$ is sometimes true" is equivalent to "(Either $\varphi x$ or $\psi x$) is sometimes true."

The further equivalences which might be expected here, namely, those between

$$(1)\ (x)\,.\,\varphi x\,.\vee.\,(x)\,.\,\psi x \quad \text{and} \quad (2)\ (x)\,.\,\varphi x \vee \psi x$$

and between

$$(1)\ (\exists x) : \varphi x\,.\,\psi x \quad \text{and} \quad (2)\ (\exists x)\,.\,\varphi x : (\exists x)\,.\,\psi x,$$

do not, in fact, obtain. For example, let $\varphi x$ = "$x$ is difficult" and $\psi x$ = "$x$ is easy": in both cases (2) will hold, but (1) will be false. In both cases, (1) is a stronger statement than (2); and instead of equivalence, we have an implication. This will be clear if, first, we prove certain similar principles which have a wider application:

**8·6** $(x) . \varphi x :\supset: (x) . \varphi x \vee \psi x$

[3·9] $\varphi a . \supset . \varphi a \vee \psi a$; $\varphi b . \supset . \varphi b \vee \psi b$; etc.

Hence [4·2] $\varphi a . \varphi b . \ldots :\supset: (\varphi a \vee \psi a)(\varphi b \vee \psi b) \ldots$

If $\varphi x$ is always true, then "Either $\varphi x$ or $\psi x$" is always true.

**8·61** $(\exists x) . \varphi x :\supset: (\exists x) . \varphi x \vee \psi x$

[4·21] $\varphi a \vee \varphi b \vee \ldots :\supset: (\varphi a \vee \psi a) \vee (\varphi b \vee \psi b) \vee \ldots$

If $\varphi x$ is sometimes true, then "Either $\varphi x$ or $\psi x$" is sometimes true.

**8·62** $(x) : \varphi x . \psi x :\supset: (x) . \varphi x$

[2·4] $\varphi a . \psi a :\supset . \varphi a$; $\varphi b . \psi b :\supset \varphi b$; etc.

Hence [4·2] $(\varphi a . \psi a)(\varphi b . \psi b) \ldots :\supset: \varphi a . \varphi b . \ldots$

If it is always true that $\varphi x$ and $\psi x$ both hold, then $\varphi x$ always holds.

**8·63** $(\exists x) : \varphi x . \psi x :\supset: (\exists x) . \varphi x$

[4·21] $(\varphi a . \psi a) \vee (\varphi b . \psi b) \vee \ldots :\supset: \varphi a \vee \varphi b \vee \ldots$

If in some cases $\varphi x$ and $\psi x$ both hold, then $\varphi x$ is sometimes true.

It will be obvious that the following similar laws also hold:

**8·64** $(x) . \psi x :\supset: (x) . \varphi x \vee \psi x$

**8·65** $(\exists x) . \psi x :\supset: (\exists x) . \varphi x \vee \psi x$

**8·66** $(x) : \varphi x . \psi x :\supset: (x) . \psi x$

**8·67** $(\exists x) : \varphi x . \psi x :\supset: (\exists x) . \psi x$

We return now to the two implications mentioned just preceding 8·6:

**8·7** $(x) . \varphi x . \vee . (x) . \psi x :\supset: (x) . \varphi x \vee \psi x$

[8·6] $(x) . \varphi x :\supset: (x) . \varphi x \vee \psi x$

[8·64] $(x) . \psi x :\supset: (x) . \varphi x \vee \psi x$

Hence [4·22] the theorem follows.

"Either $\varphi x$ is always true or $\psi x$ is always true" implies "'Either $\varphi x$ or $\psi x$' is always true."

**8·71** $(\exists x) : \varphi x . \psi x :\supset: (\exists x) . \varphi x : (\exists x) . \psi x$

[8·63] $(\exists x) : \varphi x . \psi x :\supset: (\exists x) . \varphi x$

[8·67] $(\exists x) : \varphi x . \psi x :\supset: (\exists x) . \psi x$

Hence [4·23] the theorem follows.

"Sometimes $\varphi x$ and $\psi x$ are both true" implies "$\varphi x$ is sometimes true and $\psi x$ is sometimes true."

As indicated above, the implications stated by 8·7 and 8·71 are not reversible. For example, it may be that $\varphi x$ is sometimes true and $\psi x$ is sometimes true, but that they are never true coincidently.

The relation $(x) . \varphi x \supset \psi x$, called by Russell "formal implication," is particularly important. A formal implication is not 'formal' in the strict logical sense: all logically formal relations are intensional; while formal implication shares the extensional character of material implication. It is, of course, simply the logical product of the corresponding material implications, for all values of $x$:

$$(x) . \varphi x \supset \psi x : \equiv : \varphi a \supset \psi a . \varphi b \supset \psi b . \varphi c \supset \psi c . \dots .$$

Its exact significance is most easily seen by the following equivalence:

**8·8** $(x) . \varphi x \supset \psi x : \equiv : \sim(\exists x) : \varphi x . \sim\psi x$

[2·8] $\varphi a \supset \psi a . \equiv . \sim(\varphi a . \sim\psi a)$,

$\varphi b \supset \psi b . \equiv . \sim(\varphi b . \sim\psi b)$, etc.

[3·6] $(x) . \varphi x \supset \psi x : \equiv : (x) . \sim(\varphi x . \sim\psi x)$

[8·1] $(x) . \sim(\varphi x . \sim\psi x) : \equiv : \sim(\exists x) : \varphi x . \sim\psi x$

That is, "$\varphi x$ formally implies $\psi x$" is equivalent to "It is false that $x$ exists such that $\varphi x$ is true and $\psi x$ false." For example, no $x$ exists such that "$x$ is a featherless biped" is true, but that "$x$ laughs" is false. Thus "$x$ is a featherless biped" formally implies "$x$ laughs." In fact, a formal implication holds whenever a class-inclusion, $a \subset b$, holds—e.g., the class of featherless bipeds is contained in the class of animals that laugh. But the essence of 'featherless biped' does not include or imply the attribute of laughter; and "$x$ is a featherless biped" does not imply "$x$ laughs" in the strict sense of implication.

Proof of the theorems concerning this relation is usually by some principle such as 4·2, applied to the corresponding theorem concerning material implication. Proof of 8·81, given in full, illustrates the method; later proofs will be omitted or indicated only.

**8·81** $(x) . \varphi x \supset \psi x : (x) . \psi x \supset \theta x : . \supset : (x) . \varphi x \supset \theta x$

$[8{\cdot}5]\ (x) . \varphi x \supset \psi x : (x) . \psi x \supset \theta x : .$

$\equiv : (x) : \varphi x \supset \psi x . \psi x \supset \theta x$

$[3{\cdot}7]\ \varphi a \supset \psi a . \psi a \supset \theta a : \supset . \varphi a \supset \theta a,$

$\varphi b \supset \psi b . \psi b \supset \theta b : \supset . \varphi b \supset \theta b$, etc.

Hence [4·2] the theorem follows.

That is, the relation of formal implication is transitive, like material implication and the relation of class-inclusion. This theorem is the principle of the syllogism in Barbara; e.g.: if for every $x$, "$x$ is a man" implies "$x$ is mortal"; and for every $x$, "$x$ is mortal" implies "$x$ is imperfect"; then for every $x$, "$x$ is a man" implies "$x$ is imperfect." There are two other, and equivalent, forms of this principle:

**8·82** $(x) . \varphi x \supset \psi x : \supset : . (x) . \psi x \supset \theta x : \supset : (x) . \varphi x \supset \theta x$

By 7·2, the theorem is equivalent to 8·81.

**8·83** $(x) . \psi x \supset \theta x : \supset : . (x) . \varphi x \supset \psi x : \supset : (x) . \varphi x \supset \theta x$

Other syllogistic principles also are representable in terms of this relation. We give a few illustrations:

**8·84** $(x) . \varphi x \supset \psi x : \supset . \varphi n \supset \psi n$

The theorem is a special case included under 8·2.

**8·85** $(x) . \varphi x \supset \psi x : \varphi n : . \supset . \psi n$

By 7·2, the theorem is equivalent to 8·84.

This is the principle of another form of syllogism (with one singular premise) usually classed as Barbara. For example: if, for every $x$, "$x$ is a man" implies "$x$ is mortal," and Socrates is a man, then Socrates is mortal.

**8·86** $(x) . \varphi x \supset \psi x : . (\exists x) : \varphi x . \theta x : : \supset : (\exists x) : \psi x . \theta x$

$[8{\cdot}81]\ (x) . \varphi x \supset \psi x : (x) . \psi x \supset \sim\theta x : . \supset : (x) . \varphi x \supset \sim\theta x$

By 7·3, this is equivalent to

$(x) . \varphi x \supset \psi x : \sim(x) . \varphi x \supset \sim\theta x : . \supset : \sim(x) . \psi x \supset \sim\theta x$

And [8·8] this is equivalent to the theorem.

This theorem corresponds to *I A I* in the third figure. For example: if, for every $x$, "$x$ is a man" implies "$x$ is mortal," and for some $x$, "$x$ is a man and $x$ laughs," then for some $x$, "$x$ is mortal and $x$ laughs."

The principle of other syllogisms with both premises universal, but one negative, can be derived from 8·81, by letting $\psi x$ or $\theta x$ be some negative function. The principle of other syllogisms with one particular premise can be derived from 8·86 by (1) changing the order of $\varphi x$ and $\theta x$, or of $\psi x$ and $\theta x$; or (2) letting $\psi x$ be negative, or $\theta x$ be negative; or (3) by some combination of (1) and (2).

Other important principles of formal implication are the following:

***8·87*** $(x) . \varphi x \supset \psi x : \equiv : (x) . {\sim}\varphi x \vee \psi x :\equiv: (x) . {\sim}(\varphi x . {\sim}\psi x)$

***8·88*** $(x) . \varphi x \supset \psi x : \equiv : (x) . {\sim}\psi x \supset {\sim}\varphi x$

***8·9*** $(x) . \varphi x \supset \psi x :\supset: (x) . \varphi x . \supset . (x) . \psi x$

***8·91*** $(x) . \varphi x \supset \psi x : (x) . \varphi x :. \supset : (x) . \psi x$

***8·92*** $(x) . \varphi x \supset \psi x :\supset: (\exists x) . \varphi x . \supset . (\exists x) . \psi x$

***8·93*** $(x) . \varphi x \supset \psi x : (\exists x) . \varphi x :. \supset : (\exists x) . \psi x$

The relation of 'formal equivalence' is, of course, a reciprocal formal implication:

***9·1*** $(x) . \varphi x \equiv \psi x : \equiv : (x) : \varphi x \supset \psi x . \psi x \supset \varphi x$

[2·2] $\varphi a \equiv \psi a . \equiv : \varphi a \supset \psi a . \psi a \supset \varphi a$,

$\varphi b \equiv \psi b . \equiv : \varphi b \supset \psi b . \psi b \supset \varphi b$, etc.

Hence [2·1] the theorem follows.

***9·11*** $(x) . \varphi x \equiv \psi x : \equiv :. (x) . \varphi x \supset \psi x : (x) . \psi x \supset \varphi x$

[8·5] The theorem is equivalent to 9·1.

***9·2*** $(x) . \varphi x \equiv \psi x : (x) . \psi x \equiv \theta x :. \supset : (x) . \varphi x \equiv \theta x$

The theorem follows from 9·1, by 8·5 and 8·81.

That is, the relation of formal equivalence is transitive. Alternative forms of 9·2 are:

***9·3*** $(x) . \varphi x \equiv \psi x :\supset:. (x) . \psi x \equiv \theta x :\supset: (x) . \varphi x \equiv \theta x$

***9·4*** $(x) . \psi x \equiv \theta x :\supset:. (x) . \varphi x \equiv \psi x :\supset: (x) . \varphi x \equiv \theta x$

Further theorems, similar to those for formal implication, are the following:

***9·5*** $(x) . \varphi x \equiv \psi x :\supset . \varphi n \equiv \psi n$

[8·2]

**9·6** $(x) . \varphi x \equiv \psi x :\supset: . (\exists x) . \varphi x : \equiv : (\exists x) . \psi x$

**9·7** $(x) . \varphi x \equiv \psi x :\supset: . (x) . \varphi x : \equiv : (x) . \psi x$

**9·8** $(x) . \varphi x \equiv \psi x : \equiv : (x) . \sim\varphi x \equiv \sim\psi x$

Two functions are formally equivalent if both are true of the same class of existent things: that is, the relation is extensional. Since the class of men coincides with the class of featherless bipeds, "$x$ is a man" and "$x$ is a featherless biped" are formally equivalent, though they are not equivalent in intension.

As is suggested by the correspondence which holds between laws of the syllogism and those of formal implication, there is a close analogy between the calculus of propositional functions and the calculus of classes. In fact, if we let classes $a$, $b$, $c$, etc., be determined by the corresponding propositional functions,

$a = x$ such that $\varphi x$ is true,
$b = x$ such that $\psi x$ is true,
$c = x$ such that $\theta x$ is true, etc.,

we can then derive the calculus of classes from the calculus of propositional functions of one variable. The relations of classes will follow from those of the corresponding functions, since

$x$ such that $\varphi x . \psi x = a \times b$,
$x$ such that $\varphi x \vee \psi x = a + b$,
$x$ such that $\sim\varphi x = -a$, etc.

The assertable relations of the class-calculus correspond to the 'formal' relations:

$a \subset b$ is $(x) . \varphi x \supset \psi x$,
$a = b$ is $(x) . \varphi x \equiv \psi x$.

This possibility of deriving the calculus of classes from that of propositional functions of one variable is important for what we shall later come to know as the 'logistic method.' By that method, it is necessary that the first-developed and basic principles of logic should be those of the calculus of propositions. It is possible—as is done, for example, in *Principia Mathematica* —to begin with the calculus of propositions, derive the calculus of propositional functions from that, and then deduce the calculus of classes from the calculus of propositional functions, in the manner indicated above.

The calculus of propositional functions of two variables corresponds to the calculus of relations. We shall first explain the general character of functions of two variables and give the principal theorems concerning these, and then outline briefly this calculus of relations which may be derived.

Propositional functions of two variables are of two different kinds: (1) they may be such as "$x$ is brother of $y$" or "$x$ is greater than $y$," in which the terms which are values of $x$ are the same as those which are values of $y$ [so that if $\varphi(x, y)$ has meaning, then $\varphi(y, x)$ has meaning, though one of these might be true and the other false]; or (2) the functions may be such as "$x$ is a member of $y$" or "$x$ is the sine of $y$," in which the terms which are values of $x$ are distinct from those which are values of $y$ [so that if $\varphi(x, y)$ has meaning, then $\varphi(y, x)$ is nonsense]. If $\varphi(x, y)$ is a function of type (1), then the class of couples which can be meaningfully substituted for $(x, y)$ can be represented as the two-dimensional array,

$$\begin{array}{llll} a, a & a, b & a, c & \ldots \\ b, a & b, b & b, c & \ldots \\ c, a & c, b & c, c & \ldots \\ d, a & \ldots & & \\ \text{etc., etc.} & & & \end{array}$$

But if the function is of type (2), then $\varphi(a, a)$, $\varphi(b, b)$, etc., will be meaningless; and if $\varphi(a, b)$ has meaning, then $\varphi(b, a)$ will not have meaning.

For this reason, it might be better to choose some different method of representing the values of $x$ and $y$ in $\varphi(x, y)$, such as $x_1, x_2, x_3, \ldots$ and $y_1, y_2, y_3, \ldots$ The array of couples which are values of $(x, y)$ in $\varphi(x, y)$ would then be,

$$\begin{array}{llll} x_1, y_1 & x_1, y_2 & x_1, y_3 & \ldots \\ x_2, y_1 & x_2, y_2 & x_2, y_3 & \ldots \\ x_3, y_1 & x_3, y_2 & x_3, y_3 & \ldots \\ \text{etc., etc.} & & & \end{array}$$

This mode of representation would cover functions of both types·

However, this notation with subscripts is objectionable on account of its typographical complexity. The same end can be achieved if, instead, we adopt the convention that, in $\varphi(a, a)$,

$\varphi(a, b)$, $\varphi(b, a)$, etc., the letter $a$ or $b$, etc., in the *first* position represents simply 'a distinct value of $x$ in $\varphi(x, y)$'; and that $a$ or $b$, etc., in the *second* position represents simply 'a distinct value of $y$.' Thus $\varphi(a, a)$ is to mean nothing different from $\varphi(x_1, y_1)$; $\varphi(a, b)$ is to have the same significance as would $\varphi(x_1, y_2)$, and so on. Thus if $\varphi(x, y)$ is a function of type (1), in which the same terms are values of $x$ and of $y$, both, then $\varphi(a, b)$ and $\varphi(b, a)$ will be converse propositions, such as "Tom is brother of Jack" and "Jack is brother of Tom," or "7 is greater than 5" and "5 is greater than 7." But if $\varphi(x, y)$ is a function of type (2), for which the values of $x$ are a distinct class from the values of $y$, then $\varphi(a, b)$ and $\varphi(b, a)$ will not be converses, like "0.707 is the sine of 45°," and "45° is the sine of 0.707" (since one of these would be meaningless), but will be such as "0.0175 is the sine of 1°" and "0.0349 is the sine of 0° 30′." (One of these last two statements would, of course, be false; but *both* have meaning.)

The laws of these two types of functions are not completely identical; but all the fundamental principles, such as those which will be given here, hold of both kinds. With whichever kind of function we may be dealing, it is important to remember that $\varphi(a, b)$ and $\varphi(b, a)$ are distinct: even for functions of type (1), "7 is greater than 5" and "5 is greater than 7" are different propositions. Order is of the essence in all matters connected with functions of two variables.

Two conventions adopted for functions of one variable will be continued here. We shall write $\varphi(m, n)$ with the understanding that $m$ stands for any given one of the values of $x$ in $\varphi(x, y)$, and that $n$ stands for any given one of the values of $y$. And demonstrations will be carried out as if the values of $x$ and the values of $y$ were each an exhaustible set. If the values of $x$ in $\varphi(x, y)$ should be a finite set, and the values of $y$ a finite set, the set of ordered couples $(x, y)$ for which $\varphi(x, y)$ is significant would, of course, be finite also.

The meaning of expressions involving functions of two variables, and two operators, follows from the definitions applicable to functions of one variable. For example, in $(x) : (\exists y) . \varphi(x, y)$ the force of the operator $(x)$, followed by two dots, extends over the whole of $(\exists y) . \varphi(x, y)$; and this last expression is a function of the single variable $x$. Therefore, by 8·01, we have

$$(x) : (\exists y) . \varphi(x, y) : \\ = : (\exists y) . \varphi(a, y) : (\exists y) . \varphi(b, y) : (\exists y) . \varphi(c, y) : \ldots$$

Here, $\varphi(a, y)$, $\varphi(b, y)$, etc., are functions of $y$; and hence the meaning of each constituent of the above is given by 8·02. Let us use the symbol $\times$ for the relation of logical product, indicated by $(x)$; and let us write the constituents of $(x) : (\exists y) . \varphi(x, y)$ in a column instead of a line:

$$\begin{aligned} (x) : (\exists y) . \varphi(x, y) : = : \quad & (\exists y) . \varphi(a, y) \\ & \times (\exists y) . \varphi(b, y) \\ & \times (\exists y) . \varphi(c, y) \\ & \times \ldots, \text{etc.} \end{aligned}$$

Now let us replace each of these lines by its explicit equivalent, according to 8·02:

$$\begin{aligned} (x) : (\exists y) . \varphi(x, y) : = : \quad & [\varphi(a, a) \vee \varphi(a, b) \vee \varphi(a, c) \vee \ldots] \\ & \times [\varphi(b, a) \vee \varphi(b, b) \vee \varphi(b, c) \vee \ldots] \\ & \times [\varphi(c, a) \vee \varphi(c, b) \vee \varphi(c, c) \vee \ldots] \\ & \times \ldots, \text{etc.} \end{aligned}$$

Thus an expression involving two operators can be turned into a two-dimensional array of constituent propositions as follows: (1) Each line is bracketed, and is related to the next line as a whole. (2) The inside operator, nearest the function, indicates that variable which varies from one place to the next within each line, and indicates whether the relation between constituents in each line is $\times$ or $\vee$. (3) The outside operator indicates that variable which varies from line to line, and indicates the relation between each two lines.

For example, in contrast to the above:

$$\begin{aligned} (\exists y) : (x) . \varphi(x, y) : = : \quad & [\varphi(a, a) \times \varphi(b, a) \times \varphi(c, a) \times \ldots] \\ & \vee [\varphi(a, b) \times \varphi(b, b) \times \varphi(c, b) \times \ldots] \\ & \vee [\varphi(a, c) \times \varphi(b, c) \times \varphi(c, c) \times \ldots] \\ & \vee \ldots, \text{etc.} \end{aligned}$$

To bring out the difference between $(x) : (\exists y) . \varphi(x, y)$ and

$(\exists y):(x).\varphi(x, y)$, suppose $\varphi(x, y)$ is $x < y$. Now, making our translation by reference to the preceding:

$(x):(\exists y).\varphi(x, y)$ is

$$\begin{array}{ll} & [\text{Either } a < a \text{ or } a < b \text{ or } a < c \text{ or } \ldots] \\ \text{and} & [\text{either } b < a \text{ or } b < b \text{ or } b < c \text{ or } \ldots] \\ \text{and} & [\text{either } c < a \text{ or } c < b \text{ or } c < c \text{ or } \ldots] \\ \text{and} & \ldots, \text{etc.} \end{array}$$

That is, "For every $x$, there is some $y$ or other such that $x < y$," which is equivalent to "Given any number, there is always a greater."

But $(\exists y):(x).\varphi(x, y)$ is

$$\begin{array}{ll} \text{Either} & [a < a \text{ and } b < a \text{ and } c < a \text{ and } \ldots] \\ \text{or} & [a < b \text{ and } b < b \text{ and } c < b \text{ and } \ldots] \\ \text{or} & [a < c \text{ and } b < c \text{ and } c < c \text{ and } \ldots] \\ \text{or} & \ldots, \text{etc.} \end{array}$$

That is, "There exists some $y$ such that, for every $x$, $x < y$," which is equivalent to "There is some number which is greater than every number."

In view of this difference in meaning, we must be careful to read $(x):(\exists y)$, "For every $x$, some $y$ exists such that ..."; $(\exists y):(x)$, "Some $y$ exists such that, for every $x$, ...." However, when both operators indicate the *same* relation, as $(x):(y)$, or $(\exists x):(\exists y)$, this caution is not necessary: one may read $(x):(y)$ as 'For every $x$ and $y$'; and $(\exists x):(\exists y)$ as 'For some $x$ and some $y$' or 'For some $x$ and $y$.' The reason is that, since the relations $\times$ and $\vee$ are commutative and associative, if the relation between the lines is the same as that within the lines, the order of constituents in the two-dimensional array makes no difference—one may turn the columns into lines and the lines into columns without altering the meaning.

The propositional function $\varphi(x, y)$ could be interpreted as a function of a single variable, the ordered couple $(x, y)$. Obviously whatever is true for every ordered couple $(x, y)$ will be true for every $x$ and every $y$; and conversely, what is true for every $x$ and $y$, will be true for every ordered couple $(x, y)$. Similarly, whatever is true for some $x$ and some $y$, will be true for some ordered couple $(x, y)$; and what is true for some ordered couple $(x, y)$, will be true for some $x$ and some $y$. Let us make these principles explicit:

***10·01*** $(x, y) \,.\, \varphi(x, y) : \equiv : (x) : (y) \,.\, \varphi(x, y)$

***10·02*** $(\exists x, y) \,.\, \varphi(x, y) : \equiv : (\exists x) : (\exists y) \,.\, \varphi(x, y)$

Since these principles hold; for every theorem concerning functions of one variable there is a corresponding theorem concerning functions of two; $\varphi x$ being replaced by $\varphi(x, y)$; the operator $(x)$, by $(x, y)$ or by $(x) : (y)$; and $(\exists x)$, by $(\exists x, y)$ or by $(\exists x) : (\exists y)$. Since this transcription offers no difficulty, either in the matter of symbolism or of understanding, we shall not repeat here the theorems proved for functions of one variable in the form in which they hold for two.

Of the further theorems, involving something more than such transcription of principles which hold for functions of one variable, the following are of special interest or importance:

***10·1*** $(x) : (y) \,.\, \varphi(x, y) : . \equiv : . (y) : (x) \,.\, \varphi(x, y)$

The theorem follows from the fact that $\times$ is associative and commutative.

***10·2*** $(\exists x) : (\exists y) \,.\, \varphi(x, y) : . \equiv : . (\exists y) : (\exists x) \,.\, \varphi(x, y)$

The theorem follows from the fact that $\vee$ is associative and commutative.

Since these theorems hold, we see that the order of the operators, in the second half of 10·01 and 10·02, makes no difference.

***10·3*** $(x) : (y) \,.\, \varphi(x, y) : . \supset : (y) \,.\, \varphi(m, y)$

[8·2]

What is true of every $x$ and every $y$, is true of any given value of $x$ and every $y$.

***10·31*** $(x) : (y) \,.\, \varphi(x, y) : . \supset : (x) \,.\, \varphi(x, n)$

[10·1, 8·2]

What is true of every $x$ and every $y$, is true of every $x$ and any given value of $y$.

***10·32*** $(x) : (\exists y) . \varphi(x, y) : . \supset : (\exists y) . \varphi(m, y)$
[8·2]

***10·33*** $(y) : (\exists x) . \varphi(x, y) : . \supset : (\exists x) . \varphi(x, n)$

***10·34*** $(x) : (y) . \varphi(x, y) : . \supset . \varphi(m, n)$
[10·3, 8·2]

What is true of every $x$ and every $y$, is true of any given value of $x$ and any given value of $y$.

***10·35*** $(x) : (y) . \varphi(x, y) : . \supset : . (\exists x) : (y) . \varphi(x, y)$
[8·22]

If $\varphi(x, y)$ is true for every $x$ and $y$, then there is some $x$ such that, for every $y$, $\varphi(x, y)$.

***10·36*** $(x) : (y) . \varphi(x, y) : . \supset : . (\exists y) : (x) . \varphi(x, y)$
[10·3, 8·22]

We have already called attention to the fact that changing the order of the two operators in the second half of 10·35 and 10·36 would change the meaning. But there is an implication which holds in such cases:

***10·4*** $(\exists x) : (y) . \varphi(x, y) : . \supset : . (y) : (\exists x) . \varphi(x, y)$

Let us give the proof of this law in an extended form which will go back to first principles, and will be easily understandable:

$$\begin{aligned}(\exists x) : (y) . \varphi(x, y) : = : \; & [\varphi(a, a) \times \varphi(a, b) \times \varphi(a, c) \times \ldots] \\ & \vee [\varphi(b, a) \times \varphi(b, b) \times \varphi(b, c) \times \ldots] \\ & \vee [\varphi(c, a) \times \varphi(c, b) \times \varphi(c, c) \times \ldots] \\ & \vee \ \ldots, \text{etc.}\end{aligned}$$

$$\begin{aligned}(y) : (\exists x) . \varphi(x, y) : = : \; & [\varphi(a, a) \vee \varphi(b, a) \vee \varphi(c, a) \vee \ldots] \\ & \times [\varphi(a, b) \vee \varphi(b, b) \vee \varphi(c, b) \vee \ldots] \\ & \times [\varphi(a, c) \vee \varphi(b, c) \vee \varphi(c, c) \vee \ldots] \\ & \times \ldots, \text{etc.}\end{aligned}$$

Now note that the lines in the first of these coincide with the columns in the second. That is, $(\exists x) : (y) . \varphi(x, y)$ is of the form

$$a\,b\,c \ldots \vee p\,q\,r \ldots \vee x\,y\,z \ldots \vee \ldots,$$

whereas $(y) : (\exists x) . \varphi(x, y)$ is of the form

$$(a \vee p \vee x \vee \ldots)(b \vee q \vee y \vee \ldots)(c \vee r \vee z \vee \ldots) \ldots$$

Since $\vee$ is associative with respect to $\times$, this last expression is equivalent to

$$a\,b\,c \ldots \vee p\,q\,r \ldots \vee x\,y\,z \ldots \vee \ldots \vee K,$$

where $K$ is the sum of all cross-products such as $a\,q\,z \ldots$, $p\,b\,r \ldots$, etc. That is,

$$(y) : (\exists x) \,.\, \varphi(x, y) : = :: (\exists x) : (y) \,.\, \varphi(x, y) : . \vee K,$$

where $K$ is the sum of all cross-products in the above extended expression of $(y) : (\exists x) \,.\, \varphi(x, y)$.

Hence, since [3·9] $p \,.\supset : p \vee q$, the theorem follows.

***10·41*** $(\exists y) : (x) \,.\, \varphi(x, y) : . \supset : . (x) : (\exists y) \,.\, \varphi(x, y)$

Similar proof.

The implications stated by 10·4 and 10·41 are not reversible. Let $\varphi(x, y)$ be "If $x$ is a man, then he is a member of the club $y$." Then 10·4 will be "If there is some club such that every man is a member of it, then for every man there is some club of which he is a member"—which will be true. But the converse, "If for every man there is some club of which he is a member, then there is some club such that every man is a member of it," is obviously false.

With the help of 10·4 and 10·41, we can now prove further theorems of the general type of 10·3–10·36:

***10·5*** $(\exists y) : (x) \,.\, \varphi(x, y) : . \supset : (\exists y) \,.\, \varphi(m, y)$

[10·41, 10·32]

***10·51*** $(\exists x) : (y) \,.\, \varphi(x, y) : . \supset : (\exists x) \,.\, \varphi(x, n)$

[10·4, 10·33]

***10·52*** $(x) : (y) \,.\, \varphi(x, y) : . \supset : . (y) : (\exists x) \,.\, \varphi(x, y)$

[10·4, 10·35]

***10·53*** $(x) : (y) \,.\, \varphi(x, y) : . \supset : . (x) : (\exists y) \,.\, \varphi(x, y)$

[10·41, 10·36]

The calculus of relations may be derived from the calculus of propositional functions of two variables, if we conceive that any relation $R$ is a class of ordered couples $(x, y)$ such that $x\,R\,y$ is true. That is, any function $\varphi(x, y)$ asserts some relation of

$x$ to $y$, so that $\varphi(x, y)$ and $x\,R\,y$ are merely alternative notations; and the class of ordered couples for which $\varphi(x, y)$, or $x\,R\,y$, is true, constitutes the *extension* of the relation represented by $\varphi$, or $R$. Thus relations, taken in extension as classes of ordered couples, stand to the laws of functions of two variables in precisely the same way that classes stand to the laws of functions of one variable.

Let $R$ = $(x, y)$ such that $\varphi(x, y)$ is true,
$S$ = $(x, y)$ such that $\psi(x, y)$ is true, etc.
Then, $(x, y)$ such that $\varphi(x, y) \cdot \psi(x, y)$ is true $= R \cdot S$,
$(x, y)$ such that $\varphi(x, y) \vee \psi(x, y)$ is true $= R + S$,
and $(x, y)$ such that $\sim\varphi(x, y) = -R$.

Also, the *assertable* relations of relations will correspond to the 'formal' relations of functions of two variables:

$$R \subset S \text{ is } (x) : (y) \cdot \varphi(x, y) \supset \psi(x, y),$$
$$\text{and } R = S \text{ is } (x) : (y) \cdot \varphi(x, y) \equiv \psi(x, y).$$

The exact analogy here exhibited calls attention to the fact that, since the Boole-Schröder Algebra can be interpreted as a calculus of classes, it can likewise be interpreted as a calculus of classes of ordered couples, and hence as a calculus of relations in extension. The fact that all the laws of functions of one variable likewise hold for functions of two shows that all laws of classes will correspond to similar laws of relations. But this same fact also shows us that there are laws of relations, expressible in terms of functions of two variables, which are not expressible through interpreting the Boole-Schröder Algebra as a calculus of relations. This is the case because the laws of the Algebra are exhaustively interpretable as principles holding for classes in general. Hence those laws of functions of two variables which are not exactly analogous to laws governing functions of one variable are not to be found in the Algebra when interpreted as a calculus of relations. Thus the calculus of relations, as derived from the calculus of propositional functions, is superior, because more comprehensive, to the relational interpretation of the Algebra.

Let us briefly illustrate the manner in which the principles of the calculus of propositional functions may be transcribed as explicit laws of relations; and let us note also certain derivative functions of relations which are of importance. For example, 8·81, for functions of two variables, is

$$(x) : (y) . x R y \supset x S y :. (x) : (y) . x S y \supset x T y :: \supset :. (x) : (y) . x R y \supset x T y.$$

In the other notation, this will be

$$R \subset S . S \subset T : \supset . R \subset T.$$

"If whenever the relation $R$ holds, the relation $S$ also holds, and whenever $S$ holds, $T$ holds; then whenever $R$ holds, $T$ holds." That is, the relation of implication between relations is transitive.

It is important to note that there are many laws of functions of two variables which have no analogues in terms of functions of one. Theorem 10·4 is an example. In the relational notation, this is "If there is an $x$ which has the relation $R$ to every $y$, then for every $y$, there is some $x$ which has the relation $R$ to that $y$." This is an obvious truth, and an important principle which cannot be expressed in terms of the Boole-Schröder Algebra.

A function of relations which is of fundamental importance for the logic of mathematics is the 'relative product' of two relations, which we may symbolize by $R|S$:

$$x R|S y . = : (\exists z) : x R z . z S y.$$

That is, $R|S$ is the relation of $x$ to $y$, when there is some $z$ such that $x$ has the relation $R$ to $z$ and $z$ has the relation $S$ to $y$. For example, the relative product of 'brother of' and 'parent of' is 'uncle of.' A special case of this function is the relative product of a relation with itself, $R|R$, or as it may be written, $R^2$:

$$x R^2 y . = . x R|R y . = : (\exists z) : x R z . z R y.$$

Transitive relations are distinguished as a class by the fact that, for any transitive relation $T$, $T^2 \subset T$. That is,

$$x T^2 y . \supset . x T y; \text{ or, } (\exists z) : x T z . z T y : . \supset . x T y.$$

Thus the derivation of laws governing transitive relations requires the general laws of the function of relative product, which are expressible in the calculus of propositional functions, but not expressible in terms of the Boole-Schröder Algebra.

Another function whose properties follow from laws of the calculus of propositional functions, but is not otherwise representable, is the 'converse of $R$,' $\breve{R}$.

$$x \breve{R} y . = . y R x.$$

That is, the converse of $R$ is the relation of $x$ to $y$ when $y$ has the relation $R$ to $x$. Symmetrical relations are distinguished as a class by the fact that for any symmetrical relation $S$,

$$x S y . \equiv . y S x.$$

Thus the laws peculiar to symmetrical relations require for their expression the general laws of this function, $\breve{R}$.

It is not possible in an introductory book to present the logic of relations in any detail. But if one observes the importance of various kinds of relations in mathematics—transitive relations, symmetrical relations, relations which are transitive and asymmetrical, like serial relations, one-to-one relations such as those which correlate the members of two assemblages or two series, and so on—it will be evident that this topic is fundamental for the logic of mathematics. And also it will be clear that the bases for the development of the subject are to be found in the calculus of propositional functions.[3]

In Chapters II and IV and in the present chapter, we have now presented a continuous development, beginning with an abstract algebra, capable of various interpretations, proceeding from that to the calculus of propositions, and thence to the calculus of propositional functions. Our purpose in this book being mainly to introduce the reader to the subject of symbolic logic, so that other and more special studies will be understandable, we have confined these chapters to those topics and those developments which constitute the material or provide the basis of most studies in the subject, past and present. And by fol-

[3] Any who are interested to go further will find that, on the basis of what they have now learned, they can proceed directly to *Principia Mathematica;* or they will find the more general account in Russell's *Introduction to Mathematical Philosophy* both intelligible and highly profitable.

lowing, in the main, the actual course of historical development, we have so presented this material as to enable the student to see the essential relationship which exists between the older Boole-Schröder Algebra and current developments such as the calculus of propositions and of propositional functions as one finds them to-day—for example, in *Principia Mathematica*.[4]

This mode of presentation, however, has required certain sacrifices. There are two defects, of different kinds, characterizing this development which is now concluded. One of these is methodological, and could have been avoided by adopting the 'logistic method' which has been mentioned. But if we had followed this logistic method, we should have been obliged to neglect the Boole-Schröder Algebra altogether, deriving the calculus of classes from that of propositional functions of one variable, in the manner which has been suggested. Thus the connection between the Algebra and later developments—a connection which is important both historically and intrinsically—would not have appeared. The other limitation of what has preceded merely reflects a like limitation of almost all studies in exact logic up to the present time—the limitation to the logic of extension, and the neglect of intensional relations; at least, the neglect to consider these explicitly.

Let us review what has preceded in both these respects. First, the matter of method.

In Chapter II we developed the Boole-Schröder Algebra with examples and readings of theorems which took it as a logic of terms in extension, a logic of classes. But if one notes the form of our symbolic postulates and the character of proofs, it will be observed that nothing in the mathematical development is allowed to depend on this interpretation: so far as the assumptions and the deductions from them are concerned, the system

[4] For discussion of the Boole-Schröder Algebra and the calculus of elementary propositions in *Principia Mathematica*, as related mathematical systems, see B. A. Bernstein, "Whitehead and Russell's theory of deduction as a mathematical science," *Bull. Amer. Math. Soc.*, XXXVII (1931), 480–488; and E. V. Huntington, "New sets of independent postulates for the algebra of logic, with special reference to Whitehead and Russell's *Principia Mathematica*," to appear shortly in *Trans. Amer. Math. Soc.* (see number for January, 1933).

developed may be regarded as an abstract mathematical system, independent of any particular interpretation.

The method of demonstration is no different from that by which a mathematician would deduce the laws of complex algebra or of geometry from a set of definitions and postulates. But there is a characteristic of such mathematical deductions in general which becomes somewhat paradoxical when the system to be developed is a branch of logic: such deduction necessarily makes use of the principles of deduction, and thus assumes that the laws of logic are already given or understood. Where the mathematical system deduced is not a logic, this raises no question. But in the case of logic, it would appear that this procedure involves a puzzle: unless logic is taken for granted, we can make no deduction; but it is logic which is to be deduced. Superficially, this paradox can be avoided: one takes the system—the Boole-Schröder Algebra—merely as an abstract mathematical system; and one deduces it by general mathematical methods, as one would do with any such abstract system. Its interpretation as logic is a separate matter. But as we shall see, development and interpretation cannot here be so completely separated.

Let us first observe in what manner laws of logic are presumed in the deductions of Chapter II. For example, 1·03, "$a \subset b$ is equivalent to $a \times b = a$," assumes the meaning of the equivalence of two propositions. And 1·6, "If $a \subset b$ and $a \subset -b$, then $a = 0$," assumes the meaning of the 'if-then' relation between propositions. Again, proofs quite generally depend on the principle that the premises "If $P$ then $Q$" and "$P$ holds" warrant the inference $Q$; or upon the principle that the premises "If $P$ then $Q$" and "If $Q$ then $R$" warrant the deduction "If $P$ then $R$." Other proofs depend for their validity upon the principle that propositions equivalent to the same proposition are equivalent to each other. In introducing the subject of inequations, we found it well to state explicitly some of the principles of logic by which the theorems to be proved are deduced from preceding ones—for example, that "If $P$ then $Q$" gives "If $Q$ is false, then $P$ is false." If we had omitted such explicit mention, as a mathematician engaged upon some different system would have done, they would still have been made use of, and the validity of the deduction would still have depended upon them.

In general, it is the laws of the logical relations of *propositions* which are thus presumed in demonstrations; but careful attention would reveal that at least some laws of the relations of terms are also taken for granted: for example, when we depend upon the meaning of the relation $a = b$ for the validity of 2·1, "If $a = b$, then $a\,c = b\,c$, and $c\,a = c\,b$." This also is something any mathematician would feel free to do; he would take the relation of identity, and its properties, for granted, and would use the sign $=$ as a shorthand expression of that relation, just as is done in Chapter II.

However, to assume logical principles as principles of one's deductions, in order to deduce a body of logical laws from a few which have been postulated, is obviously a circular process. In so far as the principles proved are those of the logic of classes, and the logic taken for granted consists of laws of the relations of propositions, we may escape such circularity. For the most part, this is the case in Chapter II, so long as we interpret the Algebra as a logic of classes. And, as has been said, if we take the Algebra as abstract, then no circularity whatever is involved.

If, however, we examine the development of the Two-valued Algebra in Chapter IV, we find that the situation there is quite different. The Two-valued Algebra has as its assumptions the definitions and postulates of Chapter II and the postulate which distinguishes this system from the more general Boole-Schröder Algebra: 7·1, $(p = 0) \equiv {\sim}p$. In view of this additional assumption, and its immediate consequence, 7·11, $p \equiv (p = 1)$, it is impossible to take the Two-valued Algebra as an abstract system. Unless $\equiv$ is an assertable relation, and one having a definite meaning, 7·1 states nothing. Moreover, the symbols $=$ and $\equiv$ are distinguished only by an arbitrary convention, made for convenience; and $p = 1$ and $p = 0$ must be propositions, whether $p$ itself is a proposition or not. Thus since $p$ is asserted to be equivalent to $p = 1$, and ${\sim}p$ equivalent to $p = 0$, the elements of the system are confined, in their interpretation, to propositions, and the system cannot be abstract.

In the light of these facts, the Two-valued Algebra, as developed by Schröder and as developed here, must be implicitly circular as a deductive system. The logic of propositions must be antecedently given in order that the deduction should be possible; and the principles deduced are those of the logic of propositions. It is, for example, taken for granted that "$P$ implies $Q$" gives "If $Q$ is false, then $P$ is false"; and this principle is included in what is stated by Theorem 3·8,

$$p \supset q \,.\, \equiv \,.\, {\sim}q \supset {\sim}p.$$

Again, the identity of the logic presumed and the logic to be deduced is taken for granted in transcribing "If ... then ..." by $\supset$; 'and,' by the relation of logical product; and 'is equivalent to,' by $\equiv$, as was done in Chapter IV. But even if we had avoided this, as being illegitimate, the circularity in question would not have been obviated. We should have written 3·8, for example, in the form

$$p \supset q \text{ is equivalent to } {\sim}q \supset {\sim}p.$$

But since, by 7·1, ${\sim}q \supset {\sim}p$ would be equivalent to $(q=0) \supset (p=0)$ the relations $\supset$ and $\equiv$ would still be restricted to assertable relations of propositions. As a result, theorems of the system can be given no meaning at all (even as abstract) except one which confines them to an interpretation by which they become laws of the relations of propositions.

Since the calculus of propositional functions is deduced from the laws of the Two-valued Algebra, the same circularity extends to this calculus also, as developed in the present chapter.

Thus it will be clear that any attempt to develop exact logic by the usual methods of mathematical deduction in general, must involve some circularity. The principles deduced, or at least many of them, must be taken for granted *before* they can be deduced. This is the case because the principles of deduction must be given before any deduction can be legitimately performed or its validity assessed. And this circularity cannot be removed by citing such implicit principles of deduction as explicit assumptions.

This is a highly unsatisfactory situation. That the laws of logic cannot be deduced unless they are first taken for granted as principles of their own deduction does not, of course, render them invalid. (It does suggest a serious problem concerning the ground of our knowledge of them, and the criteria of their truth. But these questions are epistemological rather than logical.) But it becomes a question what, if anything, is supposed to be accomplished by a deductive development of logic. This might satisfy some psychological or pedagogical purpose; but it would certainly be open to question whether it was of the slightest importance *logically*.

It is in order to avoid this circularity that current developments in exact logic have abandoned this older method, common to other branches of mathematics and to symbolic logic from Boole to Schröder. Instead, contemporary works, such as *Principia Mathematica*, proceed by the logistic method. Detailed discussion of this would here be premature, but the essential difference may be stated: By the logistic method, the principles of logic are not antecedently presumed as rules of demonstration. Instead, the rules in accordance with which proofs are given are rules of more or less mechanical operations upon the symbols, such as rules allowing certain substitutions to be made in the postulates or in theorems previously proved.

This logistic method requires that the first branch of logic to be developed should be the calculus of propositions; that is, the laws which can be stated for all propositions, without regard to the terms and relations of terms, into which propositions in question might be analyzed. Then, as was suggested earlier in this chapter, the calculus of propositional functions can be derived from this calculus of propositions; and, in turn, the calculus of classes and the calculus of relations can be deduced from the calculus of propositional functions. Some difference in the content of particular branches is incidental to this logistic development, as against the non-logistic type of derivation, but the important difference is methodological, and in general the content is the same—the laws of the Boole-Schröder Algebra will be found in the logistically derived calculus of classes, and the laws of the Two-valued Algebra in the logistic calculus of propositions. Thus there is nothing which the reader has so far learned, as a principle of exact logic, which has to be questioned or repudiated. The further thing which it is desirable to command is this logistic method itself.

In the next chapter we seek to meet this requirement by presenting the basic calculus of exact logic by the logistic method. But there are other aims also to be achieved in this presentation. One of these has to do with that limitation of most studies in exact logic which has been mentioned, namely restriction to the logic of extensional relations. On this point the logistic method makes no difference: older developments such as the Two-valued Algebra of Schröder and newer ones like the calculus of elementary propositions in *Principia Mathematica* have exactly the same import and the same limitations.

Let us review what has preceded with reference to this second point. In Chapter II we interpreted the Boole-Schröder Algebra as a logic of classes—of terms in extension; and in Chapter III this interpretation was further elaborated and discussed. Such extensional interpretation is the only kind which, as a matter of history, has ever been put upon the system —except incidentally and temporarily, when some writer has applied it to relations of intension without realizing precisely what he was doing. We pointed out, further, in Chapter III, that certain principles of the system, e.g., $0 \subset a$, have an air of the paradoxical because we do not commonly recognize, as principles of the logic of terms, those which hold in extension but without any corresponding relation of the same terms in intension. Such paradoxical principles are, however, necessarily true laws of the logic of classes. Also we called attention to the fact that it is possible to give the Algebra a consistent interpretation as a logic of the intensional relations of terms. On this interpretation, $a = 0$ would mean "$a$ is not logically conceivable" or "The concept $a$ is a self-contradictory notion"; and $a = 1$ would mean "Not-$a$ is logically inconceivable." The elements, $a$, $b$, $c$, etc., would not represent classes but connotations, or all the conceivable things which would, if they should exist, incorporate certain essences. All the laws of the Algebra would hold of such interpretation; but not only would their meaning be changed; their application also would be altered. Terms of which $a \subset b$ can be asserted in extension may not be such that $a \subset b$ will hold true in intension. And where $a = 0$ or $a = 1$ is true in extension, the corresponding statement in intension is often false. Thus it would be quite impossible to take the Algebra ambiguously—as applying to extensions when we choose and to intensions when we choose—because the application has to be made *de novo* and differently in the two cases. A complete logic of terms, covering relations of extension and of intension both, and allowing the denotation of terms and symbolized relations of them to remain fixed, would have to be a much more complex system than the Boole-Schröder Algebra.

In Chapter IV we pointed out, similarly, that the Two-valued Algebra covers relations of propositions in extension: and that, in consequence, the relation symbolized by $\supset$, called 'material implication,' is subject to certain paradoxes, such as "A false proposition implies any proposition" (corresponding to $0 \subset a$), and "A true proposition is implied by any proposition" (corresponding to $a \subset 1$). Nothing was there said of any possible interpretation of the Two-valued Algebra as a system of the intensional relations of propositions. Actually such interpretation is possible, but it would be quite useless as a system of the logic of propositions; for example, it would not be possible, in terms of this interpretation, to represent "$p$ is true" or "$p$ is false."

It is especially desirable that the logic of propositions should be so developed that the usual meaning of 'implies,' which is intensional, should be included. Although the relation of classes, $a \subset b$, is often important when the corresponding relation of intension does not hold, the relation of material implication is seldom, if ever, of any logical importance unless the usual intensional relation of implication also holds. It is a second purpose of the next chapter so to develop the calculus of propositions that both extensional and intensional relations will be covered —and differently symbolized—and that the meaning of the elements, $p$, $q$, etc., may remain fixed, whether it is their extensional or their intensional relations which are in question.

There is also a third aim to be realized in the next chapter. In mathematical systems in general, what are called 'existence-postulates' and theorems concerning 'existence' are usually included. In logic similarly, existence-postulates and theorems are really required as conditions of significance of the system. This has been largely ignored, up to date, by those who use the logistic method. We shall introduce such a postulate. And we shall show how, from such an assumption, existence-theorems are deducible. The method of such deduction of 'existence' in logic, has not, so far as we know, been used before.

# CHAPTER VI

## THE LOGISTIC CALCULUS OF UNANALYZED PROPOSITIONS

It is the purpose of the present chapter to derive a calculus of propositions from symbolic postulates, by the logistic method.

The qualification "unanalyzed propositions" indicates the fact that not all the laws of deduction are capable of statement in terms of symbols for propositions, *p*, *q*, *r*, etc. For example, it is a law of deduction that no proposition can be both true and false; and this principle can be stated in symbols as $\sim(p \sim p)$. But equally it is a law of deduction that if all *A*'s are *B*'s and all *B*'s are *C*'s, then all *A*'s are *C*'s. This principle, however, cannot be stated in terms of *p*, *q*, and *r*, representing propositions. It is necessary that the premises and the conclusion should be so analyzed as to indicate what terms figure in these propositions, and how these terms are related. Thus the calculus of propositions can comprise only the most general principles of deductive inference, which do not depend upon the analysis of the propositions in question.

As indicated in the preceding chapter, we have here the further purpose to develop a calculus based upon a meaning of 'implies' such that "*p* implies *q*" will be synonymous with "*q* is deducible from *p*." The relation of material implication, which figures in most logistic calculuses of propositions, does not accord with this usual meaning of 'implies.' It leads to those paradoxes such as "A false proposition implies every proposition" and "A true proposition is implied by any" which have been set forth in Chapter IV. Also, if we take "*p* is consistent with *q*" to mean "*p* does not imply the falsity of *q*," and "*q* is independent of *p*" to mean "*p* does not imply *q*," then in terms of material implication no two propositions can be at once consistent and independent. As we shall see, it is entirely possible so to develop the calculus of propositions that it accords with the usual meaning of 'implies' and includes the relation of consistency with its ordinary properties.

Since the calculus here given is not logically equivalent to the Two-valued Algebra, or to any logistic calculus which comprises the same principles, the system here to be developed needs a name. We shall call its relation of implication 'strict implication,' and the system 'the Calculus of Strict Implication'—or, for brevity, 'Strict Implication.' Similarly, we shall refer to the system based on the relation of material implication as 'Material Implication.'

Obviously the present development is to have no dependence on the theorems of previous chapters. But in order to avoid possible confusion in later reference, we give the laws of the present chapter higher numbers, beginning with 11.

## Section 1. General Properties of the Elementary Functions of Propositions

The primitive or undefined ideas assumed are the following:

1. Propositions: $p$, $q$, $r$, etc.

2. Negation: $\sim p$. This may be read either as 'not-$p$' or as "$p$ is false."

3. Logical product: $p\,q$, or $p\,.\,q$. (The dot, as a mark of punctuation, will be used only when one or both of the *members* of the product are complex.) This relation may be read as '$p$ and $q$' or "$p$ is true and $q$ is true" or "$p$ and $q$ are both true."

4. Self-consistency or possibility: $\Diamond p$. This may be read "$p$ is self-consistent" or "$p$ is possible" or "It is possible that $p$ be true." As will appear later, $\Diamond p$ is equivalent to "It is false that $p$ implies its own negation," and $\Diamond(p\,q)$ is equivalent to "$p$ and $q$ are consistent." The precise logical significance of $\Diamond p$ will be discussed in Section 4.

5. Logical equivalence: $p = q$.

In terms of product and negation, we can define the relation $p \vee q$, "At least one of the two, $p$ and $q$, is true":

***11·01*** $p \vee q\,.=.\sim(\sim p \sim q)$

This relation may be read, as before, "Either $p$ or $q$," remembering that the possibility that $p$ and $q$ both should be true is not excluded; and also that $p \vee q$ implies nothing as to connection of content or logical significance between $p$ and $q$, but has to do only with their truth or falsity.

The relation of strict implication can be defined in terms of negation, possibility, and product:

*11·02* $p \prec q . = . \sim \Diamond(p \sim q)$

Thus "$p$ implies $q$" or "$p$ strictly implies $q$" is to mean "It is false that it is possible that $p$ should be true and $q$ false" or "The statement '$p$ is true and $q$ false' is not self-consistent." When $q$ is deducible from $p$, to say "$p$ is true and $q$ is false" is to assert, implicitly, a contradiction.

The properties of this relation, and its precise significance, will become clearer with the development of the system, particularly in Section 4.

Curiously enough, it is both possible and advantageous to define the relation of logical equivalence; though the definition does not enable us to dispense with the primitive idea of equivalence, since that is the defining relation:

*11·03* $p = q . = : p \prec q . q \prec p$

That is, "$p$ and $q$ are equivalent" is equivalent to "$p$ implies $q$, and $q$ implies $p$." Thus two propositions are equivalent if, and only if, each is deducible from the other. This definition will enable us to prove other equivalences than those which are assumed; and thus to render more explicit the meaning of various logical functions in terms of one another.

The number of our undefined ideas could be smaller, and fewer postulates would be required, if logical relations which are less familiar were taken as primitive. But such a choice would render the symbolism much harder to interpret, at first, and the proofs of early theorems much more complex: we here sacrifice economy of assumption to considerations of exposition.

Not all the definitions and not all the postulates will be introduced in this section, for reasons which will appear. For the present, we assume the following postulates:

*11·1* $p q . \prec . q p$

If $p$ and $q$ are both true, then $q$ and $p$ are both true.

*11·2* $p\,q \;.⥽.\; p$

If $p$ and $q$ are both true, then $p$ is true.

*11·3* $p \;.⥽.\; p\,p$

If $p$ is true, then '$p$ and $p$' is true.

*11·4* $(p\,q)r \;.⥽.\; p(q\,r)$

"($p$ and $q$) and $r$" implies "$p$ and ($q$ and $r$)."

*11·5* $p \;.⥽.\; \sim(\sim p)$

If $p$ is true, then it is false that $p$ is false.

*11·6* $p ⥽ q \,.\, q ⥽ r \;:⥽.\; p ⥽ r$

If $p$ implies $q$, and $q$ implies $r$, then $p$ implies $r$. This law will be referred to as the Principle of the Syllogism.

*11·7* $p \,.\, p ⥽ q \;:⥽.\; q$

If $p$ is true, and $p$ implies $q$, then $q$ is true. It might be supposed that this principle would be implicit in any set of assumptions for a calculus of deductive inference. As a matter of fact, 11·7 cannot be deduced from the other postulates.

We have said that the importance of the logistic method lies in the fact that proofs take place through operations according to precise rules which are independent of any logical significance of the system. The operations to be allowed are the following:

*Substitution.*

(a) Either of two equivalent expressions may be substituted for the other. Thus if an expression of the form $p = q$ has been assumed, or subsequently established, what precedes the sign of equivalence in this expression may be substituted for what follows it; or *vice versa*.

(b) Any proposition, or any expression which has meaning in terms of the undefined ideas, may be substituted for $p$, or $q$, or $r$, etc., in any assumption or established theorem. It is understood, of course, that if $p$, for example, occurs more than once in a given postulate or theorem (as in $p\,q \;.⥽.\; q\,p$), then whatever is substituted for $p$ in one place must be substituted for it throughout.

[1] See Appendix II.

*Adjunction.*

Any two expressions which have been separately asserted may be jointly asserted. That is, if $p$ has been asserted, and $q$ has been asserted, then $p\ q$ may be asserted.

*Inference.*

If $p$ has been asserted and $p \prec q$ is asserted, then $q$ may be asserted. That is to say, a new theorem may be inferred from a previous principle which has been shown to imply it. As a logistic operation, this means that, if by either or both of the operations previously mentioned we derive an expression of the form $p \prec q$, and such that $p$ is previously asserted, $q$ may be taken as established.

It might be thought that this operation is superfluous in the light of postulate 11·7. But it is not. That postulate merely tells us that the complex premise $p \centerdot p \prec q$ implies $q$. To be sure, the logical meaning of the postulate is in accord with the operation. But it is a point of the logistic method that a symbolic expression should not be confused with an operation which gives proof.

It is to be observed that the performance of these simple operations is independent of their logical significance. They could be carried out 'mechanically,' according to the rules, by one who had no interest in the interpretation of the symbolism. Such a mechanical operator of the symbols might not produce very interesting results; but so long as he observed the rules, everything he established would be valid. One importance of this is that the precise and relatively simple character of the operations provides a check on proofs, and renders them independent of our logical intuitions. Another and even more important result is that the whole system is thus rendered abstract, in the sense that we can say, "Regardless of any interpretation which may be assigned, the initial expressions, manipulated according to certain rules of operation, give certain other expressions in result." Whether any given expression can or cannot be thus derived is absolutely determined by the initial expressions themselves and the rules. That is, the whole system is absolutely determined, quite independently of what in particular the symbols such as $p$, $q$, $r$, and ⥽ and ∨, etc., may mean, and quite independently of the logical significance of the operations.[2] When (as is, in fact, the case) different symbolic systems are possible, having different significance when taken to represent the principles of deduction, it is of the utmost importance that the question of operational or 'mathematical' integrity can be thus separated from all question of what is or is not true in logic.

Since it is important for the student to command this logistic method of derivation, we shall state proofs of the first few theorems quite fully, and explain these proofs. Later, abbreviations will be introduced, and proofs which offer no special difficulty may be omitted.

The first theorem to be demonstrated is "$p$ implies $p$" or "Every proposition implies itself."

*12·1* $p$ ⥽ $p$

[11·2: $p/q$] $p\,p$ . ⥽ . $p$ (1)

[11·6: $p\,p/q$; $p/r$] 11·3 . (1) : ⥽ . $p$ ⥽ $p$

First let us explain the conventions of notation. What appears in the square bracket preceding the first line of proof means "In 11·2, substitute $p$ for $q$." The number of the proposition in which the substitution is to be made is first given, and $p/q$ indicates the substitution of $p$ for $q$. This operation gives the line of proof set down following the bracket,

$p\,p$ . ⥽ . $p$.

That result is labeled (1). The square bracket in the second line means "In 11·6, substitute $p\,p$ for $q$, and $p$ for $r$." This gives

$p$ . ⥽ . $p\,p$ : $p\,p$ . ⥽ . $p$ : . ⥽ . $p$ ⥽ $p$.

In this expression, the first part, $p$ . ⥽ . $p\,p$, is postulate 11·3. The next part is identical with the result of the preceding step

[2] Certain critics of this conception of logistic have objected that $p$, $q$, $r$ and ⥽, ∨, etc., must be *symbols* (therefore possessing meaning), not merely marks on paper, which are different entities when they occur in different places. This is true, of course; and proves nothing—except that such critics fail to catch the point. So are $\alpha$, $\beta$, $\gamma$ in Hilbert's *Foundations of Geometry* symbols and not just ink on paper. But Hilbert's geometry is nevertheless abstract, and independent of the particular meanings which can be imposed—in great variety—upon these symbols.

of proof, $p\,p\,.\,⥽\,.\,p$. Thus the whole expression may be abbreviated:

$$11{\cdot}3\,.\,(1):⥽\,.\,p ⥽ p.$$

Since 11·3 and (1) have been asserted, the adjunction or logical product of them,

$$p\,.\,⥽\,.\,p\,p : p\,p\,.\,⥽\,.\,p,$$

may be asserted. Hence, by the operation of inference, we may assert whatever is implied by this expression. This second line of the proof states that the theorem to be proved, $p ⥽ p$, is so implied. Thus the theorem is established.

***12·11*** $p = p$

[12·1] $p ⥽ p\,.\,p ⥽ p$ (1)

[11·03: $p/q$] $p = p\,.=.\,(1)$

In this proof, the first line represents the joint-assertion of 12·1 with itself. The second line indicates that by substituting, in 11·03, $p$ for $q$, we have

$$p = p\,.=:p ⥽ p\,.\,p ⥽ p.$$

Since this holds, and equivalent expressions may be substituted for each other, $p = p$ may be substituted for the asserted expression in line (1), and is thus established.

By virtue of this theorem, that every proposition is equivalent to itself, we can assert any formal identity or expression of the form $p = p$. We can then substitute for one half of such an expression any equivalent of it which has been assumed or proved. The relation of logical equivalence is, of course, symmetrical and transitive. We could, in fact, demonstrate as theorems,

$$(1)\ p = q\,.\,⥽\,.\,q = p,$$

and

$$(2)\ p = q\,.\,q = r:⥽\,.\,p = r.$$

But the operation of substituting equivalents for one another makes it unnecessary to use these principles in proofs.

***12·15*** $p\,q\,.=.\,q\,p$

[11·1: $q/p$; $p/q$] $q\,p\,.\,⥽\,.\,p\,q$ (1)

[11·03: $p\,q/p$; $q\,p/q$] $p\,q\,.\,⥽\,.\,q\,p : q\,p\,.\,⥽\,.\,p\,q :.$

$= : p\,q\,.=.\,q\,p$

11·1 . (1) : = : $p\,q\,.=.\,q\,p$

Here we give the second line of the proof in full; then, immediately below, this is repeated in the abbreviated form, indicating that what it states is the equivalence of the theorem to be proved to the joint-assertion of 11·1 and what is proved in line (1).

*12·17* $p\,q\,.\!\prec\!.\,q$

$[11\cdot 2{:}\ q/p;\ p/q]\ q\,p\,.\!\prec\!.\,q$ (1)

$[12\cdot 11{:}\ q\,p\,.\!\prec\!.\,q/p]\ q\,p\,.\!\prec\!.\,q :=: q\,p\,.\!\prec\!.\,q$ (2)

$[12\cdot 15]\ p\,q\,. = .\,q\,p$ (3)

$[(3)]\ q\,p\,.\!\prec\!.\,q :=: p\,q\,.\!\prec\!.\,q$

$(1)\ . =: p\,q\,.\!\prec\!.\,q$

Here we first, by substitution in 11·2, derive line (1). Next, by substitution of this whole expression for $p$ in 12·11, we write the identity of line (2). The third line merely reminds us of 12·15, which allows us to substitute $p\,q$ for $q\,p$ in one half of (2). This substitution is made in the next line. We repeat that line, in abbreviated form, indicating that it states the equivalence of the theorem to be proved and the assertion of line (1). Ordinarily, we shall write a proof by such substitution of equivalents more briefly: assertion of the identity—line (2)—will be omitted, and a previously established identity will be referred to by number instead of being repeated. In this simpler form the above proof would be written:

$[11\cdot 2{:}\ q/p;\ p/q]\ q\,p\,.\!\prec\!.\,q$ (1)

$[12\cdot 15]\ (1)\,. =: p\,q\,.\!\prec\!.\,q.$

*12·2* $\sim p \prec q\,. = .\sim q \prec p$

$[12\cdot 11{:}\ \sim\Diamond(\sim p \sim q)/p]\ \sim\Diamond(\sim p \sim q) = \sim\Diamond(\sim p \sim q)$ (1)

$[12\cdot 15{:}\ \sim p/p;\ \sim q/q]\ \sim p \sim q\,. = .\sim q \sim p$ (2)

$[(1), (2)]\ \sim\Diamond(\sim p \sim q)\,. = .\sim\Diamond(\sim q \sim p)$ (3)

$[11\cdot 02{:}\ \sim p/p]\ \sim p \prec q\,. = .\sim\Diamond(\sim p \sim q)$ (4)

$[11\cdot 02{:}\ \sim q/p;\ p/q]\ \sim q \prec p\,. = .\sim\Diamond(\sim q \sim p)$ (5)

$[(4), (5)]\ (3)\,. =: \sim p \prec q\,. = .\sim q \prec p$

Here the first line is the assertion of an identity, by 12·11. Line (2) establishes the equivalence of $\sim p \sim q$ and $\sim q \sim p$, by substitutions in 12·15. In line (3) we make the substitution allowed, according to the equivalence established in (2), in the second half of line (1), thus deriving

$$\sim \Diamond(\sim p \sim q) \,.\, = \,.\, \sim \Diamond(\sim q \sim p).$$

The next two lines, by substitutions in definition 11·02, establish the equivalence of the first half of the above to $\sim p \prec q$, and of the second half to $\sim q \prec p$. The substitutions which these equivalences allow give the theorem.

*12·25* $\sim(\sim p) \prec p$

$$[12\cdot 1\colon \sim p/p] \quad \sim p \prec \sim p \qquad (1)$$

$$[12\cdot 2\colon \sim p/q] \quad \sim p \prec \sim p \,.\, = \,.\, \sim(\sim p) \prec p$$

$$(1) \quad .\, = \,.\, \sim(\sim p) \prec p$$

This is the converse of postulate 11·5. The postulate and this theorem together give the *equivalence* of $p$ and $\sim(\sim p)$:

*12·3* $p = \sim(\sim p)$

$$[11\cdot 5,\ 12\cdot 25] \quad p \prec \sim(\sim p) \,.\, \sim(\sim p) \prec p \qquad (1)$$

$$[11\cdot 03] \quad p = \sim(\sim p) \,.\, = : p \prec \sim(\sim p) \,.\, \sim(\sim p) \prec p$$

$$p = \sim(\sim p) \,.\, = \,. \qquad (1)$$

The first step in this proof is an operation of adjunction; the joint-assertion of 11·5 and 12·25. Next, by substitution in definition 11·03, the theorem is proved to be equivalent to this assertion of line (1); and hence it may be substituted for that assertion. The substitution made in definition 11·03 is not indicated, since it is obvious.

Theorem 12·2 contains an implication, which can be separately asserted:

*12·4* $\sim p \prec q \,.\, \prec \,.\, \sim q \prec p$

$$[11\cdot 2] \quad \sim p \prec q \,.\, \prec \,.\, \sim q \prec p : \sim q \prec p \,.\, \prec \,.\, \sim p \prec q : . \prec :$$

$$\sim p \prec q \,.\, \prec \,.\, \sim q \prec p \qquad (1)$$

$$[11\cdot 03] \quad (1) \,.\, = : . \sim p \prec q \,.\, = \,.\, \sim q \prec p : \prec : \sim p \prec q \,.\, \prec \,.\, \sim q \prec p$$

$$12\cdot 2 \qquad . \prec : \sim p \prec q \,.\, \prec \,.\, \sim q \prec p$$

Line (1) is here an expression of the form $p\,q \,.\, \prec \,.\, p$. The substitutions to be made in 11·2 in order to give this line are omitted, being obvious. The first half of line (1) is equivalent to

$$\sim p \prec q \,.\, = \,.\, \sim q \prec p,$$

by definition 11·03. Again, the substitutions made in the definition are not indicated. The second line, being thus equivalent to (1), may be asserted. This second line is found to state that 12·2 implies the theorem to be proved. Hence the theorem may be asserted, by the operation of inference.

***12·41*** $\sim p \prec \sim q \,.\prec.\, q \prec p$

$[12{\cdot}4\colon \sim q/q]\ \sim p \prec \sim q \,.\prec.\, \sim(\sim q) \prec p$ (1)

$[12{\cdot}3]$ (1) = Q.E.D.

Here line (1), established by substituting $\sim q$ for $q$ in 12·4, is equivalent to the theorem to be proved, when we substitute $q$ for its equivalent $\sim(\sim q)$, by 12·3. We here introduce the abbreviation Q.E.D. for the theorem to be proved, instead of repeating the theorem in the last line of the proof. This abbreviation will be continued.

***12·42*** $p \prec \sim q \,.\prec.\, q \prec \sim p$

$[12{\cdot}41\colon \sim p/p]\ \sim(\sim p) \prec \sim q \,.\prec.\, q \prec \sim p$ (1)

$[12{\cdot}3]$ (1) = Q.E.D.

***12·43*** $p \prec q \,.\prec.\, \sim q \prec \sim p$

$[12{\cdot}42\colon \sim q/q]\ p \prec \sim(\sim q) \,.\prec.\, \sim q \prec \sim p$ (1)

$[12{\cdot}3]$ (1) = Q.E.D.

***12·44*** $p \prec q \,.=.\, \sim q \prec \sim p$

$[12{\cdot}41\colon q/p;\, p/q]\ \sim q \prec \sim p \,.\prec.\, p \prec q$ (1)

$[11{\cdot}03]\ 12{\cdot}43\,.\,(1) : =$ Q.E.D.

The last line of this proof states that, by definition 11·03, the joint-assertion of theorem 12·43 and what is established in line (1) is equivalent to the theorem to be proved.

***12·45*** $p \prec \sim q \,.=.\, q \prec \sim p$

$[12{\cdot}42\colon q/p;\, p/q]\ q \prec \sim p \,.\prec.\, p \prec \sim q$ (1)

$[11{\cdot}03]\ 12{\cdot}42\,.\,(1) : =$ Q.E.D.

The general principle of all the theorems, 12·2 and 12·4–12·45, is that any implication may be reversed by negating both its members. That the result of this operation is *implied by* the original expression is established in 12·4–12·43; that it is *equivalent to* the original expression (and hence may be substituted for it) is proved in 12·2, 12·44, and 12·45.

***12·5*** $(p\,q)r \,.=.\, p(q\,r) \,.=.\, q(p\,r) \,.=.\, (q\,p)r$, etc., etc.

[12·15] $p(q\,r) \,.=.\, (q\,r)p \,.=.\, (r\,q)p$ (1)

[11·4] $(r\,q)p \,.⥽.\, r(q\,p)$ (2)

[(1), (2)] $p(q\,r) \,.⥽.\, r(q\,p)$ (3)

[12·15] $r(q\,p) \,.=.\, (q\,p)r \,.=.\, (p\,q)r$ (4)

[(3), (4)] $p(q\,r) \,.⥽.\, (p\,q)r$ (5)

[11·03] 12·15 . (5) $: = : (p\,q)r \,.=.\, p(q\,r)$

Remainder of the theorem by similar proofs.

The force of 12·5 is that in any product of three propositions, the order of the propositions and the placing of the parentheses are immaterial. Since this holds, we may hereafter omit such parentheses, or place them as we choose, giving reference to this theorem.

The next principle to be proved is the law of the 'antilogism,' mentioned in Chapter III:

***12·6*** $p\,q \,.⥽.\, r : = : q \sim r \,.⥽.\, \sim p : = : p \sim r \,.⥽.\, \sim q$

[12·11] $\sim \Diamond(p\,q \,.\, \sim r) : = : \sim \Diamond(p\,q \,.\, \sim r)$ (1)

[12·5] (1) $. = :. \sim \Diamond(p\,q \,.\, \sim r) : = : \sim \Diamond(q \sim r \,.\, p)$ (2)

[12·3] (2) $. = :. \sim \Diamond(p\,q \,.\, \sim r) : = : \sim \Diamond[q \sim r \,.\, \sim(\sim p)]$ (3)

[11·02] (3) $. = :. p\,q \,.⥽.\, r : = : q \sim r \,.⥽.\, \sim p$

By similar proof: $p\,q \,.⥽.\, r : = : p \sim r \,.⥽.\, \sim q$

That two premises $p$ and $q$ together give the conclusion $r$, is equivalent to "If $p$ is true but $r$ is false, then $q$ is false" and to "If $q$ is true but $r$ is false, then $p$ is false." The equivalences stated by this theorem obviously give rise to implications, by the principles 11·2 and 12·17:

***12·61*** $p\,q \,.⥽.\, r : ⥽ : p \sim r \,.⥽.\, \sim q$

***12·62*** $p\,q \,.⥽.\, r : ⥽ : q \sim r \,.⥽.\, \sim p$

It will be convenient to have certain of the principles stated by the postulates in alternative forms which can now be proved.

***12·7*** $p \,.=.\, p\,p$

[11·2: $p/q$] $p\,p \,.⥽.\, p$ (1)

[11·03] 11·3 . (1) : = Q.E.D.

***12·72*** $\sim p ⥽ \sim(p\,q)$

[12·43: $p\,q/p$; $p/q$] $p\,q \,.⥽.\, p : ⥽ . \sim p ⥽ \sim(p\,q)$ (1)

11·2 ⥽ Q.E.D.

**12·73** $\sim q \prec \sim(p\, q)$

$[12{\cdot}43:\ p\, q/p]\ 12{\cdot}17 \prec$ Q.E.D.

**12·75** $q \prec r\,.\,p \prec q :\prec .\, p \prec r$

$[12{\cdot}15]\ 11{\cdot}6 =$ Q.E.D.

From this point on, proofs will be increasingly abbreviated. But indication will always be given sufficient for complete reconstruction of the proof; and any step likely to be troublesome will be stated in full.

The next two theorems are extensions of the Principle of the Syllogism, 11·6. The first of these is of considerable importance.

**12·77** $p \prec q : q\, r\,.\prec .\, s :.\prec : p\, r\,.\prec .\, s$

$[11{\cdot}6]\quad r \sim s\,.\prec .\sim q : \sim q \prec \sim p :.\prec : r \sim s\,.\prec .\sim p$ (1)

$[12{\cdot}6]\quad r \sim s\,.\prec .\sim q : = : q\, r\,.\prec .\, s$ (2)

$[12{\cdot}6]\quad r \sim s\,.\prec .\sim p : = : p\, r\,.\prec .\, s$ (3)

$[12{\cdot}44]\quad \sim q \prec \sim p\,.=.\, p \prec q$ (4)

$[(2), (3), (4), 12{\cdot}15]\ (1) =$ Q.E.D.

**12·78** $p \prec q\,.\,q \prec r\,.\,r \prec s :\prec .\, p \prec s$

$[11{\cdot}6]\quad q \prec r\,.\,r \prec s :\prec .\, q \prec s$ (1)

$[12{\cdot}75]\quad q \prec s\,.\,p \prec q :\prec .\, p \prec s$ (2)

$[12{\cdot}77]\quad (1)\,.\,(2) :\prec : q \prec r\,.\,r \prec s\,.\,p \prec q :\prec .\, p \prec s$ (3)

$[12{\cdot}15]\ (3) =$ Q.E.D.

Theorem 12·78 extends the Principle of the Syllogism from the case of two antecedents to the case of three. By continued use of 12·77, it could be extended from three antecedents to four, from four to five, and so on; and hence proved to hold for any given number of antecedents.

So far, no use has been made of postulate 11·7. The next group of theorems are consequences of it.

**12·8** $p \sim q\,.\prec .\sim(p \prec q)$

$[12{\cdot}61:\ p \prec q/q;\ q/r]\ 11{\cdot}7 \prec$ Q.E.D.

If $p$ is true and $q$ false, then $p$ does not imply $q$; a true proposition does not imply any which is false.

**12·81** $p \prec q\,.\prec .\sim(p \sim q)$

$[12{\cdot}42:\ p \sim q/p;\ p \prec q/q]\ 12{\cdot}8 \prec$ Q.E.D.

If $p$ implies $q$, then it is not the case that $p$ is true and $q$ false. The converse of 12·81, which would be

$$\sim(p \sim q) . \prec . p \prec q,$$

cannot be proved from our postulates.[3] This is a main distinction between strict implication and material implication. On this point, the properties of strict implication are in accord with the usual meaning of 'implies,' where those of material implication are not. Let $p$ = "Roses are red" and $q$ = "Sugar is sweet." It is here not the case that $p$ is true and $q$ false—since $q$ is true. Thus in this example $\sim(p \sim q)$ holds. But $p$ does not imply $q$: "Sugar is sweet" cannot be inferred from "Roses are red."

***12·84*** $p\, q . \prec . \sim(p \prec \sim q)$

[12·8: $\sim q/q$] $p . \sim(\sim q) : \prec . \sim(p \prec \sim q)$ (1)

[12·3] (1) = Q.E.D.

***12·85*** $p \prec \sim q . \prec . \sim(p\, q)$

[12·45] 12·84 = Q.E.D.

***12·86*** $p . \prec . \sim(p \prec \sim p)$

[12·84: $p/q$] $p\, p . \prec . \sim(p \prec \sim p)$ (1)

[12·7] (1) = Q.E.D.

A true proposition does not imply its own denial. The correlative principle, "If a proposition implies its own denial, it is false," is, of course, the principle of the *reductio ad absurdum*. This comes next:

***12·87*** $p \prec \sim p . \prec . \sim p$

[12·42: $p \prec \sim p/q$] 12·86 $\prec$ Q.E.D.

***12·88*** $\sim p \prec p . \prec . p$

[12·87: $\sim p/p$] $\sim p \prec \sim(\sim p) . \prec . \sim(\sim p)$ (1)

[12·3] (1) = Q.E.D.

If a proposition is implied by its own denial, it is true. This might be called the 'principle of necessary truth.' Its correlative, "A false proposition is never implied by its own denial," is less familiar, but obviously follows:

[3] See Appendix II.

*12·89* ~p ⥽ ~(~p ⥽ p)

[12·43] 12·88 ⥽ Q.E.D.

As a corollary of 12·81, we have the Law of Contradiction:

*12·9* ~(p ~p)

[12·81: p/q] 12·1 ⥽ Q.E.D.

The fundamental properties of the relation p ∨ q are deducible from those of p q, in terms of which it is defined. The next group of theorems exhibit such properties.

*13·1* p ∨ q . ⥽ . q ∨ p

[11·1: ~q/p; ~p/q] ~q ~p . ⥽ . ~p ~q (1)

[12·44] (1) . = . ~(~p ~q) ⥽ ~(~q ~p) (2)

[11·01] (2) = Q.E.D.

The 'either . . . or . . .' relation is symmetrical.

*13·11* p ∨ q . = . q ∨ p

[13·1: q/p; p/q] q ∨ p . ⥽ . p ∨ q (1)

[11·03] 13·1 . (1) : = Q.E.D.

*13·2* p . ⥽ . p ∨ q

[11·2] ~p ~q . ⥽ . ~p (1)

[12·45] (1) . = . p ⥽ ~(~p ~q) (2)

[11·01] (2) = Q.E.D.

If p is true, then at least one of the two, p and q, is true.

*13·21* q . ⥽ . p ∨ q

[12·17: ~p/p; ~q/q] ~p ~q . ⥽ . ~q (1)

[12·45] (1) . = : q . ⥽ . ~(~p ~q) (2)

[11·01] (2) = Q.E.D.

*13·3* p ∨ p . ⥽ . p

[11·3: ~p/p] ~p . ⥽ . ~p ~p (1)

[12·4] (1) . ⥽ . ~(~p ~p) ⥽ p (2)

[11·01] (2) = Q.E.D.

*13·31* p . = . p ∨ p

[13·21: p/q] p . ⥽ . p ∨ p (1)

[11·03] 13·3 . (1) : = Q.E.D.

*13·4* $p \vee (q \vee r) . \prec . (p \vee q) \vee r$

$[11\cdot4]\ (\sim p \sim q) \sim r . \prec . \sim p(\sim q \sim r)$ (1)

$[12\cdot3]\ (1) . = :. \sim[\sim(\sim p \sim q)] \sim r : \prec : \sim p \sim[\sim(\sim q \sim r)]$ (2)

$[11\cdot01]\ (2) . = : \sim(p \vee q) \sim r . \prec . \sim p \sim(q \vee r)$ (3)

$[12\cdot44]\ (3) . = : \sim[\sim p \sim(q \vee r)] . \prec . \sim[\sim(p \vee q) \sim r]$ (4)

$[11\cdot01]\ (4) =$ Q.E.D.

It is obvious that 13·4 can be extended in the same manner in which 11·4 is extended in 12·5. The mode of proof will be apparent from that of the preceding theorems, and need not be given:

*13·41* $p \vee (q \vee r) . = . (p \vee q) \vee r . = . q \vee (p \vee r) . = . (q \vee p) \vee r,$ etc., etc.

The Law of the Excluded Middle, "Every proposition is either true or false," concludes this group of theorems:

*13·5* $p \vee \sim p$

$[12\cdot9 : \sim p/p]\ \sim[\sim p \sim(\sim p)]$ (1)

$[11\cdot01]\ (1) =$ Q.E.D.

## Section 2. Material Implication

If we add to our previous assumptions definitions of the relation of material implication and the relation of material equivalence, the entire system of Material Implication can then be deduced.

*14·01* $p \supset q . = . \sim(p \sim q)$

That is, "$p$ materially implies $q$" means "It is not the case that $p$ is true and $q$ false."

The definition of material equivalence is in terms of material implication:

*14·02* $p \equiv q . = : p \supset q . q \supset p$

Replacing the material implications here by their defined equivalents, this becomes

$$p \equiv q . = : \sim(p \sim q) . \sim(q \sim p).$$

Hence $p \equiv q$ means "$p$ and $q$ are either both true or both false."

First, we shall prove that, from the definition 14·01 and our previous assumptions, the symbolic postulates for the system of

Material Implication, as given in section A of *Principia Mathematica,* can be deduced. We shall then discuss (1) the properties which material implication and strict implication have in common and (2) the properties peculiar to material implication, which distinguish it from strict implication.

It follows from our postulate 11·7 that if $p$ strictly implies $q$, then also $p$ materially implies $q$:

***14·1*** $p \prec q . \prec . p \supset q$

[12·81] $p \prec q . \prec . \sim(p \sim q)$ (1)

[14·01] (1) = Q.E.D.

By virtue of this principle, whenever a strict implication can be asserted, the corresponding material implication can also be asserted. The converse does not hold: strict implication is a *narrower* relation than material implication; the assertion of a strict implication is a *stronger* statement than the assertion of the corresponding material implication. This will become apparent —at least it will be apparent how wide the meaning of material implication is—if we consider what is involved in negating it:

***14·12*** $\sim(p \supset q) . = . p \sim q$

[14·01, 12·3] $\sim(p \supset q) . = . \sim[\sim(p \sim q)] . = . p \sim q$

The relation $p \supset q$ fails to hold when and only when $p$ is true and $q$ false. A true proposition does not materially imply a false one; but the relation holds if $p$ and $q$ are both true, or both false, or if $p$ is false and $q$ true, regardless of the meaning or logical significance of $p$ and $q$.

Proof of the symbolic assumptions for the system of Material Implication, as given in *Principia Mathematica,* is as follows:

***14·2*** $p \supset q . = . \sim p \vee q$ (*Principia,* ∗1·01.)

[11·01 $\sim p/p$] $\sim p \vee q . = . \sim[\sim(\sim p) \sim q]$

[12·3] $= . \sim(p \sim q)$

[14·01] $= . p \supset q$

***14·21*** $p q . = . \sim(\sim p \vee \sim q)$ (*Principia,* ∗3·01.)

[12·11] $\sim(\sim p \vee \sim q) = \sim(\sim p \vee \sim q)$

[11·01] $= \sim[\sim\{\sim(\sim p) \sim(\sim q)\}]$

[12·3] $= p q$

In *Principia*, 14·2 and 14·21 are definitions.

*14·22* $p \vee p . \supset . p$ (*Principia*, $*$1·2.)

[14·1] 13·3 $\dashv$ Q.E.D.

It should be noticed that 13·3, from which 14·22 is derived, asserts the corresponding strict implication $p \vee p . \dashv . p$. Similarly 13·21, $q . \dashv . p \vee q$, gives the next:

*14·23* $q . \supset . p \vee q$ (*Principia*, $*$1·3.)

[14·1] 13·21 $\dashv$ Q.E.D.

Also our theorem 13·1, $p \vee q . \dashv . q \vee p$, gives:

*14·24* $p \vee q . \supset . q \vee p$ (*Principia*, $*$1·4.)

[14·1] 13·1 $\dashv$ Q.E.D.

*14·25* $p \vee (q \vee r) . \dashv . q \vee (p \vee r)$

[13·4] $p \vee (q \vee r) . \dashv . (p \vee q) \vee r$ (1)

[13·41] (1) = Q.E.D.

The asserted relation in 14·25 is a strict implication. This gives immediately:

*14·251* $p \vee (q \vee r) . \supset . q \vee (p \vee r)$ (*Principia*, $*$1·5.)

[14·1] 14·25 $\dashv$ Q.E.D.

Before proving the last postulate of the set in *Principia Mathematica*, we require one further general principle connecting strict and material implication—one which is in point whenever we have a triadic relation of the form $p\,q . \dashv . r$:

*14·26* $p\,q . \dashv . r : = : p . \dashv . q \supset r : = : q . \dashv . p \supset r$

[12·6] $p\,q . \dashv . r : = : q \sim r . \dashv . \sim p$

[12·45] $= : p . \dashv . \sim(q \sim r)$

[14·01] $= : p . \dashv . q \supset r$

By similar proof: $p\,q . \dashv . r : = : q . \dashv . p \supset r$

*14·27* $q \supset r . \dashv : p \vee q . \supset . p \vee r$

[11·1] $\sim r\, q . \dashv . q \sim r$ (1)

[12·61: $\sim r/p$; $q \sim r/r$] (1) $. \dashv :. \sim r . \sim(q \sim r) : \dashv . \sim q$ (2)

[11·1] $\sim q \sim p . \dashv . \sim p \sim q$ (3)

[12·77: $\sim r . \sim(q \sim r)/p$; $\sim q/q$; $\sim p/r$; $\sim p \sim q/s$]

(2) . (3) $: \dashv :. \sim r . \sim(q \sim r) . \sim p : \dashv . \sim p \sim q$ (4)

[12·5] (4) $. = :. \sim(q \sim r) . \sim p \sim r : \dashv . \sim p \sim q$ (5)

[12·6] (5) . = : . ∼(q ∼r) . ∼(∼p ∼q) : ⥽ . ∼(∼p ∼r) (6)
[11·01] (6) . = : . ∼(q ∼r) . p ∨ q : ⥽ . p ∨ r (7)
[14·01] (7) . = : . q ⊃ r . p ∨ q : ⥽ . p ∨ r (8)
[14·26] (8) = Q.E.D.

The *asserted* relation in 14·27 is a strict implication. This gives immediately:

***14·28*** q ⊃ r . ⊃ : p ∨ q . ⊃ . p ∨ r (*Principia*, ∗1·6.)
[14·1] 14·27 ⥽ Q.E.D.

In *Principia Mathematica*, the derivation of theorems from the above set of postulates requires that the operation of inference be extended to material implication: that is, when *p* is asserted, and *p* ⊃ *q* is asserted, it must be possible to assert *q*.[4] Now it is a point of the comparison between strict and material implication that *p* ⥽ *q* is equivalent to "*q* is deducible from *p*," while *p* ⊃ *q* is not. It is a fact, however, that for every material implication which is asserted in any theorem in the system of Material Implication, the corresponding strict implication also holds. We could not prove this here without a long and complex discussion; but it will be noticed that, for each of the above set of postulates, the corresponding principle in which the *asserted* relation is a strict implication also holds. (It is certain *un*asserted, or subordinate, material implications which cannot validly be replaced by the corresponding strict implications.) This fact is of considerable theoretical importance in logic: we shall discuss the significance of it in Chapter VIII. This comparison suggests that we can deduce the theorems of Material Implication without extending the operation of inference to material implication, but does not really prove it. However, the same point can be demonstrated in another way—by means of the following theorem:

***14·29*** p . p ⊃ q : ⥽ . q
[12·1] p ∼q . ⥽ . p ∼q (1)
[12·61: ∼q/q; p ∼q/r] (1) . ⥽ : . p . ∼(p ∼q) : ⥽ . q (2)
[14·01] (2) = Q.E.D.

If any material implication *p* ⊃ *q* is asserted, and *p* is asserted, *p* . *p* ⊃ *q* may be asserted by the operation of adjunction; and

[4] See postulates ∗1·1 and ∗1·11 in *Principia*.

since 14·29 holds, $q$ may then be asserted, by the principle of inference as applied to *strict* implication. Hence any result of applying the operation of inference to an asserted material implication can be derived from our assumptions.

Since the above definitions and postulates, from which the calculus of Material Implication is derived in *Principia Mathematica,* have now been deduced from our postulates, together with the definition of the relation of material implication, it follows that the whole system of Material Implication is contained in the system of Strict Implication.

The further main point of comparison between the two systems can be briefly indicated by examination of our postulates. Postulates 11·1–11·5 each contain only one implication—the asserted strict implication. Since by 14·1,

$$p \prec q \,.\, \prec \,.\, p \supset q,$$

it follows that these five postulates also hold when the asserted relation is a material implication.

Postulates 11·6 and 11·7 contain unasserted, or subordinate, strict implications. But the analogous theorems for material implication also hold:

***15·1*** $p \supset q \,.\, q \supset r \,:\prec .\, p \supset r$

[14·27] $q \supset r \,.\prec :\, {\sim}p \vee q \,.\supset .\, {\sim}p \vee r$ (1)

[14·26] (1) . $= \,:.\, {\sim}p \vee q \,.\, q \supset r \,:\prec .\, {\sim}p \vee r$ (2)

[11·01, 12·3] (2) . $= \,:.\, {\sim}(p\, {\sim}q) \,.\, q \supset r \,:\prec .\, {\sim}(p\, {\sim}r)$ (3)

[14·01] (3) $=$ Q.E.D.

In 15·1, the *asserted* relation is still strict; but this gives immediately:

***15·11*** $p \supset q \,.\, q \supset r \,:\supset .\, p \supset r$

[14·1] 15·1 $\prec$ Q.E.D.

Theorem 15·11 is the analogue of postulate 11·6. Theorems 15·1 and 15·11 also hold, of course, for the other order of the antecedents:

***15·12*** $q \supset r \,.\, p \supset q \,:\prec .\, p \supset r$

***15·13*** $q \supset r \,.\, p \supset q \,:\supset .\, p \supset r$

The analogue of postulate 11·7 follows immediately from 14·29:

***15·14*** $p \,.\, p \supset q : \supset . \, q$

[14·1] 14·29 ⥽ Q.E.D.

Thus if, in our postulates, each strict implication were replaced by a material implication, all of them would hold. In consequence of this and of the facts above pointed out about the operation of inference, it follows that every theorem so far proved would also hold if, in every occurrence of strict implication, this were replaced by a material implication. *All theorems, so far, hold of both relations.* The reader must not hastily assume that, therefore, there is no important difference between the two: we have so ordered the development here as to bring this coincidence about. Their *differences* are to be indicated in the remainder of the present section, and in Section 4.

First, we prove one further principle in which the two relations are alike:

***15·15*** $p \supset q \,. = .\, {\sim}q \supset {\sim}p$

[12·15, 12·25] $\sim(p \sim q) \,. = .\, \sim[\sim q \sim(\sim p)]$ (1)

[14·01] (1) = Q.E.D.

Material implication, like strict implication, is subject to the law that its terms may be interchanged by negating both. Immediate corollaries of 15·15 are:

***15·16*** $p \supset q \,.$ ⥽ $.\, {\sim}q \supset {\sim}p$

***15·17*** $p \supset q \,. \supset .\, {\sim}q \supset {\sim}p$

We proceed now to theorems which hold of material implication but do *not* hold of strict implication. The definition of material implication, 14·01, has the force of the following pair:

(1) $p \supset q$ . ⥽ . $\sim(p \sim q)$,

(2) $\sim(p \sim q)$ . ⥽ . $p \supset q$.

The analogue of (1) for strict implication holds: it is 12·81,

$p$ ⥽ $q$ . ⥽ . $\sim(p \sim q)$.

A true proposition does not imply a false one, either strictly or materially. But the analogue of (2), which would be

$$\sim(p \sim q) \mathrel{.} \prec \mathrel{.} p \prec q,$$

is false. It can be proved that it is not deducible from our postulates.[5] This principle (2), contained in the definition of material implication, is the source of all the paradoxes of material implication which were given in Chapter IV. We repeat the most important of them here, giving the proof of a sufficient number to illustrate the manner of their derivation.

***15·2*** $p \mathrel{.} \prec \mathrel{.} q \supset p$

[12·17] $q \sim p \mathrel{.} \prec \mathrel{.} \sim p$ (1)

[12·45] (1) $. = :$ $p \prec \sim(q \sim p)$ (2)

[14·01] (2) = Q.E.D.

***15·21*** $p \mathrel{.} \supset \mathrel{.} q \supset p$

[14·1] 15·2 $\prec$ Q.E.D.

If $p$ is true, then any proposition $q$ materially implies $p$. The main or asserted implication is strict in 15·2, material in 15·21; but the unasserted implication in the consequent is material in both. The theorems do not hold in the form in which this unasserted relation is strict:

$$p \mathrel{.} \prec \mathrel{.} q \prec p$$

cannot be proved from our postulates.

The manner in which one passes from the assertion of a strict implication, as in 15·2, to the assertion of the corresponding material implication, as in 15·21, is always the same—by means of 14·1. We may, then, omit the proof of this step hereafter.

***15·22*** $\sim p \mathrel{.} \prec \mathrel{.} p \supset q$

[11·2] $p \sim q \mathrel{.} \prec \mathrel{.} p$ (1)

[12·43] (1) $. \prec :$ $\sim p \mathrel{.} \prec \mathrel{.} \sim(p \sim q)$ (2)

[14·01] (2) = Q.E.D.

***15·23*** $\sim p \mathrel{.} \supset \mathrel{.} p \supset q$

If $p$ is false, then $p$ materially implies any proposition $q$. As before, $\sim p \mathrel{.} \prec \mathrel{.} p \prec q$ cannot be proved from our postulates, and is false.

[5] See Appendix II.

Theorem 15·2 gives two further principles which are interesting and of much importance:

*15·24* $p . = . \sim p \supset p$

[15·2: $\sim p/q$] $p . \prec . \sim p \supset p$ (1)

[11·5] $\sim(\sim p) \prec p$ (2)

[12·7] (2) $. = . \sim(\sim p \sim p) \prec p$ (3)

[14·01] (3) $. = : \sim p \supset p . \prec . p$ (4)

[11·03] (1) . (4) : = Q.E.D.

That is, "$p$ is true" and "$p$ is materially implied by its own negation" are logically equivalent. Similarly we have:

*15·25* $\sim p . = . p \supset \sim p$

[15·24: $\sim p/p$] $\sim p . = . \sim(\sim p) \supset \sim p$ (1)

[12·3] (1) = Q.E.D.

That is, "$p$ is false" and "$p$ materially implies its own negation" are logically equivalent statements.

In terms of our ordinary logical conceptions, we should say that a proposition which is implied by its own negation is *logically necessary;* and a proposition which implies its own negation is *self-contradictory* or *logically impossible.* Thus, in terms of material implication—as 15·24 shows—a merely true proposition is indistinguishable from one which is logically necessary; and —as 15·25 shows—a merely false proposition is indistinguishable from one which is self-contradictory or absurd.

In terms of *strict* implication, as we shall see in Section 4, the logically necessary is distinguished from the merely true, and the logically impossible from the merely false.

Further consequences of the definition of material implication, which bear upon the consistency and independence of propositions, are the following:

*15·3* $\sim(p \supset q) . \prec . p \supset \sim q$

[12·17] $p \sim q . \prec . \sim q$ (1)

[11·6] (1) . 12·73 $: \prec : p \sim q . \prec . \sim(p\, q)$ (2)

[12·3] (2) $. = : \sim[\sim(p \sim q)] . \prec . \sim[p \sim(\sim q)]$ (3)

[14·01] (3) = Q.E.D.

*15·31* $\sim(p \supset q) . \supset . p \supset \sim q$

As before, $\sim(p \prec q) . \prec . p \prec \sim q$ cannot be proved, and is false.

*15·32* $\sim(p \supset \sim q) . \prec . p \supset q$

*15·33* $\sim(p \supset \sim q) . \supset . p \supset q$

As 15·3 and 15·32 indicate, if we take any pair of propositions, $p$ and $q$, then $p$ must materially imply $q$ or $p$ will materially imply that $q$ is false. This is of considerable importance, because it means that if material implication, $p \supset q$, should be taken as equivalent to "$q$ is deducible from $p$," then no pair of propositions could be at once consistent and independent. Because if $p$ and $q$ are consistent, then $p$ cannot imply that $q$ is false: and if $q$ is independent of $p$, then $p$ cannot imply that $q$ is true. Thus the ordinary procedures of deduction—as, for instance, in the usual mathematical requirement that the members of a set of postulates should be consistent and independent—would not be possible if $p \supset q$ and "$q$ is deducible from $p$" should be synonymous.

*15·4* $\sim(p \supset q) . \prec . q \supset p$

[12·17] $p \sim q . \prec . \sim q$ (1)

[12·72] $\sim q . \prec . \sim(q \sim p)$ (2)

[11·6] (1) . (2) $: \prec :$ $p \sim q . \prec . \sim(q \sim p)$ (3)

[12·3, 14·01] (3) = Q.E.D.

*15·41* $\sim(p \supset q) . \supset . q \supset p$

By 15·4, if one of a pair of propositions does not materially imply the other, then the other implies the one. The analogue for strict implication,

$$\sim(p \prec q) . \prec . q \prec p,$$

cannot be proved, and is false.

*15·5* $\sim(p \supset q) . \prec . \sim p \supset q$

*15·51* $\sim(p \supset q) . \supset . \sim p \supset q$

By 15·5, if $p$ does not materially imply $q$, then the denial of $p$ implies $q$. But the analogue, $\sim(p \prec q) . \prec . \sim p \prec q$, does not hold.

*15·6* $\sim(p \supset q) . \prec . q \supset \sim p$

*15·61* $\sim(p \supset q) . \supset . q \supset \sim p$

If $p$ does not materially imply $q$, then $q$ implies that $p$ is false. The analogue, $\sim(p \prec q) . \prec . q \prec \sim p$, does not hold.

*15·7* $\sim(p \supset q) \,.\, ⥽ \,.\, \sim p \supset \sim q$

*15·71* $\sim(p \supset q) \,.\supset.\, \sim p \supset \sim q$

The analogue, $\sim(p ⥽ q) \,.\, ⥽ \,.\, \sim p ⥽ \sim q$, does not hold.

*15·72* $p \supset q \,.\vee.\, p \supset \sim q$

[12·81] 15·3 $.⥽.\ \sim[\sim(p \supset q)\ \sim(p \supset \sim q)]$ (1)

[11·01] (1) = Q.E.D.

At least one of the two, "$p$ materially implies $q$" and "$p$ materially implies that $q$ is false," is always true. The analogue,

$$p ⥽ q \,.\vee.\, p ⥽ \sim q,$$

cannot be proved: we shall assume the contradictory of it in Section 6.

A point to be noted concerning all these paradoxical theorems of Material Implication is that while the *asserted* relation in each may be either material or strict, the proposition does not hold when the subordinate or unasserted implications are strict, but only when they are material.

Inspection of theorems 15·3–15·72 reveals a rather startling ubiquity of material implication. Perhaps as good a way as any of summarizing these peculiar properties of this relation, which strict implication does not share, is the following: Let an equal number of true and false statements—chosen at random, and regardless of their subject-matter—be written on slips of paper and put in a hat. Let two of these then be drawn at random. The chance that the first drawn will materially imply the second is 3/4. The chance that the second will materially imply the first is 3/4. The chance that each will materially imply the other is 1/2. And the chance that neither will materially imply the other is 0.

Certain further principles governing material implication will be needed in Section 3. The first of these is the analogue of 14·26:

*15·8* $p\,q \,.\supset.\, r := : p \,.\supset.\, q \supset r := : q \,.\supset.\, p \supset r$

[12·3, 12·5] $\sim(p\,q \,.\, \sim r) = \sim[p \sim\{\sim(q \sim r)\}]$

$= \sim[q \sim\{\sim(p \sim r)\}]$ (1)

[14·01] (1) = Q.E.D.

Since $p = q$ gives $p ⥽ q$ and $q ⥽ p$, and hence $p \supset q$ and $q \supset p$, 15·8 has the corollaries:

*15·81* $p\,q \,.\supset.\, r :⥽: p \,.\supset.\, q \supset r$

*15·82* $p \,.\supset.\, q \supset r :⥽: p\,q \,.\supset.\, r$

*15·83* $p\,q \,.\supset.\, r :\supset: p \,.\supset.\, q \supset r$

*15·84* $p \,.\supset.\, q \supset r :\supset: p\,q \,.\supset.\, r$

But $p\,q \,.⥽.\, r :⥽: p \,.⥽.\, q ⥽ r$ does not hold: if two premises strictly imply a certain conclusion, and one of these premises is true, it does not generally follow that the conclusion can be deduced from the other premise alone. This is an important difference between the two relations.

By virtue of 14·26 and 15·8, the Principle of the Syllogism has a second form in the case of material implication:

*15·9* $p \supset q \,.⥽:\, q \supset r \,.\supset.\, p \supset r$

[15·8] 15·1 = Q.E.D.

*15·91* $p \supset q \,.\supset:\, q \supset r \,.\supset.\, p \supset r$

*15·92* $q \supset r \,.⥽:\, p \supset q \,.\supset.\, p \supset r$

[15·8] 15·12 = Q.E.D.

*15·93* $q \supset r \,.\supset:\, p \supset q \,.\supset.\, p \supset r$

We shall also need the analogues of 12·6 and 12·77:

*15·95* $p\,q \,.\supset.\, r : = : p \sim r \,.\supset.\, \sim q : = : q \sim r \,.\supset.\, \sim p$

[12·3, 12·5] $\sim(p\,q \,.\, \sim r) = \sim[p \sim r \,.\, \sim(\sim q)]$

$= \sim[q \sim r \,.\, \sim(\sim p)]$ (1)

[14·01] (1) = Q.E.D.

*15·96* $p \supset q : q\,r \,.\supset.\, s :.⥽: p\,r \,.\supset.\, s$

[15·1] $r \sim s \,.\supset.\, \sim q : \sim q \supset \sim p :.⥽: r \sim s \,.\supset.\, \sim p$ (1)

[15·95, 12·15, 15·15] (1) = Q.E.D.

*15·97* $p \supset q : q\,r \,.\supset.\, s :.\supset: p\,r \,.\supset.\, s$

The properties of material equivalence are not important for us, and will be omitted. As has been noted, $p \equiv q$ holds whenever $p$ and $q$ are both true or both false; and fails to hold when one is true and the other false. It holds whenever strict equivalence, $p = q$, holds; but $p = q$ is a much narrower relation, and the assertion that it holds is a much stronger statement.

All the functions of $p$ and $q$ which figure in the system of Material Implication—that is, $\sim p$, $p\,q$, $p \vee q$, $p \supset q$, and $p \equiv q$—are 'truth-functions' of $p$ and $q$: the truth or falsity of any one of these functions is categorically determined by the truth or falsity of $p$ and $q$ alone. The strict relations, $p ⥽ q$, and $p = q$ (and the relation of consistency, to be introduced in Section 4), are *not* such truth-functions: that $p ⥽ q$ or $p = q$ holds cannot generally be determined merely by knowing whether $p$ and $q$ are true or false. We shall revert to this topic in Chapters VII and VIII.

## Section 3. Further Theorems

In the present section we will develop certain more complex principles, partly as a further means of comparison between strict and material implication, and partly because some of these are key-theorems, such that their presence or absence in a calculus of propositions is an important point about the structure of it. A number of these, which concern strict implication, are consequences of 12·77, and have the form of what we shall call '*T*-principles.' The first one will be explained in full.

***16·1*** $p ⥽ q \,.\, T : ⥽ : p\,r \,.\, ⥽ \,.\, q\,r$

$T = : q\,r \,.\, ⥽ \,.\, q\,r$

[12·77: $q\,r/s$] $p ⥽ q : q\,r \,.\, ⥽ \,.\, q\,r : . ⥽ : p\,r \,.\, ⥽ \,.\, q\,r$

In the statement of this theorem, $T$ represents a proposition, $q\,r \,.\, ⥽ \,.\, q\,r$, such that *every proposition of this form is true*, by some previous principle—in this case, by 12·1. Thus if we have any premise of the form of the *other* member in the antecedent, $p ⥽ q$, the corresponding conclusion of the form $p\,r \,.\, ⥽ \,.\, q\,r$ can always be deduced, since the further premise needed to give this conclusion can always be asserted. Thus, as a principle of inference, 16·1 can be used exactly as if the $T$ did not occur in it. We shall not, for the present, take advantage of that fact, but shall use 16·1 in the complete form,

$$p ⥽ q : q\,r \,.\, ⥽ \,.\, q\,r : . ⥽ : p\,r \,.\, ⥽ \,.\, q\,r,$$

in order that it may be perfectly clear that ignoring the presence of $T$, when the theorem is used as a principle of inference, commits no fallacy. When such a $T$-principle is used as a *premise*, the presence of the expression represented by $T$ obviously *cannot* be ignored.

The corresponding theorem for material implication can be proved without the $T$, by virtue of the fact that if two premises materially imply a conclusion, and one of them is true, then the other premise alone will *materially* imply the conclusion. (See 15·9–15·93.)

***16·11*** $p \supset q \,.\, ⥽ : p\,r \,.\, \supset .\, q\,r$

[14·27] $\sim q \supset \sim p \,.\, ⥽ : \sim r \vee \sim q \,.\, \supset .\, \sim r \vee \sim p$ (1)

[15·15] (1) . $=$ $: . \, p \supset q \,.\, ⥽ : \sim(\sim r \vee \sim p) \,.\, \supset .\, \sim(\sim r \vee \sim q)$ (2)

[11·01, 12·15] (2) = Q.E.D.

By 14·1, 16·11 gives immediately

$$p \supset q \,.\, \supset : p\,r \,.\, \supset .\, q\,r.$$

From this point on, we shall not repeat such theorems as 16·11 in the second form in which the asserted relation is a material implication, since this second form always follows from the first, by 14·1.

***16·15*** $p ⥽ q \,.\, T : ⥽ : p \vee r \,.\, ⥽ .\, q \vee r$

$T = \, : \sim q \sim r \,.\, ⥽ .\, \sim q \sim r$

[16·1] $\sim q ⥽ \sim p \,.\, T : ⥽ : \sim q \sim r \,.\, ⥽ .\, \sim p \sim r$ (1)

[12·44] (1) . $=$ $: . \, p ⥽ q \,.\, T : ⥽ : \sim(\sim p \sim r) \,.\, ⥽ .\, \sim(\sim q \sim r)$ (2)

[11·01] (2) = Q.E.D.

***16·16*** $p \supset q \,.\, ⥽ : p \vee r \,.\, \supset .\, q \vee r$

[14·27] $p \supset q \,.\, ⥽ : r \vee p \,.\, \supset .\, r \vee q$ (1)

[13·11] (1) = Q.E.D.

***16·2*** $p ⥽ q \,.\, p ⥽ r \,.\, T : ⥽ : p \,.\, ⥽ .\, q\,r$

$T = \, : q\,r \,.\, ⥽ .\, q\,r$

[12·77: $q\,r/s$] $p ⥽ q \,.\, T : ⥽ : p\,r \,.\, ⥽ .\, q\,r$ (1)

[12·77] $p ⥽ r : r\,p \,.\, ⥽ .\, q\,r : . ⥽ : p\,p \,.\, ⥽ .\, q\,r$ (2)

[12·15, 12·7] (2) . $=$ : :

$p\,r \,.\, ⥽ .\, q\,r : p ⥽ r : . ⥽ : p \,.\, ⥽ .\, q\,r$ (3)

[12·77] (1) . (3) : ⥽ : :

$p ⥽ q : q\,r \,.\, ⥽ .\, q\,r : p ⥽ r : . ⥽ : p \,.\, ⥽ .\, q\,r$

The next group of theorems are each of some interest; but it is 16·33 and 16·35 for the sake of which they are developed.

*16·3* $p . p \supset q : \prec . p q$

[16·11] $p \supset q . \prec : p p . \supset . q p$ (1)

[14·26] $(1) . = : . p \supset q . p p : \prec . q p$ (2)

[12·15, 12·7] (2) = Q.E.D.

*16·31* $p . p \supset q : = . p q$

[15·2] $q . \prec . p \supset q$ (1)

[11·6] 12·17. $(1) : \prec : p q . \prec . p \supset q$ (2)

[12·1] $p . p \supset q : \prec : p . p \supset q$ (3)

[16·2] 11·2 . (2) . $(3) : \prec : . p q . \prec : p . p \supset q$ (4)

[11·03] 16·3 . (4) : = Q.E.D.

In the fourth line of the above proof, 16·2 is used as a principle of inference. If we had used this in the briefer manner which is permissible in the case of *T*-principles, the third line would have been omitted, and this fourth line would have been written

[16·2] 11·2 . (2) . $(T) : \prec : . p q . \prec : p . p \supset q$.

The reader will observe that this procedure would not have affected the result.

*16·32* $p q . = : p . \sim(p \sim q)$

[14·01] 16·31 = Q.E.D.

*16·33* $p \prec q . = : p . \prec . p q$

[12·11] $\sim\Diamond(p \sim q) = \sim\Diamond(p \sim q)$ (1)

[16·32, 12·3] $(1) . = . \sim\Diamond(p \sim q) = \sim\Diamond[p \sim(p q)]$ (2)

[11·02] (2) = Q.E.D.

*16·34* $p \prec q . = : p \vee q . \prec . q$

[16·33] $\sim q \prec \sim p . = : \sim q . \prec . \sim q \sim p$ (1)

[12·44, 12·15] $(1) . = : . p \prec q . = : \sim(\sim p \sim q) \prec \sim(\sim q)$ (2)

[11·01, 12·3] (2) = Q.E.D.

*16·35* $p . = : p \vee q . p$

[16·33] 13·2 . $= : . p . \prec : p . p \vee q$

[12·15] $= : . p . \prec : p \vee q . p$ (1)

[12·17] $p \vee q . p : \prec . p$ (2)

[11·03] (1) . (2) : = Q.E.D.

Theorems 16·1 and 16·2 give rise to other and similar theorems:

***16·4*** $p ⥽ r . q ⥽ r . T :⥽: p \vee q . ⥽ . r$

$T = : \sim p \sim q . ⥽ . \sim p \sim q$

[16·2] $\sim r ⥽ \sim p . \sim r ⥽ \sim q . T :⥽: \sim r . ⥽ . \sim p \sim q$ (1)

[12·44] (1) . = :. $p ⥽ r . q ⥽ r . T :⥽: \sim(\sim p \sim q) ⥽ r$ (2)

[11·01] (2) = Q.E.D.

***16·5*** $p . ⥽ . q r : T :. ⥽ : p ⥽ q . p ⥽ r$

$T = :. q r . ⥽ . q : q r . ⥽ . r$

[12·17] $p . ⥽ . q r : T :. ⥽ :. p . ⥽ . q r : q r . ⥽ . q$ (1)

[12·17] $p . ⥽ . q r : T :. ⥽ :. p . ⥽ . q r : q r . ⥽ . r$ (2)

[11·6] $p . ⥽ . q r : q r . ⥽ . q :. ⥽ . p ⥽ q$ (3)

[11·6] $p . ⥽ . q r : q r . ⥽ . r :. ⥽ . p ⥽ r$ (4)

[11·6] (1) . (3) $:⥽:: p . ⥽ . q r : T :. ⥽ . p ⥽ q$ (5)

[11·6] (2) . (4) $:⥽:: p . ⥽ . q r : T :. ⥽ . p ⥽ r$ (6)

[12·1] $p ⥽ q . p ⥽ r :⥽: p ⥽ q . p ⥽ r$ (7)

[16·2] (5) . (6) . (7) $:⥽:: p . ⥽ . q r : T :. ⥽ : p ⥽ q . p ⥽ r$

***16·51*** $p \vee q . ⥽ . r : T :. ⥽ : p ⥽ r . q ⥽ r$

$T = :. \sim p \sim q . ⥽ . \sim p : \sim p \sim q . ⥽ . \sim q$

[16·5] $\sim r . ⥽ . \sim p \sim q : T :. ⥽ : \sim r ⥽ \sim p . \sim r ⥽ \sim q$ (1)

[12·44] (1) . = :: $\sim(\sim p \sim q) ⥽ r . T :⥽: p ⥽ r . q ⥽ r$ (2)

[11·01] (2) = Q.E.D.

***16·6*** $p ⥽ r . q ⥽ s . T :⥽: p q . ⥽ . r s$

$T = :. r q . ⥽ . q r : s r . ⥽ . r s$

[11·2, 12·5] $p ⥽ r . q ⥽ s . T :⥽:. p ⥽ r : r q . ⥽ . q r$ (1)

[12·17, 12·5] $p ⥽ r . q ⥽ s . T :⥽:. q ⥽ s : s r . ⥽ . r s$ (2)

[12·77: $r/q$; $q/r$; $q\,r/s$]

$p ⥽ r : r q . ⥽ . q r :. ⥽ : p q . ⥽ . q r$ (3)

[12·77] $q ⥽ s : s r . ⥽ . r s :. ⥽ : q r . ⥽ . r s$ (4)

[11·6] (1) . (3) $:⥽:. p ⥽ r . q ⥽ s . T :⥽: p q . ⥽ . q r$ (5)

[11·6] (2) . (4) $:⥽:. p ⥽ r . q ⥽ s . T :⥽: q r . ⥽ . r s$ (6)

[12·1] $p q . ⥽ . q r : q r . ⥽ . r s :. ⥽ :.$

$p q . ⥽ . q r : q r . ⥽ . r s$ (7)

[16·2] (5) . (6) . (7) $:⥽:: p ⥽ r . q ⥽ s . T :⥽:.$

$p q . ⥽ . q r : q r . ⥽ . r s$ (8)

[11·6] $pq . \dashv . qr : qr . \dashv . rs : . \dashv : pq . \dashv . rs$ (9)

[11·6] (8) . (9) : $\dashv$ Q.E.D.

***16·61*** $p \dashv r . q \dashv s . T : \dashv : p \vee q . \dashv . r \vee s$

$T = : . \sim p \sim s . \dashv . \sim s \sim p : \sim q \sim p . \dashv . \sim p \sim q$

[16·6] $\sim r \dashv \sim p . \sim s \dashv \sim q . T : \dashv : \sim r \sim s . \dashv . \sim p \sim q$ (1)

[12·44] (1) . = : $p \dashv r . q \dashv s . T : \dashv : \sim(\sim p \sim q) \dashv \sim(\sim r \sim s)$ (2)

[11·01] (2) = Q.E.D.

***16·62*** $p \dashv q . p \dashv r . T : \dashv : p . \dashv . q \vee r$

$T = : . \sim p \sim r . \dashv . \sim r \sim p : \sim p \dashv \sim p$

[16·61] $p \dashv q . p \dashv r . T : \dashv : p \vee p . \dashv . q \vee r$ (1)

[13·31] (1) = Q.E.D.

All the above $T$-principles follow from the three basic ones, 16·1, 16·2, and 16·5. In Section 5 of this chapter, we shall show how these three theorems, and hence the $T$-principles in general, can be proved without the $T$. For this, however, a further postulate will be necessary.[6]

Having illustrated, in the preceding proofs, that for any $T$-theorem, $p\,T . \dashv . q$, $q$ can be deduced if $p$ is given, we shall hereafter ignore the presence of the $T$ in using such theorems as principles of inference.

The analogues of 16·1 and 16·15, for material implication, have been given in 16·11 and 16·16. Analogues of the remaining $T$-principles are most easily derived from the Distributive Law, 16·72 below:

***16·7*** $pq . \vee . pr : \dashv : p . q \vee r$

[12·17] $pq . \dashv . q$ (1)

[11·2] $pq . \dashv . p$ (2)

[12·17] $pr . \dashv . r$ (3)

[11·2] $pr . \dashv . p$ (4)

[16·61] (1) . (3) . ($T$) : $\dashv$ : . $pq . \vee . pr : \dashv . q \vee r$ (5)

[16·61] (2) . (4) . ($T$) : $\dashv$ : . $pq . \vee . pr : \dashv . p \vee p$ (6)

[13·31] (6) . = : . $pq . \vee . pr : \dashv . p$ (7)

[16·2] (7) . (5) . ($T$) : $\dashv$ Q.E.D.

[6] No positive proof that 16·1, 16·2, and 16·5, without the $T$, are independent of the postulates of Section 1 has been discovered. But persistent efforts to derive them in this form have failed.

***16·71*** $p . q \vee r : ⥽ : p q . \vee . p r$

$[11·2]\ p . p \supset \sim q . \sim q \supset r : ⥽ . p$ (1)

$[12·17]\ p . p \supset \sim q . \sim q \supset r : ⥽ . p \supset \sim q . \sim q \supset r$ (2)

$[15·1]\ p \supset \sim q . \sim q \supset r : ⥽ . p \supset r$ (3)

$[16·2]\ (1) . (3) . (T) : ⥽ : .$

$p . p \supset \sim q . \sim q \supset r : ⥽ : p . p \supset r$ (4)

$[16·31]\ (4) . = : . p . p \supset \sim q . \sim q \supset r : ⥽ . p r$ (5)

$[14·26]\ (5) . = : . p . \sim q \supset r : ⥽ : p \supset \sim q . \supset . p r$ (6)

$[14·2, 12·3]\ (6) . = : . p . q \vee r : ⥽ : \sim p \vee \sim q . \supset . p r$ (7)

$[14·2]\ (7) . = : . p . q \vee r : ⥽ : \sim(\sim p \vee \sim q) . \vee . p r$ (8)

[11·01, 12·3] (8) = Q.E.D.

***16·72*** $p . q \vee r : = : p q . \vee . p r$

[11·03] 16·71 . 16·7 : = Q.E.D.

A corresponding principle to 16·72 is:

***16·73*** $p . \vee . q r : = : p \vee q . p \vee r$

[12·11, 16·72]

$\sim(\sim p . \sim q \vee \sim r) : = : \sim(\sim p \sim q . \vee . \sim p \sim r)$ (1)

$[11·01, 12·3]\ (1) . = : .$

$p . \vee . \sim(\sim q \vee \sim r) : = : \sim(\sim p \sim q) . \sim(\sim p \sim r)$ (2)

[11·01, 12·3] (2) = Q.E.D.

***16·8*** $p . \supset . q r : = : p \supset q . p \supset r$

$[16·73]\ \sim p . \vee . q r : = : \sim p \vee q . \sim p \vee r$ (1)

[14·2] (1) = Q.E.D.

16·8 contains the analogues of 16·2 and 16·5. It is to be observed that these analogues would be

$$p . \supset . q r : ⥽ : p \supset q . p \supset r,$$

and $p \supset q . p \supset r : ⥽ : p . \supset . q r,$

the *asserted* relation being a strict implication. The similar theorems in which the asserted relation is material would follow immediately. Proof of the other analogues of the above *T*-principles would be from 16·8, in a manner similar to the proof of other *T*-theorems from 16·2 and 16·5. These analogues will not be needed later, and may be listed only:

***16·81*** $p \supset r . q \supset r : ⥽ : p \vee q . \supset . r$

***16·82*** $p \vee q . \supset . r : ⥽ : p \supset r . q \supset r$

*16·83* $p \supset q . \vee . p \supset r : ⥽ : p . \supset . q \vee r$

*16·84* $p \supset r . \vee . q \supset r : ⥽ : p q . \supset . r$

*16·85* $p \supset r . q \supset s : ⥽ : p q . \supset . r s$

*16·86* $p \supset r . q \supset s : ⥽ : p \vee q . \supset . r \vee s$

There are two *T*-principles which have been omitted because they can be proved without the *T* in Section 5. (See 19·46 and 19·5.)

## Section 4. Consistency and the Modal Functions

Up to this point, the modal function $\Diamond p$, "*p* is possible" or "*p* is self-consistent," has not appeared explicitly in any theorem, and has been made use of in only three proofs. We have proceeded, so far as possible, in the same manner as if $p ⥽ q$ had been taken as a primitive idea, instead of $\Diamond p$. That method would, in fact, have been adopted, and $\Diamond p$ introduced for the first time in the present section, were it not that two additional postulates would then have been required in Section 1.

In the present section we shall introduce the relation of consistency, $p \circ q$, and the ideas of possibility, impossibility, and necessity. The definition of $p \circ q$ and the equivalences to be established between this function and the modal propositions will serve to clarify and sharpen the significance of all these ideas, as well as that of $p ⥽ q$.

When we speak of two propositions as 'consistent,' we mean that it is not possible, with either one of them as premise, to deduce the falsity of the other. Thus if $p ⥽ q$ has the intended meaning "*q* is deducible from *p*," then "*p* is consistent with *q*" may be defined as follows:

*17·01* $p \circ q . = . \sim(p ⥽ \sim q)$

We have seen (12·42) that $\sim(p ⥽ \sim q) = \sim(q ⥽ \sim p)$. Hence $p \circ q$, defined to mean "It is false that *p* implies the falsity of *q*," has exactly the same force as "*p* does not imply that *q* is false, and *q* does not imply that *p* is false." The properties which result from this definition will serve as a check upon the accord between the usual meanings of 'implies' and of 'consistency' and the functions $p ⥽ q$ and $p \circ q$.

*17·1* $p\,q\,.\!\prec\!.\,p \circ q$

[12·84] $p\,q\,.\!\prec\!.\sim(p \prec \sim q)$ (1)

[17·01] (1) = Q.E.D.

Any two propositions, both of which are true, must be consistent. This implication is not reversible: two propositions may be consistent though one is false and the other true, or though both are false.

*17·12* $p \prec q\,.=.\sim(p \circ \sim q)$

[17·01, 12·3] $p \prec q\,.=.\,p \prec \sim(\sim q)\,.$

$=.\sim[\sim\{p \prec \sim(\sim q)\}]\,.=.\sim(p \circ \sim q)$

That $p$ strictly implies $q$ means that $p$ is inconsistent with the denial of $q$. Compare this with the definition of material implication, 14·01,

$$p \supset q\,.=.\sim(p \sim q).$$

For example, let $p$ = "Roses are green" and $q$ = "Sugar is sweet." Since $p$ is false (or since $q$ is true), $\sim(p \sim q)$ holds for this example; and hence $p \supset q$ holds: "Roses are green" materially implies "Sugar is sweet." But, so far as one can see, "Roses are green" and "Sugar is not sweet" are not inconsistent with one another: $\sim(p \circ \sim q)$ does not hold, and hence $p \prec q$ does not hold.

*17·13* $\sim(p \circ \sim p)$

[17·12] 12·1 = Q.E.D.

No proposition is consistent with its own denial.

*17·2* $p \circ q\,.\!\prec\!.\,q \circ p$

[12·1] $\sim(p \prec \sim q) \prec \sim(p \prec \sim q)$ (1)

[12·45] (1) $.=.\sim(p \prec \sim q) \prec \sim(q \prec \sim p)$ (2)

[17·01] (2) = Q.E.D.

The relation of consistency is symmetrical. The *equivalence* of $p \circ q$ and $q \circ p$ is an obvious corollary:

*17·21* $p \circ q\,.=.\,q \circ p$

[12·42] $\sim(p \prec \sim q) = \sim(q \prec \sim p)$ (1)

[17·01] (1) = Q.E.D.

*17·3* $p \prec q \,.\, p \circ r :\prec .\, q \circ r$

[11·6] $p \prec q \,.\, q \prec {\sim} r :\prec .\, p \prec {\sim} r$ (1)

[12·6] (1) $.\, = :.\, p \prec q \,.\, {\sim}(p \prec {\sim} r) :\prec .\, {\sim}(q \prec {\sim} r)$ (2)

[17·01] (2) = Q.E.D.

If a proposition $r$ is consistent with another, $p$, then $r$ is consistent with any proposition $q$ which $p$ implies.

*17·31* $p \prec q \,.\, {\sim}(q \circ r) :\prec .\, {\sim}(p \circ r)$

[12·6] 17·3 = Q.E.D.

If $p$ has some implication, $q$, with which $r$ is not consistent, then $p$ and $r$ are not consistent.

*17·32* $p \prec r \,.\, q \prec s \,.\, p \circ q :\prec .\, r \circ s$

[12·78] $p \prec r \,.\, r \prec {\sim} s \,.\, {\sim} s \prec {\sim} q :\prec .\, p \prec {\sim} q$ (1)

[12·5, 12·44, 12·15] (1) $.\, = :.$

$p \prec r \,.\, q \prec s \,.\, r \prec {\sim} s :\prec .\, p \prec {\sim} q$ (2)

[12·6] (2) $.\, = :.\, p \prec r \,.\, q \prec s \,.\, {\sim}(p \prec {\sim} q) :\prec .\, {\sim}(r \prec {\sim} s)$ (3)

[17·01] (3) = Q.E.D.

For example, if a postulate $p$ implies a theorem $r$, and a postulate $q$ implies a theorem $s$, and the two postulates are consistent, then the theorems will be consistent. A system deduced from consistent postulates will be consistent throughout.

*17·33* $p \prec r \,.\, q \prec s \,.\, {\sim}(r \circ s) :\prec .\, {\sim}(p \circ q)$

[12·6] 17·32 = Q.E.D.

If there is some consequence of $p$ which is not consistent with some consequence of $q$, then $p$ and $q$ are not consistent.

*17·4* $p q \,.\circ .\, r := : q r \,.\circ .\, p := : p r \,.\circ .\, q :$

$= : p \,.\circ .\, q r := : q \,.\circ .\, p r := : r \,.\circ .\, p q$

[12·6, 12·3] ${\sim}(p q \,.\prec .\, {\sim} r) := : {\sim}(q r \,.\prec .\, {\sim} p) :$

$= : {\sim}(p r \,.\prec .\, {\sim} q)$ (1)

[17·01] (1) $.\, = :.\, p q \,.\circ .\, r := : q r \,.\circ .\, p := : p r \,.\circ .\, q$

[17·21] $p q \,.\circ .\, r := : r \,.\circ .\, p q$, etc.

It is important to note that the statement "$p$, $q$, and $r$ are all consistent" does *not* mean $p \circ (q \circ r)$ or $(p \circ q) \circ r$. For example, let

$p$ = Grass is red,
$q$ = Grass has color,
and $r$ = Grass is green.

Here though $p$ is false, $p$ and $q$ are obviously consistent: $p \circ q$ is *true*. Also $r$ is true. Since two propositions which are true must be consistent (17·1), it follows that $(p \circ q) \circ r$ will hold in this example. But "$p$, $q$, and $r$ are all consistent" is false. Also it might be thought that "$p$, $q$, and $r$ form a consistent set" may be expressed by the complex proposition $p \circ q \,.\, p \circ r \,.\, q \circ r$. But this also would be a mistake: let

$$p = \text{To-day is Monday,}$$
$$q = \text{To-day is July 4th,}$$
$$\text{and } r = \text{July 5th is not Tuesday.}$$

Here any two of the three, $p$, $q$, and $r$, are consistent: $p \circ q$, $p \circ r$, and $q \circ r$ are all true; hence $p \circ q \,.\, p \circ r \,.\, q \circ r$ is true. But it is false that $p$, $q$, and $r$ form a consistent set. Or we may form the 'inconsistent triad' corresponding to any syllogism all of whose propositions are contingent (not necessarily true or necessarily false); any two propositions of this triad will be consistent with one another—they will be related like $p$, $q$, and $r$ above—but any two together will be incompatible with the third. The statement "$p$, $q$, and $r$ are all consistent" *does* mean $p\,q \,.\!\circ\!.\, r$, or any of its equivalents according to 17·4. In more general terms, "$p$, $q$, $r$, ... form a consistent set" means "The joint-assertion of any selection from $p$, $q$, $r$, ... is consistent with the joint-assertion of the remainder of the set."

Many of the laws governing the relation of consistency follow from the Principle of the Syllogism, 11·6:

***17·5*** $\sim(p \circ r) \,.\, \sim(q \circ \sim r) \,:\, \prec \,.\, \sim(p \circ q)$

[11·6] $p \prec \sim r \,.\, \sim r \prec \sim q \,:\, \prec \,.\, p \prec \sim q$ (1)

[12·45] (1) $. = :.\ p \prec \sim r \,.\, q \prec \sim(\sim r) \,:\, \prec \,.\, p \prec \sim q$ (2)

[17·12, 12·3] (2) = Q.E.D.

If $p$ is not consistent with $r$, but $q$ is not consistent with the denial of $r$, then $p$ and $q$ are not consistent with each other.

***17·51*** $p \prec \sim r \,.\, q \prec r \,:\, \prec \,.\, \sim(p \circ q)$

[17·12, 12·3] 17·5 = Q.E.D.

If $p$ implies one of a pair of contradictories, and $q$ implies the other, then $p$ and $q$ are not consistent.

***17·52*** $p \prec q \,.\, p \prec {\sim}q :\prec. {\sim}(p \circ p)$

$[17{\cdot}51: p/q;\ q/r]\ p \prec {\sim}q \,.\, p \prec q :\prec. {\sim}(p \circ p)$

A proposition which implies both of any contradictory pair is not consistent with itself.

***17·53*** $p \prec q \,.\, p \circ p :\prec. q \circ q$

$[12{\cdot}7]\ p \prec q : q \prec {\sim}q := : p \prec q \,.\, p \prec q \,.\, q \prec {\sim}q$ (1)

$[12{\cdot}44, 12{\cdot}15]\ = : p \prec q \,.\, q \prec {\sim}q \,.\, {\sim}q \prec {\sim}p$ (2)

$[12{\cdot}78]\ p \prec q \,.\, q \prec {\sim}q \,.\, {\sim}q \prec {\sim}p :\prec. p \prec {\sim}p$ (3)

$[(2), (3)]\ p \prec q \,.\, q \prec {\sim}q :\prec. p \prec {\sim}p$ (4)

$[12{\cdot}6]\ (4) \,.\, = :. p \prec q \,.\, {\sim}(p \prec {\sim}p) :\prec. {\sim}(q \prec {\sim}q)$ (5)

$[17{\cdot}01]\ (5) =$ Q.E.D.

What is implied by a self-consistent proposition is self-consistent.

***17·54*** $p \prec q \,.\, {\sim}(q \circ q) :\prec. {\sim}(p \circ p)$

$[12{\cdot}6]\ 17{\cdot}53 =$ Q.E.D.

If $q$ is not self-consistent, and $p$ implies $q$, then $p$ is not self-consistent.

***17·55*** $p \circ p \,.\, {\sim}(q \circ q) :\prec. {\sim}(p \prec q)$

$[12{\cdot}6]\ 17{\cdot}54 =$ Q.E.D.

A self-consistent proposition does not imply one that is not self-consistent.

***17·56*** $p \prec q \,.\, p \circ p :\prec. p \circ q$

$[12{\cdot}6]\ 17{\cdot}52 \,.\, = :. p \prec q \,.\, p \circ p :\prec. {\sim}(p \prec {\sim}q)$ (1)

$[17{\cdot}01]\ (1) =$ Q.E.D.

If $p$ implies $q$, and $p$ is self-consistent, then $p$ is consistent with $q$; or, a self-consistent proposition is consistent with all its implications. The principle

$$p \prec q \,.\prec.\, p \circ q,$$

which might be expected to hold, does not, in fact, hold without exceptions. There are propositions which are not consistent with any other proposition; yet such propositions have implications. Hence if $p \prec q$ holds, it requires the further condition $p \circ p$ to assure that $p$ is consistent with $q$.

***17·57*** $p \prec q \,.\, \sim(p \circ q) :\prec.\, \sim(p \circ p)$

[12·6] 17·56 = Q.E.D.

A proposition which implies anything with which it is not consistent, is not consistent with itself.

***17·58*** $p \circ p \,.\, \sim(p \circ q) :\prec.\, \sim(p \prec q)$

[12·6] 17·56 = Q.E.D.

A self-consistent proposition does not imply any with which it is not consistent.

***17·59*** $p \circ p \,.\, p \prec q :\prec.\, \sim(p \prec \sim q)$

[12·15, 12·3] 17·56 . $= :. \, p \circ p \,.\, p \prec q :\prec.\, \sim[\sim(p \circ q)]$ (1)

[12·3, 17·12] (1) = Q.E.D.

If $p$ is self-consistent, and $p$ implies $q$, then $p$ does not also imply the falsity of $q$.

***17·591*** $p \circ p \,.\prec: \sim(p \prec q \,.\, p \prec \sim q)$

[12·45] 17·52 = Q.E.D.

A self-consistent proposition does not imply both of any contradictory pair.

***17·592*** $p \circ p \,.\prec: p \circ q \,.\vee.\, p \circ \sim q$

[14·21, 12·3] 17·591 . = :.

$p \circ p \,.\prec: \sim(p \prec q) \,.\vee.\, \sim(p \prec \sim q)$ (1)

[12·3, 17·01] (1) = Q.E.D.

If $p$ is self-consistent, then it is consistent with one or other of any contradictory pair.

It is to be observed that the relation of consistency is not, in general, transitive. If it were, then no pair of propositions could be at once consistent and independent: if we should have as a theorem

$$p \circ q \,.\, q \circ r :\prec.\, p \circ r, \tag{1}$$

then we should also have, as a special case of this,

$$p \circ q \,.\, q \circ \sim p :\prec.\, p \circ \sim p. \tag{2}$$

Since, by 17·13, $\sim(p \circ \sim p)$, (2) would have the consequence,

$$\sim(p \circ q \,.\, q \circ \sim p). \tag{3}$$

And (3) is equivalent to $\sim(p \circ q) \,.\vee.\, q \prec p$.

The next two theorems state an obvious relation between truth and self-consistency.

***17·6*** $p . \prec . p \circ p$

$[17·1]\ p\, p . \prec . p \circ p$ (1)

$[12·7]\ (1) =$ Q.E.D.

Every true proposition is self-consistent.

***17·61*** $\sim(p \circ p) \prec \sim p$

$[12·44]\ 17·6 =$ Q.E.D.

Any proposition which is not consistent with itself is false.

We have, as $T$-principles concerning consistency, the correlates of 16·2 and 16·5:

***17·7*** $p . \circ . q \vee r : T : . \prec : p \circ q . \vee . p \circ r$

$T = : \sim q \sim r . \prec . \sim q \sim r$

$[16·2]\ p \prec \sim q . p \prec \sim r . T : \prec : p . \prec . \sim q \sim r$ (1)

$[12·6]\ (1) . = : .$

$\sim(p . \prec . \sim q \sim r) : T : . \prec : \sim(p \prec \sim q . p \prec \sim r)$ (2)

$[11·01]\ (2) . = : : \sim[p . \prec . \sim(q \vee r)] : T : . \prec :$

$\sim(p \prec \sim q) . \vee . \sim(p \prec \sim r)$ (3)

$[17·01]\ (3) =$ Q.E.D.

***17·71*** $p \circ q . \vee . p \circ r : T : . \prec : p . \circ . q \vee r$

$T = : . \sim q \sim r . \prec . \sim q : \sim q \sim r . \prec . \sim r$

$[16·5]\ p . \prec . \sim q \sim r : T : . \prec : p \prec \sim q . p \prec \sim r$ (1)

$[12·6]\ (1) . = : .$

$\sim(p \prec \sim q . p \prec \sim r) . T : \prec : \sim(p . \prec . \sim q \sim r)$ (2)

$[11·01]\ (2) . = : : \sim(p \prec \sim q) . \vee . \sim(p \prec \sim r) : T : . \prec :$

$\sim[p . \prec . \sim(q \vee r)]$ (3)

$[17·01]\ (3) =$ Q.E.D.

If the modal function $\Diamond p$ had not been taken as a primitive idea, it could now be defined as equivalent to $p \circ p$. Its properties in the system are precisely those which would follow from such definition.

***18·1*** $\Diamond p . = . p \circ p . = . \sim(p \prec \sim p)$

$[12·3, 12·7]\ \Diamond p . = . \sim(\sim\Diamond p) . = . \sim[\sim\Diamond(p\, p)] .$

$= . \sim[\sim\Diamond \{p \sim(\sim p)\}]$

$[11·02, 17·01]\ \sim[\sim\Diamond \{p \sim(\sim p)\}] . = . \sim(p \prec \sim p) . = . p \circ p$

Thus $\Diamond p$ means "$p$ is self-consistent" or "$p$ does not imply its own negation." If we read $\Diamond p$ as "$p$ is possible," then $\sim(\Diamond p)$ will be "It is false that $p$ is possible" or "$p$ is impossible"; $\Diamond(\sim p)$ will be "It is possible that $p$ be false" or "$p$ is not necessarily true"; and $\sim[\Diamond(\sim p)]$ will be "It is impossible that $p$ be false" or "$p$ is necessarily true." For convenience, these expressions will be written without parentheses: $\sim\Diamond p$, $\Diamond\sim p$, and $\sim\Diamond\sim p$. If at first one forgets what these represent, it is only necessary to read the constituent symbols, in the order written.

*18·12* $\sim\Diamond p \,.\!=.\, \sim(p \circ p) \,.\!=.\, p \prec \sim p$

[18·1] $\sim\Diamond p \,.\!=.\, \sim(p \circ p) \,.\!=.\, \sim[\sim(p \prec \sim p)]$

The modal proposition "$p$ is impossible" means "$p$ is not self-consistent" or "From $p$, its own negation can be deduced."

*18·13* $\Diamond\sim p \,.\!=.\, \sim p \circ \sim p \,.\!=.\, \sim(\sim p \prec p)$

[18·1] $\Diamond\sim p \,.\!=.\, \sim p \circ \sim p \,.\!=.\, \sim[\sim p \prec \sim(\sim p)]$

It is to be observed that $\Diamond\sim p$ and $\sim\Diamond\sim p$ are mutually contradictory.

*18·14* $\sim\Diamond\sim p \,.\!=.\, \sim(\sim p \circ \sim p) \,.\!=.\, \sim p \prec p$

[18·13] $\sim\Diamond\sim p \,.\!=.\, \sim(\sim p \circ \sim p) \,.\!=.\, \sim[\sim(\sim p \prec p)]$

That $p$ is necessarily true means "The denial of $p$ is not self-consistent" or "The truth of $p$ can be deduced from its own denial."

The above equivalences may be compared with the following, which hold for material implication:

18·1 with $p \,.\!=.\, p \sim(\sim p) \,.\!=.\, \sim(p \supset \sim p)$,
18·12 with $\sim p \,.\!=.\, \sim[p \sim(\sim p)] \,.\!=.\, p \supset \sim p$,
18·13 with $\sim p \,.\!=.\, \sim p \sim p \,.\!=.\, \sim(\sim p \supset p)$,
18·14 with $p \,.\!=.\, \sim(\sim p \sim p) \,.\!=.\, \sim p \supset p$.

As this comparison illustrates, "$p$ is possible" and "$p$ is necessary" are indistinguishable, in terms of material implication, from "$p$ is true"; and "$p$ is impossible" and "$p$ is possibly false" are indistinguishable from "$p$ is false."

It should also be noted that the words 'possible,' 'impossible,' and 'necessary' are highly ambiguous in ordinary discourse. The meaning here assigned to $\Diamond p$ is a *wide* meaning of 'possibility'—namely, logical conceivability or the absence of self-contradiction. And the resultant meanings of $\sim\Diamond p$ and $\sim\Diamond\sim p$ are correspondingly *narrow* meanings of 'impossibility' and 'necessity': $\sim\Diamond p$ means "$p$ is logically inconceivable"; and $\sim\Diamond\sim p$ means "It is not logically conceivable that $p$ should be false."

A second—and colloquially more frequent—meaning of 'possible,' 'impossible,' and 'necessary' has reference to the relation which the proposition or thing considered has to some state of affairs, such as given data, or to our knowledge as a whole. In this second sense, 'possible' means 'consistent with the data' or 'consistent with everything known'; 'impossible' means 'not consistent with the data, or with what is known'; and 'necessary' means 'implied by what is given or known.' Such meaning of 'possible,' etc., is *relative*—'possible in relation to ———': by contrast, the meanings which we symbolize are *absolute;* they concern only the relation which the fact or proposition has to itself or to its negative—what can be analyzed out of the proposition by sheer logic. The two sets of meanings can be compared if, for the moment, we represent what is given, or what is known, by $Q$:

| *Relative* | $p$ is | *Absolute* |
|---|---|---|
| $p \circ Q$ | possible | $p \circ p$ |
| $\sim(p \circ Q)$ | impossible | $\sim(p \circ p)$ |
| $\sim(\sim p \circ Q)$ or $Q \prec p$ | necessary | $\sim(\sim p \circ \sim p)$ or $\sim p \prec p$ |

It is the more important to understand the distinction of these two meanings of 'possible,' 'impossible,' and 'necessary' because frequently they are confused, even by logicians, with consequences which are fatal to the understanding of logical principles.

Relative possibility implies absolute possibility; absolute impossibility implies relative impossibility; and absolute necessity implies relative necessity. But these relations between the absolute and the relative are not reversible.

Since $p \prec q$ is defined in terms of logical impossibility, as $\sim\Diamond(p \sim q)$, it is a narrow, or strict, meaning of 'implies.' If our various definitions and assumptions are in accord with one another, and with the meanings assigned, it should be possible to prove that $p \prec q$ is equivalent to "$p \sim q$ implies its own denial."

This is the case. The proof of this which we give below *depends solely upon the assumed properties of* $p \prec q$, and would hold even if the function $\Diamond p$ and the relation $p \circ q$ did not appear in the system.

***18·2*** $p \prec q . = : p \sim q . \prec . \sim(p \sim q) : = : \sim(p \sim q . \circ . p \sim q)$

[12·44] $p \prec q . = . \sim q \prec \sim p$

[12·7] $= : \sim q \sim q . \prec . \sim p$

[12·6] $= : p \sim q . \prec . q$

[12·7] $= : (p\, p) \sim q . \prec . q$

[12·5] $= : p(p \sim q) . \prec . q$

[12·6] $= : p \sim q . \prec . \sim(p \sim q)$

[17·12] $= : \sim(p \sim q . \circ . p \sim q)$

No principle of the present section figures in this proof until the last line, which gives the second equivalence stated in the theorem.

Incidentally, the above theorem demonstrates a point which has sometimes been questioned, namely, whether there are any propositions which genuinely imply their own negation. Unless some one or more of our assumptions in Section 1 is a false principle, there must be as many such self-contradictory propositions as there are instances of valid deduction: if $q$ is deducible from $p$, then the proposition "$p$ is true but $q$ is false" implies its own denial.

Similarly, if our various definitions and assumptions are in accord with one another, we should be able to prove that $p \circ q$ is equivalent to $p\, q . \circ . p\, q$. This equivalence is, in fact, deducible from the same principles upon which the proof of 18·2 depends:

Since $p \prec q . = : p \sim q . \prec . \sim(p \sim q)$,

we have $\sim(p \prec \sim q) . = . \sim[p\, q . \prec . \sim(p\, q)]$.

Hence, by the definition of the relation $p \circ q$,

$$p \circ q . = : p\, q . \circ . p\, q.$$

This equivalence is included in the following:

***18·3*** $\Diamond(p\, q) . = : p\, q . \circ . p\, q : = . p \circ q . = . \sim(p \prec \sim q)$

[18·1] $\Diamond(p\, q) . = : p\, q . \circ . p\, q$

[17·01] $p\, q . \circ . p\, q : = : \sim[p\, q . \prec . \sim(p\, q)]$

[18·2, 12·3] $\sim[p\,q\,.\!\prec\!.\sim(p\,q)] = \sim(p \prec \sim q)$
[17·01] $\sim(p \prec \sim q)\,.=.\,p \circ q$

"It is logically possible that $p$ and $q$ be both true" means that the statement "$p$ and $q$ are both true" is self-consistent; and this is equivalent to "$p$ is consistent with $q$."

*18·31* $\sim\Diamond(p\,q)\,.=.\sim(p\,q\,.\circ.\,p\,q)\,.=.\sim(p \circ q)\,.=.\,p \prec \sim q$

This follows immediately from 18·3. The manner in which 18·3 extends to consistent sets in general is important. As has been indicated, $\Diamond(p\,q\,r\,\ldots)$ means "$p, q, r, \ldots$ are all consistent" or "$p, q, r, \ldots$ form a consistent set." The extension of 18·3 is a step-by-step process: in 18·35 we give the equivalents of $\Diamond(p\,q\,r)$; and in 18·36 we indicate the further extension which would result by letting $r$ be a compound proposition, $r\,s$, $r\,s\,t$, etc.:

*18·35* $\Diamond(p\,q\,r)\,.=:p\,q\,r\,.\circ.\,p\,q\,r$
$= :p\,q\,.\circ.\,r : = :q\,r\,.\circ.\,p : = :p\,r\,.\circ.\,q,$
etc.
$= :\sim(p\,q\,.\prec\sim r) : = :\sim(q\,r\,.\prec.\sim p) :$
$= :\sim(p\,r\,.\prec.\sim q)$

The theorem follows immediately from 18·3 and 17·4.

*18·36* $\Diamond(p\,q\,r\,s\,\ldots) : = :p\,.\circ.\,q\,r\,s\,\ldots : = :q\,.\circ.\,p\,r\,s\,\ldots :$
$= :\,p\,q\,.\circ.\,r\,s\,\ldots$, etc.
$= :\sim(q\,r\,s\,\ldots\,.\prec.\sim p)$
$= :\sim(p\,r\,s\,\ldots\,.\prec.\sim q)$, etc.

The next group of theorems—all obvious—are consequences of the postulate 11·7:

*18·4* $p \prec \Diamond p$
[18·1] 17·6 = Q.E.D.

What is true is logically possible or conceivable.

*18·41* $\sim\Diamond p \prec \sim p$
[12·44] 18·4 = Q.E.D.

What is impossible is false.

*18·42* $\sim\Diamond\sim p \prec p$
[18·41] $\sim\Diamond\sim p \prec \sim(\sim p)$

What is necessary is true.

***18·43*** $\sim\Diamond\sim p \prec \Diamond p$

[11·6] 18·42 . 18·4 : $\prec$ Q.E.D.

***18·44*** $\sim p \prec \Diamond\sim p$

[18·4: $\sim p/p$] $\sim p \prec \Diamond\sim p$.

***18·45*** $\sim\Diamond p \prec \Diamond\sim p$

[11·6] 18·41 . 18·44 : $\prec$ Q.E.D.

The next six theorems are consequences of the Principle of the Syllogism.

***18·5*** $p \prec q \,.\, \sim\Diamond q :\prec .\, \sim\Diamond p$

[12·7] $p \prec q \,.\, q \prec \sim q : = : p \prec q \,.\, p \prec q \,.\, q \prec \sim q$

[12·5, 12·43] $= : p \prec q \,.\, q \prec \sim q \,.\, \sim q \prec \sim p$ (1)

[12·78] $p \prec q \,.\, q \prec \sim q \,.\, \sim q \prec \sim p :\prec .\, p \prec \sim p$ (2)

[(1), 18·12] (2) = Q.E.D.

A proposition which implies something impossible is itself impossible.

***18·51*** $p \prec q \,.\, \Diamond p :\prec .\, \Diamond q$

[12·6, 12·3] 18·5 = Q.E.D.

Anything implied by a proposition the truth of which is conceivable is itself conceivably true.

***18·52*** $p \prec q \,.\, \Diamond\sim q :\prec .\, \Diamond\sim p$

[18·51] $\sim q \prec \sim p \,.\, \Diamond\sim q :\prec .\, \Diamond\sim p$ (1)

[12·43] (1) = Q.E.D.

A proposition which implies anything whose falsity is conceivable, is itself conceivably false.

***18·53*** $p \prec q \,.\, \sim\Diamond\sim p :\prec .\, \sim\Diamond\sim q$

[12·6] 18·52 = Q.E.D.

Anything implied by a necessary proposition is itself necessarily true.

***18·6*** $p q \,.\prec .\, r : p \sim q \,.\prec .\, r :.\prec .\, p \prec r$

[17·52] $p \sim r \,.\prec .\, \sim q : p \sim r \,.\prec .\, q :.\prec : \sim(p \sim r \,.\circ .\, p \sim r)$ (1)

[18·31] (1) . = :: $p q \,.\prec .\, r : p \sim q \,.\prec .\, r :.\prec .\, \sim\Diamond(p \sim r)$ (2)

[11·02] (2) = Q.E.D.

***18·61*** $\sim\Diamond\sim p : p\,q \,.\!\prec\!.\, r :.\prec.\, q \prec r$

[12·77] $\sim p \prec p : p\,q \,.\!\prec\!.\, r :.\prec: \sim p\,q \,.\!\prec\!.\, r$ (1)

[16·33] (1) $. = :: \sim p \prec p : p\,q \,.\!\prec\!.\, r :.\prec::. \sim p \prec p : p\,q \,.\!\prec\!.\, r : \sim p\,q \,.\!\prec\!.\, r$ (2)

[18·14] (2) $. = :: \sim\Diamond\sim p : p\,q \,.\!\prec\!.\, r :.\prec:. \sim p \prec p : p\,q \,.\!\prec\!.\, r : \sim p\,q \,.\!\prec\!.\, r$ (3)

[12·17] $\sim p \prec p : p\,q \,.\!\prec\!.\, r : \sim p\,q \,.\!\prec\!.\, r :.\prec:. p\,q \,.\!\prec\!.\, r : \sim p\,q \,.\!\prec\!.\, r$ (4)

[18·6] $p\,q \,.\!\prec\!.\, r : \sim p\,q \,.\!\prec\!.\, r :.\prec.\, q \prec r$ (5)

[12·78] (3) . (4) . (5) : $\prec$ Q.E.D.

In terms of *material* implication, if $p\,q \,.\!\supset\!.\, r$ and $p$ is true, then $q \supset r$, since $p\,q \,.\!\supset\!.\, r : = : p \,.\!\supset\!.\, q \supset r$. But in terms of *strict* implication, if two premises, $p$ and $q$, together imply $r$, and $p$ is true, it does not follow in general that $q \prec r$; since $p\,q \,.\!\prec\!.\, r$ is *not* equivalent to $p \,.\!\prec\!.\, q \prec r$. But as 18·61 indicates, if $p\,q \,.\!\prec\!.\, r$, and $p$ is *necessarily* true, then $q \prec r$. That is, in stating a strict implication one cannot omit a merely true premise which is one of a set of premises which together give the conclusion; but one *can* omit a *necessarily* true premise. The omission of a premise which is *a priori* or logically undeniable does not affect the validity of deduction: but the omission of a required premise which is true but not *a priori* leaves the deduction incomplete and, as it stands, invalid. Since this is a distinguishing feature of strict implication, as compared with various other 'implication relations,' let us illustrate its logical significance. The two premises "Socrates is a man" and "All men are mortal" together imply "Socrates is mortal." But does the single premise "Socrates is a man" imply "Socrates is mortal"? If the omitted premise "All men are mortal" is necessarily true (e.g., if 'immortal man' is a contradiction in terms), it does: but if this omitted premise is merely a contingent truth, it does not.

***18·7*** $p \prec q \,.\!=\!.\, \sim\Diamond\sim(p \supset q)$

[11·02, 12·3] $p \prec q \,. = .\, \sim\Diamond(p \sim q) \,. = .\, \sim\Diamond\sim[\sim(p \sim q)]$

A strict implication is equivalent to a material implication which holds of necessity, or by purely logical analysis. This is the reason for the fact—illustrated at length in Section 2—that the material implications which are *asserted* in *theorems of logic* are strict implications as well as material.

Two simple but important principles are the following:

*18·8* $\sim\Diamond(p \sim p)$

[11·02] 12·1 = Q.E.D.

*18·81* $\sim\Diamond\sim(p \vee \sim p)$

[11·01, 12·3, 13·11] 18·8 = Q.E.D.

From 18·81 and 18·61 the Principle of Expansion, 18·92 below, can be deduced:

*18·9* $p \,.\!\prec\!: p\, q \,.\vee.\, p \sim q$

[18·81] $\sim\Diamond\sim(q \vee \sim q)$ (1)

[16·71, 12·15] $q \vee \sim q \,.\, p :\prec: p\, q \,.\vee.\, p \sim q$ (2)

[18·61] (1) . (2) : $\prec$ Q.E.D.

*18·91* $p\, q \,.\vee.\, p \sim q :\prec.\, p$

[11·2] $p\, q \,.\prec.\, p$ (1)

[11·2] $p \sim q \,.\prec.\, p$ (2)

[16·4] (1) . (2) . (*T*) : $\prec$ Q.E.D.

*18·92* $p \,.=: p \,.\, q \vee \sim q :=: p\, q \,.\vee.\, p \sim q$

[11·03] 18·9 . 18·91 : $=:. \, p \,.=: p\, q \,.\vee.\, p \sim q$

[16·7] $p\, q \,.\vee.\, p \sim q := : p \,.\, q \vee \sim q$

## Section 5. The Consistency Postulate and Its Consequences

In this section we introduce an additional postulate concerning the relations of modal functions. As will be pointed out later, this assumption, and all the consequences of it, can be proved in the form of *T*-principles from the seven postulates of Section 1. But this further assumption allows such *T*-theorems, and also *all the T-theorems of previous sections,* to be replaced by the corresponding theorems in which *T* does not occur.

The additional postulate is:

*19·01* $\Diamond(p\, q) \prec \Diamond p$

The correlate of this principle can be proved directly from it:

***19·02*** $\Diamond p \prec \Diamond(p \vee q)$

[19·01] $\Diamond(p \vee q \,.\, p) :\prec . \Diamond(p \vee q)$ (1)

[16·35] (1) = Q.E.D.

An alternative and equivalent form of this assumption is:

***19·1*** $\sim(p \circ p) \prec \sim(p \circ q)$

[12·45] 19·01 . = . $\sim\Diamond p \prec \sim\Diamond(p\,q)$ (1)

[18·12, 18·3] (1) = Q.E.D.

If $p$ is not consistent with itself, then $p$ is not consistent with any proposition. Thus the force of this assumption is to the effect that no group of propositions can form a consistent set if they include one which is not self-consistent. This principle, either in the form of 19·01 or 19·1, will be referred to hereafter as the "Consistency Postulate." Its accord with the usual meaning of 'consistency,' as in mathematics, is obvious.

The first group of theorems are simple and obvious consequences of 19·01:

***19·11*** $p \circ q \,.\prec.\, p \circ p$

[12·45] 19·1 = Q.E.D.

A proposition which is consistent with any other is consistent with itself.

***19·13*** $\Diamond(p\,q) \prec \Diamond q$

[19·01] $\Diamond(q\,p) \prec \Diamond q$ (1)

[12·15] (1) = Q.E.D.

***19·14*** $\Diamond(p\,q) \,.\prec.\, \Diamond p\, \Diamond q$

[16·2] 19·01 . 19·13 . (*T*) : $\prec$ Q.E.D.

If it is possible that $p$ and $q$ be both true, then $p$ is possible and $q$ is possible. This implication is not reversible. For example: it is possible that the reader will see this at once. It is also possible that he will not see it at once. But it is not possible that he will both see it at once and not see it at once.

This last theorem could be extended, by successive substitutions—as $q\,r$ for $q$, etc.—to any number of propositions:

***19·15*** $\Diamond(p\,q\,r\,\ldots) \,.\prec.\, \Diamond p\, \Diamond q\, \Diamond r \ldots$

Every member of any consistent set must be a self-consistent proposition.

*19·16* $\sim\Diamond p \prec \sim\Diamond(p\, q)$

[12·44] 19·01 = Q.E.D.

*19·17* $\sim\Diamond q \prec \sim\Diamond(p\, q)$

*19·18* $\sim\Diamond p \vee \sim\Diamond q \,.\prec.\, \sim\Diamond(p\, q)$

[16·4] 19·16 . 19·17 . (*T*) : ⥽ Q.E.D.

*19·19* $\sim\Diamond\sim p \vee \sim\Diamond\sim q \,.\prec.\, \sim\Diamond\sim(p \vee q)$

[19·18: $\sim p/p$; $\sim q/q$] $\sim\Diamond\sim p \vee \sim\Diamond\sim q \,.\prec.\, \sim\Diamond(\sim p \sim q)$ (1)

[12·3] (1) . = : $\sim\Diamond\sim p \vee \sim\Diamond\sim q \,.\prec.\, \sim\Diamond\sim[\sim(\sim p \sim q)]$ (2)

[11·01] (2) = Q.E.D.

As in 19·14, so also in 19·18 and 19·19, the implication is not reversible. If it is impossible that *p* and *q* be both true, it does not follow that at least one of the two, *p* and *q*, is an impossible proposition. And if it is necessary that at least one of the two, *p* and *q*, be true, it does not follow that either of them is a necessary proposition. This will be apparent if, for *q*, one substitutes $\sim p$, as the theorems allow.

The last two theorems could be extended to any number of propositions, as 19·14 is extended in 19·15.

The next group of theorems are corresponding consequences of 19·02:

*19·2* $\Diamond\sim p \prec \Diamond\sim(p\, q)$

[19·02: $\sim p/p$; $\sim q/q$] $\Diamond\sim p \prec \Diamond(\sim p \vee \sim q)$ (1)

[12·3] (1) . = . $\Diamond\sim p \prec \Diamond\sim[\sim(\sim p \vee \sim q)]$ (2)

[11·01, 12·3] (2) = Q.E.D.

*19·21* $\Diamond\sim q \prec \Diamond\sim(p\, q)$

*19·22* $\Diamond\sim p \vee \Diamond\sim q \,.\prec.\, \Diamond\sim(p\, q)$

[16·4] 19·2 . 19·21 . (*T*) : ⥽ Q.E.D.

*19·23* $\sim\Diamond\sim(p\, q) \prec \sim\Diamond\sim p$

[12·44] 19·2 = Q.E.D.

*19·24* $\sim\Diamond\sim(p\, q) \prec \sim\Diamond\sim q$

*19·25* $\sim\Diamond\sim(p\, q) \,.\prec.\, \sim\Diamond\sim p \sim\Diamond\sim q$

[16·2] 19·23 . 19·24 . (*T*) : ⥽ Q.E.D.

*19·26* $\sim\Diamond(p \vee q) \prec \sim\Diamond p$

$[19{\cdot}23\colon \sim p/p;\ \sim q/q]\ \sim\Diamond[\sim(\sim p \sim q)] \prec \sim\Diamond[\sim(\sim p)]$ (1)

$[11{\cdot}01,\ 12{\cdot}3]\ (1) =$ Q.E.D.

By the same method used in the proofs of 19·19 and 19·26, we get a theorem in terms of $p \vee q$ from each of the preceding theorems in terms of $p\,q$. Proofs of the remainder of these will be omitted, only the preceding theorem which is transformed being indicated:

*19·27* $\sim\Diamond(p \vee q) \prec \sim\Diamond q$ [19·24]

*19·28* $\sim\Diamond(p \vee q) \,.\!\prec\!.\, \sim\Diamond p \sim\Diamond q$ [19·25]

*19·3* $\Diamond p \prec \Diamond(p \vee q)$ [19·2]

*19·31* $\Diamond q \prec \Diamond(p \vee q)$ [19·21]

*19·32* $\Diamond p \vee \Diamond q \,.\!\prec\!.\, \Diamond(p \vee q)$ [19·22]

*19·33* $\sim\Diamond\sim p \prec \sim\Diamond\sim(p \vee q)$ [19·16]

*19·34* $\sim\Diamond\sim q \prec \sim\Diamond\sim(p \vee q)$ [19·17]

The next group of theorems are laws governing triadic relations of the type $\Diamond(p\,q\,r)$, or $p\,q\,.\circ.\,r$, etc., which follow from the Consistency Postulate:

*19·4* $p\,.\circ.\,q\,r :\prec. \,p \circ q$

$[19{\cdot}11]\ p\,q\,.\circ.\,r :\prec: p\,q\,.\circ.\,p\,q$ (1)

$[17{\cdot}4,\ 18{\cdot}3]\ (1) =$ Q.E.D.

*19·41* $p\,.\circ.\,q\,r :\prec. \,p \circ r$

*19·43* $p\,.\circ.\,q\,r :\prec. \,q \circ r$

*19·44* $p\,.\circ.\,q\,r :\prec: p \circ q \,.\, p \circ r$

$[16{\cdot}2]\ 19{\cdot}4 \,.\, 19{\cdot}41 \,.\, (T) :\prec$ Q.E.D.

*19·45* $p\,.\circ.\,q\,r :\prec: p \circ q \,.\, p \circ r \,.\, q \circ r$

$[16{\cdot}2]\ 19{\cdot}44 \,.\, 19{\cdot}43 \,.\, (T) :\prec$ Q.E.D.

The complete statement of the consequences of $\Diamond(p\,q\,r)$, or $p\,.\circ.\,q\,r$, is given by the next theorem, which is an obvious consequence of 19·45 and 19·11, by 11·6 and 16·2.

*19·451* $p\,.\circ.\,q\,r :\prec: p \circ p \,.\, q \circ q \,.\, r \circ r \,.\, p \circ q \,.\, p \circ r \,.\, q \circ r$

We have already called attention to the fact that the implication of 19·45 is not reversible. Even more obviously, the implication of 19·44 is not reversible. This represents an exception to the general analogy between $p\,q$ and $p \circ q$, since

$$p\,.\,q\,r : = : p\,q\,.\,p\,r : = : p\,q\,.\,p\,r\,.\,q\,r.$$

***19·46*** $p \prec q\,.\vee.\,p \prec r :\prec: p\,.\prec.\,q \vee r$

[19·44] $p\,.\circ.\,{\sim}q\,{\sim}r :\prec: p \circ {\sim}q\,.\,p \circ {\sim}r$ (1)

[12·44] (1) $. = :.$
$${\sim}(p \circ {\sim}q\,.\,p \circ {\sim}r) :\prec: {\sim}(p\,.\circ.\,{\sim}q\,{\sim}r) \quad (2)$$

[11·01, 12·3] (2) $. = :.$
$${\sim}(p \circ {\sim}\,q)\,.\vee.\,{\sim}(p \circ {\sim}\,r) :\prec: {\sim}(p\,.\circ.\,{\sim}q\,{\sim}r) \quad (3)$$

[17·12, 12·3, 11·01] (3) = Q.E.D.

The implication of 19·46 is not reversible. If we had

$$p\,.\prec.\,q \vee r :\prec: p \prec q\,.\vee.\,p \prec r,$$

then we should also have, through transforming it by means of 12·6,

$$p\,q\,.\prec.\,r :\prec: p \prec r\,.\vee.\,q \prec r.$$

This last does not hold for strict implication: it is frequently the case that two premises $p$ and $q$ strictly imply a conclusion $r$, although neither premise alone implies this conclusion. Almost any syllogism is an illustration. This is another point of difference between strict and material implication, and explains the fact that

$$p\,.\supset.\,q \vee r :\prec: p \supset q\,.\vee.\,p \supset r$$
and $$p\,q\,.\supset.\,r :\prec: p \supset r\,.\vee.\,q \supset r$$

both hold, though their analogues for strict implication do not.

***19·47*** $p \prec q\,.\vee.\,p \prec r\,.\vee.\,{\sim}q \prec r :\prec: p\,.\prec.\,q \vee r$

Proof similar to 19·46, using 19·45 in place of 19·44.

Theorem 19·46 gives the obvious corollaries:

***19·48*** $p \prec q\,.\prec: p\,.\prec.\,q \vee r$

***19·49*** $p \prec r\,.\prec: p\,.\prec.\,q \vee r$

***19·5*** $p \prec r\,.\vee.\,q \prec r :\prec: p\,q\,.\prec.\,r$

[19·44, 17·4] $p\,q\,.\circ.\,{\sim}r :\prec: p \circ {\sim}r\,.\,q \circ {\sim}r$ (1)

[12·44] (1) $. = :.\,{\sim}(p \circ {\sim}r\,.\,q \circ {\sim}r) :\prec: {\sim}(p\,q\,.\circ.\,{\sim}r)$ (2)

[11·01, 12·3, 17·01] (2) = Q.E.D.

We have already noted that the implication of 19·5 is not reversible. This theorem gives the corollaries:

***19·51*** $p \prec r . \prec : p q . \prec . r$

***19·52*** $q \prec r . \prec : p q . \prec . r$

It may be observed that, in 19·46 and 19·5, we have in this section proved two principles of the general type of the *T*-principles which occur in Section 3. In fact, 19·46 and 19·5 could there have been proved as *T*-theorems, but were omitted because they would not be needed for later proofs and because demonstration of them would have been long and involved. *All* previous *T*-principles can now be proved, with omission of the *T*. We called attention, in Section 3, to the fact that the basic theorems of this type, from which all others are deduced, are:

16·1 $p \prec q . T : \prec : p r . \prec . q r,$

16·2 $p \prec q . p \prec r . T : \prec : p . \prec . q r,$

and 16·5 $p . \prec . q r : T : . \prec : p \prec q . p \prec r.$

In order to prove these, without the *T*, we need first two simple principles which are consequences of 19·16 and 18·8:

***19·57*** $p . q \sim q : = . q \sim q$

[18·8] $\sim\Diamond(q \sim q)$ (1)

[19·16: $q \sim q/p$; $\sim(p . q \sim q)/q$]

$(1) . \prec : \sim\Diamond[(q \sim q) . \sim(p . q \sim q)]$ (2)

[11·02] $(2) . = : . q \sim q . \prec : p . q \sim q$ (3)

[12·17] $p . q \sim q : \prec . q \sim q$ (4)

[11·03] $(3) . (4) : =$ Q.E.D.

The adjunction of any proposition $p$ with the impossible proposition $q \sim q$, is equivalent to $q \sim q$. This theorem corresponds to the principle of certain other systems, $p \times 0 = 0$, $q \sim q$ here behaving like the zero-element of the system.

***19·58*** $p . = : p . \vee . q \sim q$

[19·16] $18{\cdot}8 . \prec : \sim\Diamond[(q \sim q) . \sim p]$ (1)

[11·02] $(1) . = : q \sim q . \prec . p$ (2)

[16·34] $(2) . = : . p . \vee . q \sim q : \prec . p$ (3)

[13·2] $p . \prec : p . \vee . q \sim q$ (4)

[11·03] $(3) . (4) : =$ Q.E.D.

This theorem corresponds to the principle $p = p + 0$ in certain other systems.

Using 19·57 and 19·58, proof of 16·1, without the $T$, is as follows:

***19·6*** $p ⥽ q . ⥽ : p\,r . ⥽ . q\,r$

[19·16] $\sim\Diamond(p \sim q) ⥽ \sim\Diamond(p \sim q\,r)$ (1)

[19·58] $(1) . = :. \sim\Diamond(p \sim q) . ⥽ : \sim\Diamond(p \sim q\,r . \vee . r \sim r)$ (2)

[19·57] $(2) . = :. \sim\Diamond(p \sim q) . ⥽ : \sim\Diamond(p \sim q\,r . \vee . p\,r \sim r)$ (3)

[16·72] $(3) . = :. \sim\Diamond(p \sim q) . ⥽ : \sim\Diamond(p\,r . \sim q \vee \sim r)$ (4)

[11·01, 12·3] $(4) . = :. \sim\Diamond(p \sim q) . ⥽ : \sim\Diamond[p\,r . \sim(q\,r)]$ (5)

[11·02] (5) = Q.E.D.

The other two $T$-principles mentioned above may be replaced as follows:

***19·61*** $p ⥽ q . p ⥽ r : ⥽ : p . ⥽ . q\,r$

[11·6, 12·15] $p\,r . ⥽ . q\,r : p . ⥽ . p\,r :. ⥽ : p . ⥽ . q\,r$ (1)

[12·77] $19·6 . (1) : ⥽ :: p ⥽ q : p . ⥽ . p\,r :. ⥽ : p . ⥽ . q\,r$ (2)

[16·33] (2) = Q.E.D.

***19·62*** $p . ⥽ . q\,r : ⥽ : p ⥽ q . p ⥽ r$

[19·28] $\sim\Diamond(p \sim q . \vee . p \sim r) : ⥽ : \sim\Diamond(p \sim q) . \sim\Diamond(p \sim r)$ (1)

[16·72] $(1) . = :.$

$\sim\Diamond(p . \sim q \vee \sim r) : ⥽ : \sim\Diamond(p \sim q) . \sim\Diamond(p \sim r)$ (2)

[11·01, 12·3] $(2) . = :.$

$\sim\Diamond[p . \sim(q\,r)] : ⥽ : \sim\Diamond(p \sim q) . \sim\Diamond(p \sim r)$ (3)

[11·02] (3) = Q.E.D.

***19·63*** $p . ⥽ . q\,r : = : p ⥽ q . p ⥽ r$

[11·03] 19·61 . 19·62 : = Q.E.D.

Since 16·1 can now be replaced by 19·6, 16·2 by 19·61, and 16·5 by 19·62, it will be obvious from the proofs of other $T$-principles, given in previous sections, how they may now be proved with omission of the $T$. Accordingly we shall simply list such theorems without demonstration:

***19·64*** $p ⥽ q . ⥽ : p \vee r . ⥽ . q \vee r$ (See 16·15)

***19·65*** $p ⥽ r . q ⥽ r : ⥽ : p \vee q . ⥽ . r$ (See 16·4)

***19·66*** $p \vee q . ⥽ . r : ⥽ : p ⥽ r . q ⥽ r$ (See 16·51)

*19·67* $p \prec r . q \prec r : = : p \lor q . \prec . r$

[11·03] 19·65 . 19·66 : = Q.E.D.

*19·68* $p \prec r . q \prec s : \prec : p q . \prec . r s$ (See 16·6)

*19·681* $p \prec r . q \prec s : \prec : p \lor q . \prec . r \lor s$ (See 16·61)

*19·682* $p \prec q . p \prec r : \prec : p . \prec . q \lor r$ (See 16·62)

*19·69* $p . \circ . q \lor r : \prec : p \circ q . \lor . p \circ r$ (See 17·7)

*19·691* $p \circ q . \lor . p \circ r : \prec : p . \circ . q \lor r$ (See 17·71)

*19·692* $p . \circ . q \lor r : = : p \circ q . \lor . p \circ r$

[11·03] 19·69 . 19·691 : = Q.E.D.

The next two theorems are alternative forms of a very important consequence of the Consistency Postulate:

*19·7* $p \circ p . = : p \circ q . \lor . p \circ {\sim} q$

[19·11] $p \circ q . \prec . p \circ p$ (1)

[19·11] $p \circ {\sim} q . \prec . p \circ p$ (2)

[19·65] (1) . (2) $: \prec : . p \circ q . \lor . p \circ {\sim} q : \prec . p \circ p$ (3)

[11·03] 17·592 . (3) : = Q.E.D.

*19·71* $\Diamond p . = : p \circ q . \lor . p \circ {\sim} q : = : \Diamond (p q) . \lor . \Diamond (p \, {\sim} q)$

[18·1, 18·3] 19·7 = Q.E.D.

Theorem 19·71 could be extended, since the same principle gives

$$\Diamond (p q) . = : \Diamond (p q r) . \lor . \Diamond (p q \, {\sim} r),$$
$$\Diamond (p \, {\sim} q) . = : \Diamond (p \, {\sim} q r) . \lor . \Diamond (p \, {\sim} q \, {\sim} r),$$
$$\Diamond (p q r) . = : \Diamond (p q r s) . \lor . \Diamond (p q r \, {\sim} s),$$

and so on, for any number of elements. Thus the familiar Principle of Expansion holds for $\Diamond p$ as well as for $p$.

It will be noted that one of the two implications involved in the equivalences stated by 19·7 and 19·71—that if $p$ is self-consistent, then it is consistent with one or other of every contradictory pair—has been previously proved, as 17·592, and does not depend on the Consistency Postulate. But the other implication—that if $p$ is consistent with $q$ or with ${\sim} q$, then it is self-consistent—depends directly upon the Consistency Postulate.

The correlates for $\sim\Diamond p$ and $\sim\Diamond\sim p$ are as follows:

*19·72* $\sim\Diamond p \,.\, = : \sim(p \circ q) \,.\, \sim(p \circ \sim q) : = : p \prec \sim q \,.\, p \prec q$

[19·71] $\sim\Diamond p \,.\, = : \sim(p \circ q \,.\, \vee \,.\, p \circ \sim q)$

[11·01] $= : \sim(p \circ q) \,.\, \sim(p \circ \sim q)$

[17·12] $= : p \prec \sim q \,.\, p \prec q$

Here also, one implication involved in the equivalence stated by the theorem does not require the Consistency Postulate: that if $p \prec q$ and $p \prec \sim q$, then $p$ is impossible, follows from the Principle of the Syllogism. But that "an impossible proposition implies both of any contradictory pair" depends on the Consistency Postulate.

*19·73* $\sim\Diamond\sim p \,.\, = : q \prec p \,.\, \sim q \prec p$

[19·72: $\sim p/p$] $\sim\Diamond\sim p \,.\, = : \sim(\sim p \circ q) \,.\, \sim(\sim p \circ \sim q)$

[17·12, 17·21] $= : q \prec p \,.\, \sim q \prec p$

That if $p$ is implied both by $q$ and by $\sim q$, then $p$ is necessarily true, follows from the Principle of the Syllogism. But that "a necessary proposition is implied by both of any contradictory pair" depends on the Consistency Postulate.

The last two equivalences involve what are sometimes called the 'paradoxes of strict implication.' The principle in question becomes explicit in the next four theorems:

*19·74* $\sim\Diamond p \,.\, \prec \,.\, p \prec q$

[19·1: $\sim q/q$] $\sim(p \circ p) \prec \sim(p \circ \sim q)$ (1)

[18·12, 17·12] (1) = Q.E.D.

A proposition which is self-contradictory or impossible implies any proposition.

*19·75* $\sim\Diamond\sim p \,.\, \prec \,.\, q \prec p$

[19·74: $\sim p/p$; $\sim q/q$] $\sim\Diamond\sim p \,.\, \prec \,.\, \sim p \prec \sim q$ (1)

[12·44] (1) = Q.E.D.

A proposition which is necessarily true is implied by any proposition.

*19·76* $\sim(p \prec q) \prec \Diamond p$

[12·4] 19·74 $\prec$ Q.E.D.

If there is any proposition $q$ which $p$ does not imply, then $p$ is self-consistent or possible.

***19·77*** $\sim(q \prec p) \prec \Diamond\sim p$

[12·4] 19·75 $\prec$ Q.E.D.

If there is any proposition $q$ which does not imply $p$, then $p$ is possibly false (not necessarily true).

Unlike the corresponding paradoxes of material implication, these paradoxes of strict implication are inescapable consequences of logical principles which are in everyday use. They are paradoxical only in the sense of being commonly overlooked, because we seldom draw inferences from a self-contradictory proposition. Further discussion of this point will be found in Chapter VIII.

The three theorems which follow represent equivalences one implication of which, in each case, has been proved already; the other implication depends on the principle of the paradoxes:

***19·8*** $\sim\Diamond p \sim\Diamond q \,.\, = \,.\, \sim\Diamond(p \vee q)$

[11·2] $\sim\Diamond p \sim\Diamond q \,.\, \prec \,.\, \sim\Diamond p$ (1)

[12·17] $\sim\Diamond p \sim\Diamond q \,.\, \prec \,.\, \sim\Diamond q$ (2)

[19·74] $\sim\Diamond p \,.\, \prec : p \,.\, \prec \,.\, \sim p \sim q$ (3)

[19·74] $\sim\Diamond q \,.\, \prec : q \,.\, \prec \,.\, \sim p \sim q$ (4)

[11·6] (1) . (3) $: \prec :. \sim\Diamond p \sim\Diamond q \,.\, \prec : p \,.\, \prec \,.\, \sim p \sim q$ (5)

[11·6] (2) . (4) $: \prec :. \sim\Diamond p \sim\Diamond q \,.\, \prec : q \,.\, \prec \,.\, \sim p \sim q$ (6)

[19·61] (5) . (6) $: \prec ::$

$\sim\Diamond p \sim\Diamond q \,.\, \prec :. p \,.\, \prec \,.\, \sim p \sim q : q \,.\, \prec \,.\, \sim p \sim q$ (7)

[19·65] $p \,.\, \prec \,.\, \sim p \sim q : q \,.\, \prec \,.\, \sim p \sim q :. \prec : p \vee q \,.\, \prec \,.\, \sim p \sim q$ (8)

[11·6] (7) . (8) $: \prec :. \sim\Diamond p \sim\Diamond q \,.\, \prec : p \vee q \,.\, \prec \,.\, \sim p \sim q$ (9)

[11·01, 12·3] (9) $. = :.$

$\sim\Diamond p \sim\Diamond q \,.\, \prec : p \vee q \,.\, \prec \,.\, \sim(p \vee q)$ (10)

[18·12] (10) $. = : \sim\Diamond p \sim\Diamond q \,.\, \prec \,.\, \sim\Diamond(p \vee q)$ (11)

[11·03] (11) . 19·28 : = Q.E.D.

The compound proposition "$p$ is impossible and $q$ is impossible" is equivalent to "It is impossible that either $p$ or $q$ be true." (It should be remembered that $p \vee q$ means exactly "At least one of the two, $p$ and $q$, is true.")

***19·81*** $\sim\Diamond\sim p \sim\Diamond\sim q \,.\, = \,.\, \sim\Diamond\sim(p\, q)$

[19·8: $\sim p/p$; $\sim q/q$] $\sim\Diamond\sim p \sim\Diamond\sim q \,.\, = \,.\, \sim\Diamond(\sim p \vee \sim q)$

[12·3] $= \,.\, \sim\Diamond\sim[\sim(\sim p \vee \sim q)]$

[11·01] $= \,.\, \sim\Diamond\sim(p\, q)$

The compound proposition "$p$ is necessary and $q$ is necessary" is equivalent to "'$p$ and $q$ both' is necessarily true."

*19·82* $\Diamond p \vee \Diamond q . = . \Diamond(p \vee q)$

[19·8, 12·3] $\sim(\sim\Diamond p \sim\Diamond q) = \Diamond(p \vee q)$ (1)

[11·01] (1) = Q.E.D.

The compound proposition "Either $p$ is possible or $q$ is possible" is equivalent to "It is possible that 'either $p$ or $q$' is true."

It will be noticed that there is nothing paradoxical about these last three equivalences, although they depend on the principle of the paradoxes. Two further principles which might be classed as paradoxes follow:

*19·83* $\sim\Diamond p \sim\Diamond q . \prec . p = q$

[11·2] $\sim\Diamond p \sim\Diamond q . \prec . \sim\Diamond p$ (1)

[12·17] $\sim\Diamond p \sim\Diamond q . \prec . \sim\Diamond q$ (2)

[19·74] $\sim\Diamond p . \prec . p \prec q$ (3)

[19·74] $\sim\Diamond q . \prec . q \prec p$ (4)

[11·6] (1) . (3) $: \prec : \sim\Diamond p \sim\Diamond q . \prec . p \prec q$ (5)

[11·6] (2) . (4) $: \prec : \sim\Diamond p \sim\Diamond q . \prec . q \prec p$ (6)

[19·61] (5) . (6) $: \prec : . \sim\Diamond p \sim\Diamond q . \prec : p \prec q . q \prec p$ (7)

[11·03] (7) = Q.E.D.

Any two self-contradictory propositions are logically equivalent.

*19·84* $\sim\Diamond\sim p \sim\Diamond\sim q . \prec . p = q$

Similar proof, using 19·75 in place of 19·74.

Any two necessarily true propositions are logically equivalent.

It does not follow from these principles that any two propositions which are self-consistent or possible will be logically equivalent. If that should be the case, then no two propositions could be at once consistent and independent. Nor does it follow from the above that any two propositions both of which are possibly false (not necessarily true) will be equivalent. As a fact, *nothing* follows, from the postulates so far assumed, as to the equivalence or non-equivalence of propositions which are neither self-contradictory nor logically undeniable. But we shall assume, in the next section, that not all merely true propositions are equivalent;

from which it will follow that not all merely false propositions are equivalent.

We have now shown in this section that, assuming 19·01, all the $T$-principles of preceding sections can be replaced by the corresponding principle without the $T$. It is also a fact that, *without* the assumption of 19·01, all the theorems of the present section can be deduced, *in the form of T-principles*, from the postulates of Section 1 alone. In order that this may be clear, we give below such proof of 19·01, 19·02, and 19·1, in the form of $T$-theorems. The proof of their consequences—all the theorems of this section—in similar form, follows readily, and the general method of it will be obvious.

***19·9*** $\Diamond(p\,q) \,.\, T :\prec .\, \Diamond p$ (See 19·01)

$T = : p\,q \,.\prec .\, p$

[18·51] $T \,.\, \Diamond(p\,q) :\prec .\, \Diamond p$

***19·91*** $\Diamond p \,.\, T :\prec .\, \Diamond(p \vee q)$ (See 19·02)

$T = : p \,.\prec .\, p \vee q$

[18·51] $T \,.\, \Diamond p :\prec .\, \Diamond(p \vee q)$

***19·92*** $\sim(p \circ p) \,.\, T :\prec .\, \sim(p \circ q)$ (See 19·1)

$T = : p\,q \,.\prec .\, p$

[17·54] $T \,.\, \sim(p \circ p) :\prec : \sim(p\,q \,.\circ .\, p\,q)$ (1)

[12·15, 18·3] (1) = Q.E.D.

Thus we have demonstrated, by the manner in which this chapter is developed, that there are two systems, related but distinct. System 1, deduced from the definitions which have been given and the postulates 11·1–11·7 of Section 1, contains all the theorems of previous sections, as there printed; and it contains all the theorems of the present section in the form of $T$-principles. System 2, deduced from the definitions and the postulates of Section 1, with the addition of the postulate 19·01, contains all the theorems of this section, as here printed, and all the theorems of previous sections, any $T$-principle being replaced by the corresponding theorem without the $T$.

These two systems, and others which are related, will be discussed in Appendix II. Although System 1 is more economical in its assumptions, and although there is no usable principle of inference in System 2 which is not also contained (in more complex form perhaps) in System 1, nevertheless we regard System 2 as superior on account of its slightly greater simplicity. It is this System 2 which we desire to indicate as the System of Strict Implication.

### Section 6. The Existence Postulate and Existence Theorems

Our postulates, up to this point, do not include any one which categorically distinguishes the System of Strict Implication from that of Material Implication. That is, while there are theorems in terms of the relation $p \supset q$ which cannot be proved to hold of $p \prec q$, there is no assumption which asserts or implies that any theorem which is true of $p \prec q$ would be *definitely false* of $p \supset q$. What distinguishes our assumptions from a possible set for Material Implication is only that the converse of 12·81, which would be

$$\sim(p \sim q) \,.\prec.\, p \prec q,$$

is not assumed, and cannot be proved from our postulates. But this is *consistent with* our previous symbolic assumptions; hence nothing so far (except the *meanings* assigned) positively prevents interpretation of our postulates as an incomplete set for Material Implication.

If the converse of 12·81, above, were added to the previous assumptions, the result would be to reduce the whole system to a redundant form of Material Implication; in which $p \circ q$ would be merely a second mode of symbolizing $p\,q$; $\sim\Diamond\sim p$ and $\Diamond p$ would both be superfluous equivalents of $p$ ($p$ is true); $\sim\Diamond p$ and $\Diamond\sim p$ would be superfluous equivalents of $\sim p$; and $p \prec q$ would be equivalent to $p \supset q$. A postulate which makes this interpretation impossible is now to be added.

We have pointed out that one way in which material implication, $p \supset q$, fails to have the properties of the relation "$q$ is deducible from $p$" is that, in terms of material implication, no two propositions can be at once consistent and independent. That $p$ is consistent with $q$ means "$p$ does not imply the falsity of $q$," $\sim(p \prec \sim q)$. And that $q$ is independent of $p$ means "$p$ does not imply $q$," $\sim(p \prec q)$. Thus if $p \prec q$ is to express a meaning of 'implies' in terms of which $q$ can be at once consistent with and independent of $p$, then it must be the case that there are *some* propositions, $p$ and $q$, such that

$$\sim(p \prec q) \,.\, \sim(p \prec \sim q).$$

But this could not be assumed to hold for *every* pair of propositions, $p$ and $q$. If the above symbolic expression were asserted as a postulate, it would mean "No proposition implies anything; and any two propositions are consistent with each other."

Thus the postulate we require cannot be expressed without introducing the ideas 'for some $p$,' 'for some $p$ and $q$,' etc. Let us represent any statement which can be expressed in the symbols of the system, and involves the proposition-sign $p$, by $\varphi(p)$ or $\psi(p)$, etc.; any such statement involving the two proposition-signs $p$ and $q$, by $\varphi(p, q)$ or $\psi(p, q)$, etc. And let us express "For some $p$, $\varphi(p)$ is true," by $(\exists p) \,.\, \varphi(p)$; "For some $p$ and $q$, $\varphi(p, q)$ is true," by $(\exists p, q) \,.\, \varphi(p, q)$. The postulate which categorically distinguishes strict implication from material implication will then be:

***20·01*** $(\exists p, q) : \sim(p \prec q) \,.\, \sim(p \prec \sim q)$

For some $p$ and $q$, $p$ does not strictly imply $q$, and $p$ does not strictly imply that $q$ is false; or, there is some pair of propositions, $p$ and $q$, so related that $p$ implies nothing about the truth or falsity of $q$.

For *material* implication, we have proved (15·72) that

$$p \supset q \,.\vee.\, p \supset \sim q.$$

For every $p$ and $q$, either $p$ materially implies $q$ or $p$ materially implies that $q$ is false. Thus 20·01 and 15·72 would be exact contradictories if $p \prec q$ should coincide with $p \supset q$. Hence the consistency of 20·01 with our previous assumptions (proved in Appendix II) demonstrates categorically that $p \prec q$ in this system is distinct from $p \supset q$.

The reader may be puzzled by the necessity of introducing a postulate of the general form $(\exists p) \,.\, \varphi(p)$. The laws of logic, one may say, are all universal. But without meaning to beg any question of truth or falsity in logic, we may here point out a general fact about the distinction of any system of 'good' logic —adequate to and true of deductive inference—and various 'bad' logics.[7] For example, suppose we wish to deny the validity of deducing "$p$ is true and $q$ false" from "$p$ and $q$ are both true": that is, to deny that

$$p\, q \,.\, \prec\!\!\!\dashv \,.\, p \sim q$$

is a valid logical principle. We cannot do this by asserting

$$\sim(p\, q \,.\, \prec\!\!\!\dashv \,.\, p \sim q),$$

because this affirms altogether too much. For example, substituting $\sim p$ for $q$, it asserts

$$\sim[p \sim p \,.\, \prec\!\!\!\dashv \,.\, p \sim(\sim p)] \quad \text{or} \quad \sim(p \sim p \,.\, \prec\!\!\!\dashv \,.\, p).$$

If this last should hold, then we should have contradictory principles in our logic, since $p\, q \,.\, \prec\!\!\!\dashv \,.\, p$ is a valid law of logic; and this gives $p \sim p \,.\, \prec\!\!\!\dashv \,.\, p$ as a special case. Thus any system containing the two principles,

$$p\, q \,.\, \prec\!\!\!\dashv \,.\, p \quad \text{and} \quad \sim(p\, q \,.\, \prec\!\!\!\dashv \,.\, p \sim q),$$

would not be a consistent system; and with the first of these in the system, the second cannot be.

It is for such reasons that it is impossible to distinguish a 'good' logic from various other strange and bizarre systems by universal principles alone. If a 'bad' logic should be 'bad' only by including as universal principles such laws as genuinely hold in some single instance or special case, then no 'good' logic could include any postulate or law, of the form of those in earlier sections, which would be categorically incompatible with this 'bad' logic.

Even the particular existence postulate which we here assume does not distinguish Strict Implication from various other systems any one of which might be put forward as a calculus of propositions. It does, however, distinguish it from Material Implication, as has been pointed out.[8]

[7] We shall revert to the question of the truth about deductive inference in Chapter VIII.

[8] In a doctoral dissertation presented to the Department of Philosophy in Harvard University, Dr. W. T. Parry has reached certain important results

It has not been customary heretofore to introduce in logic principles of the form of our existence postulate. But it is only through such principles that the outlines of a logical system can be positively delineated.[9]

Given a postulate of existence, theorems of the same form can be proved. In fact, certain theorems of this form can be proved without any postulate of existence.

The technique adequate to such demonstration would require a discussion and development too long to be introduced here. We shall simply set down, and explain where necessary, certain general principles to be made use of. The analogy of these to the laws of propositional functions in Chapter V will be an aid to the understanding of their significance.

It will be well that the idea of universality, implicit in the assertion of the principles of previous sections, should be explicitly symbolized. Let us represent 'for every $p$' by the prefix $(p)$; 'for every $p$ and $q$,' by $(p, q)$, etc. This idea can be defined in terms of $(\exists\, p)$, $(\exists\, p, q)$, etc.:

***20·02*** $(p) \,.\, \varphi(p) :=: \sim[(\exists\, p) \,.\, \sim\varphi(p)]$

***20·03*** $(p, q) \,.\, \psi(p, q) :=: \sim[(\exists\, p, q) \,.\, \sim\psi(p, q)]$

The same principle extends to expressions involving three or more proposition-signs.

The following principles will be used in the demonstration of existence theorems. These are stated in terms of $\varphi(p)$ only, but are meant to extend also to $\varphi(p, q)$, $\varphi(p, q, r)$, etc.:

(A) If $\varphi(p)$ is asserted as a law, $(p) \,.\, \varphi(p)$ may be asserted as its equivalent.

---

which bear upon this point. In the light of his work, it seems to us probable that any calculus of propositions must be such that either (1) it has the above-indicated non-categorical character, or (2) the class of its distinct elements is assumed to be infinite, or (3) it is capable of interpretation as a truth-value system. This means that any system such as Strict Implication must either be capable of more than one interpretation as a logical system, or it must be assumed that there are an infinite number of propositions which are consistent and independent. This last is very likely true; but it would be a very awkward assumption.

[9] This has been recognized by Professors Lukasiewicz and Tarski. See Lukasiewicz, "Philosophische Bemerkungen zu mehrwertigen Systemen des Aussagenkalküls," *Comptes Rendus des séances de la Société des Sciences et des Lettres de Varsovie*, XXIII (1930), *Classe* III, 58 and elsewhere.

(B) If $\varphi(p)$, or $(p) \cdot \varphi(p)$, is asserted, then $(\exists p) \cdot \varphi(p)$ may be asserted. That is, what is true of all propositions is true of some. This is valid if, and only if, there *are* propositions. But the existence of at least two distinct propositions has been assumed, in 20·01.[10]

(C) If $(\exists p) \cdot \varphi(p)$ holds, and we have, as a postulate or proved principle, $\varphi(p) \prec \psi(p)$, or $(p) \cdot \varphi(p) \prec \psi(p)$, then $(\exists p) \cdot \psi(p)$ holds.

(D) If $\varphi(p)$, or $(p) \cdot \varphi(p)$, holds, and $(\exists p) \cdot \psi(p)$ holds, then $(\exists p) : \varphi(p) \cdot \psi(p)$ holds.

(E) What is true universally is true of any chosen proposition:

$$(p) \cdot \varphi p : \prec \cdot \varphi q$$

Hence also, $(p) \cdot \varphi(p) : \prec : (\exists p) \cdot \varphi(p)$.

(F) If two logical expressions $P$ and $Q$ are so related that $Q$ is a value of $P$ in $\varphi(P)$, then

(a) if an *existence* principle $(\exists -) \cdot \varphi(Q)$ is asserted, the *existence* principle $(\exists -) \cdot \varphi(P)$ can be asserted;

(b) if $\varphi(Q)$ is asserted universally, the existence principle $(\exists -) \cdot \varphi(P)$ can be asserted.

(The dash following $\exists$ here represents the variable, or variables, in the expression $P$ or $Q$.)

Use of any of the above principles, when not obvious, will be indicated by letter. (F) above covers a principle which is

[10] The idea of 'existence' here involved, and symbolized by $(\exists p)$, $(\exists p, q)$, etc., is the same as that which characterizes 'existence postulates' and 'existence theorems' in mathematics in general. But the designation is doubtfully appropriate: logic and deductive systems are never concerned with existence except in a hypothetical sense—the sense in which "*A* exists" means "There is a definable entity, *A*, such that . . . ." Thus 'existence' has to do with the possibility of intellectual construction, or of definite conception which is free from inconsistency. The conception of 'existence' involves theoretical and methodological problems of the first magnitude, which cannot be discussed here. The most accurate reading of $(\exists p) \cdot \varphi(p)$, etc., in the above is "For some choice of $p$, $\varphi(p)$ holds"; where 'choice' refers to the alternatives covered by the range of significance of the variable $p$. Thus nothing is asserted by writing a theorem of the form $(\exists p) \cdot \varphi(p)$ except exactly what is proved, for example, by the fact that $\varphi(\sim p)$ or $\varphi(p \vee q)$, etc., holds, and $\sim p$ or $p \vee q$, etc., is a 'value' of $p$ in $\varphi(p)$. Furthermore, the inference that if $\varphi(p)$ holds, then $(\exists p) \cdot \varphi(p)$, does *not* involve the principle that whatever is universally true, is true of some existent thing or things, which would be false. It *does* involve the assumption that there are instances of what the symbol $p$ in $\varphi(p)$ represents; that where $\varphi(p)$ is a formula of logic, it is true, and is true for a different reason than that it is 'vacuously satisfied.'

difficult to express and requires explanation. We have referred to an expression $Q$ being a 'value' of an expression $P$. It would be more appropriate to speak of $P$ being in the 'generic-specific' relation to $Q$.

If $Q$ can be derived from $P$ by substitution, according to the principle of substitution, (b), in Section 1, let us say that $P$ stands to $Q$ in the 'generic-specific' relation; that $Q$ stands to $P$ in the 'specific-generic' relation; and that, relative to each other, $P$ is the 'generic' proposition, $Q$ the 'specific' proposition. Thus $\varphi(p)$ stands to $\varphi(\sim p)$, or to $\varphi(p \vee q)$, or $\varphi(p \prec q)$, etc., in the generic-specific relation: $\varphi(p)$ is the generic proposition with respect to which $\varphi(\sim p)$, $\varphi(p \vee q)$, $\varphi(p \prec q)$, etc., are specific. (It is to be noted that, as the terms are here used, $\varphi(p)$ stands to $\varphi(q)$ in *both* the generic-specific and the specific-generic relation: that is, given $p \prec p$, for example, $q \prec q$ can be derived by substitution, and *vice versa*.)

The operation of substitution, (b), in Section 1, holds for universal propositions, of the form $\varphi(p)$, or $(p) \cdot \varphi(p)$. The validity of it reflects the fact that if a principle is universally true of the generic proposition—e.g., if $p \prec p$ holds—then the same principle holds for any specific proposition—e.g., $\sim p \prec \sim p$ holds, $p \vee q \,.\prec.\, p \vee q$ holds, $p \prec q \,.\prec.\, p \prec q$ holds, etc. What is true of every proposition $p$ is true of every *negative* proposition, $\sim p$, of every 'either . . . or . . .' proposition, $p \vee q$, of every hypothetical proposition, $p \prec q$, etc.

This operation of substituting the specific for the generic is *not valid* for existence principles. If there is some proposition $p$ such that $(\exists p) \cdot \varphi(p)$, it *does not follow*, for example, that there is some *negative* proposition, $\sim p$, such that $(\exists p) \cdot \varphi(\sim p)$, or some hypothetical proposition, $p \prec q$, such that $(\exists p) \cdot \varphi(p \prec q)$, etc. But the *converse* substitution *is* valid for principles of the form $(\exists p) \cdot \varphi(p)$. That is, if $(\exists p) \cdot \varphi(\sim p)$, or $(\exists p, q) \cdot \varphi(p \vee q)$, or $(\exists p, q) \cdot \varphi(p \prec q)$ holds, then $(\exists p) \cdot \varphi(p)$ holds; because whatever negative proposition $\sim p$ it is for which $\varphi(\sim p)$ holds, is *some* proposition; whatever hypothetical proposition $p \prec q$ it is which is such that $\varphi(p \prec q)$ holds, is *some* proposition; and so on.

An analogy here may be helpful. What is universally true of the genus 'birds' is universally true of the species 'swans.' It does not follow that what is true of some birds will be true of some swans. Instead, it follows that what is true of some swan, is true of some bird.

We shall represent the 'converse substitution' of the generic for the specific, which is valid in existence principles, as follows: $p \int p \vee q$, for example, will mean 'substituting $p$ for $p \vee q$,' just as, in universal principles, $p \vee q/p$ means 'substituting $p \vee q$ for $p$.' Thus if $p \vee q/p$ represents a substitution which is valid in *universal* principles, then the converse substitution, $p \int p \vee q$, will be valid in *existence* principles. This is the simplest and the final test of the validity of any converse substitution. The principle of such converse substitutions is stated above in (F, a); (F, b) merely combines, in one operation, (F, a) and (B).

It is to be noted that this principle does not allow us to substitute the same symbol, $p$, for two expressions which are symbolically distinct. For example, in our existence postulate,

$$(\exists p, q) : {\sim}(p \prec q) \,.\, {\sim}(p \prec {\sim}q),$$

it would not be legitimate to substitute $p$ for *both* ${\sim}(p \prec q)$ and $(p \prec {\sim}q)$, thus deriving

$$(\exists p) : p \,.\, {\sim}p.$$

This is the case, because if we were given, as a universal principle, $p \,{\sim}p$, we could not, by substitution in this, derive

$${\sim}(p \prec q) \,.\, {\sim}(p \prec {\sim}q).$$

We could substitute ${\sim}(p \prec q)$ for $p$; but that would give us, instead of the above,

$${\sim}(p \prec q) \,.\, {\sim}[{\sim}(p \prec q)].$$

We proceed to the proof of theorems.

***20·1*** $(\exists p) \,.\, p$

[12·1] $p \prec p$ (1)

[(F), (1): $p \int p \prec p$] $(\exists p) \,.\, p$

The theorem states that "There exists at least one proposition $p$ which is true." To prove it, we take 12·1, $p \prec p$ (we might have taken any other asserted principle), as *some* proposition. By principle (F), since $p \prec p$ is asserted to be true, the converse substitution, $p \int p \prec p$, gives $(\exists p) \,.\, p$.

***20·11*** $(\exists p) . \sim p$

[12·9] $\sim(p \sim p)$ (1)

[(F), (1): $p \int p \sim p$] $(\exists p) . \sim p$

For some $p$, $p$ is false; or, there exists at least one false proposition. Here we take the fact that the falsity of $p \sim p$ is asserted, in 12·9, as our demonstration that there is some proposition which is false.

***20·2*** $(\exists p) . \sim \Diamond p$

[12·1] $p \prec p$ (1)

[11·02] (1) $= \sim \Diamond (p \sim p)$ (2)

[(F), (2): $p \int p \sim p$] $(\exists p) . \sim \Diamond p$

There is at least one proposition which is impossible, not self-consistent.

***20·21*** $(\exists p) . \sim \Diamond \sim p$

[12·1] $p \prec p$ (1)

[11·02, 12·3] (1) $= \sim \Diamond \sim [\sim (p \sim p)]$ (2)

[(F), (2): $p \int \sim (p \sim p)$] $(\exists p) . \sim \Diamond \sim p$

There is at least one necessarily true proposition. It might be supposed that the existence of *more* than one necessary proposition, and of more than one impossible proposition, could be proved. But by 19·84, any two necessary propositions are logically equivalent, hence not distinct; and by 19·83, any two impossible propositions are equivalent.

***20·25*** $(\exists p, q) . \sim (p = q)$

[12·86] 12·1 $. \prec : \sim [p \prec p . \prec . \sim (p \prec p)]$ (1)

[(F), (1): $p \int p \prec p$; $q \int \sim (p \prec p)$] $(\exists p, q) . \sim (p \prec q)$ (2)

[12·72] $\sim (p \prec q) . \prec : \sim (p \prec q . q \prec p)$ (3)

[11·03] (3) $. = : \sim (p \prec q) . \prec . \sim (p = q)$ (4)

[(C), (2), (4)] $(\exists p, q) . \sim (p = q)$

There are at least two propositions which are distinct (not equivalent).

***20·26*** $(\exists p) . \Diamond p$

[18·4] $p \prec \Diamond p$ (1)

[(C), 20·1, (1)] $(\exists p) . \Diamond p$

There is at least one proposition which is possible or self-consistent.

*20·27* $(\exists p) . \Diamond{\sim}p$

$[18·44]\ {\sim}p \prec \Diamond{\sim}p$ (1)

$[(C), 20·11, (1)]\ (\exists p) . \Diamond{\sim}p$

There is at least one proposition which is possibly false (not necessarily true).

So far, we have made no use of our Existence Postulate. Hence, without that principle, it can be proved that there exist one true and one false proposition, one necessary and one impossible, one possible and one which is possibly false. It might be supposed that we have here proved the existence of six distinct propositions. But in fact, no more than two have been proved to exist (20·25); or *could* be proved to exist without the Existence Postulate. All the above theorems are satisfied if there exist two distinct propositions: one which is necessarily true (hence true and possible), and its negative which is impossible (hence false and possibly false). As has been pointed out, all the principles so far made use of could be interpreted in terms of Material Implication; and the system of Material Implication is incompatible with the existence of more than two non-equivalent propositions—such that ${\sim}(p \equiv q)$—since

$$p\,q . \prec : p \supset q . q \supset p,$$

and $${\sim}p\,{\sim}q . \prec : p \supset q . q \supset p.$$

Beginning with 20·5, we derive the similar consequences of the Existence Postulate. Theorem 20·4 is a lemma which is needed:

*20·4* $(p) . {\sim}(p = {\sim}p)$

$[12·87]\ p \prec {\sim}p . \prec . {\sim}p$ (1)

$[12·89]\ {\sim}p . \prec . {\sim}({\sim}p \prec p)$ (2)

$[11·6]\ (1) . (2) : \prec : p \prec {\sim}p . \prec . {\sim}({\sim}p \prec p)$ (3)

$[12·81]\ (3) . \prec : {\sim}(p \prec {\sim}p . {\sim}p \prec p)$ (4)

$[11·03]\ (4) . = . {\sim}(p = {\sim}p)$

No proposition is equivalent to its own negative.

*20·5* $(\exists p, q, r) : \Diamond p \,.\, \Diamond q \,.\, \Diamond r \,.\, \sim(p = q) \,.\, \sim(p = r) \,.\, \sim(q = r)$

[12·7] 20·01 . = : . $(\exists p, q) : \sim(p \prec q) \,.\, \sim(p \prec q) \,.$
$\sim(p \prec \sim q) \,.\, \sim(p \prec \sim q)$ (1)

[12·44, 12·45] (1) . = : .
$(\exists p, q) : \sim(p \prec q) \,.\, \sim(\sim q \prec \sim p) \,.$
$\sim(p \prec \sim q) \,.\, \sim(q \prec \sim p)$ (2)

Let $H = : \sim(p \prec q) \,.\, \sim(\sim q \prec \sim p) \,.\, \sim(p \prec \sim q) \,.\, \sim(q \prec \sim p)$

[11·2] $H \prec \sim(p \prec q)$ (3)

[12·17] $H \prec \sim(\sim q \prec \sim p)$ (4)

[12·17] $H \prec \sim(q \prec \sim p)$ (5)

[12·17] $H \prec \sim(p \prec \sim q)$ (6)

[19·76] $\sim(p \prec q) \,.\prec .\, \Diamond p$ (7)

[19·76] $\sim(\sim q \prec \sim p) \,.\prec .\, \Diamond(\sim q)$ (8)

[19·76] $\sim(q \prec \sim p) \,.\prec .\, \Diamond q$ (9)

[12·72, 11·03] $\sim(p \prec q) \,.\prec .\, \sim(p = q)$ (10)

[12·72, 11·03] $\sim(p \prec \sim q) \,.\prec .\, \sim(p = \sim q)$ (11)

[11·6] (3) . (7) : $\prec$ . $H \prec \Diamond p$ (12)

[11·6] (4) . (8) : $\prec$ . $H \prec \Diamond(\sim q)$ (13)

[11·6] (5) . (9) : $\prec$ . $H \prec \Diamond q$ (14)

[11·6] (3) . (10) : $\prec$ . $H \prec \sim(p = q)$ (15)

[11·6] (6) . (11) : $\prec$ . $H \prec \sim(p = \sim q)$ (16)

[16·2] (12) . (13) . (14) . (15) . (16) . (*T*) : $\prec$ : .
$H : \prec : \Diamond p \,.\, \Diamond q \,.\, \Diamond(\sim q) \,.\, \sim(p = q) \,.\, \sim(p = \sim q)$ (17)

[(C), (1), (17)] $(\exists p, q) : \Diamond p \,.\, \Diamond q \,.\, \Diamond(\sim q) \,.\, \sim(p = q) \,.$
$\sim(p = \sim q)$ (18)

[(D), (18), 20·4] $(\exists p, q) : \Diamond p \,.\, \Diamond q \,.\, \Diamond(\sim q) \,.\, \sim(p = q) \,.$
$\sim(p = \sim q) \,.\, \sim(q = \sim q)$ (19)

[(F), (19): $r \int \sim q$] $(\exists p, q, r) : \Diamond p \,.\, \Diamond q \,.\, \Diamond r \,.$
$\sim(p = q) \,.\, \sim(p = r) \,.\, \sim(q = r)$

There are at least three distinct propositions which are self-consistent.

We could similarly prove:

*20·51* $(\exists p, q, r) : \Diamond\sim p \,.\, \Diamond\sim q \,.\, \Diamond\sim r \,.\, \sim(p = q) \,.\, \sim(p = r) \,.\, \sim(q = r)$

There are at least three distinct propositions which are possibly false (not necessarily true).

The next theorem establishes the existence in the system of at least four distinct propositions:

**20·6** $(\exists p, q, r, s) : \sim(p = q) . \sim(p = r) . \sim(p = s) . \sim(q = r) . \sim(q = s) . \sim(r = s)$

[20·01] $(\exists p, q) : \sim(p \prec q) . \sim(p \prec \sim q)$ (1)

Let $H = : \sim(p \prec q) . \sim(p \prec \sim q)$

[11·2] $H \prec \sim(p \prec q)$ (2)

[12·17] $H \prec \sim(p \prec \sim q)$ (3)

[12·44] $(2) . = . H \prec \sim(\sim q \prec \sim p)$ (4)

[12·45] $(3) . = . H \prec \sim(q \prec \sim p)$ (5)

[12·72, 11·03] $\sim(p \prec q) \prec \sim(p = q)$ (6)

[12·72, 11·03] $\sim(p \prec \sim q) \prec \sim(p = \sim q)$ (7)

[12·72, 11·03] $\sim(q \prec \sim p) \prec \sim(q = \sim p)$ (8)

[12·72, 11·03] $\sim(\sim q \prec \sim p) \prec \sim(\sim q = \sim p)$ (9)

[11·6] $(2) . (6) : \prec : H \prec \sim(p = q)$ (10)

[11·6] $(3) . (7) : \prec . H \prec \sim(p = \sim q)$ (11)

[11·6] $(5) . (8) : \prec . H \prec \sim(q = \sim p)$ (12)

[11·6] $(4) . (9) : \prec . H \prec \sim(\sim q = \sim p)$ (13)

[16·2] $(10) . (11) . (12) . (13) . (T) : \prec : .$
$H : \prec : \sim(p = q) . \sim(p = \sim q) . \sim(q = \sim p) . \sim(\sim q = \sim p)$ (14)

[(C), (1), (14)] $(\exists p, q) : \sim(p = q) . \sim(p = \sim q) . \sim(q = \sim p) . \sim(\sim q = \sim p)$ (15)

[20·4] $(p) . \sim(p = \sim p)$ (16)

[20·4] $(q) . \sim(q = \sim q)$ (17)

[(D), (15), (16), (17)]
$(\exists p, q) : \sim(p = q) . \sim(p = \sim q) . \sim(q = \sim p) . \sim(\sim q = \sim p) . \sim(p = \sim p) . \sim(q = \sim q)$ (18)

[(F), (18): $r \int \sim q$; $s \int \sim p$]
$(\exists p, q, r, s) : \sim(p = q) . \sim(p = r) . \sim(q = s) . \sim(r = s) . \sim(p = s) . \sim(q = r)$

The last three theorems merely make explicit what is implicit in the Existence Postulate; namely, that there are at least four distinct propositions—the $p$ and $q$ of the postulate and their negatives—three of which, $p$, $q$, and $\sim q$, are logically possible, since for each there is a proposition which it does not imply (see 19·76); and three of which, $q$, $\sim p$, and $\sim q$, are possibly false, since for each there is a proposition which does not imply it (see 19·77). Two of these, consequently, $q$ and $\sim q$, must be both possible and possibly false—self-consistent but not logically necessary; but they cannot be both true or both false. Of the other two, $p$ and $\sim p$, one must be true and one false; but $p$ is not required to be possibly false, and hence may be both true and necessary. And $\sim p$ is not required to be possible; hence it may be both false and impossible.

Previous theorems—not dependent on the Existence Postulate—require that there be at least one true and one false proposition; one necessary and one impossible proposition. Thus to satisfy the minimum requirements of the system, there must be four distinct propositions, distributed as follows: one true and necessary, one true but not necessary, one false and impossible, and one false but not impossible. This could be proved as a theorem, but the symbolic demonstration would be unduly long.

It may be a matter for surprise that, in view both of the symbolic diversity of the propositions of logic itself and of obvious facts about the existence of consistent and independent propositions, it is not easily possible to prove the existence of an indefinitely large number of distinct propositions. But three facts should be borne in mind: (1) The only 'examples' of propositions which are available to us for use in demonstrating existence theorems here, are the propositions of logic itself. (2) Symbolic diversity is no guarantee of distinctness.[11] Not only may different complexes of symbols represent propositions which are equivalent, but also it is frequently impossible to prove the distinctness of non-equivalent expressions. For example, it cannot be proved that

$$\sim(p \prec q \,.=.\, p \prec p),$$

because it is the case that $(\exists p, q) : p \prec q \,.=.\, p \prec p$. (3) In the nature of the case, no greater number of distinct propositions can be proved to exist, from the laws of logic, than that minimum number which, for some distribution of them, would permit these laws to be simultaneously true. Furthermore, no larger number can be proved to exist than is required by each and every possible interpretation of the symbolic assumptions. It is

[11] Use of the operation of substitution (for universals) tacitly assumes that if $p$ is a proposition, $\sim p$ is a proposition; and that if $p$ and $q$ are propositions, then $pq$, $p \vee q$, $p \prec q$, and $p = q$ are propositions. However, it assumes nothing about the equivalence or distinctness of any pair of expressions.

for this reason that the Existence Postulate could not be proved: the other assumptions, by themselves, allow the interpretation by which $p \circ q . = . p\, q$, etc., and the system coincides with Material Implication.

Existence propositions of a different type may be demonstrated by 'generalizing' with respect to some only of the elements, $p$, $q$, $r$, etc., in previous theorems. This process may give important results when there is an element which occurs on one side only of the asserted relation: in such cases it is sometimes possible to prove the equivalence of an existence proposition to a universal. Certain equivalences of this sort throw further light on the logical significance of the Consistency Postulate and of such functions as $\Diamond p$ and $\sim\Diamond p$. As a first example of this kind of generalization, let us take postulate 11·6,

$$p \prec q . q \prec r : \prec . p \prec r.$$

Here $q$ occurs only in the hypothesis. Let us generalize the expression with respect to $q$ alone: that is, instead of reading it with the preface (expressed or implied) 'Whatever propositions $p$, $q$, and $r$ may be,' let us take $p$ and $r$ as constant or given propositions, and read it with the preface 'Whatever proposition $q$ may be.' This will be symbolized by

$$(q) :. p \prec q . q \prec r : \prec . p \prec r.$$

By principle (A) this is assertable as equivalent to the postulate. The logical significance of this will become evident if, for the moment, we give $p$ and $r$ fixed meanings. Let $p$ = "To-day is Wednesday" and $r$ = "To-morrow will be fair." Then the above symbolic statement reads: "Whatever proposition $q$ may be; if 'To-day is Wednesday' implies $q$, and $q$ implies 'To-morrow will be fair,' then 'To-day is Wednesday' implies 'To-morrow will be fair.'" One sees that this is true, and that the truth of it is included in the postulate as generalized.

As another example, we may take 11·2, $p\, q . \prec . p$. Generalized with respect to $q$ alone, this becomes,

$$(q) : p\, q . \prec . p;$$

that is, "Whatever proposition $q$ may be, if $p$ and $q$ are both true, then $p$ is true." A further and most important point, in this case, is that

$$(q) : p\,q \,.\!\prec\!.\, p \quad \text{is equivalent to} \quad (\exists q) \,.\, p\,q : \prec .\, p.$$

[Note the dots in these expressions: the force of $(q)$, in $(q) : p\,q \,.\!\prec\!.\, p$, extends to the whole of $p\,q \,.\!\prec\!.\, p$; but $(\exists q)$, in $(\exists q) \,.\, p\,q : \prec .\, p$, modifies only the hypothesis, $p\,q$.] Thus "Whatever proposition $q$ may be, if $p$ and $q$ are both true, then $p$ is true" is equivalent to "If there is some (any) proposition $q$ such that $p$ and $q$ are both true, then $p$ is true."

To revert to the previous example:

$$(q) :.\, p \prec q \,.\, q \prec r : \prec .\, p \prec r$$

is equivalent to

$$(\exists q) : p \prec q \,.\, q \prec r :. \prec .\, p \prec r.$$

The second of these equivalents reads "If there is some (any) $q$ such that $p \prec q$ and $q \prec r$, then $p \prec r$." This is obviously equivalent to the first.

The general principle of such equivalences might be expressed as follows:

$$(p) : \varphi(p, q, r, \ldots) \,.\!\prec\!.\, \psi(q, r, \ldots)$$

is equivalent to

$$(\exists p) \,.\, \varphi(p, q, r, \ldots) : \prec .\, \psi(q, r, \ldots).$$

In fact, this is merely a special case of a still more general principle:

***21·01*** $(p) : \varphi(p) \,.\!\prec\!.\, K :. = :. (\exists p) \,.\, \varphi(p) : \prec .\, K$

where $K$ is any proposition whatever. [It should be remembered, in applying this principle, that $\psi(p, q, \ldots)$ is an instance of $\varphi(p)$.]

When we generalize with respect to an element which occurs only in the *consequent* of an asserted implication, the situation is quite different. Let us take as our example, 12·72, $\sim p \,.\!\prec\!.\, \sim(p\,q)$. The assertion of this is equivalent to

$$(q) : \sim p \,.\!\prec\!.\, \sim(p\,q);$$

"Whatever proposition $q$ may be; if $p$ is false, then it is false that $p$ and $q$ are both true." But also it is equivalent to

$$\sim p \,.\, \prec : (q) \,.\, \sim(p\,q);$$

"If $p$ is false, then, whatever proposition $q$ may be, it is false that $p$ and $q$ are both true."

Here also, it holds generally that

$$(p) : \varphi(q, r, \ldots) . \dashv . \psi(p, q, r, \ldots)$$

is equivalent to

$$\varphi(q, r, \ldots) . \dashv : (p) . \psi(p, q, r, \ldots).$$

And this is a special case covered by the principle:

*21·02* $(p) : K . \dashv . \varphi(p) : . = : . K . \dashv : (p) . \varphi(p)$

A similar principle holds for propositions of the form $(\exists p) : K . \dashv . \varphi(p)$:

*21·03* $(\exists p) : K . \dashv . \varphi(p) : . = : . K . \dashv : (\exists p) . \varphi(p)$

If a technique sufficient for demonstrating logical principles which involve functions of the type in question were here available, 21·01, 21·02, and 21·03 would be provable theorems. (See the analogous principles, 8·41, 8·42, and 8·43, in Chapter V.) We must here rely upon the reader's intuition to recognize their truth.

We shall thus generalize, below, certain previous theorems, in which a particular element appears only on one or the other side of an asserted implication. Sometimes this procedure allows us to replace an implication by an equivalence, due to the fact that $(\exists p) . \varphi(p)$ is satisfied by $\varphi(q)$; and if $\varphi(p, q)$ does not contain or imply $\sim(p = q)$, then $(\exists p, q) . \varphi(p, q)$ is satisfied by $\varphi(p, p)$. Some of the equivalences thus arrived at give the clearest and most specific meanings of the logical functions which are in question.

First, we give two or three obvious and unimportant examples, to illustrate the method. After that, only those theorems will be given which are logically important.

*21·1* $(\exists q) . p\, q : \dashv . p$

[(A), 11·2] $(q) : p\, q . \dashv . p$ (1)

[21·01] (1) = Q.E.D.

If there is some proposition $q$ such that $p$ and $q$ are both true, then $p$ is true.

*21·11* $p . = : (\exists\, q) . p\, q$

$[11·3]\ p . ⥽ . p\, p$ (1)

$[(F), (1): q \int p]\ (\exists\, q) : p . ⥽ . p\, q$ (2)

$[21·03]\ (2) . = :. p . ⥽ : (\exists\, q) . p\, q$ (3)

$[11·03]\ 21·1 . (3) : =$ Q.E.D.

The statement "$p$ is true" is equivalent to "There is some proposition $q$ such that $p$ and $q$ are both true." In line (2) of this proof, it will be noted that the substitution is of $q$ for $p$ in one place only: this is valid on the general principle that, if we were given as a *universal* principle $p . ⥽ . p\, q$, $p . ⥽ . p\, p$ could be derived by the substitution $p/q$. That is, $p . ⥽ . p\, q$ stands to $p . ⥽ . p\, p$ in the generic-specific relation. In line (3), we have an example of 21·03: "There is some $q$ such that $p$ implies $p\, q$" is equivalent to "If $p$ is true, then for some $q$, $p\, q$ is true."

*21·12* $\sim p . ⥽ : (q) . \sim(p\, q)$

$[(A), 12·72]\ (q) : \sim p . ⥽ . \sim(p\, q)$ (1)

$[21·02]\ (1) =$ Q.E.D.

If $p$ is false, then whatever proposition $q$ may be, it is false that $p$ and $q$ are both true.

*21·15* $(\exists\, q) : p ⥽ q . q ⥽ r :. ⥽ . p ⥽ r$

$[(A), 11·6]\ (q) :. p ⥽ q . q ⥽ r : ⥽ . p ⥽ r$

$[21·01]\ (1) =$ Q.E.D.

This theorem has been discussed above.

*21·2* $p . ⥽ : (q) . q \supset p$

$[15·2]\ (q) : p . ⥽ . q \supset p$ (1)

$[21·02]\ (1) =$ Q.E.D.

If $p$ is true, then whatever proposition $q$ may be, $q$ materially implies $p$. It is, in fact, 21·2 rather than 15·21 which validates the usual reading of $p . ⥽ . q \supset p$ as "A true proposition is materially implied by any proposition."

*21·21* $p . = : (q) . q \supset p$

$[(E)]\ (q) . q \supset p : ⥽ . \sim p \supset p$ (1)

$[15·24, 12·17]\ \sim p \supset p . ⥽ . p$ (2)

$[11·6]\ (1) . (2) : ⥽ :. (q) . q \supset p : ⥽ . p$ (3)

$[11·03]\ 21·2 . (3) : =$ Q.E.D.

This theorem states a most important property of material implication: "$p$ is true" and "Every proposition $q$ materially implies $p$" are equivalent statements.

*21·22* $\sim p \,.\, ⥽ : (q) \,.\, p \supset q$

$[(A), 15\cdot 22]\ (q) : \sim p \,.\, ⥽ \,.\, p \supset q$ (1)

$[21\cdot 02]$ (1) = Q.E.D.

*21·23* $\sim p \,.\, = : (q) \,.\, p \supset q$

$[(E)]\ (q) \,.\, p \supset q : ⥽ \,.\, p \supset \sim p$ (1)

$[15\cdot 25, 12\cdot 17]\ p \supset \sim p \,.\, ⥽ \,.\, \sim p$ (2)

$[11\cdot 6]$ (1) . (2) $: ⥽ :. (q) \,.\, p \supset q : ⥽ \,.\, \sim p$ (3)

$[11\cdot 03]$ 21·22 . (3) : = Q.E.D.

The statement "$p$ is false" is equivalent to "$p$ materially implies every proposition $q$."

We shall next generalize certain theorems of Section 4. These are not dependent on the Consistency Postulate; and the comparison between them and later theorems which depend on that postulate will be important.

*21·3* $(\exists q) : p ⥽ q \,.\, p ⥽ \sim q :. ⥽ \,.\, \sim\Diamond p$

$[11\cdot 6]\ p ⥽ q \,.\, q ⥽ \sim p : ⥽ \,.\, p ⥽ \sim p$ (1)

$[12\cdot 45, 18\cdot 12]$ (1) . = :. $p ⥽ q \,.\, p ⥽ \sim q : ⥽ \,.\, \sim\Diamond p$ (2)

$[(A), (2)]\ (q) :. p ⥽ q \,.\, p ⥽ \sim q : ⥽ \,.\, \sim\Diamond p$ (3)

$[21\cdot 01]$ (3) = Q.E.D.

If there is some (any) proposition, $q$, such that $p$ strictly implies both $q$ and $\sim q$, then $p$ is impossible. The converse of this principle takes the form of a $T$-principle:

*21·31* $\sim\Diamond p \,.\, T : ⥽ :. (\exists q) : p ⥽ q \,.\, p ⥽ \sim q$

$T = : p \,.\, ⥽ \,.\, \sim(p \sim p)$

$[12\cdot 1]\ p ⥽ \sim p \,.\, T : ⥽ : p ⥽ \sim p \,.\, T$ (1)

$[16\cdot 33]$ (1) . = :: $p ⥽ \sim p \,.\, T : ⥽ :.$

$p \,.\, ⥽ \,.\, p \sim p : p \,.\, ⥽ \,.\, \sim(p \sim p)$ (2)

$[(F), (2): \ q \int p \sim p]$ (2) . = ::

$p ⥽ \sim p \,.\, T : ⥽ :. (\exists q) \,.\, p ⥽ q \,.\, p ⥽ \sim q$ (3)

$[18\cdot 12]$ (3) = Q.E.D.

If $p$ is impossible, then for some $q$, $p ⥽ q$ and $p ⥽ \sim q$ both hold. That in such a case $p ⥽ q$ and $p ⥽ \sim q$ both hold is not deducible from $\sim\Diamond p$ alone, however, but from this together with the principle that $p \prec \sim(p \sim p)$. There are other principles also which could replace $T$ here: for example, the theorem could be proved with $T = . p \prec p$.

From 21·3 and 21·31 together, we may say that "$p$ is impossible" and "There is some proposition $q$ such that $p \prec q$ and $p \prec \sim q$ both hold" are equivalent in the sense that when either of these is true the other is also [since $p . \prec . \sim(p \sim p)$ is always true].

*21·4* $\Diamond p . \prec :. (q) : \sim(p \prec q) . \vee . \sim(p \prec \sim q)$

[12·2] 21·3 $. \prec :: \Diamond p . \prec :. \sim[(\exists q) : p \prec q . p \prec \sim q]$ (1)

[20·02] (1) $. = :: \Diamond p . \prec :. (q) : \sim(p \prec q . p \prec \sim q)$ (2)

[11·01] (2) = Q.E.D.

If $p$ is possible, then for every proposition $q$, either $p$ does not strictly imply $q$ or it does not imply $\sim q$. The converse of this also takes the form of a $T$-principle. Proof is from 21·31, by 12·6:

*21·41* $(q) : \sim(p \prec q) . \vee . \sim(p \prec \sim q) :. T :: \prec . \Diamond p$

$T = : p . \prec . \sim(p \sim p)$

If, for every $q$, either $p$ does not strictly imply $q$ or $p$ does not imply $\sim q$, then $p$ is possible or self-consistent.

*21·5* $(\exists q) : q \prec p . \sim q \prec p :. \prec . \sim\Diamond\sim p$

[11·6] $\sim p \prec \sim q . \sim q \prec p : \prec . \sim p \prec p$ (1)

[12·44, 18·14] (1) $. = :. q \prec p . \sim q \prec p : \prec . \sim\Diamond\sim p$ (2)

[(A), (2)] $(q) :. q \prec p . \sim q \prec p : \prec . \sim\Diamond\sim p$ (3)

[21·01] (3) = Q.E.D.

If there is some (any) proposition $q$ such that $q \prec p$ and $\sim q \prec p$ both hold, then $p$ is a necessary truth. The converse is again a $T$-principle:

*21·51* $\sim\Diamond\sim p . T : \prec :. (\exists q) : q \prec p . \sim q \prec p$

$T = . p \prec p$

[11·1] $\sim p \prec p . p \prec p : \prec : p \prec p . \sim p \prec p$ (1)

[18·14] (1) $. = :. \sim\Diamond\sim p . T : \prec : p \prec p . \sim p \prec p$ (2)

[(F), (2): $q \int p$] $\sim\Diamond\sim p . T : \prec :. (\exists q) : q \prec p . \sim q \prec p$

Other such principles, of less importance, follow. The proofs are obvious: only the theorem generalized will be indicated.

**21·6** $(\exists p) : p \prec q \,.\, p \circ r :. \prec .\, q \circ r$ [17·3]

**21·61** $(\exists q) : p \prec q \,.\, \sim(q \circ r) :. \prec . \sim(p \circ r)$ [17·31]

**21·62** $(\exists p, q) : p \prec r \,.\, q \prec s \,.\, p \circ q :. \prec .\, r \circ s$ [17·32]

**21·63** $(\exists r, s) : p \prec r \,.\, q \prec s \,.\, \sim(r \circ s) :. \prec . \sim(p \circ q)$ [17·33]

**21·64** $(\exists r) : \sim(p \circ r) \,.\, \sim(q \circ \sim r) :. \prec . \sim(p \circ q)$ [17·5]

**21·65** $(\exists q) : p \prec q \,.\, p \prec \sim q :. \prec . \sim(p \circ p)$ [17·52]

**21·66** $(\exists p) : p \prec q \,.\, p \circ p :. \prec .\, q \circ q$ [17·53]

**21·67** $(\exists q) : p \prec q \,.\, \sim(q \circ q) :. \prec . \sim(p \circ p)$ [17·54]

**21·68** $p \circ p \,.\, \prec :. (q) : \sim(p \prec q \,.\, p \prec \sim q)$ [17·591]

**21·69** $p \circ p \,.\, \prec :. (q) : p \circ q \,.\vee.\, p \circ \sim q$ [17·592]

Each of these theorems gives another, by 12·44 and 21·01 or 21·02. Where, in the above, the operator is of the form $(\exists p)$ and appears in the antecedent, the theorem derived from it by 12·44 will have an operator of the form $(p)$ in the consequent. Thus 21·6 gives

$$\sim(q \circ r) \,.\prec :. (p) : \sim(p \prec q \,.\, p \circ r),$$

$$\text{or} \quad \sim(q \circ r) \,.\prec :. (p) : \sim(p \prec q) \,.\vee. \sim(p \circ r).$$

And where, in the above, an operator of the form $(q)$ appears in the consequent, the derived theorem will have the operator $(\exists q)$ in the antecedent. Thus 21·68 gives

$$(\exists q) : p \prec q \,.\, p \prec \sim q :. \prec . \sim(p \circ p).$$

Some of the above also have a converse in the form of a *T*-principle. For example, since

$$\sim(p \circ p) = \sim\Diamond p,$$

it is evident from 21·31 that 21·68 has such a converse.

As has been said, the theorems immediately preceding have no dependence on the Consistency Postulate. The theorems which follow are corresponding consequences of that postulate.

**21·7** $\sim\Diamond p \,. = .\, \sim(p \circ p) \,. = :. (q) : p \prec q \,.\, p \prec \sim q$

[18·12] $\sim\Diamond p \,. = .\, \sim(p \circ p)$ (1)

[(E)] $(q) : p \prec q \,.\, p \prec \sim q :. \prec :. (\exists q) : p \prec q \,.\, p \prec \sim q$ (2)

[11·6] (2) . 21·3 : ⥽ : : $(q)$ : $p$ ⥽ $q$ . $p$ ⥽ ~$q$ : . ⥽ . ~◊$p$ (3)

[19·1] ~($p$ ∘ $p$) . ⥽ . ~($p$ ∘ $q$) (4)

[19·1] ~($p$ ∘ $p$) . ⥽ . ~($p$ ∘ ~$q$) (5)

[16·2] (4) . (5) . ($T$) : ⥽ : .

~($p$ ∘ $p$) . ⥽ : ~($p$ ∘ $q$) . ~($p$ ∘ ~$q$) (6)

[18·31] (6) . = : . ~($p$ ∘ $p$) . ⥽ : $p$ ⥽ $q$ . $p$ ⥽ ~$q$ (7)

[(A), (7)] $(q)$ : . ~($p$ ∘ $p$) . ⥽ : $p$ ⥽ $q$ . $p$ ⥽ ~$q$ (8)

[21·02] (8) . = : : ~($p$ ∘ $p$) . ⥽ : . $(q)$ : $p$ ⥽ $q$ . $p$ ⥽ ~$q$ (9)

[11·03] (3) . (9) : = : : ~($p$ ∘ $p$) . = : . $(q)$ : $p$ ⥽ $q$ . $p$ ⥽ ~$q$

In 21·3 and 21·31, we have proved, *without* the Consistency Postulate, that ~◊$p$ is equivalent in logical force to "There is *some* proposition $q$ such that $p$ strictly implies $q$ and $p$ implies ~$q$." In 21·7, we prove, *with* the Consistency Postulate, that ~◊$p$ is equivalent to "For *every* proposition $q$, $p$ implies $q$ and $p$ implies ~$q$." This leads to the further consequence stated by the next theorem, which also depends on the Consistency Postulate:

***21·71*** (∃ $q$) : $p$ ⥽ $q$ . $p$ ⥽ ~$q$ : . = : . $(q)$ : $p$ ⥽ $q$ . $p$ ⥽ ~$q$

[21·3] (∃ $q$) : $p$ ⥽ $q$ . $p$ ⥽ ~$q$ : . ⥽ . ~◊$p$ (1)

[11·2] 21·7 . ⥽ : : ~◊$p$ . ⥽ : . $(q)$ : $p$ ⥽ $q$ . $p$ ⥽ ~$q$ (2)

[11·6] (1) . (2) : ⥽ : : (∃ $q$) : $p$ ⥽ $q$ . $p$ ⥽ ~$q$ : . ⥽ : .

$(q)$ : $p$ ⥽ $q$ . $p$ ⥽ ~$q$ (3)

[(E)] $(q)$ : $p$ ⥽ $q$ . $p$ ⥽ ~$q$ : . ⥽ : . (∃ $q$) : $p$ ⥽ $q$ . $p$ ⥽ ~$q$ (4)

[11·03] (3) . (4) : = Q.E.D.

If there is *any* proposition $q$ such that $p$ ⥽ $q$ and $p$ ⥽ ~$q$, then for *every* proposition $q$, $p$ ⥽ $q$ and $p$ ⥽ ~$q$; and *vice versa*.

The same general comparison which holds between 21·3 and 21·31, on the one hand, and the stronger statement of 21·7, on the other, extends to the equivalents of the other modal functions, as the following theorems indicate:

***21·72*** ◊$p$ . = . $p$ ∘ $p$ . = : . (∃ $q$) : ~($p$ ⥽ $q$) . ∨ . ~($p$ ⥽ ~$q$)

[18·1] ◊$p$ . = . $p$ ∘ $p$ (1)

[21·7] ~(~◊$p$) . = : . ~[$(q)$ : $p$ ⥽ $q$ . $p$ ⥽ ~$q$] (2)

[20·02, 11·01] (2) = Q.E.D.

The statement "$p$ is possible or self-consistent" is equivalent to "There is some proposition $q$ such that either it is false that $p$ implies $q$ or it is false that $p$ implies ~$q$."

***21·73*** $(\exists q) : \sim(p \dashv q) . \vee . \sim(p \dashv \sim q) :. = :.$
$(q) : \sim(p \dashv q) . \vee . \sim(p \dashv \sim q)$

[11·03, 12·17] 21·72 . $\dashv$ : :
$(\exists q) : \sim(p \dashv q) . \vee . \sim(p \dashv \sim q) :. \dashv . \Diamond p$ (1)

[11·6] (1) . 21·4 : $\dashv$ : :
$(\exists q) : \sim(p \dashv q) . \vee . \sim(p \dashv \sim q) :. \dashv :.$
$(q) : \sim(p \dashv q) . \vee . \sim(p \dashv \sim q)$ (2)

[(E)] $(q) : \sim(p \dashv q) . \vee . \sim(p \dashv \sim q) :. \dashv :.$
$(\exists q) : \sim(p \dashv q) . \vee . \sim(p \dashv \sim q)$ (3)

[11·03] (2) . (3) : = Q.E.D.

***21·74*** $\sim\Diamond\sim p . = :. (q) : q \dashv p . \sim q \dashv p$

[21·7: $\sim p/p$] $\sim\Diamond\sim p . = :. (q) : \sim p \dashv q . \sim p \dashv \sim q$ (1)

[12·44] (1) = Q.E.D.

The statement "$p$ is necessarily true" is equivalent to "For every proposition $q$, $q \dashv p$, and $\sim q \dashv p$.

***21·75*** $(\exists q) : q \dashv p . \sim q \dashv p :. = :. (q) : q \dashv p . \sim q \dashv p$

[21·74] $\sim\Diamond\sim p . \dashv :. (q) : q \dashv p . \sim q \dashv p$ (1)

[11·6] 21·5 . (1) : $\dashv$ : :
$(\exists q) : q \dashv p . \sim q \dashv p :. \dashv :. (q) : q \dashv p . \sim q \dashv p$ (2)

[(E)] $(q) : q \dashv p . \sim q \dashv p :. \dashv :. (\exists q) : q \dashv p . \sim q \dashv p$ (3)

[11·03] (2) . (3) : = Q.E.D.

These equivalences, 21·7—21·75, are perhaps the clearest and the crucial examples of the logical significance of the Consistency Postulate. It is to be observed that if that postulate were omitted, these equivalences would be replaced, in the system, by those of 21·3—21·51.

# CHAPTER VII

## TRUTH-VALUE SYSTEMS AND THE MATRIX METHOD

As we have seen in Chapter IV, the Two-valued Algebra, in mathematical terms, is a class of elements, $p$, $q$, etc., each of which is either $= 0$ or $= 1$. Otherwise put, it is a class of two distinct elements, 0 and 1—$p$, $q$, etc., representing ambiguously one or other of these two. When $p = 1$ is interpreted, in the usual way, as "$p$ is true," and $p = 0$ as "$p$ is false," the algebra coincides with the system of Material Implication. Any other pair of properties, one or other of which is assignable to every $p$ or $q$, etc., would also constitute a possible interpretation, provided that the relations of the system could also be interpreted in the chosen fashion.

It is a distinctive feature of this two-valued system that when the property, 0 or 1, of the elements $p$, $q$, etc., is given, any function of the elements which is in the system is thereby determined to have the property 0 or the property 1. In the usual terms, this means that the truth or falsity of $p$ and $q$ being given, the truth or falsity of $\sim p$, of $p \supset q$, of $p \vee \sim q$, of $p \,.\!\supset\!.\, q \supset p$, and of every other function of $p$ and $q$ which can figure in the system is thereby categorically determined. Any system having this character—that there is no function or relation of the elements which is in the system except such as are categorically determined to be true or to be false by the truth or falsity of their elementary terms—may be called a 'truth-value system.'

For example, contrast the relation of material implication, $p \supset q$, with strict implication, $p \prec q$, on this point:

| $p$ | $q$ | $p \supset q$ | $p \prec q$ |
|---|---|---|---|
| 1 | 1 | 1 | undetermined |
| 1 | 0 | 0 | 0 |
| 0 | 1 | 1 | undetermined |
| 0 | 0 | 1 | undetermined |

In the first two columns at the left are represented the four possible combinations of the truth-values of $p$ and $q$. And in the columns under $p \supset q$ and $p \prec q$ is set down, for each of these four possible cases, the result for the truth or falsity of the implication. In the case of $p \supset q$, this is always determined; $p \supset q$ definitely holds except when $p$ is true and $q$ false, in which case it definitely fails to hold. This is, in fact, exactly what is expressed by its definition,

$$p \supset q \,.\! = .\, \sim(p \sim q).$$

By contrast, $p \prec q$ is definitely false if $p$ is true and $q$ false, but is not determined to be either true or false in the other three cases: whether it holds or not depends upon something else than merely the truth or falsity of $p$ and $q$.

If we use the term 'truth-function' for relations and functions, such as $p \supset q$, whose truth-status (truth or falsity, etc.) is categorically determined by the truth-status of the elements, then $\sim p$, $p\,q$, $p \vee q$, $p \supset q$, and $p \equiv q$ are, all of them, truth-functions.[1] But $\Diamond p$, $\sim\Diamond p$, $\Diamond\sim p$, $\sim\Diamond\sim p$, $p \circ q$, $p \prec q$, and $p = q$ are not truth-functions: it may be the case that these last are determined to be true, or to be false, by some *particular* truth-value of the elements—as $p \circ q$ must be true if $p$ and $q$ are both true, and $\sim\Diamond\sim p$ must be false if $p$ is false—but it is *not* the case that whatever the truth-value of the elements, the truth or falsity of these expressions is thereby determined. The relations and other functions in the system of Material Implication are exclusively such truth-functions: the system of Strict Implication contains both kinds.

Material Implication is the only truth-value system which has been extensively investigated. But it is by no means the only possible one: there are an unlimited number. Some of these others are of interest on their own account. Also there are certain problems of logic which may be illuminated by a comparison of Material Implication with other truth-value systems. We shall exhibit two such, as further examples, in this chapter.

Any truth-value system can be developed by a method which is independent of interpretations, or of meanings, to a degree which even the logistic method does not attain. Even proofs,

[1] The exact meaning of 'truth-value' and of derivative conceptions will become clearer as the chapter progresses.

in the ordinary sense of inference from postulates, can be dispensed with: that any principle, expressible in the symbols of the system, holds or does not hold can be determined by investigating its truth-status for all combinations of the truth-values of the elements. This is the matrix method.

In order to apply this method, all that is required is that the 'definition' of each function of the elements should be given in the form of a matrix or truth-table, which determines the truth or falsity of the function for each combination of the truth-values of the elements. The table given above, for $p \supset q$, is such a definition of that relation; and the definition of $\sim p$ can be very simply given in the same way:

| $p$ | $\sim p$ |
|---|---|
| 1 | 0 |
| 0 | 1 |

That is, $\sim p$ is that function of $p$ which is false when $p$ is true, and true when $p$ is false.[2]

As further examples, let us observe the matrix-definitions of $p\,q$ and $p \vee q$:

| $p$ | $q$ | $p\,q$ | $p \vee q$ |
|---|---|---|---|
| 1 | 1 | 1 | 1 |
| 1 | 0 | 0 | 1 |
| 0 | 1 | 0 | 1 |
| 0 | 0 | 0 | 0 |

[2] Another form of matrix-definition than the one here used is more common, because more economical of space and more in line with usual mathematical modes of representation. For example, the defining matrix for $p \supset q$ would be given as

| $\supset$ | 1 | 0 |
|---|---|---|
| 1 | 1 | 0 |
| 0 | 1 | 1 |

Here the column at the left represents the truth-value of the antecedent ($p$ in $p \supset q$), and the truth-values of the consequent ($q$) are at the top. Since the functions which figure in the system of Material Implication can all be defined in terms of two, $\sim p$ and $p \supset q$, the whole system can be specified by the matrix

| $\supset$ | 1 | 0 | $\sim$ |
|---|---|---|---|
| 1 | 1 | 0 | 0 |
| 0 | 1 | 1 | 1 |

However, any extensive use of the method requires also the truth-table form of matrix, which we use in this chapter.

That is, $p\,q$ is that function which is true when $p$ and $q$ are both true, and is false for all other values of the elements; $p \vee q$ is that function which is true except when $p$ and $q$ are both false. These definitions could be given originally in this matrix form, or they might be arrived at as consequences of the more usual form of definition, in terms of some other relation for which the matrix has been given. For example, the definitions,

$$p\,q \,.\!=\!.\, \sim(p \supset \sim q) \quad \text{and} \quad p \vee q \,.\!=\!.\, \sim p \supset q,$$

together with the matrix-definitions of $p \supset q$ and $\sim p$, would give results the same as those set down above.

When matrices for the elementary functions have been given, it is possible to determine directly whether any expression in terms of these functions is or is not a law of the system. This is done by determining the truth-value of the expression for every combination of the truth-values of its ultimate constituents, $p$, $q$, etc. If for every such combination the truth-value of the expression itself is 1, it is a law of the system; otherwise, it is not a law. In other words, the laws of the system are those expressions, in terms of $p$, $q$, etc., which are always true, whether $p$ and $q$ themselves are true or false.

This may be determined by taking the expression to pieces and determining the truth-value of each of its constituents by reference to the original defining matrix for functions of that form. One builds up any complex constituent out of its simpler members, thus proceeding from simple to complex until the expression as a whole is reached; at each step determining the truth-value of whatever is in question by reference to the truth-values of its members (which will have been determined already) together with the rule given by the defining matrix for functions of that form.

As an example, let us test the proposition,

$$p \supset q \,.\supset.\, \sim q \supset \sim p,$$

using the defining matrices for $\sim p$ and $p \supset q$ which have been given above:

| $p$ | $q$ | $\sim p$ | $\sim q$ | $p \supset q$ | $\sim q \supset \sim p$ | $p \supset q . \supset . \sim q \supset \sim p$ |
|---|---|---|---|---|---|---|
| 1 | 1 | 0 | 0 | 1 | 1 | 1 |
| 1 | 0 | 0 | 1 | 0 | 0 | 1 |
| 0 | 1 | 1 | 0 | 1 | 1 | 1 |
| 0 | 0 | 1 | 1 | 1 | 1 | 1 |

The proposition to be tested contains only two element-symbols, $p$ and $q$. So in the first two columns at the left, we indicate the four possible combinations of $p$, true or false, with $q$, true or false. Next, we set down the truth-values for $\sim p$ which correspond to the values of $p$ in the first column. Similarly, the values of $\sim q$ are determined by reference to the values of $q$ in the second column. Then the truth-values of $p \supset q$ are determined by reference to the values of $p$ and $q$, according to the rule given by the matrix-definition of $p \supset q$. Similarly, the truth-values of $\sim q \supset \sim p$ are determined by this rule from the values of $\sim q$ and $\sim p$. (One has to remember here that $\sim q$ is the antecedent, $\sim p$ the consequent, in $\sim q \supset \sim p$.) Finally, the truth-values of the whole expression,

$$p \supset q . \supset . \sim q \supset \sim p,$$

are determined by reference to the values of its constituents, $p \supset q$ and $\sim q \supset \sim p$, and the rule for the relation $\supset$ which holds between them. Since this truth-value turns out to be always 1, the expression is always true, and is a law of the system.

Next, let us take a proposition which we know does not always hold: $p . \supset . p \supset q$:

| $p$ | $q$ | $p \supset q$ | $p . \supset . p \supset q$ |
|---|---|---|---|
| 1 | 1 | 1 | 1 |
| 1 | 0 | 0 | 0 |
| 0 | 1 | 1 | 1 |
| 0 | 0 | 1 | 1 |

This is not a law of the system, being false when $p$ is true and $q$ false. One might be inclined to say that it is never true, but that would be a mistake: it is not a universal principle, but it is true when $p$ and $q$ are both true, or both false, or when $p$ is false and $q$ is true. Or, to put it otherwise:

$$p\, q . \supset : p . \supset . p \supset q,$$

$$\sim p\, q . \supset : p . \supset . p \supset q,$$

and $$\sim p \sim q . \supset : p . \supset . p \supset q.$$

That is the fact which the three 1's in the last column represent. But

$$p \sim q . \supset : \sim (p . \supset . p \supset q).$$

That is the fact represented by the 0 in the second line of the last column. These *four implications* are themselves laws of the system, verifiable as always true.

Let us take one further example, so as to illustrate the procedure when a third element is involved:

$$p\, q . \supset . r : \supset : p . \supset . \sim q \vee r:$$

| $p$ | $q$ | $r$ | $pq$ | $\sim q$ | $\sim q \vee r$ | $pq . \supset . r$ | $p . \supset . \sim q \vee r$ | $pq . \supset . r : \supset : p . \supset . \sim q \vee r$ |
|---|---|---|---|---|---|---|---|---|
| 1 | 1 | 1 | 1 | 0 | 1 | 1 | 1 | 1 |
| 1 | 1 | 0 | 1 | 0 | 0 | 0 | 0 | 1 |
| 1 | 0 | 1 | 0 | 1 | 1 | 1 | 1 | 1 |
| 1 | 0 | 0 | 0 | 1 | 1 | 1 | 1 | 1 |
| 0 | 1 | 1 | 0 | 0 | 1 | 1 | 1 | 1 |
| 0 | 1 | 0 | 0 | 0 | 0 | 1 | 1 | 1 |
| 0 | 0 | 1 | 0 | 1 | 1 | 1 | 1 | 1 |
| 0 | 0 | 0 | 0 | 1 | 1 | 1 | 1 | 1 |

The important difference of this example from the preceding ones is that here all the combinations of the three elements, $p$, $q$, and $r$, true or false, must be given in the first three columns, so that the matrix has eight lines instead of four. If there were a fourth element, $s$, in the proposition to be tested, sixteen lines would be required.

The order of columns in such a matrix or truth-table does not matter, except for convenience: the only important points are the obvious ones, already illustrated, and no further principle is involved in testing even the most complex expressions. However, the reader for whom the matrix method is a novelty will do well to give himself some further practice. The laws of the Two-valued Algebra, or propositions of the system of Material Implication, afford material; and they will provide a check upon results, since any such proposition should turn out to have the value 1 for all values of the elements. Every postulate and theorem of Material Implication is verifiable by this method from the matrices given above for the functions $\sim p$, $p \supset q$, $p\, q$, and $p \vee q$, together with a similar matrix for the relation of material equivalence, which results from its definition,

$$p \equiv q \,.\! = : p \supset q \,.\, q \supset p.$$

| $p$ | $q$ | $p \equiv q$ |
|---|---|---|
| 1 | 1 | 1 |
| 1 | 0 | 0 |
| 0 | 1 | 0 |
| 0 | 0 | 1 |

Since this system has been sufficiently dealt with in preceding chapters, further consideration of it here would be superfluous.

It is of more importance to consider certain facts about truth-value systems in general which the method itself brings to light, and the bearing of these facts upon the nature of logical principles, so far as these principles are capable of statement in the form of truth-relations. First, let us consider the possible variety (in a two-valued system) of truth-functions of a given number of elements. The functions of two elements—that is, relations—are the most important.

All relations in any calculus of propositions are dyadic. Any triadic relation, such as $p\, q \,.\!\supset\!.\, p$ or $p \,.\!\supset\!.\, p \vee q$, is a dyad one member of which is itself a dyad. Any tetradic relation is either a dyad both members of which are dyads, like

$$p \supset q \,.\!\supset\!.\, {\sim}q \supset {\sim}p,$$

or it is a dyad one member of which is triadic, like

$$p \,.\!\supset :\, q \,.\!\supset\!.\, q \supset p.$$

All relations of a higher order can be similarly resolved, eventually into dyads. Thus consideration of dyadic relations covers the whole topic: examination of possible dyadic truth-relations will be exhaustive of truth-relations in general. Any such truth-relation, $T(p, q)$, in a two-valued system must be definable by some matrix:

| $p$ | $q$ | $T(p, q)$ |
|---|---|---|
| 1 | 1 | $A$ |
| 1 | 0 | $B$ |
| 0 | 1 | $C$ |
| 0 | 0 | $D$ |

where $A$, $B$, $C$, and $D$ are either 0 or 1. Hence there are as many distinct (non-equivalent) truth-relations as there are different ways of replacing these letters with 0 or 1—that is, sixteen. Let us designate any one of these relations by naming the letters which are replaced by 1 in its defining matrix, those replaced by 0 being omitted. The possible truth-relations are, then, as follows: (1) $ABCD$; (2) $ABC$; (3) $ABD$; (4) $ACD$; (5) $BCD$; (6) $AB$; (7) $AC$; (8) $AD$; (9) $BC$; (10) $BD$; (11) $CD$; (12) $A$; (13) $B$; (14) $C$; (15) $D$; (16) the 0-relation, or combination 0000.

All of these can be expressed in terms of two relations, $p\,q$ ($p$ and $q$ are both true) and $p \vee q$ (at least one of $p$ and $q$ is true), together with the idea of negation, $\sim p$. That is, if we wish to state the meaning of any one of these sixteen possible relations of $p$ to $q$, defined by any one of these sixteen different matrices, this can always be done, in some more or less complex fashion, by means of the three ideas just mentioned. Thus $p\,q$ itself is $A$; it is defined, as we have seen, by a matrix in which $A$, above, is 1, and $B$, $C$, and $D$ are each 0. The relation $p \vee q$ is $ABC$; its defining matrix has 1 in the first three lines and 0 in the last. The relation designated by $B$ is $p \sim q$, as may be seen by forming the matrix for $p \sim q$ according to rule:

| $p$ | $q$ | $\sim q$ | $p \sim q$ |
|---|---|---|---|
| 1 | 1 | 0 | 0 |
| 1 | 0 | 1 | 1 |
| 0 | 1 | 0 | 0 |
| 0 | 0 | 1 | 0 |

Likewise $\sim p\, q$ is $C$; and $\sim p \sim q$ is D. The relation designated by $AB$ is $p\,q \,.\!\vee\!.\, p \sim q$:

| $p$ | $q$ | $\sim q$ | $p\,q$ | $p \sim q$ | $p\,q \,.\!\vee\!.\, p \sim q$ |
|---|---|---|---|---|---|
| 1 | 1 | 0 | 1 | 0 | 1 |
| 1 | 0 | 1 | 0 | 1 | 1 |
| 0 | 1 | 0 | 0 | 0 | 0 |
| 0 | 0 | 1 | 0 | 0 | 0 |

If the reader will note that the relation designated $A$ is $p\,q$, and the relation $B$ is $p \sim q$, while $AB$ is $p\,q \,.\!\vee\!.\, p \sim q$, he will be able to 'translate' the remainder of these relations for himself.

Thus the matrix designated by *AC* defines the relation $p\,q\,.\vee.\sim p\,q$; that designated by *ABD* defines

$$p\,q\,.\vee.\,p\sim q\,.\vee.\sim p\sim q,$$

and so on. It may seem a little strange to call some of these truth-functions 'relations' of $p$ to $q$; but that is precisely one of the ways in which consideration of the matrix method should broaden our ideas: the 'simplicity' of the relations we are accustomed to call such, and have simple names for, is purely psychological or due to practical importance; logically what any one of these sixteen matrices defines is as much a relation of $p$ to $q$ as any other.

The possible truth-functions of a *single* element are, of course, four in number:

| (1) | | (2) | | (3) | | (4) | |
|---|---|---|---|---|---|---|---|
| $p$ | $T(p)$ | $p$ | $T(p)$ | $p$ | $T(p)$ | $p$ | $T(p)$ |
| 1 | 1 | 1 | 1 | 1 | 0 | 1 | 0 |
| 0 | 1 | 0 | 0 | 0 | 1 | 0 | 0 |

Of these, it will be obvious that (2) is $p$ itself, or "$p$ is true"; and that (3) is $\sim p$, the function which is false when $p$ is true, and true when $p$ is false. The other two, (1) and (4), will be considered shortly.

The next point to be observed is the manner in which a function of one element may be considered as a function of two, a function of two as a function of three, and so on. Any truth-function of a single element $p$ is expressible also as a truth-function of $p$ and any other element $q$. Thus, in terms of $p$ and $q$, (2) above becomes:

| $p$ | $q$ | $T(p, q)$ |
|---|---|---|
| 1 | 1 | 1 |
| 1 | 0 | 1 |
| 0 | 1 | 0 |
| 0 | 0 | 0 |

This is the matrix for $p\,q\,.\vee.\,p\sim q$; which is in accord with the fact that

$$p\,.=.\,p(q\vee\sim q)\,.=:\,p\,q\,.\vee.\,p\sim q.$$

That is, the matrix (2) above, which defines the function "$p$ is true" is equivalent to that which defines "Either $p$ and $q$ are both true or $p$ is true and $q$ false."

Similarly, (3) above, which defines the function "$p$ is false," becomes, in terms of $p$ and $q$, the equivalent function

$$\sim p\, q \,.\vee.\, \sim p \sim q.$$

In the same way, any function of two elements, $p$ and $q$, is expressible as a function of three, $p$, $q$, and $r$; and in general, a function of any number of elements is expressible as a function of any larger number of elements, in accordance with the principle that, for any expression $p$,

$$p \,.=.\, p(q \vee \sim q) \,.=.\, p(q \vee \sim q)(r \vee \sim r) \ldots$$

A truth-function of a larger number of elements cannot always be expressed as a function of any smaller number: for example, $p \sim q$ cannot be expressed as a function of $p$ or a function of $q$.

These matters are of some interest on their own account, but are of particular importance in connection with the universal function, 'always true,' and the null-function, 'always false.' Consideration of the universal function will lead to some of the most significant results which the matrix method is capable of demonstrating.

For a single element $p$, the universal function is (1) on page 207. And (4) on that page is the null-function. It will be obvious that the universal function is expressible as $p \vee \sim p$. The null-function is the negative of this; it may be expressed as $p \sim p$.

It is a fact of much importance that the universal function is identical for every number of elements. In terms of two, it is *ABCD*, or

$$p\, q \,.\vee.\, p \sim q \,.\vee.\, \sim p\, q \,.\vee.\, \sim p \sim q.$$

This is, of course, equivalent to

$$p(q \vee \sim q) \,.\vee.\, \sim p(q \vee \sim q); \quad \text{and hence to} \quad p \vee \sim p,$$

which is the universal function in terms of a single variable. It is also equivalent to

$$p\,q(r \vee {\sim}r) \,.\vee.\, p\,{\sim}q(r \vee {\sim}r) \,.\vee.\, {\sim}p\,q(r \vee {\sim}r) \,.\vee.\, {\sim}p\,{\sim}q(r \vee {\sim}r),$$

or $p\,q\,r \,.\vee.\, p\,q\,{\sim}r \,.\vee.\, p\,{\sim}q\,r \,.\vee.\, p\,{\sim}q\,{\sim}r \,.\vee.\, {\sim}p\,q\,r \,.\vee.$

$${\sim}p\,q\,{\sim}r \,.\vee.\, {\sim}p\,{\sim}q\,r \,.\vee.\, {\sim}p\,{\sim}q\,{\sim}r,$$

which is the universal function for three elements. In short, the universal function is the same in all cases; and is always equivalent to the 'sum' of all the combinations represented by the left-hand columns of any truth-table.

The null-function also is identical for every number of elements, being expressible as $p\,{\sim}p \,.\vee.\, q\,{\sim}q \,.\vee.\, r\,{\sim}r \,.\vee\, \ldots$

Any law, being an expression which is always true, is equivalent to the universal function. This is the famous principle of 'Tautology.' (There are other ways of stating the principle, but all of them, of course, come to the same thing.) The principle is of considerable importance in understanding the nature of truth in logic, and has been much discussed. Let us, therefore, give attention to certain elementary considerations which will make clear the precise significance of it.

First, let us observe the relation which the matrix method establishes between the truth-values of the elements, represented in the left-hand columns of any truth-table, and the resultant truth or falsity of any expression to be tested. This relation will be clearer if we take an example which is true for some values of the elements, and false for others, than if we take a law which is always true. Consider the following:

| $p$ | $q$ | $p\,q$ | $p\,q \,.\vee.\, p$ |
|---|---|---|---|
| 1 | 1 | 1 | 1 |
| 1 | 0 | 0 | 1 |
| 0 | 1 | 0 | 0 |
| 0 | 0 | 0 | 0 |

In the first two columns (together), the first line represents $p\,q$ ($p$ and $q$ are both true); the second line represents $p\,{\sim}q$; the third line, ${\sim}p\,q$; and the fourth, ${\sim}p\,{\sim}q$. The four lines together (or the matrix itself) represent the fact that at least one of these four, $p\,q$, $p\,{\sim}q$, ${\sim}p\,q$, and ${\sim}p\,{\sim}q$, must be true; which is precisely what is stated by the universal function,

$$p\,q \,.\vee.\, p\,{\sim}q \,.\vee.\, {\sim}p\,q \,.\vee.\, {\sim}p\,{\sim}q.$$

This represents an exhaustion of the possible alternatives as to truth and falsity; and is, therefore, true *a priori*.

Consider, now, the last column of the matrix. Here 1 in the first line represents

$$\text{If } p\,q, \text{ then } p\,q\,.\vee.\,p;$$

1 in the second line represents

$$\text{If } p\sim q, \text{ then } p\,q\,.\vee.\,p;$$

0 in the third line represents

$$\text{If } \sim p\,q, \text{ then } p\,q\,.\vee.\,p \text{ is false;}$$

and 0 in the fourth line represents,

$$\text{If } \sim p\sim q, \text{ then } p\,q\,.\vee.\,p \text{ is false.}$$

Thus the four lines together represent "If one of the two, $p\,q$ and $p\sim q$, is true, then $p\,q\,.\vee.\,p$ is true; and otherwise it is false." Thus $p\,q\,.\vee.\,p\sim q$ (the logical sum of those lines in the first two columns in which the value of $p\,q\,.\vee.\,p$ is 1) is a sufficient and a necessary condition of the truth of $p\,q\,.\vee.\,p$. It is a sufficient condition because, if $p\,q\,.\vee.\,p\sim q$ is true, then $p\,q\,.\vee.\,p$ is true. And it is a necessary condition because (the value of $p\,q\,.\vee.\,p$ in the other two lines being 0) if $p\,q\,.\vee.\,p\sim q$ is not true, then $p\,q\,.\vee.\,p$ is false.

Now to say that something, *A*, is a necessary and a sufficient condition of something else, *B*, is the same as to say that *A* and *B* are logically equivalent: when either is true, the other is true; and when either is false, the other is false. Thus in general, for any function $T(p, q)$ whose truth is tested by this method,

$$T(p, q) := : (1/0)p\,q\,.\vee.\,(1/0)p\sim q\,.\vee.\,(1/0)\sim p\,q\,.\vee.\,(1/0)\sim p\sim q,$$

where (1/0) represents the 1 or 0 under $T(p, q)$ in the corresponding line of the matrix; and any term whose coefficient is 0 drops out. (We have taken advantage of this fact in specifying the sixteen distinct functions of two elements, on page 206.)

Next, let us ask how the distribution of 0 and 1 under any function, $T(p, q)$, is determined. In one of two ways: (1) arbitrarily, as a 'definition' of $T(p, q)$, which fixes its possible interpretation or meaning; (2) according to the rules of the method, by reference to *previous* definition—definition of functions of the form of those which figure in $T(p, q)$. Thus the exact significance of the 0's and 1's under $p\,q \,.\!\vee\!.\, p$, above, is this: "By virtue of the definitions of the relations $p\,q$ and $p \vee q$,

$$p\,q \,.\!\vee\!.\, p :=: p\,q \,.\!\vee\!.\, p \sim q."$$

Now let us take any truth-value principle or law, $L(p, q)$. It is proved to be such by the fact that, in every line under it in the matrix, the truth-value is 1. The exact significance of this, therefore, is: "By virtue of definitions of functions of the form which figure in $L(p, q)$,

$$L(p, q) :=: p\,q \,.\!\vee\!.\, p \sim q \,.\!\vee\!.\, \sim p\,q \,.\!\vee\!.\, \sim p \sim q."$$

Since this equivalent of $L(p, q)$ exhausts the possibilities, and is true *a priori*, $L(p, q)$ likewise is necessarily true. There is no conceivable alternative to the truth of $L(p, q)$. It is a very important fact that every law of logic has this 'tautological' character.

The *source* of this necessary truth, be it observed, is in *definitions*, arbitrarily assigned. Thus the tautology of any law of logic is merely a special case of the general principle that what is true by definition cannot conceivably be false: it merely explicates, or follows from, a meaning which has been assigned, and requires nothing in particular about the universe or the facts of nature. Thus any logical principle (and, in fact, any other truth which can be certified by logic alone) is tautological in the sense that it is an analytic proposition. The only truth which logic requires, or can state, is that which is contained in our own conceptual meanings—what our language or our symbolism represents. Or to put it otherwise: there are no laws of logic, in the sense that there are laws of physics or biology; there are only certain analytic propositions, explicative of 'logical' meanings, and these serve as the 'principles' which thought or inference which involves these meanings must, in consistency, adhere to.

Such tautologies are by no means confined to what is traditionally subsumed under 'logic.' All the laws of pure mathematics, for example, are similarly tautological. If 2 were represented somewhat more graphically by 11, 3 by 111, and 5 by 11111, it could not escape notice that $2 + 3 = 5$ is a tautology, true by the definitions of $+$ and $=$.

There has always been some confusion about the nature of analytic propositions, which are true by definition or follow from the meanings of terms; and there has been a tendency to say that such propositions 'make no assertion' or 'are not significant,' or even that they 'are not propositions.' They are not, of course, 'assertions' or 'significant' in the sense that synthetic propositions are, such as generalizations from experience, like the physical law $v = gt$. Such natural laws state something which could quite conceivably be false. Whether what could *not* conceivably be false—such as logical principles and arithmetical sums—is 'significant' or not, or 'makes an assertion' or not, is merely a question of propriety in the use of language, and is not worth arguing. We can only ask that those who deny significance or the quality of assertion to analytic propositions should be a little more explicit as to what they mean by 'significant' or 'an assertion.'

On the other hand, there have always been those who take logical truth to state some peculiar and miraculous property of reality or the universe, and thus fall into a state of mystic wonderment about nothing. The facts which the principles of logic state are simply facts of our own meanings in the use of language: they have nothing to do with any character of reality, unless of reality as exhibited in human language-habits. The universe can 'be what it likes'; it cannot make a definition false; and it cannot exhibit what is logically inconceivable, for the simple reason that logical conception exhausts the possibilities.

Furthermore, we must not allow preoccupation with the matrix method to draw us into supposing that the particular kind of tautologies which it reveals—namely, those of truth-value—are in any sense proved to be exhaustive of logical truth, or even logically fundamental. There are other relations of propositions than such truth-functions, and these also will give rise to analytic or tautological principles which are necessary truths. But the matrix method (as here used) will not apply to them, because the question whether such a relation holds or does not hold will not be categorically determined by the truth-values of its elements but will depend on something else. The laws of the relation of strict implication, for example, are tautologies, but they are not truth-value tautologies. Such truths as the matrix method establishes are necessarily true; but they are not necessarily the whole of logic, or even an important part of it.

Moreover, there are other truth-value systems than this two-valued calculus. And these alternative systems are not necessarily inconsistent with the principle that "Every proposition is either true or false, and none is both," which might be supposed to dictate the two-valued character of the logic of propositions. One such alternative is the Three-valued Calculus, developed by Lukasiewicz and Tarski,[3] based upon the matrix

| $C$ | 0 | ½ | 1 | $N$ |
|---|---|---|---|---|
| 0 | 1 | 1 | 1 | 1 |
| ½ | ½ | 1 | 1 | ½ |
| 1 | 0 | ½ | 1 | 0 |

Let us read $pCq$ as "$p$ implies $q$"; and $Np$ as 'not-$p$' or "$p$ is false." It should be remembered, however, that the appropriateness or inappropriateness of these readings is something which the development of the system must itself determine, through the properties of these functions which result from the above matrix.

[3] Lukasiewicz, "Philosophische Bemerkungen zu mehrwertigen Systemen des Aussagen-kalküls," *Comptes rendus des séances de la Société des Sciences et des Lettres de Varsovie*, XXIII (1930), Classe III, 57–77. In this article, a general method is indicated for the erection of any number of such systems: "If $p$ and $q$ designate certain numbers of the interval 0–1, then

$$\begin{aligned} Cpq\ [p \text{ implies } q] &= 1 \text{ for } p \leq q, \\ Cpq &= 1 - p + q \quad \text{for } p > q, \\ Np\ [p \text{ is false}] &= 1 - p. \end{aligned}$$

"If from the interval 0–1 only the limits are chosen, then the above definition represents the matrix of the usual two-valued calculus of propositions. If, in addition, the number ½ is taken, then we have the matrix of the three-valued system. In similar fashion, 4, 5, . . . $n$-valued systems can be erected." (Translation ours.)

In presenting, in outline, this three-valued system, we here alter somewhat the symbolism of the authors, to avoid certain difficulties incident to their notation.

It inevitably suggests itself that $p=1$ may be read "$p$ is certainly true"; $p=0$, "$p$ is certainly false"; and $p=1/2$, "$p$ is doubtful"; after the analogy to the calculus of probabilities. As a matter of convenience, let us tentatively adopt these readings also. It must be remembered that $p$ and $p=1$ may not be equivalent in this system: that remains to be determined.

In terms of the relation $C$, three further relations are defined, as follows:

$$pOq. = :pCq.Cq \qquad \text{Def.}$$

Read $pOq$ as "$p$ or $q$": this relation is the analogue of $p \vee q$ in the Two-valued Calculus.

$$pAq. = N(Np.O.Nq) \qquad \text{Def.}$$

Read $pAq$ as "$p$ and $q$": this relation is the analogue of $p\ q$.

$$pEq. = :pCq.A.qCp \qquad \text{Def.}$$

Read $pEq$ as "$p$ is equivalent to $q$": this relation is the analogue of $p \equiv q$.

In the truth-table form, the above matrix-definition of $pCq$, and these three further definitions in terms of this relation, can all be summarized as follows (for typographical reasons, we substitute ? for the truth-value 1/2):

| $p$ | $q$ | $pCq$ | $pOq$ | $pAq$ | $pEq$ |
|---|---|---|---|---|---|
| 1 | 1 | 1 | 1 | 1 | 1 |
| 1 | ? | ? | 1 | ? | ? |
| 1 | 0 | 0 | 1 | 0 | 0 |
| ? | 1 | 1 | 1 | ? | ? |
| ? | ? | 1 | ? | ? | 1 |
| ? | 0 | ? | ? | 0 | ? |
| 0 | 1 | 1 | 1 | 0 | 0 |
| 0 | ? | 1 | ? | 0 | ? |
| 0 | 0 | 1 | 0 | 0 | 1 |

It will be necessary to examine with care the truth-values of these different relations for the corresponding values of $p$ and $q$. Our logical intuitions will at first be useless here. But if the readings we have suggested are kept in mind, the properties of these relations will for the most part seem 'natural' and right, with the possible exception of $pCq$. The best way to remember the properties of this relation is through its analogy to $p \supset q$; and by means of the rule given in the foot-note on page 213:

taking ? as 1/2, the value of $pCq$ is 1 when the value of $p$ is equal to or less than the value of $q$; when $p>q$, the value of $pCq$ is $1-p+q$.

In terms of $Np$ and $pCq$, a further function of one element, $Mp$, is defined as follows:

$$Mp. = :Np.Cp \qquad \text{Def.}$$

The truth-table for $Np$ and $Mp$ is:

| $p$ | $Np$ | $Mp$ |
|---|---|---|
| 1 | 0 | 1 |
| ? | ? | 1 |
| 0 | 1 | 0 |

As would be expected, $Np$ is false when $p$ is true; true when $p$ is false; and doubtful when $p$ is doubtful. Lukasiewicz and Tarski read $Mp$ as "$p$ is possible" ("Es ist möglich, dass $p$"). It is *not* analogous to $\Diamond p$ in the Calculus of Strict Implication. We shall develop the basic properties of $Mp$ later.[4]

In this calculus, it is important to distinguish the truth-*values*, 1, ?, and 0, from the truth-*functions*, $p$, $Mp$, and $Np$. The latter are propositions. The former would best be taken, for the present, merely as part of the machinery of the matrix

[4] Lukasiewicz and Tarski treat $Mp$ ($p$ is possible), $NMp$ ($p$ is impossible), $MNp$ ($p$ is possibly false), and $NMNp$ ($p$ is necessary) as analogues of the modal propositions of traditional logic. They find that the properties of these functions coincide only partially with what traditional dicta require. The principal reason for this failure of accord is the ambiguity of the words 'possible,' 'impossible,' and 'necessary' in ordinary usage. One precisely correct interpretation of $Mp$ is as the *relative* 'possibility' of the calculus of probabilities, $p \neq 0$, "Nothing is known which requires that $p$ be false" or "$p$ is not certainly-false." $Mp$ can*not* validly be interpreted as the absolute or logical possibility, "$p$ is logically conceivable" or "$p$ is self-consistent ($p \circ p$)." An excellent example of the difficulties which beset the modal conceptions in ordinary language is the following principle, put forward by these authors for consideration but not included in the calculus above: "Wird vorausgesetzt, dass nicht-$p$, so ist es (unter dieser Voraussetzung) nicht möglich, dass $p$" (*loc. cit.*, p. 54). They translate this into symbols as

$$Np.C.NMp.$$

But the statement "When $p$ is false, then it is not possible that $p$ be true" is highly ambiguous: if it means "It is not possible that $p$ should be true when it is false," it is obviously valid; but if it means "When $p$ is false, $p$ is logically inconceivable, not self-consistent," then it is invalid, since it equates conceivability with actual truth.

method. The interrelation of truth-values and truth-functions will be considered later.

Since truth-tables in this calculus require considerable space, and since no new principle of the matrix method is required for dealing with it, we shall give only one example of the verification of a law. In order that this example may be as extended as any with which the reader need trouble himself, we choose a principle involving three elements:

$$pC.qCr{:}C{:}qC.pCr$$

(In the table, in order to save space, the antecedent of this expression, *pC.qCr*, is represented by *A*; the consequent, *qC.pCr*, by *B*; and the whole expression by *A.C.B.*)

| *p* | *q* | *r* | *qCr* | *pCr* | *A* | *B* | *A.C.B* |
|---|---|---|---|---|---|---|---|
| 1 | 1 | 1 | 1 | 1 | 1 | 1 | 1 |
| 1 | 1 | ? | ? | ? | ? | ? | 1 |
| 1 | 1 | 0 | 0 | 0 | 0 | 0 | 1 |
| 1 | ? | 1 | 1 | 1 | 1 | 1 | 1 |
| 1 | ? | ? | 1 | ? | 1 | 1 | 1 |
| 1 | ? | 0 | ? | 0 | ? | ? | 1 |
| 1 | 0 | 1 | 1 | 1 | 1 | 1 | 1 |
| 1 | 0 | ? | 1 | ? | 1 | 1 | 1 |
| 1 | 0 | 0 | 1 | 0 | 1 | 1 | 1 |
| ? | 1 | 1 | 1 | 1 | 1 | 1 | 1 |
| ? | 1 | ? | ? | 1 | 1 | 1 | 1 |
| ? | 1 | 0 | 0 | ? | ? | ? | 1 |
| ? | ? | 1 | 1 | 1 | 1 | 1 | 1 |
| ? | ? | ? | 1 | 1 | 1 | 1 | 1 |
| ? | ? | 0 | ? | ? | 1 | 1 | 1 |
| ? | 0 | 1 | 1 | 1 | 1 | 1 | 1 |
| ? | 0 | ? | 1 | 1 | 1 | 1 | 1 |
| ? | 0 | 0 | 1 | ? | 1 | 1 | 1 |
| 0 | 1 | 1 | 1 | 1 | 1 | 1 | 1 |
| 0 | 1 | ? | ? | 1 | 1 | 1 | 1 |
| 0 | 1 | 0 | 0 | 1 | 1 | 1 | 1 |
| 0 | ? | 1 | 1 | 1 | 1 | 1 | 1 |
| 0 | ? | ? | 1 | 1 | 1 | 1 | 1 |
| 0 | ? | 0 | ? | 1 | 1 | 1 | 1 |
| 0 | 0 | 1 | 1 | 1 | 1 | 1 | 1 |
| 0 | 0 | ? | 1 | 1 | 1 | 1 | 1 |
| 0 | 0 | 0 | 1 | 1 | 1 | 1 | 1 |

The following elementary laws—all of them analogues of those in the Two-valued Calculus—may be verified as holding in this Three-valued Calculus:

(1) $pCp$.

(2) $pAq.C.qAp$, $pAq.E.qAp$.

(Where an implication and an equivalence both hold, we shall state both.)

(3) $pC.NNp$, $pE.NNp$.

(4) $pC.pOq$,

(5) $qC.pOq$.

(6) $pAq.Cp$.

(7) $pAq.Cq$.

(8) $pCq.C{:}Nq.C.Np$.

(9) $Np.C.Nq{:}C.qCp$, $pCq.E{:}Nq.C.Np$.

(10) $pC.Nq{:}C{:}qC.Np$, $pC.Nq{:}E{:}qC.Np$.

(11) $Np.Cq{:}C{:}Nq.Cp$, $Np.Cq{:}E{:}Nq.Cp$.

(12) $pC.qCr{:}C{:}qC.pCr$, $pC.qCr{:}E{:}qC.pCr$.

(13) $pCq.C{:}qCr.C.pCr$.

(14) $qCr.C{:}pCq.C.pCr$.

The operation of 'inference,' based upon the relation $C$, can validly be used in this calculus to derive further theorems from the above. Any theorem so derived will be found to be verifiable from the matrices of the calculus. This fact will be understood if one observes, in the defining matrix for the relation $C$, that *when* $p=1$, the relation $pCq$ has the value 1 when and only when it is also the case that $q=1$. That is, when $p$ is an assertable proposition (certainly true) in the system, $pCq$ will be assertable if and only if $q$ also is assertable.

The correspondences and differences between the body of propositions which hold in this calculus and those of the two-valued system are both interesting and important. We can do no more than indicate the salient features of this comparison here. What it is of the utmost importance to note is that for every principle which holds in this system, its analogue must hold in the Two-valued Calculus; but that the reverse is not the case. We can see that this is so, very simply, by noting what would happen, in any matrix of this system, if each line in which the truth-value ? occurs should be struck out. The defining-matrix on page 214 would then become:

| $p$ | $q$ | $pCq$ | $pOq$ | $pAq$ | $pEq$ |
|---|---|---|---|---|---|
| 1 | 1 | 1 | 1 | 1 | 1 |
| 1 | 0 | 0 | 1 | 0 | 0 |
| 0 | 1 | 1 | 1 | 0 | 0 |
| 0 | 0 | 1 | 0 | 0 | 1 |

Thus, as comparison of this with the matrices of the Two-valued Calculus will show, $pCq$ would coincide with $p \supset q$; $pOq$ with $p \vee q$; $pAq$ with $p\,q$; and $pEq$ with $p \equiv q$. Now in order to have the value 1 for all values of the elements in this three-valued system, any expression must of course hold (1) for the values 0 and 1 of the elements, and combinations of these two values, and (2) for the value ?, and combinations of ? with 0 and 1. Hence every law of this system (1) must be true in the Two-valued Calculus (when the relations are interpreted as those of the two-valued system) and (2) must satisfy certain further conditions.

It is important to understand what this means: in particular, to avoid the error of supposing that, because the Two-valued Calculus contains all the laws of this system and certain others besides, therefore this calculus is merely the two-valued system with part of it left out. It is true that, for every law of this calculus, its analogue holds in the two-valued system; and that certain laws of the Two-valued Calculus are absent here because, although they hold for the values 0 and 1 of the elements, they fail when some element has the value ?. But suppose we were dealing with two mathematical systems: System A, containing the laws which hold of the rational fractions between 0 and 1, including 0 and 1 as limits; and System B, containing the laws which hold of 0 and 1. Every law of system *A* would belong to System *B* also; and there would be laws of *B* (which held of the limits only) which would not hold in *A*. But which of the two would be the 'more comprehensive' mathematical system?

The analogy here is exact: the Two-valued Calculus is the system of laws which hold of the limits 0 and 1; the laws of the Three-valued Calculus must hold also of the intermediate value represented by ?. Also, the distinction of *Mp* from *p*, *NMNp* from *p*, *NMp* from *Np*, and *MNp* from *Np* would disappear with the elimination of the value ?; hence these distinctions are not possible in the two-valued system.

One point of difference between the two systems concerns the triadic relations. In the Two-valued Calculus,

$$pq\,.\supset.\,r \qquad \text{and} \qquad p\,.\supset.\,q\supset r$$

are always equivalent. But in the Three-valued Calculus,

$$pAq.Cr \qquad \text{and} \qquad pC.qCr$$

are not, in general, equivalent. They have the same truth-value in every case but one, namely, when *p* and *q* both have the value ? and *r* has the value 0. For that combination, the defining matrices give the following results:

| *p* | *q* | *r* | *pAq* | *qCr* | *pAq.Cr* | *pC.qCr* |
|---|---|---|---|---|---|---|
| ? | ? | 0 | ? | ? | ? | 1 |

Thus *pAq.Cr:C:pC.qCr* holds, but the converse implication fails to hold; it has the truth-value ? for the above values of *p*, *q*, and *r*.

As a result of this difference, the laws of triadic relations, in the Three-valued Calculus, ordinarily require that the relation have the form *pC.qCr*, though (6) and (7), above, indicate a certain kind of exception. One important case in point is the following proposition, which might be regarded as stating the principle of inference:

(15) *pC:pCq.Cq.*

(This is a triadic relation of the general form *pC.qCr*, with one complex member.) If this principle be given the other triadic form,

$$pA.pCq:Cq,$$

it fails to hold. Thus it would seem that, in this calculus, we ought not to say "If *p* is true *and* *p* implies *q*, then *q* is true" but instead "If $p$ is true, *then if* $p$ implies $q$, $q$ is true." But the point that, given $p$ and $pCq$, $q$ can be derived, is not affected: if $p$ is given, then by (15), $pCq.Cq$ can be inferred; from which, if $pCq$ is given, $q$ can be inferred.

Further important points of comparison can be brought out by considering together certain principles which hold, and certain other and similar propositions which fail to hold. (In listing the propositions which *fail*, we shall give them a number, for convenience of reference, but this number will be *primed.*)

(16) $pC.qCp$.

In this system, as in the two-valued, an assertable proposition ($p$) is implied by any proposition ($q$).

(17) $Np.C.pCq$.

If not-$p$ can be asserted, $p$ implies every proposition. (In reading these last two theorems, we say "assertable" and "can be asserted," instead of 'true' and 'is true' because a proposition which is asserted must have the value 1. Precisely what $p=1$ means in this calculus we shall see shortly.)

As a special case included in (16), we have:

(18) $pC{:}Np.Cp$, $\quad pC.Mp$.

An assertable proposition is implied by its own negation. By definition $Mp$ is $Np.Cp$; hence the second form of the law, which would be read "$p$ implies '$p$ is possible (not certainly-false).'" In the Two-valued Calculus, the converse of (18) would also hold; but here

(19′) $Np.Cp{:}Cp$ does not hold.

If (18) and (19′) should both hold, then $p$ and $Np.Cp$ would be equivalent; $p$ and $Mp$ would be equivalent; and this calculus would collapse into the two-valued system.

But note the next two, and compare them with (19′):

(20) $pC{:}.Np.Cp{:}Cp$.

(21) $Np.C{:}.Np.Cp{:}Cp$.

If either $p$ or $Np$ holds, then $Np.Cp{:}Cp$ holds. But this does not hold generally, because it fails when $p$ has the value ?. If we should suppose that what is implied by $p$ and likewise by $Np$

can therefore be asserted as always true—since always either $p$ or $Np$ must be true—we are met by the further fact that

(22′) $pO.Np$ does not hold.

This likewise fails when $p$ has the value ?. This is, perhaps, the most important point of comparison between the three-valued and the two-valued system, since $pO.Np$ might be taken to express the Law of the Excluded Middle.

There are other examples of propositions in this calculus which hold with the hypothesis $p$ and likewise with the hypothesis $Np$, and yet fail to hold generally:

(23′) $pC.N(pC.Np)$ does not hold: it has the value ? when $p$ and $Np$ have that value.

But the two following hold:

(24) $pC{:}pC.N(pC.Np)$.

(25) $Np.C{:}pC.N(pC.Np)$.

(26′) $pC.Np{:}C.Np$ does not hold; it has the value ? when $p$ and $Np$ have that value.

But the two following hold:

(27) $pC{:}.pC.Np{:}C.Np$.

(28) $Np.C{:}.pC.Np{:}C.Np$.

We might suppose that the same thing holds generally; *i. e.*, that for any function, $T(p, q,..)$, in the symbols of the system, which is such that (1) $T(p, q,..)$ is not provable in this Three-valued Calculus, but (2) the analogue of $T(p, q,..)$ is a theorem of the Two-valued Calculus, it will be provable that $pC.T(p, q,..)$ and $Np.C.T(p, q,..)$. Indeed statement to that effect was made in the original edition of this book, in the paragraph replaced by this one. But J. C. C. McKinsey found a somewhat curious exception:*

$$N(Np.Cp{:}Cp{:}.C{::}N{:}.Np.Cp{:}Cp)$$

The analogue of this is a provable theorem of the Two-valued Calculus. But as may be established by use of the truth-table method, neither this expression itself nor this expression preceded by the hypothesis $p$ or the hypothesis $Np$ is a theorem of the

* J. C. C. McKinsey, "A Correction to Lewis and Langford's *Symbolic Logic*," *Jour. Symbolic Logic*, Vol. 5 (1940), p. 149.

Three-valued Calculus. Thus this three-valued logic lacks even that manner of approximation to the two-valued logic which the author responsible for this chapter had supposed. Nevertheless, what is illustrated by (26′), (27), and (28) on the preceding page, will also hold in many instances.

**Thus there are many propositions which are true if, or when, $p=1$, and likewise true if $Np=1$ (if $p=0$), which nevertheless are not valid laws of the Three-valued Calculus. If $p$ having the value 1 in this system represents simply "$p$ is true"; and $p=0$, or $Np=1$, represents simply "$p$ is false"; then the calculus obviously requires that the Law of the Excluded Middle, "Every proposition is either true or false," must be repudiated as a false principle.**

Shall we, then, say that the calculus itself is merely a *jeu d'esprit*, and false in so far as it has this consequence? That is impossible: all its laws are necessarily true; the matrix method makes it certain that any principle whose value is always 1 is a truth-value tautology, which could not conceivably be false.

In the light of this, shall we decide that the laws of this system must be accepted, and the Law of the Excluded Middle, therefore, repudiated? In that case, we are met by the fact that the laws of the Two-valued Calculus likewise are tautologies; and that system requires the *acceptance* of the Law of the Excluded Middle.

The way out of this dilemma lies in the reflection that the tautological laws of any truth-value system are necessarily true; but that the symbolic system itself does not tell us what it is true *of*. It is true for whatever interpretation of its truth-values will make them exhaustive of the possibilities, and for any interpretation of its relations and other truth-functions which will then be consonant with their matrix-properties. But such an interpretation—for this or any other symbolic system—is something which has to be found; and something concerning which it is easily possible to make a mistake. To suppose that because of the rigorous character of its method, it must therefore represent 'the truth of logic' would be excessively naïve.

This Three-valued Calculus simply does not admit of that interpretation which takes $p=1$ to represent "$p$ is true," and $p=0$ to represent "$p$ is false"—unless the Law of the Excluded

Middle is, in fact, a false principle, in which case we might find here an exact determination of the truth of logic.

Let us try whether the suggested interpretation of 1 as representing 'certainly true'; 0, 'certainly false'; and ?, 'doubtful (neither certainly true nor certainly false)' will be compatible with the properties of the calculus which we have discovered. For these meanings, 0 and 1 do not exhaust the possibilities; but 0, ?, and 1 do exhaust the possibilities, and are mutually exclusive. This, of itself, is absolute assurance that this interpretation is possible: all functions are defined in terms of these truth-values, and hence must admit any interpretation which can be imposed upon the truth-values. It does *not* assure us that any particular reading of these functions will be correct: what interpretation of them will be valid must be determined from their defining-matrices. As a fact, none of the suggested readings is quite satisfactory. In particular, *pOq* cannot validly be interpreted as "At least one of the two, *p* and *q*, is true," because *pOq* has the truth-value ? when *p* and *q* have that value. It is not universally the case that, when *p* and *q* are both doubtful propositions, "At least one of the two, *p* and *q*, is true" is a doubtful proposition. This fails when *p* and *q* are propositions so related that if one of them is false, the other must be true; in particular, it fails for *p* and *Np*. Thus the fact that the proposition *pO.Np* does not hold generally in this calculus proves nothing whatever about the Law of the Excluded Middle.[5] Similarly, the reading of *pAq*, "*p* and *q* are both true," is inaccurate, because this function has the value ? when *p* and *q* have that value. It is not universally the case that, when *p* and *q* are both doubtful, "*p* and *q* are both true" is doubtful. When *p* and *q* are propositions so related that the truth of one is incompatible with the truth of the other, *p* may be doubtful, and *q* doubtful, but "*p* and *q* are both true" is certainly false. The exactly valid

[5] It should not be supposed that, in originating this calculus, Lukasiewicz and Tarski think that anything is proved about the Law of the Excluded Middle, or any other principle of logic. Their brief paper demonstrates the existence of this system, and of an unlimited number of other such truth-value systems—a contribution of the greatest importance. It also points out problems and makes suggestions concerning possible interpretation; but discussion of these is not sufficient to be final.

meanings of $pOq$ and $pAq$ are a little difficult in ordinary language: $pOq$ is "At least a designatable one of the two, $p$ and $q$, is true"; and $pAq$ is "It is not the case that a designatable one of the two, $p$ and $q$, is false." The relations $pCq$ and $pEq$ are hardly expressible at all in simple English, with strict accuracy: $pCq$ is best characterized by the fact that its truth-value is 1 when and only when the value of $q$ equals or exceeds the value of $p$; and $pEq$, by the fact that its value is 1 when and only when the values of $p$ and $q$ are identical.[6] It should be understood, however, that even if there be no way of rendering these meanings in precise English, except to recite the truth-values of the functions for the corresponding values of the elements, these functions are still perfectly definite logical relations. Their properties are completely determined: there is an absolutely fixed logical truth about them.

Interpretation of the functions of a single element is simpler. Also, it will prove decisive of certain important questions about the calculus. If we take $Mp$ provisionally to mean "$p$ is possible," then

$NMp$ is "$p$ is impossible";
$MNp$ is "$p$ is possibly false";
$NMNp$ is "$p$ is necessarily true."

The matrix-definition of $Mp$ gives the following determination of these:

| $p$ | $Np$ | $Mp$ <br> $Np.Cp$ | $NMp$ <br> $N(Np.Cp)$ | $MNp$ <br> $pC.Np$ | $NMNp$ <br> $N(pC.Np)$ |
|---|---|---|---|---|---|
| 1 | 0 | 1 | 0 | 0 | 1 |
| ? | ? | 1 | 0 | 1 | 0 |
| 0 | 1 | 0 | 1 | 1 | 0 |

[6] Perhaps the following will make clearer the difference between "at least one" and "at least a designatable one" as used above: Let the probability of $p$ be $\frac{1}{2}$, and the probability of $q$ be $\frac{1}{2}$. If, then, one be allowed to designate either $p$ or $q$ at will, what is the probability that the designated proposition will be true? The answer is $\frac{1}{2}$, even when $p$ and $q$ are contradictory propositions such that when one is false the other must be true.

The meaning of $pCq$ might be suggested by "$q$ is at least as believable as $p$." But this is not really accurate: 'believability' here cannot mean 'probability,' because when $p = 1$ and $q = \frac{1}{2}$, $pCq$ is doubtful ($= \frac{1}{2}$). And it cannot refer to actual truth or falsity, because when $p$ and $q$ are doubtful, $pCq$ has the value 1. One strictly accurate reading of $pCq$ is "Disregarding *degrees* of uncertainty, a bet on $q$ is at least as good as a bet on $p$."

There are in the system two other definable truth-functions of one element, which are omitted in this table, and in the calculus as presented by its originators. One of these may be symbolized by $Dp$: it is defined by

$$Dp. = :pE.Np \qquad \text{Def.}$$

The other is the negative of this, $NDp$. Matrix values of $Dp$ and $NDp$ are:

| $p$ | $Dp$ | $NDp$ |
|---|---|---|
| 1 | 0 | 1 |
| ? | 1 | 0 |
| 0 | 0 | 1 |

Reading these last two truth-tables, for the 'modal' functions of one variable, we have the following:

(1) $Mp$ is that function which holds except when $p=0$ (i.e., except when $p$ is certainly false).

(2) $NMp$ is that function which holds only when $p=0$ (i.e., only when $p$ is certainly false).

(3) $MNp$ is that function which holds except when $p=1$ (i.e., except when $p$ is certainly true).

(4) $NMNp$ is that function which holds only when $p=1$ (i.e., only when $p$ is certainly true).

(5) $Dp$ is that function which holds only when $p=?$ (i.e., only when $p$ is not certainly true and not certainly false).

(6) $NDp$ is that function which holds except when $p=?$ (i.e., which holds when $p$ is either certainly true or certainly false).

Thus the obviously correct interpretations of these functions are as follows:

$NMNp$, or $p=1$, means "$p$ is certainly true."
$MNp$, or $p\neq 1$, means "$p$ is not certainly true."
$NMp$, or $p=0$, means "$p$ is certainly false."
$Mp$, or $p\neq 0$, means "$p$ is not certainly false."
$Dp$, or $p=?$, means "$p$ is doubtful (not certainly true and not certainly false)."
$NDp$, or $p\neq ?$, means "$p$ is not doubtful."

All of these six functions are themselves categorically determined to have the value 0 or the value 1 under all circumstances (see the matrices). Herein they differ from $p$ and $Np$, which admit the value ?. But this is quite as it should be: when $p=?$ (and hence $Np=?$), "$p$ is certainly true" is false, "$p$ is certainly false" is false, and "$p$ is not doubtful" is false; while "$p$ is not certainly true," "$p$ is not certainly false," and "$p$ is doubtful" are all true.[7]

It should be understood that "certainly" does not here connote a psychological status, or belief-status: "certainly true" has here exactly the meaning of $p=1$ in the calculus of probabilities—a status of *logical believability.* One may, as a fact, disbelieve a proposition whose probability-value is 1—but one may not *rationally* do so.

The proposition $p$ and the proposition $p=1$ are seen to be distinct: when $p$ has the value ?, $NMNp$, which is equivalent to $p=1$, has the value 0. But the *assertion* of $p$ is equivalent to $p=1$, in this as in the two-valued system, because whatever is asserted must have the value 1 for all values of the elements —which means, by the matrix method, that it is a tautology whose falsity is inconceivable.

Particular interest attaches to the relation $pCq$ and to the validity of its use as a basis of inference. It occurs to us that the properties of this relation do not coincide with those of $p \supset q$ in the Two-valued Calculus. We might, therefore, be inclined to say, "If one of these truly has the properties of the relation 'implies,' the other does not. It cannot be the case that the laws of both represent principles of valid inference, since these laws are not the same in the two cases."

The matrix method never uses the operation of inference; that is to say, by the matrix method one never establishes a theorem $q$ by taking some previous proposition $p$ and establishing that $pCq$ (or $p \supset q$) holds. Instead, one proves any proposition by establishing the fact that its truth-value is 1 for all values of the elements, and hence that it is a tautology. Nevertheless,

[7] It may be objected that when $NMNp$, for example, has the value 1 in the matrix, we should, to be consistent, read this "It is certainly true that $p$ is certain." As a fact, this reading is permissible but not obligatory: it is a property of this calculus that $p = 1$ is equivalent to $(p = 1) = 1$; $NMNp.E.NMN(NMNp)$. However, the law $p = (p = 1)$, which characterizes the Two-valued Calculus, does *not* hold in this three-valued system.

the matrix method provides a simple test for determining whether inferences based upon a given 'implication'-relation—call it $pIq$—will be valid. In any truth-value system, if $pIq$ is a relation so defined that when $p$ has the value 1, and $pIq$ has the value 1, $q$ also has the value 1, then any inference, $q$, based on the fact that "$p$ is assertable, and $pIq$ holds," will be a true proposition.

This does not depend upon any peculiar 'logical' significance of such a relation, $pIq$. Whatever more it may be, the matrix method at least is a kind of game which we play with recognizable marks, according to certain rules. If in any game which deals with any kind of things, $p$'s and $q$'s, there is an operation or move, $pIq$, which according to the rules can be taken, when $p$ has the property $A$, only if $q$ also has the property $A$, then *ipso facto* if $p$ has $A$ and $pIq$ is allowable, then $q$ has $A$.

Thus it does not matter whether $p=1$ represents "$p$ is true" or "$p$ is a curly wolf," nor whether $pIq$ represents "$p$ implies $q$" or "$p$ bites $q$"; if the rules of the matrix game are such that when $p=1$, $pIq$ holds only if $q=1$, then in the nature of the case, any $q$ such that, for some $p$ which always has the value 1, $pIq$ holds, will be such that $q$ always has the value 1. Thus the use of the operation of inference, based on such a relation $pIq$ will, when the antecedent is assertable as a law of the system, give only such results as are also assertable laws of the system, as tested by the matrix method.

Now a glance at the matrix definition of $pCq$ will show that when $p$ has the value 1, $pCq$ has the value 1 only if $q$ also has the value 1. Therefore if any set of propositions, each of which always has the value 1 in this system (as tested by the matrix method), be taken as postulates or as already proved, and these propositions include some concerning the relation $pCq$, which are used as 'principles of inference,' the result of any such inference will always be a law of the system (as tested by the matrix method).

The nature of such an 'implication'-relation is not by any means completely determined by this requirement which enables it to function as a basis of inference in the system—because this requirement concerns only what will be the case when $p$ has the value 1. Thus even in a single system there can be more than one such 'implication'-relation: two such may be different by virtue of having different truth-values when $p$ does not have the value 1. For example, in the Two-valued Calculus, there are four such relations, $p\,q$, $p \equiv q$, $p\,q\,.\vee.\,{\sim}p\,q$, and $p \supset q$. If $pIq$ be any one of these four, it will universally be the case that "If $p$ is true, and $pIq$ holds, then $q$ is true." If, for the moment, we call any one of these relations 'implies,' they coincide with one another in what a true proposition implies, and differ from one another in what a false proposition implies. A glance at the matrix definitions of them will reveal this:

| $p$ | $q$ | $p\,q$ | $p \equiv q$ | $p\,q\,.\vee.\,{\sim}p\,q$ | $p \supset q$ |
|---|---|---|---|---|---|
| 1 | 1 | 1 | 1 | 1 | 1 |
| 1 | 0 | 0 | 0 | 0 | 0 |
| 0 | 1 | 0 | 0 | 1 | 1 |
| 0 | 0 | 0 | 1 | 0 | 1 |

The choice of $p\,q$ would mean "A false proposition implies nothing"; of $p \equiv q$, "A false proposition implies every false proposition, but no true one"; of $p\,q\,.\vee.\,{\sim}p\,q$, "A false proposition implies every true proposition, but no false one"; of $p \supset q$, "A false proposition implies every proposition."

In a three-valued system, there is even wider choice of definable relations, any one of which will be such that true propositions imply only true consequences. The following table indicates the alternatives:

| $p$ | $q$ | $pIq$ |
|---|---|---|
| 1 | 1 | 1 |
| 1 | 2 | 2 or 3 |
| 1 | 3 | 2 or 3 |
| 2 | 1 | 1 or 2 or 3 |
| 2 | 2 | 1 or 2 or 3 |
| 2 | 3 | 1 or 2 or 3 |
| 3 | 1 | 1 or 2 or 3 |
| 3 | 2 | 1 or 2 or 3 |
| 3 | 3 | 1 or 2 or 3 |

Any one of the possible combinations indicated by the column under $pIq$ will define a relation such that "If $p=1$, and $pIq$ holds, then $q=1$."[8] There are, thus, $2^2 \times 3^6$ or 2,916 different

[8] It might be supposed that, for every such relation, $pIq$, there would be some finite set of postulates from which, using this relation as the basis of

relations, each having the required property that "What an assertable proposition implies is assertable," which can be defined in a three-valued system.

The nature of the matrix method and the characteristics of 'implication'-relations which have just been considered make it obvious that there is an immense variety of truth-value systems, every one of them having its determined structure and its definite laws, and any one of which might conceivably be taken as a calculus of propositions. We do not need to *discover* such systems: they can be *devised* in various simple ways. The following matrix, on five values, illustrates a method (due to Lukasiewicz and Tarski) which can be extended to systems on any finite number of values: (1) the value of $pIq$ ("$p$ implies $q$") is 1 if $q \leq p$; and if $q > p$, then $pIq = q + 1 - p$; (2) the value of $Np$ ("$p$ is false") is $5 + 1 - p$:

| $I$ | 1 | 2 | 3 | 4 | 5 | $N$ |
|---|---|---|---|---|---|---|
| 1 | 1 | 2 | 3 | 4 | 5 | 5 |
| 2 | 1 | 1 | 2 | 3 | 4 | 4 |
| 3 | 1 | 1 | 1 | 2 | 3 | 3 |
| 4 | 1 | 1 | 1 | 1 | 2 | 2 |
| 5 | 1 | 1 | 1 | 1 | 1 | 1 |

(The values of $p$ are in the left-hand column, and the values of $q$ in the top line. Corresponding values of $pIq$ are at the intersection of column and line. Values of $Np$, corresponding to those of $p$, are in the right-hand column.)

Let us, as before, assert as laws of the system only such expressions as have the value 1 for all values of the variables. Any $q$ such that, for some $p$ which has the value 1, $pIq$ holds, will be such that $q$ has the value 1. Thus $pIq$ will be an 'implication'-relation, or possible basis of inference.

Let us try the following interpretation:

---

inference, all the laws of the system could be deduced. This, however, is far from being the case. The connection between a truth-value system as determined by a set of postulates, and as determined by the matrix method, is rather intricate. One point of some importance is the fact that there is a certain subclass of relations of the form $pIq$ which do not give rise to laws of 'inference,' because they hold *only* when $q = 1$.

$p=1$; $p$ is certainly true.
$p=2$; $p$ is more probable than not, but not certain.
$p=3$; $p$ is exactly as probable as not.
$p=4$; $p$ is less probable than not, but not certainly false.
$p=5$; $p$ is certainly false.

These meanings represent mutually exclusive alternatives, which together exhaust a certain set of possibilities; hence this interpretation is possible. And the meaning assigned to $p=1$ is compatible with taking this truth-value to be equivalent to assertability. Therefore all laws of this system will be truth-value tautologies.

The matrix-definition of $pIq$ involves the principle: A proposition implies any which is equally or more probable; and is implied by any which is equally or less probable. This principle holds of $pCq$ in the Three-valued Calculus; and, in its limiting forms, appears as the two theorems of Material Implication: (1) A true proposition is implied by any; and (2) A false proposition implies any. The further properties of $pIq$, as here defined, present an obvious uniformity, but not one which allows the general meaning of the relation to be simply expressed in English. However, if one should not be satisfied with this relation, there are billions of other definable relations $(4^4 \times 5^{20}-1)$, in the system, each of which has the required property of 'implication.'

The function $Np$, as defined, is obviously "$p$ is false."

The following summary statement concerning truth-value systems goes a little beyond what has been exemplified in the preceding, but in ways which will be easily understood:

(1) Truth-value systems are such as contain only functions which are categorical in terms of the truth-values of the system. A function is thus categorical if it is such that its truth-value, for every truth-value of its elementary terms, is unambiguously determined.

(2) The number of non-equivalent functions of one element, functions of two elements, etc., and the matrix values of such functions, is fixed simply by the number of truth-values of the system. If $n$ be the number of truth-values, the number of definable functions of one element will be $n^n$; the number of

definable relations (functions of two elements) will be $n$ with the exponent $n^2$.

If there be one designated truth-value which is equated with assertability, then the laws of the system are similarly determined simply by the number of the truth-values. (But the *meaning* of these laws is *not:* that depends on the interpretation of the system.) The manner in which functions—and hence laws—shall be symbolized is of course subject to arbitrary choice. Also, if some only of the mathematically definable functions are given symbolic representation, the laws which can be symbolically expressed will be a selection only of the mathematical laws of the system.

Let us call an $n$-valued system 'symbolically complete' if it is such that every function which could be determined by an $n$-valued matrix—the totality of functions mentioned in the last paragraph but one—can also be represented in the symbols of the system. For example, the two-valued system in the early part of this chapter is symbolically complete, as was there pointed out. *Mathematically*, there is only *one* symbolically complete system for any given number of truth-values. But a particular $n$-valued system, as determined by a matrix and definitions—*e.g.*, the three-valued system of Lukasiewicz and Tarski—may or may not be symbolically complete. That is, it may or may not be the case that all $n$-valued truth-functions are definable in terms of the chosen two or three which appear in the fundamental matrix. Whether this is so or not will depend in part on the functions so chosen and in part on the mathematical properties of the system. Thus two $n$-valued systems, as determined by given matrices, may differ by being symbolically incomplete in different ways. In that case, they may be regarded mathematically as different *selections* from the complete $n$-valued mathematical system. (Also, of course, two such systems may differ in interpretation through assignment of a different set of meanings to the $n$ truth-values.)

(3) The conditions on which any truth-value system, taken as an abstract mathematical system, can be interpreted as a calculus of propositions, are two: (a) The truth-values must

represent properties such that every proposition will have at least one of this set of properties. (It will be logically 'neater' if they are also such that no proposition can have *more* than one property of the set. But it is not required that they should be such mutually exclusive alternatives.) This condition will be satisfied if the truth-values, together, represent an exhaustive classification of propositions according to some particular principle of division. (b) The property represented by any 'designated' truth-value must be such that whatever proposition has this property will be validly assertable. It should be noted here that 'assertability' is a general character which is common to a considerable variety of more specific properties—*e.g.*, truth, universal truth, probability-value = 1, logical necessity.

There are no further conditions of interpretation, since the valid meaning of every function, and hence of every asserted law, depends upon that of the truth-values. Incidentally, it is quite generally, if not universally, the case that a system will admit of more than one valid interpretation.

(4) The meaning of any function is determined by its defining matrix, together with the interpretation imposed upon the truth-values. For different interpretations of the truth-values, the same matrix-function, in the abstract $n$-valued system, will have the same matrix-properties (and hence the same laws) but different meanings (and hence the laws will be of different significance). A logical relation, for example, which represents the assignable meaning of a certain matrix-function on one interpretation, will not generally be the assignable meaning of that function on another interpretation. In fact, for a different interpretation it may not be assignable as the meaning of any function in the system. Practically, the selection of functions to be symbolized and considered will be likely to depend upon the importance of the entity or relation which they mean.

(5) It follows from condition (b) under (3) above, that if there be one designated truth-value equated with assertability, the laws of any truth-value system will be truth-value tautologies for any valid interpretation of the system. The laws of the $n$-valued abstract system will not vary from one to another

interpretation, since whether any symbolic expression is a law depends only on its matrix-properties. But the *meaning* of a symbolic law will, of course, vary with the interpretation.

(There are some truth-value systems in which more than one of the truth-values may be taken as meaning 'is assertable': for example, 1 can be interpreted as 'necessarily true,' and 2 as 'true but not necessary.' However, the complications thus introduced are not of fundamental importance.)

(6) If an 'implication'-relation, $pIq$, be defined as any such that, when $p$ is assertable and $pIq$ is assertable, $q$ is assertable, then in the $n$-valued system, the number of definable 'implication'-relations is $(n-1)^{n-1}$ multiplied by $n$ with the exponent $(n^2-n)$. Each of these will be distinguished from every other which is in the system with respect to what *non*-assertable propositions 'imply.' The laws of any such relation do not alter with interpretation of the truth-values, so long as the same designated truth-value is equated with assertability; but the meaning both of the relation and of its laws does alter with interpretation. However, what is an 'implication'-relation for one interpretation, will remain an 'implication'-relation for any interpretation which can validly be imposed.

(7) A truth-value system is essentially an abstract mathematical structure. It becomes a system of logical truth only by interpretation. That the structure of a logical calculus can be thus considered in abstraction from its logical meaning is a fact of the greatest importance, and one which has commonly been overlooked. Nevertheless, any interpretation of such a system presumes antecedent logical meanings and an antecedent logical truth in terms of these meanings. Otherwise the validity of the interpretation could not be tested, and the meaning of abstract functions could not be assigned. The logical truth exhibited by the system, as interpreted, is implicit in the logical truth which tests the validity of the interpretation and assigns the meanings of the functions. Development of the system determines logical truth only in the sense (the very important sense) of exhibiting in detail the necessary consequences of the truth and meanings which the interpretation implicitly presumes.

Such truth-value systems are only beginning to be investigated, in their generality. The wealth of facts awaiting exposition here is obvious. It is to be hoped, however, that students will not be so preoccupied with these as to overlook the fact that not all logical meanings are truth-value functions, and not all logical principles are capable of statement in truth-value terms.

## Note Concerning Many-valued Logical Systems.

In Chapter VII of Lewis and Langford, *Symbolic Logic*, in the discussion of multiply-valued matrix systems, and of a three-valued system in particular, reference is made throughout to "Łukasiewicz and Tarski." It would have been more appropriate if such references had been to Professor Łukasiewicz alone, with an accompanying explanatory footnote.

Professor Łukasiewicz is sole author of these systems, having originated the three-valued system in 1920, and *n*-valued systems in 1922.[1] The matrices determining the systems, the original definitions of their fundamental ideas, and the philosophic interpretation of them are exclusively his.

In 1921, Dr. Tarski contributed the definition of the modal function *Mp*, which appears in the three-valued system as sketched in *Symbolic Logic*. This definition is adopted by Professor Łukasiewicz, as he notes, in place of his own earlier and more complex one, which is somewhat narrower in meaning.[2] The collaboration of Dr. Tarski in the further development of these systems—on the methodological side—is also indicated in the published papers.[3]

The same correction applies also to references in my article on "Alternative Systems of Logic" in *The Monist* for October, 1932.

C. I. Lewis.

Harvard University.

[1] See J. Łukasiewicz and A. Tarski, "Untersuchungen über den Aussagenkalkül," *C. R. Soc. d. Sc. et d. Let. de Varsovie*, XXIII (1930), Classe III, p. 10, footnote 17.

[2] See J. Łukasiewicz, "Philosophische Bemerkungen zu mehrwertigen Systemen des Aussagenkalküls," *ibid.*, pp. 65 ff.

[3] See "Philosophische Bemerkungen . . . ," p. 74, and "Untersuchungen . . . ," pp. 11 ff.

## CHAPTER VIII

### IMPLICATION AND DEDUCIBILITY

Exact logic can be taken in either of two ways: (1) as a vehicle and canon of deductive inference, or (2) as that subject which comprises all principles the statement of which is tautological. The two conceptions are by no means equivalent; the second is much more inclusive. Those who take logic in this second fashion have—perhaps unnoticed by themselves—usually confined attention to truth-value tautologies which approximate to principles of deductive inference. But how multifarious and how varied in type tautologies may be the preceding chapter has made evident. To debate which of these two conceptions is correct would be to argue the meaning of a word. All that is important here is to apprehend the facts and to perceive certain connections between the laws of deduction and the wider field which includes tautologies of all kinds.

The chief business of a canon of deduction is to delineate correctly the properties of that relation which holds between any premise, or set of premises, and a conclusion which can validly be inferred. Commonly this relation is called 'implication.' But as the preceding chapter has shown, there is more than one relation which can be made the basis of inference. If we conceive that the distinguishing mark of an implication-relation, $pIq$, is that if $p$ is a true premise and $pIq$ holds, $q$ also will be true, then, as we have seen, the number of relations having this property, but distinguished one from another in other respects and answering to different laws, is indefinitely large.

This variety of implication-relations came to our attention in the previous chapter exclusively in connection with truth-value systems. We are aware that there are other than truth-value relations which give rise to inference through having observed, in Chapter VI, that strict implication is such a relation. It is a further fact—though it is nowhere established in this book—that there exist also a variety of non-truth-value relations which may give rise to inference, incident to a similar variety of systems which are not of the truth-value type, each having the general form of a calculus of propositions.[1]

Now in some sense or other there must be a truth about deducibility which is not relative to this variety and difference of systems and their relations. Either a given proposition *q* is genuinely deducible from another, *p*, or it is not. Either, then, there is some one system which alone is true when *pIq* is translated "*q* is deducible from *p*," or none of them states the truth of logic in that sense. On the other hand, there is a certain kind of consistency and rigor which characterizes truth-value systems, as well as systems of other than the truth-value type. There appears to be a sense in which any law of any such system represents an undeniable truth. The systems themselves are developed by a procedure which evidently possesses some kind of logical compulsion. Inference, based on any one of these truth-implications, may be used to derive the laws of the system from postulates or previously established theorems. And that such inference does not lead us astray is evidenced by the fact that all principles thus derived are verifiable by the matrix method. If the 'truth about deducibility' does not somehow include and account for this fact, then we shall have an unsolved puzzle left on our hands.

Any two implication-relations will be such that one of them holds in some class of cases in which the other does not. They cannot, then, each of them hold when and only when the consequent in the relation is genuinely deducible from the antecedent —if the truth about deducibility is unambiguous and fixed. Yet any one of them may genuinely give rise to inference; if the antecedent is a proposition known to be true, then the consequent will not be false. It becomes a problem, then, in what sense, if any, there can be a single relation answering to laws which are unambiguously determined, which holds when and only when *q* is deducible from *p*.

Let us first inquire what, if anything, is common to all the relations which can give rise to inference. All of them have the

[1] The systems indicated as S1, S2, etc., at the end of Appendix II, may be taken as such different determinations of the relation there represented by $\prec$.

property that when the antecedent $p$ in any such relation $pIq$ is assertable as true, the consequent $q$ cannot fail to have this status also.[2] This property must belong not only to truth-implications but also to any relation, whether of the truth-value type or not, which could give rise to inference. The very meaning of inferring or deducing, and the purpose for which we perform any such operation, require that it should never be the case that a proposition which is true should imply one which is not.

All *truth*-implications have the *additional* property in common that if $p$ and $q$ are both assertable as true, then $pIq$ holds, regardless of any further consideration. That is, for any meaning of 'implies' which is definable in any truth-value system, it must be the case that, of any pair of true propositions (those having the value 1), each implies the other. The reason for this is simple: any relation whatever, of the truth-value type, must either hold always when the terms it relates are both true, or it must always fail to hold when both are true. For by the very nature of a truth-value function, given the fact that $p$ and $q$ are both true, any truth-relation must, by that fact alone, be categorically determined to hold between these terms, or it must be categorically determined not to hold. Hence, for any truth-implication, either *every* true proposition must imply *every* true proposition, or *no* true proposition will imply *any* true proposition. This latter alternative would mean that the relation could never give rise to inference, since either true propositions would imply

[2] In the Two-valued Calculus, $p = 1$ means simply "$p$ is true"; in a three-valued calculus, as we have seen, $p = 1$ must be given the narrower interpretation, "$p$ is certain" or "$p$ is known to be true," if the Law of the Excluded Middle is to be retained. In a four-valued calculus, $p = 1$ may take the interpretation "$p$ is certain" or—for some systems—it may be interpreted "$p$ is implied by its own negation" or "$p$ is logically necessary." It would be awkward, in the remainder of this chapter, to be obliged continually to allow for such differences of interpretation. We shall, therefore, write with the Two-valued Calculus in mind as our principal illustration: any qualification or correction of language required in the case of other systems, will be such as the reader can make himself. No conclusion reached will be affected by this. The properties which all relations of truth-implication have in common are three: (1) the truth-value of $pIq$ is categorically determined when the values of $p$ and $q$ are given; (2) if $p = 1$ and $pIq = 1$, then $q = 1$; (3) when $p = 1$ and $q = 1$, $pIq = 1$. In every case, our conclusions will be found to depend only upon these properties.

only those which are not true, or no true proposition would imply anything.[3]

Thus any truth-implication, appearing in any truth-value system whatever, will be such that not only does no true proposition imply any which is not true, but also every true proposition implies every other which is true. This second property of such relations leads to a very important consequence: if we should take any such truth-implication, $pIq$, to be equivalent to "$q$ is deducible from $p$," then every pair of true propositions must be such that each can validly be deduced from the other. Thus, in terms of any truth-implication, two propositions could be independent (one not deducible from the other) only if one of them be true and the other false.

As a statement about deducibility, this is quite surely an absurdity. Otherwise, any mathematical system which, for any conceivable interpretation, could represent the truth about something or other, would be deducible *in toto* from any single proposition of it taken as a postulate.[4] It seems to us that the falsity

[3] There is a class of four-valued systems in which $p = 1$ takes the interpretation "The negation of $p$ implies $p$" or "$p$ is logically undeniable." (Any one of the matrices given in Appendix II may be taken as an example. These are there used to prove consistency and independence of postulates. But they could also be taken as the generating matrices of truth-value systems. If so taken, each of them would give a four-valued system belonging to the class in question.) For systems of this class, any two propositions having the value 1 are genuinely deducible from one another—if it be granted that all propositions which are logically necessary have this property. But the same problem pointed out above recurs in these systems in another form. The indicated interpretation of $p = 2$ is "$p$ is true but not necessary." Therefore, since these are truth-value systems, in which $pIq$ always has the *same* determined value when $p = 2$ and $q = 2$, either *every* proposition which is true but not necessary will imply *every other* such proposition, or *no* proposition which is true but not necessary will imply *any other* such proposition. (In the examples referred to above, this implication always holds, and any proposition which is true but not necessary implies every true proposition.) This paradox inevitably recurs, in some form, in every truth-value system.

[4] An attempt might be made to escape this consequence by maintaining that mathematical systems do not consist of propositions but of propositional functions; or by maintaining that, when properly interpreted, a mathematical system does not assert its postulates and theorems, but asserts only that the postulates imply the theorems. Discussion of these points would involve issues too complex to be inserted here. (We may observe, in passing, that in *Principia Mathematica*, for example, the propositions of mathematics which

of the assertion "Every true proposition is deducible from every other" hardly requires proof. But if this *is* false, then we have the unavoidable consequence that there can be no relation of truth-implication, *pIq*, which holds whenever *q* is deducible from *p*, and *fails* to hold when *q* is *not* deducible from *p*. Since all such truth-implications hold whenever *p* and *q* are both true, every such relation is *too inclusive* in its meaning to be equivalent to "*q* is deducible from *p*."

This conclusion is inescapable. But in that case, how can a truth-implication validly give rise to inference? How can it be true, at one and the same time, that (1) a relation of truth-implication, *pIq*, which is definable in a given system, is not equivalent to "*q* is deducible from *p*," but holds sometimes when *q* is *not* deducible from *p*, and that (2) when *p* is any proposition in the system, and *pIq* is assertable as a law of the system, we can validly infer that *q* is a proposition in the system?

The answer is that, if *pIq* is a relation which sometimes holds when *q* is not deducible from *p*—and every truth-implication is such—then obviously, *q* cannot validly be inferred from *p* merely

are demonstrated are not merely asserted to be implied by something: with a few explicit exceptions, they are asserted unconditionally.) But certain facts may be noted which will, in all probability, be sufficient to satisfy the reader.

If a mathematical system, in the abstract, consists of statements which are not definitely true or false, being ambiguous as to what they are about or what their terms denote, at least it has been commonly assumed by mathematicians that there must be one or more interpretations—one or more ways of assigning fixed meanings to its ambiguous terms—for which all its statements become true propositions. The usual test of consistency requires the finding of such an interpretation. It may be that such tests are not of the essence of consistency; but, however that may be, at least it is a fact that, for the great majority of all mathematical systems ever presented, such interpretation has been found.

Now the claim that, although the mathematical system in its abstract form is such that it contains statements (for example, the postulates) one of which may be not-deducible from another, an interpretation for which the system becomes true will not exhibit any similar independence of the propositions arising from such interpretation—if any one would make this claim—is something the plausibility of which the reader can judge for himself. It would mean, for example, that, although a system of geometry in its modern abstract form exhibits independence of certain of its propositions from certain others, any geometry which should be the truth about space would be such that every proposition of it could be deduced from the single assumption "A triangle has more than two sides."

because $pIq$ is true. *But this is never done* when $pIq$ is made the basis of an inference in a truth-value system. The inference is made on the ground that $pIq$ is a *tautology*. Nothing is ever asserted in a truth-value system unless it is a tautology. And the relation of $p$ to $q$ when $pIq$ is a tautology is quite different from the relation when $pIq$ is true but not tautological. Thus we may propound the conundrum: "When is a truth-implication not a truth-implication?" And the answer is: "When it is a tautology."

Every truth-implication is such that it is sometimes true when it is not tautological. And when $pIq$ is true but not tautological, $q$ cannot validly be deduced from $p$. But the truth of $q$ *can* validly be deduced from the truth of $p$ together with the fact that $pIq$ is a tautology. And it is only in such cases that any truth-implication is made the basis of inference, in any truth-value system. Thus in all cases of such inference within the system, the truth-value system makes use of a relation—the relation of $p$ to $q$ when $pIq$ is a tautology—which it symbolizes merely as $pIq$, but which is in reality a more special relation which often fails to hold when $pIq$ is true.

The problem which thus appears, though at bottom simple, is one which is marked by small distinctions which are apparently trivial but really essential to understanding. It suggests itself, in the light of the foregoing, that a clue to the relation of deducibility may be discovered by attention to the nature of truth-implications when they have the character of tautologies. If we are to investigate this, there are three points which should be kept in mind.

First, as has been stated in the preceding chapter, there are other tautologies than those of truth-value, because there are other principles of division, and hence other ways of exhausting the possibilities, than by reference to alternatives of truth-value.[5]

[5] It is a fact that any principle of division operates in such wise that the result of it can be exhibited as the necessity that some one of a given set of alternatives must, in any particular case, be true. If the alternatives are mutually exclusive, then it is further required that, in any particular case, all the alternatives but one must be false. Thus *every* tautology must be capable of statement by reference to alternatives of truth or falsity. But that has nothing to do with the question whether the *principle of division* has reference to truth and falsity.

But it is at least plausible that any law of logic, in whatever terms, must be a tautology, i.e., a principle whose truth is demonstrable by exhaustion of some set of alternative possibilities.

Second, if we make this supposition that the laws of logic must be tautological or necessary truths, then any law of deductive inference, being a statement that something, *q*, can be inferred from something, *p*, must be a tautology. If this be the case, then in order to elicit such principles of valid deduction, we require to discover a relation, "*p* implies *q*," which *when it holds* represents a tautology. But it will not and cannot be a relation which is tautological *in general*: it cannot be a relation *R* such that the function *pRq* is equivalent to the universal function, or always has the value 'truth.' It must be a relation which fails to hold sometimes—when *q* is *not* deducible from *p*—and no relation which is sometimes false can be such that the mere statement *pRq* is a tautology.

Third—and this is the important point, the other two being set down to guard it from misunderstanding—if "*p* implies *q*" is to be synonymous with "*q* is deducible from *p*"; and if *q is* deducible from *p* when and only when "*p* implies *q*" expresses a tautology; then "*p* implies *q*," in this required meaning, must be true when, for a particular *p* and *q*, it expresses a tautology; and it must be false when, for a particular *p* and *q*, it does not express a tautology.

No truth-value relation can meet this requirement. Any truth-implication must be such that, in some cases, it is true when it does not express a tautology.

Inference in a truth-value system, based upon a relation of truth-implication, is really a special case of the kind of inference to which such a relation may give rise. Where such inference occurs in the system itself, the premise *p* will be some law (i.e., a tautology), *pIq* will likewise be assertable as a law, and the inferred *q* will also be a law of the system. Let us first consider the *general* case, in which a truth-implication may validly give rise to inference; that is, the case in which the premise *p* need not be a law of the system but may be any proposition, and *pIq* need not be a tautology. Consideration of this general case will lead us to the heart of the whole matter.

Any truth-implication $pIq$ gives rise to inference through the fact that—no matter what particular implication-relation it may be, or to what truth-value system it may belong—

$$(p \text{ and } pIq)\ I\ q$$

expresses a tautology.[6] And this may be a tautology when $pIq$ is not a tautology. Notice that it is only the second $I$ in the above expression which is asserted: it is only this $I$ which is required to express a tautology if the inference from '$p$ and $pIq$' to $q$ is to be a valid deduction; the unasserted $I$, in $pIq$, need not express a tautology.

Suppose that $p$ and $q$ be some pair of true but independent propositions—neither deducible from the other. For example, let $p$ = "Vinegar tastes sour" and $q$ = "Some men have beards." Since any truth-implication, $pIq$, will hold when $p$ and $q$ are both true, it will hold in this case. For these meanings, $pIq$ will not express a tautology: the statement "It is not the case that ('Vinegar tastes sour' is true and 'Some men have beards' is false)" is a true statement; but it is not tautological or necessarily true, since it has a conceivable alternative. Nevertheless, '($p$ and $pIq$) $I$ $q$' *will* be a tautology. This is the case because: (1) Any truth-implication $pIq$ will fail to hold if $p$ is true and $q$ false. So that when $pIq$ holds, we may be sure that "It is not the case that $p$ is true and $q$ false" is a true statement. And (2) from the premises "$p$ is true" and "It is not the case that $p$ is true and $q$ false," the truth of $q$ can validly be deduced. That is (and now we read the meaning of the second, or asserted, $I$), "It is false that ($p$ is true, and it is not the case that $p$ is true and $q$ false, but $q$ is not true)" is a tautology.

This is a bit involved; perhaps the point will be clearer if we put the matter in more completely symbolic form. Let us choose,

[6] This cannot be expressed symbolically in the same way in every system. For example, in the Three-valued Calculus it requires to be symbolized by

$$pC{:}pCq.Cq.$$

But in every case, the expression of the principle will contain an asserted implication-relation which will be tautological, and an unasserted implication, represented by the same symbol, which need not be tautological.

as our relation of truth-implication, material implication of the Two-valued Calculus, $p \supset q$. By definition, this means "It is false that '$p$ is true and $q$ false'":

$$p \supset q \,.\, = \,.\, \sim(p \sim q).$$

Given the meanings mentioned above, $p \supset q$ is true, but it is not a tautology: "It is false that 'Vinegar tastes sour and no men have beards,'" is a true statement, but it is not tautological. Nevertheless, for these or any other meanings of $p$ and $q$,

$$p \,.\, p \supset q : \supset . \, q$$

*is* a tautology. Substituting for the first or unasserted implication here its defined equivalent, we have:

$$p \,.\, \sim(p \sim q) : \supset . \, q.$$

The implication-relation which still remains is the tautological one which is asserted. That this *is* a tautology will be apparent if we transform this relation also into its defined equivalent:

$$\sim[p \,.\, \sim(p \sim q) : \sim q].$$

The expression in brackets here is a logical product, the order of whose members is indifferent. Changing this order, we have:

$$\sim[p \sim q \,.\, \sim(p \sim q)].$$

Thus $p \,.\, p \supset q : \supset . \, q$ is equivalent to "It is false that $p \sim q$ is both true and false": and that statement is an obvious tautology. It is a tautology even when $p$ and $q$ are independent propositions; it is always a tautology.

Let us return to our example. "Some men have beards" ($q$) cannot be deduced from "Vinegar tastes sour" ($p$). But from the two premises, (1) "Vinegar tastes sour" ($p$), and (2) "It is false that 'Vinegar tastes sour and no men have beards,'" $\sim(p \sim q)$, the conclusion "Some men have beards" can validly be deduced. In ordinary discourse, we seldom have occasion to make an inference which has this form, but it should be noted that it accords completely with our logical intuitions.

Thus we find a very simple answer to the question how an implication-relation which is rather 'queer,' and not at all equivalent to the relation of deducibility, may nevertheless give rise to completely valid inference. Define this relation—in English or any other terms which make its meaning really clear—and choose an instance in which the relation actually holds and the antecedent is actually true. The consequent also will then be true; for if the antecedent were true but the consequent false, the relation would not hold. Moreover, if for the relation $pIq$ its meaning as defined be substituted, it will be found that from the two premises (1) "$p$ is true" and (2) "$pIq$ (read in English) holds," the truth of $q$ can validly be deduced, by the commonly accepted principles of deduction. And yet if one take $pIq$ to express "$q$ is deducible from $p$," the relation may not hold at all: it may be as absurd as it would be to say, "From 'Vinegar tastes sour,' we deduce 'Some men have beards.'"

We see further that if we wish to elicit that relation which holds whenever, in terms of any one of the variety of possible implication-relations, a deduction can validly be made, it is required that we should be able to distinguish between "$pIq$ is true" and "$pIq$ is a *tautology*." When $pIq$ is true but not tautological, $q$ can be deduced from the two premises, $p$ and $pIq$; but only because "($p$ and $pIq$) $I$ $q$" is a tautology. When $pIq$ is a *tautology*, $q$ can be deduced from $p$.

This is precisely the logical significance of the relation $p \prec q$ in the system of Strict Implication. The one requirement of all implication-relations is that $pIq$ must *not* hold when $p$ is true and $q$ false. Thus in order to express "$pIq$ is a tautology," what is needed is to elicit a relation $R$ such that $pRq$ will mean "$p$ true and $q$ false, is a logically impossible combination," or "It is necessarily true—true under all conceivable circumstances—that it is not the case that $p$ is true and $q$ false." This is exactly the meaning of strict implication, as is evidenced by the equivalences:

$$p \prec q \;.=.\; \sim\Diamond(p \sim q) \;.=.\; \sim\Diamond\sim[\sim(p \sim q)].$$ [7]

Whenever any truth-implication, $pIq$, expresses a tautology (is necessarily true) the relation $p \prec q$ holds: when $pIq$ is true but does not express a tautology, $p \prec q$ does not hold. So far,

[7] See Chapter VI, 11·02 and 18·7.

then, *p* ⥽ *q* has the property requisite to that relation which holds when *q* is deducible from *p*, and does *not* hold when *q* is *not* deducible from *p*.

The same fact is evidenced, in more striking fashion, by the relation which exists between strict implication and any truth-implication, of any truth-value calculus. Let any relation of truth-implication be introduced into the system of Strict Implication, by suitable definition. (This can always be done: if in no other way, by explicit introduction of the truth-values and definition in terms of these.) The laws of this relation of truth-implication will then be provable theorems in the system of Strict Implication. And in these laws, in any case in which this truth-implication, *I*, is tautological, it will be possible to replace it by ⥽ ; but in any case in which *pIq* is true but is not tautological, the relation *I* will *not* be replaceable by ⥽ . Every instance in which this truth-implication *I* gives rise to *inference*, in the truth-value system in which it occurs, will be a case in which *I* can be replaced by ⥽ . For example, we introduced the relation of material implication into the system of Strict Implication, in Chapter VI, by definition of $p \supset q$. From this definition, it was possible (using the propositions of Strict Implication as principles of deduction) to deduce every theorem of the system of Material Implication. This was demonstrated by deducing the postulates for Material Implication, as given in *Principia Mathematica*. In such theorems, as deduced in the system of Strict Implication, in every case in which the relation $\supset$ is assertable in a law (i.e., is tautological), $\supset$ can be replaced by ⥽ . But when an unasserted (non-tautological) relation $\supset$ appears in a theorem, it cannot, in general, be replaced by ⥽ .

We set down below two columns for comparison. Under (1), is given a proposition in the form in which it appears in the system of Material Implication. Each of the theorems cited can be proved in that form, from the definition of $p \supset q$, in the system of Strict Implication. But also it can be proved in the form given under (2), where any relation $\supset$ which is tautological is replaced by ⥽ . Where the relation $\supset$ appears under (2), it is not tautological in the theorem; and if $\supset$ were here replaced by ⥽ , the theorem would be false. (Reference numbers are, of course, those of the theorems in Chapter VI, where proof is given.)

| | (1) | | (2) |
|---|---|---|---|
| 15·21 | $p . \supset . q \supset p.$ | 15·2 | $p . ⥽ . q \supset p.$ |
| 15·23 | $\sim p . \supset . p \supset q.$ | 15·22 | $\sim p . ⥽ . p \supset q.$ |
| 15·31 | $\sim(p \supset q) . \supset . p \supset \sim q.$ | 15·3 | $\sim(p \supset q) . ⥽ . p \supset \sim q.$ |
| 15·41 | $\sim(p \supset q) . \supset . q \supset p.$ | 15·4 | $\sim(p \supset q) . ⥽ . q \supset p.$ |

Of special interest is 14·29, $p . p \supset q : ⥽ . q$. Let us presume, for the moment, that $p ⥽ q$ is precisely equivalent to "$q$ is deducible from $p$." Then 14·29 means "$q$ is deducible from the two premises, '$p$' and '$p$ materially implies $q$.'" It does *not* mean that when $p \supset q$ holds, $q$ is deducible from $p$. Inability to distinguish between (1) "If $p$ is true and $p \supset q$ holds, then $q$ is true" and (2) "When $p \supset q$ holds, $q$ is deducible from $p$" is responsible for most of the confusion about material implication and deducibility. This distinction may be subtle, and the confusion understandable; but remembering our illustration, $p$ = "Vinegar tastes sour" and $q$ = "Some men have beards," we should see clearly that (1) is true but (2) is false.

Let us now turn back, briefly, to what we have said is a special case in which truth-implications give rise to inference, namely, the case in which such a relation is used in deducing one law of the system in which it occurs from another which has been assumed or already established. In that special case, the antecedent $p$ in the relation will be a tautology (since it is a law of the system); $pIq$ will also express a tautology; and the $q$ which is deduced must also be a tautology. We have seen that in any case in which a truth-implication $pIq$ gives rise to inference, '($p$ and $pIq$) $I$ $q$' will be a tautology. Where the truth-implication in question is the relation of material implication, this principle is what is expressed by 14·29,

$$p . p \supset q : ⥽ . q.$$

The further fact that if $p$ is a tautology, or necessary truth, and $p \supset q$ is a tautology, then $q$ is a tautological or necessary truth, is what is stated by 18·53:

$$p ⥽ q . \sim\Diamond\sim p : ⥽ . \sim\Diamond\sim q.$$

Since $p \prec q . = . \sim\Diamond\sim[\sim(p \sim q)] . = . \sim\Diamond\sim(p \supset q)$, this may be transformed into

$$\sim\Diamond\sim p . \sim\Diamond\sim(p \supset q) : \prec . \sim\Diamond\sim q.$$

That is, if $q$ is deducible from $p$ (as it is when $pIq$ is a tautology), then from this and the fact that $p$ is a tautological or necessary truth we can deduce that $q$ is a tautology also. Thus not only may a relation of truth-implication give rise to inference, but also it gives rise to inference in such a manner that when the premise is a law of the system, the consequent also will be a law of the system. The principles of Strict Implication express the facts about any such deduction in an explicit manner in which they cannot be expressed within the truth-value system itself, for the reason that, in Strict Implication, what is tautological is distinguishable from what is merely true, whereas this difference does not ordinarily appear in the symbols of a truth-value system.

In the light of all these facts, it appears that the relation of strict implication expresses precisely that relation which holds when valid deduction is possible, and fails to hold when valid deduction is not possible. In that sense, the system of Strict Implication may be said to provide that canon and critique of deductive inference which is the desideratum of logical investigation. All the facts about those cases in which any other implication-relation may genuinely give rise to inference are incorporated in and explained by the laws of this system—or they may be so incorporated by introducing the implication-relation in question into the system by definition. Also Strict Implication explains the paradoxes incident to truth-implications, such as

15·2 $p . \prec . q \supset p$ and 15·21 $p . \supset . q \supset p$,

"If $p$ is true, then any proposition $q$ implies $p$"; and

15·22 $\sim p . \prec . p \supset q$ and 15·23 $\sim p . \supset . p \supset q$,

"If $p$ is false, then $p$ implies any proposition $q$." It explains these by making it clear that "$p$ implies $q$" in these cases is not equivalent to "$q$ is deducible from $p$," but is a relation which may hold when $p$ and $q$ are independent propositions.

The one serious doubt which can arise concerning the equivalence of $p \prec q$ to the relation of deducibility and concerning the adequacy of Strict Implication to the problems of deduction in general arises from the fact that strict implication has its corresponding paradoxes:

$$19{\cdot}74 \quad \sim\Diamond p \,.\prec.\, p \prec q,$$

"If $p$ is impossible, then $p$ strictly implies any proposition $q$"; and

$$19{\cdot}75 \quad \sim\Diamond\sim p \,.\prec.\, q \prec p,$$

"If $q$ is necessary, then any proposition $p$ strictly implies $q$." If $p \prec q$ is equivalent to "$q$ is deducible from $p$," then to satisfy these theorems it must be the case that, from any proposition which negates a necessary or tautological truth, anything whatever can be deduced; and that any proposition whose truth is necessary or tautological can be deduced from anything whatever.

We wish to show that this is indeed the case, and that these theorems, as well as others in the system of Strict Implication which may be subject to a similar doubt, are paradoxical only in the sense of expressing logical truths which are easily overlooked.

But there are certain ambiguities which may cloud the issue. First, it must be understood that 'deducible' here means 'deducible by some mode of inference which is valid.' It might seem that this meaning is the obvious one which could not be missed, but, as we shall see, it might easily be confused with another which is of quite different import.

Second, we must observe the meaning of 'necessary' and 'impossible' here. By definition,

$$18{\cdot}14 \quad \sim\Diamond\sim p \,.=.\, \sim p \prec p \,.=.\, \sim(\sim p \circ \sim p);$$

To say "$p$ is necessary" means "$p$ is implied by its own denial" or "The denial of $p$ is not self-consistent."

$$18{\cdot}12 \quad \sim\Diamond p \,.=.\, p \prec \sim p \,.=.\, \sim(p \circ p);$$

To say "$p$ is impossible" means "$p$ implies its own negation" or "$p$ is not self-consistent." Necessary truths, so defined, coincide with the class of tautologies, or truths which can be certified by logic alone; and impossible propositions coincide with the class of those which deny some tautology.

Every tautology is expressible as some proposition of the general form $p \vee {\sim}p$. Probably this fact is already evident from the considerations of the preceding chapter. Complete demonstration of it would run to greater length than can be afforded here, but it may be of value to give a few examples, which will also serve to make clear the manner in which theorems of Strict Implication express tautologies. The simplest of all tautologies is ${\sim}p \vee p$. And, remembering that ${\sim}\Diamond{\sim}p$ means "$p$ is a tautology," we may observe that the theorem $p \prec p$ states "${\sim}p \vee p$ is a tautology":

$$ {\sim}\Diamond{\sim}({\sim}p \vee p) \,.\, = \,.\, {\sim}\Diamond(p\, {\sim}p) \,.\, = \,.\, p \prec p. $$

A tautology of more complex form is:

$$ {\sim}[{\sim}\Diamond(p\, {\sim}q)] \,.\, \vee \,.\, {\sim}\Diamond(p\, {\sim}q), $$

"Either it is false that $p\, {\sim}q$ is impossible, or $p\, {\sim}q$ is impossible." The statement that this is a tautology becomes the theorem:

$$ p \prec q \,.\, \prec \,.\, {\sim}q \prec {\sim}p. $$

Because $\qquad p \prec q \,.\, = \,.\, {\sim}\Diamond(p\, {\sim}q),$

and $\qquad {\sim}q \prec {\sim}p \,.\, = \,.\, {\sim}\Diamond({\sim}q\, p) \,.\, = \,.\, {\sim}\Diamond(p\, {\sim}q).$

And $\qquad {\sim}\Diamond{\sim}[{\sim}(p \prec q) \,.\, \vee \,.\, {\sim}q \prec {\sim}p] \,:\, = \,:\, p \prec q \,.\, \prec \,.\, {\sim}q \prec {\sim}p$

by the general principle that

$$ {\sim}\Diamond{\sim}({\sim}p \vee q) \,.\, = \,.\, {\sim}\Diamond(p\, {\sim}q) \,.\, = \,.\, p \prec q. $$

Let us take one more example, beginning this time with the theorem and producing the tautology. Let us choose as our theorem number 12·61,

$$ p\, q \,.\, \prec \,.\, r \,:\, \prec \,:\, p\, {\sim}r \,.\, \prec \,.\, {\sim}q. $$

By successive transformations this becomes:

$$ {\sim}\Diamond{\sim}[{\sim}(p\, q \,.\, \prec \,.\, r) \,:\, \vee \,:\, p\, {\sim}r \prec {\sim}q], $$
$$ {\sim}\Diamond{\sim}\{{\sim}[{\sim}\Diamond(p\, q \,.\, {\sim}r)] \,:\, \vee \,:\, {\sim}\Diamond[p\, {\sim}r \,.\, {\sim}({\sim}q)]\}, $$
$$ {\sim}\Diamond{\sim}[\Diamond(p\, q \,.\, {\sim}r) \,:\, \vee \,:\, {\sim}\Diamond(p\, {\sim}r \,.\, q)]. $$

Thus what the theorem asserts to be a tautology is the proposition "Either it is possible that $p$ be true, $q$ true, and $r$ false, or it is impossible that $p$ be true, $r$ false, and $q$ true."

Oftentimes the tautologies to which theorems are reducible would be more complicated than this; but it is a fact that all valid logical principles may be thus reduced. (There are certain complicating considerations, but in the end this statement holds.) And any tautology whatever may be given the general form $p \vee {\sim}p$; something bearing on that point will appear in what follows.

We may now indicate the manner in which, from a proposition whose truth is impossible, anything whatever may be deduced. The negation of any proposition which is of the form ${\sim}p \vee p$ is a corresponding proposition of the form $p\,{\sim}p$:

$${\sim}p \vee p \,.\, = \,.\, {\sim}(p\,{\sim}p).$$

From any proposition of the form $p\,{\sim}p$, any proposition whatever, $q$, may be deduced as follows:

$$\text{Assume } p\,{\sim}p. \qquad (1)$$

$$(1) \prec p \qquad (2)$$

If $p$ is true and $p$ is false, then $p$ is true.

$$(1) \prec {\sim}p \qquad (3)$$

If $p$ is true and $p$ is false, then $p$ is false.

$$(2) \,.\!\prec\!.\, p \vee q \qquad (4)$$

If, by (2), $p$ is true, then at least one of the two, $p$ and $q$, is true.

$$(3) \,.\, (4) :\prec .\, q$$

If, by (3), $p$ is false; and, by (4), at least one of the two, $p$ and $q$, is true; then $q$ must be true.

This demonstration is a paradigm, in which $p$ may be any proposition so chosen that ${\sim}p \vee p$ will express the tautology which is in question; and $q$ may be any proposition whatever. Thus any proposition one chooses may be deduced from the denial of a tautological or necessary truth: the theorem

$$\sim\Diamond p \,.\, \prec \,.\, p \prec q$$

states a fact about deducibility.

Similarly, from any proposition whatever, $p$, every proposition of the form $\sim q \vee q$ may be deduced, as follows:

Assume $p$. (1)

$$(1) \,.\, \prec \,:\, p \sim q \,.\, \vee \,.\, p\, q \quad (2)$$

If $p$ is true, then either $p$ is true and $q$ false or $p$ and $q$ are both true.

$$(2) \,.\, = \,:\, p \,.\, \sim q \vee q \quad (3)$$

"Either $p$ is true and $q$ false or $p$ and $q$ are both true" is equivalent to "$p$ is true, and either $q$ is false or $q$ is true."

$$(3) \,.\, \prec \,.\, \sim q \vee q$$

If $p$ is true, and either $q$ is false or $q$ is true, then either $q$ is false or $q$ is true.

This demonstration, likewise, is a paradigm, in which $p$ may be any proposition whatever, and $q$ may be so chosen as to give any desired tautology, $\sim q \vee q$. Thus tautologies in general are deducible from any premise we please: the theorem

$$\sim\Diamond\sim q \,.\, \prec \,.\, p \prec q$$

states a fact about deducibility.

Hence the two paradoxical theorems cited are no ground of objection to the supposition that strict implication, $p \prec q$, coincides in its properties with the relation "$q$ is deducible from $p$."

Another general property of the system of Strict Implication which may seem paradoxical is the fact that, in its terms, all tautological or necessary propositions are equivalent; and hence all impossible propositions likewise are equivalent. These also are inevitable consequences of any genuinely valid logic. Any two tautologies, $\sim p \vee p$ and $\sim q \vee q$, however unrelated in their content, are logically equivalent, in the general fashion in which any proposition $p$ is equivalent to its division into the alternatives

$p \sim q$ and $p\, q$:

$$\begin{aligned} \sim p \vee p \,.\, &= : (\sim p \vee p) \sim q \,.\vee.\, (\sim p \vee p) q \\ &= : \sim p \sim q \,.\vee.\, p \sim q \,.\vee.\, \sim p\, q \,.\vee.\, p\, q \\ &= : \sim p(\sim q \vee q) \,.\vee.\, p(\sim q \vee q) : = .\, \sim q \vee q. \end{aligned}$$

For example, "Either it is raining or it is not raining" is equivalent to "Either it is raining or not, and is hot, or it is raining or not, and is not hot"; which is equivalent to "Either it is raining and hot, or raining and not hot, or not raining and hot, or not raining and not hot." This, in turn, is equivalent to "Either it is hot or not, and raining, or it is hot or not, and not raining"; which is equivalent to "Either it is hot or it is not hot."

For the validity of the trains of reasoning in these proofs we must, of course, appeal to intuition. A point of logic being in question, no other course is possible. But let the reader ask himself whether they involve any mode of inference which he is willing to be deprived of—for instance, in making deductions in geometry. The proofs have the air of clumsy legerdemain, not because they are sophistical, but because they are 'so unnecessary.' They merely emphasize the fact that the logical division of any proposition $p$ with respect to any exhaustive set of other alternatives, $\sim q \vee q$, does not alter the logical force of the assertion $p$. That is to say, the tautological character of tautologies is something which ordinary logical procedures assume; and in that sense, all tautologies are presumed as already given. This merely reflects the inevitable fact that, when deductions are to be made, logical principles themselves are already implicit.

However, one may object that to assume implicitly what is to be deduced is not legitimate. Let us examine this possible objection with care. The problem is whether something is deducible from something else. This something to be deduced may happen to be a logical principle. But if I want to know whether $B$ is deducible from $A$, and I find that there is a valid mode of reasoning which allows me to take $A$ as premise and derive $B$ as conclusion, do I or do I not thereby discover that $B$ is genuinely deducible from $A$? It is here that we encounter the ambiguity of 'deducibility' which has been mentioned. It may mean (1) 'deducible by *some* valid mode of inference'; or it may mean (2) 'deducible in accordance with some principle of inference *which has been assumed or already proved.*' The first is the only meaning which ever occurs outside of logic itself: in mathematics or politics or what not, to say that something is deducible means that it may be inferred by some valid mode of reasoning (all such valid modes being taken for granted). But in logic itself, the propositions of the system have a double use: they are used as premises *from* which conclusions are drawn; and as principles of inference *in accord with* which conclusions are drawn. Therefore in *logic*, 'deducible' may have the first meaning above, or it may have the second meaning, which is here quite different. This is the importance of the logistic method: by that method, one assumes a set of postulates and definitions to begin with; and the problem is to deduce the further principles of the system from the propositions assumed (or previously proved) *in accordance with* these same propositions as principles of inference. Thus in logic, something $B$ may be deducible from something $A$, in the first sense, when it is not deducible in the second—because the principle of inference required for the deduction is valid but has not yet been proved in the system. To avoid the ambiguity, then, let us call this second meaning of the word 'logistic deducibility.'

What has been shown above is that the properties of strict implication (paradoxical ones included) coincide with those of deducibility in the first or general sense. That is, $p \prec q$ can validly be interpreted to mean "Given $p$ as premise, $q$ may be deduced by some valid mode of inference." But the properties of strict implication do *not* coincide with those of *logistic* deducibility; and the paradoxical theorems are, in general, false of logistic deducibility. For example, if the theorem

$$\sim\Diamond\sim q \,.\prec .\, p \prec q$$

should hold when $p \prec q$ is interpreted "$q$ is logistically deducible from $p$," then (since the laws of any properly constructed logistic system are all tautologies) the whole of any logistic system could be derived from a single postulate, or from any assumption whatever. This is not, of course, the case.

However, this failure to accord with the properties of logistic deducibility is no ground of possible objection to strict implication. For there can be *no* relation having fixed logical properties which is such that it holds between *A* and *B* whenever *B* is logistically derivable from *A*, and fails to hold when this is not the case.

Let us investigate the reason for this. Suppose that a complete calculus of logic can be derived in the logistic manner from five postulates, *A*, *B*, *C*, *D*, and *E*. If the postulate-set is well devised, it will be the case that, if any one of these five postulates should be omitted, there would be a certain body of theorems, belonging to the calculus and expressing truths of logic, which could not be derived from the remaining four. This would likewise be the case for *any* selection of the postulates: from *A*, *B*, and *C*, or from *B*, *D*, and *E*, etc., certain theorems would be logistically deducible, but certain others belonging to the system would not. For example, it might be the case that, using postulate *E* as a principle of inference, we can derive theorem *Q* from postulate *A* as premise; but that without postulate *E*, no principle of inference can be derived from the other four which will serve as the principle by which theorem *Q* can be deduced. Theorem *Q* would, in this case, not be logistically deducible from the four postulates, *A*, *B*, *C*, and *D*. This would be so in spite of the fact that a sufficient premise for the theorem—postulate *A*—is given, and that the theorem can be inferred from this premise by a valid mode of inference—according to the omitted postulate *E*. Thus if we omit any postulate in our set, not only have we lost a premise from which theorems might be derived, but we have lost *certain modes of inference* which, in the absence of this postulate, are not allowable.

Also it is the case that, for any logistic system derived from any set of postulates, the allowable modes of inference vary with the stage of development of the system. The reason is obvious: no principle of inference can be used (except the postulates) until it has been proved. In deriving the first few theorems, the allowable modes are very much restricted; later, when a considerable number and variety of theorems have been proved, the modes of inference available are similarly multiplied. If it were not for this fact, then any proper and complete calculus of logic *could* be derived logistically from a single assumption. For such a calculus will, when completely developed, contain all genuinely valid modes of inference amongst its theorems; and if all of these were available from the beginning, then, as we have shown, a single postulate would be sufficient.

Thus it cannot be demanded that any implication-relation should be such that "$p$ implies $q$" will hold when and only when $q$ is *logistically* deducible from $p$, or that its properties should be those of logistic deducibility in general. Logistic deducibility *has* no general logical properties, but only such as are relative to the antecedently given modes of inference. No reliable logical relation could be such that it will hold, for example, between postulate $A$ and Theorem $Q$ when $A$, $B$, $C$, $D$, and $E$ are given, but will fail to hold when $A$, $B$, $C$, and $D$ are given and $E$ is not given.

It is not, therefore, a legitimate objection to strict implication, or to any other implication-relation, that it fails to coincide with logistic deducibility in logic itself.[8] The only legitimate demand which can be made is that a relation shall hold between a premise and a conclusion whenever, *all valid modes of deduction being allowed*, that conclusion can be derived from that premise; and that it shall fail to hold when such deductive derivation is not possible. The relation of strict implication satisfies this requirement: no relation of truth-implication does. In this sense, the system of Strict Implication constitutes an adequate canon (for unanalyzed propositions) of deductive inference.

However, it would be a mistake if this should be taken to mean that the principles of other systems are false as laws of logic. It needs to be understood that what is usually called 'logic'—meaning the canon of inference—represents simply a selection of relations, with their laws, which are found useful for certain purposes, notably those commonly connoted by 'deduction.' *There is no peculiar and exclusive truth of these, as against some other selection of the relations of propositions, and the laws*

[8] Material implication likewise lacks this property. According to it, any true proposition is implied by anything. But obviously one cannot derive the system, logistically, from a single arbitrarily chosen assumption.

*of these other relations.* It is in this sense that it is accurate to say that there is no such thing as 'logic'; there are only the indefinitely large number of different relations of propositions, every one of them having its own fixed properties, the expression of which are the 'laws' of it. These different relations, and their laws, may each be elicited by some particular mode of classifying and comparing propositions, and conveyed by a definition expressing the criterion of such classification.

It is obvious enough, in the light of this and earlier chapters, that whether a particular relation is included or omitted in a 'system' is a matter of choice. Systems are thoroughly man-made, even in that sense in which relations and the truth about them are not. When we include a given relation in a system, or omit it, we may do well or ill; but such inclusion creates no truth, and such omission indicates no falsity. The justification of one's procedure, in this respect, is purely pragmatic; it depends upon the relevance of what is included or omitted to the purposes which the system is designed to satisfy. If, for example, it is important to be able to express in logic those facts about the relations of propositions commonly denoted by 'consistency' and 'independence,' then any calculus comprising truth-value relations exclusively is ill-devised, because it cannot express or deal with the consistency or independence of unanalyzed propositions. If, on the other hand, these relations of propositions are irrelevant to the purposes for which the system is intended, then the complexity incident to their inclusion would merely be a nuisance.

Traditional logic is a highly selected body of truth within an immensely greater body of truth (tautologies in general) of the same fundamental type. The same is true also of any 'logic' devised to accord with and convey the significance of proofs in mathematics and other exact sciences—to which purpose traditional logic is hopelessly inadequate. Just as the weight of every grain of sand on the seashore is a physical fact, though no part of 'physics,' so the truths about the relations of propositions are all of them logical facts, and the multiplicity and variety of such facts is beyond all imagining; but to be a logical fact in this sense does not mean to be a part of 'logic.' Logic represents a certain order or arrangement of facts; a very fundamental type of order, since it is the order of our chosen ways of ordering in general. Nevertheless it is not the only type of such order which is possible. We could not arrange facts in a certain order if the facts did not have certain relations. But facts do not arrange themselves; and quite generally the relations which facts actually have allow an almost unlimited variety of different orderings. This is true even in logic.

We cannot do justice to the importance of this matter here. But something of its bearing on logic must be understood if we are to appreciate the sense in which *there are alternatives with respect to the canon of inference*, and the relation which holds between any such canon and the wider field of logical facts or tautologies in general.

The facts summarized by a system, and the relations of these facts, are not created by the system nor dependent on the process of inference by which the system grows. Geometry did not wait for Euclid, nor logic for Aristotle. Inference or other system-building sets up guide-posts or makes a map of facts, but it does not create the geography of them. This is true even of logical facts. We cannot 'relate them in certain ways': they either are so related or they are not. We can only *select* certain relations to be our guides. But it is important to realize that there are genuine alternatives for such selection of relations and consequent types of order utilized. And so far as such choice is possible, the result of our system-making answers to pragmatic criteria which are quite outside any question of absolute truth. We can select the relations to be followed as guides and thus delineate a structure of facts in ways which are suited to our purposes. But also we might do this in some other fashion which would still be true to the facts but relatively useless to us.

Perennial purposes may, in the main, be relied upon to elicit and integrate that body of truth which is relevant and adequate to them. Thus accord with tradition is a valuable test in logic, especially if by 'tradition' we denote practice rather than precept. But we should guard ourselves against designating what is falsely put forward as best satisfying certain purposes as therefore 'false.'

Inference is not something which we are forced to perform in certain ways because 'reality is what it is.' Even so far as a system exhibits a certain set of facts in their relations, it is still true that the inferences which represent our ways of devising the system stand quite outside the facts and their relations, which the system serves to summarize. Inference is something which we *do,* upon observation of certain relationships amongst the facts with which we are dealing. We make the inference of *B* from *A* when we observe that a certain relation exists between *A* and *B*. But the relation exists whether it is observed or not. (This is true—and most curiously so—even in logic itself. In dealing with a calculus of propositions, for example, we find *A* in the system, and we find the relation "*A* implies *B*" in the system; whereupon, if we choose, we 'infer *B* from *A*.' But '*B* inferred from *A*' is nothing which happens in the system of logical facts. The three facts, *A*, *B*, and "*A* implies *B*," stand side by side in the system, and are unaffected by our inferring. Inference remains an *operation* even when implication is a relation of the system. The logistic rule which controls or allows this operation of inference reveals its externality to the facts within the system itself by being incapable of expression in the symbols of the system. The system may be discovered or delimited in terms of inference: nevertheless the fact of the inference is nothing in the system.)

The point—the very important point—of what immediately precedes is this: We make an inference upon observation of a certain relation between facts. Whether the facts have that relation or not we do not determine. But whether we shall *be observant of* just this particular relation of the facts and whether we shall *make that relation the basis of our inferences* are things which we do determine. It is quite universally the case that the facts with which we are dealing have *other* logical relations, which we do not choose to be observant of. And these unobserved relationships may *also* be such that, when they exist, it is valid to make an inference. Thus that relation upon observation of which we shall make an inference is not something unambiguously determined by the nature of logical facts. There are alternatives: in fact, an extraordinarily large number of alternatives.

The fact that logical order is immensely wider than traditionally observed relationships, and the fact that quite other relations might serve as guides in our exploration of facts and as the basis of our inferences, have been obscured by the settled character of our intellectual habits. It has seemed to us that there was only one basic type of order, in terms of certain chosen logical relations, which could possess validity. We are familiar with the fact that there is a variety of abstract geometries, for example, no more than one of which is true of space, but all of which are valid. But that there may be a variety of 'logics,' each comprising certain selected relationships of propositions, any one of which might validly become the chosen basis of our inferences, has escaped us. It has seemed to us that there must be one unambiguously true canon of inference, based upon a single implication-relation, and that any inference not sanctioned by the laws of this relation would be invalid. But this is not the case. The number of relations which can validly give rise to inference is indefinitely large. At least their number is so great that it is practically impossible for our human minds to be observant of them all, or even aware of them. Thus, practically, it is necessary that we make our inferences upon observation of some chosen one—or at least some chosen few—of these relations. This choice will, of course, be determined, in part at least, by conformity to our capacities, our bent of mind, and our characteristic intellectual purposes. Thus logic, as the canon of deductive inference, must necessarily be something which, *in addition* to being absolutely true, is pragmatically determined.

We have tried to make clear the sense in which the laws of valid inference are truly unambiguous. They must, indeed, be laws of some relation, $pIq$, which is such that when $p$ is true, or assertable, and this relation holds, $q$ will not be false. It is a further fact that all such relations, which can give rise to inference, coincide with one another in the property that

$$(p \text{ and } pIq)\ I\ q$$

represents a tautology; and that the relation $I$, in its *asserted* occurrence here, coincides with strict implication. Thus attention to this relation of strict implication isolates and generalizes the properties of valid inference. But it remains a fact that such implication-relations exist in great variety, incident to possible systems which arise when the basic classification of propositions is made in different ways. The laws of such systems are as various as the systems themselves, and the implication-relations appearing in them are distinct from one another. Moreover, it does not require attention to precisely that property in which they coincide to secure that inferences drawn in accordance with their laws will always be true when the propositions used as premises are true. The nature of any implication-relation itself secures that.

Thus there are an indefinitely large number of 'logics,' or possible canons of inference, every one of which is true throughout and states true laws of inference. If our intellectual habits and interests were slightly different, we might choose some other than the logic of traditional deduction to be our guide. For example, if the fundamental division, (1) known for a fact, (2) known not to be a fact, (3) doubtful, should seem to us more important, natural, and simpler than the basic dichotomy into true or false, then we might choose the Three-valued Calculus of Lukasiewicz and Tarski as our canon, and draw our inferences on the basis of some one or more of the 2,916 implication-relations which are definable in terms of the truth-values of that system. In that case, we should not (if we were consistent) *deny* the Law of the Excluded Middle: we should *ignore* it; because we should be unobservant of that principle of division to which alone it is pertinent. Similarly, if consistency and independence of propositions should not be important to us, we might choose the system of Material Implication as the canon of our inferences. We should then observe the basic dichotomy of true and false, and the Law of the Excluded Middle, but we should ignore the basic trichotomy of consistency, "Either $p$ is consistent with $q$, or $p$ is consistent with '$q$ is false,' or $p$ is not consistent with itself," which represents the fundamental tautology of strict implication. (Most of us do ignore this trichotomy in precept, though whether we ignore it in practice, or can ignore it with safety to our prevailing intellectual interests, are different questions.)

The real defect which all truth-value logics have, in use, is pragmatic. It is one which is very simple and easily observed. What a proposition implies, in any truth-value meaning of the word, is different, if the proposition is true, from what it implies if false. And this dependence of what implies what upon truth or falsity defeats one of the most important interests which we have in our observation of logical relationships. This characteristic interest moves us to note, primarily if not exclusively, only those relations which remain invariant whether the terms of them are true or false. One notable example of the interest in question is the desire to be able to draw the consequences of an hypothesis whose truth or falsity is undetermined.

If we choose a truth-implication as the basis of inference, there are two ways, and only two, in which this implication-relation can be known to hold: (1) it may be known from the import, content, or meaning of $p$ and $q$, that it is *impossible* under any circumstances that $p$ should be true and $q$ false; (2) it may be known that it is not the case that $p$ is true and $q$ false, through knowing the truth of $q$ or knowing the falsity of $p$. But the second alternative here has no value for any of our characteristic interests in drawing inferences. And the first alternative means that the relation coincides with strict implication.

Let us examine this second alternative. Here we should know $pIq$ to hold either because we know $q$ to be true or because we know $p$ to be false. But if we know $p$ to be false, we discover nothing about the truth of $q$ from the fact that $pIq$ holds. If $p$ is false, and $pIq$ holds, $q$ may, of course, be likewise false. Furthermore we cannot, in this case, infer $q$ *hypothetically* from $p$: that is, we cannot say "$q$ *would* be true if $p$ *were* true," because a truth-implication which holds when $p$ is false might or might not hold if $p$ were true. Again, if we know that $pIq$ holds because we know that $q$ is true, this serves none of the purposes which we have in drawing inferences. First, because if we know $q$ to be true, why infer it? And second, because a truth-implication which holds when $q$ is true might or might not hold if $q$ were false. Thus no relation of truth-implication has any possible use in the investigation of hypotheses. For example, in terms of material implication any known fact is implied equally by *all* hypotheses. And for *any* such relation, if $h$ be an hypothesis and $f$ be some known fact, then either $hIf$ holds for *all* hypotheses equally or the truth-value of $hIf$ cannot be determined until the value of $h$ is known.

Thus the only case in which any truth-implication can be known to hold, under circumstances which make that fact useful for the purposes of inference, is the case in which $pIq$ is known to hold through knowing that the conjunction '$p$ true but $q$ false' is impossible under any circumstances. To know this, however, means precisely to know that $pIq$ is a *tautology*—to know that $p \prec q$ holds. Thus the only case in which any truth-implication is likely to have any value in application, as the basis of inference, is the case in which it coincides with strict implication.

There can be no reasonable doubt that it is such pragmatic considerations which account for the accord between traditional logical principles and Strict Implication, and the failure of such accord in the case of truth-value systems. The laws of all such formal systems are equally true—of their own relations. But pragmatically the laws of truth-value systems, where these diverge from those of Strict Implication, are 'false' or unacceptable in the sense that they have no useful application to inference.

# CHAPTER IX

## THE GENERAL THEORY OF PROPOSITIONS

In previous chapters we have dealt with propositions constructed on elementary propositional functions, that is to say, on functions built up by the use of the variables $p, q, \ldots$, and in terms of the ideas symbolized by $\vee$, $.$, $\sim$, $\dashv$, together with certain derivative conceptions. Thus, we have constructed such propositions as $(p) . p \vee \sim p$ and $(\exists p, q) . p \vee q$ on functions like $p \vee \sim p$ and $p \vee q$. Elementary functions provide a framework on which more explicit functions can be constructed; and it is these more explicit functions, together with the propositions that can be formulated in connection with them, which we have to consider in this chapter. The way in which elementary functions are related to the ones with which we are now concerned can be seen from the following consideration. If we have an elementary function $F(p_1, \ldots, p_n)$, such that

$$(p_1, \ldots, p_n) . F(p_1, \ldots, p_n)$$

is true, we can replace the variables involved by more explicit expressions, such as $f(x)$ and $g(x, y)$, and obtain a true proposition that is a logical consequence of the original one, because the resulting function will simply be a specific form of $F(p_1, \ldots, p_n)$, and what holds for all propositions denoted by $p_1, \ldots, p_n$ will hold for the narrower range of propositions denoted by the more specific expressions $f(x)$, $g(x, y)$, etc. Thus, from $(p) . p \vee \sim p$ we can derive $(f(x)) . f(x) \vee \sim f(x)$, $(g(x, y)) . g(x, y) \vee \sim g(x, y)$, and the like. And this means, of course, that all universal propositions constructed on elementary functions which have been previously established can be extended without further argument to the functions with which we are immediately concerned.

In order to make clear the significance of such expressions as $f(x)$, let us take two propositions which can be expressed by the words "*a* is round" and "*b* is round" respectively, where *a* and *b* are names of assigned particulars; and let us observe what these propositions have in common. It is clear, in this case, that if the subjects $a$ and $b$ were not distinct, we should have one proposition in place of two; so that the only point of difference arises in connection with a diversity of subjects. If, therefore, we remove $a$ and $b$, we shall have left only what is common to the two propositions; and what we have to do is to devise a way of representing this common factor. It might be supposed that we could do this, quite simply, by writing "is round"; but that would hardly be sufficient, because, in addition to having their predicates in common, these propositions are both of the subject-predicate kind, and so have their *forms* in common as well. It will be better to write "$x$ is round," where $x$ is to be understood, not as being a name of an assigned thing, but simply as representing an element of syntax. This complex factor, "$x$ is round," is, then, the ground of the resemblance of the two propositions; it is an incomplete entity, of such a kind that, when completed in an appropriate manner, a proposition, true or false, arises: if $a$ is, as we say, substituted for $x$, the first proposition results; if $b$ is substituted, the second. In referring here to the 'substitution of $a$ for $x$,' however, we must not be supposed to be referring directly to anything other than the symbols in question; what $x$ stands for, namely, an element of syntax, does not vanish when substitution is carried out; it is simply that the symbol $x$ is no longer required, its function being performed by $a$.

Now, in "$x$ is round," the element of form represented by $x$ is referred to as being a *variable*, $a$, $b$, etc., being called values of that variable; and "$x$ is round" is itself said to be a propositional function, of which "$a$ is round," "$b$ is round," etc., are values or instances. The situation here is, of course, exactly analogous to the one we have in the case of elementary functions. Thus, $p \vee q$ is a function of the two variables $p$ and $q$, and takes such propositions as "To-day is Monday or to-day is Tuesday" as values, where the variables themselves denote the separate propositions. By using propositional functions, we are able to speak of *all* the propositions that are instances of a given function; we are, for instance, able to refer to all propositions of the form

"$x$ is round" without being acquainted with the several members of the class of propositions in question.

Let us take now the propositions "$a$ is round" and "$b$ is square," with a view to examining their points of resemblance. These propositions have distinct predicates, as well as distinct subjects, but they resemble each other in that they are both of the subject-predicate kind; so that we may replace $a$ and $b$ by $x$, and "round" and "square" by $f$, and thus obtain a function of the form "$x$ is $f$," of which each proposition is an instance. This function will denote any subject-predicate proposition, and we shall be able, accordingly, to refer to all such propositions by referring to all that are of the form "$x$ is $f$," just as we can refer to all disjunctive propositions by referring to all values of the function $p \vee q$. Again, let us compare "$a$ is round" with, say, "$b$ is perceived by some one," where the latter proposition is not, strictly, of the subject-predicate kind. Here the two propositions seem to resemble each other only in that each is a proposition with regard to an assigned entity, to the effect that that entity possesses a certain property; and we may, as is customary, represent this common factor by writing $f(x)$. The function so expressed is more generic than any heretofore considered, and it will therefore denote a wider range of propositions: we can speak of any proposition that is one with regard to an assigned thing—to the effect that that thing possesses a certain property, however complex—as being of the form $f(x)$.

Let us consider now the proposition "$a$ is larger than $b$," where $a$ and $b$ are given particulars. We can, just as before, replace $a$ and $b$ by variables, so that we have "$x$ is larger than $y$"; and then, if we replace the relation "being larger than" by $R$, we shall have the function $x\,R\,y$, which will denote any proposition consisting of two terms connected by a dyadic relation. And we may, of course, write $f(x, y)$ to denote such propositions as "$a$ and $b$ are perceived by some one," which are not strictly of the dyadic-relational kind, as well as such as "$a$ is larger than $b$," which are of that kind. In the same way, we may take the proposition "$a$ gives $b$ to $c$," which involves three terms asserted to be connected by a triadic relation, and from it derive $f(x, y, z)$; and, again, we may write $f(x, y, z, w)$, which will denote propositions like "$a$ gives $b$ to $c$ at $t$."

We must endeavor to make more explicit the exact way in which propositions are related to the functions that denote them. In general, a proposition admits of several different analyses, and each analysis reveals a function which denotes the proposition. Thus, "$a$ is larger than $b$" can be analyzed into $a$ and 'being larger than $b$,' and is therefore an instance of the function "$x$ is larger than $b$"; it can be analyzed into $b$ and '$a$ as being larger than,' and so is an instance of "$a$ is larger than $y$"; and it can be analyzed into $a$, $b$, and 'being larger than,' and is therefore an instance of "$x$ is larger than $y$." An assigned function will, then, denote a proposition, if at all, only with respect to some analysis of which the proposition admits, or, in other words, only in virtue of the way in which certain factors in the proposition are related; and since a proposition is complex, there may be many such functions, more or less generic. Observe, for instance, that $f(x)$ is simply a more generic function than "$x$ is larger than $b$" and will therefore denote any proposition denoted by this latter function. Moreover, the function "$a$ is larger than $y$" is also of the form $f(x)$; and since both "$x$ is larger than $b$" and "$a$ is larger than $y$" denote the proposition "$a$ is larger than $b$," the function $f(x)$ will denote this proposition in virtue of two different analyses. Any proposition of the form $f(x, y)$ must be of the form $f(x)$ in at least two respects, and any one of the form $f(x, y, z)$ must be of the form $f(x)$ in at least three respects; so that when we speak of all propositions that are instances of $f(x)$, we are speaking of all that are instances of $f(x, y)$, and of all that are instances of $f(x, y, z)$; though, of course, the converse does not hold. Again, consider the conjunctive proposition "$a$ is round and $b$ is not square." This is an instance of each of the functions $p . \sim q$, $p . q$, and $p$; but it is also an instance of $f(x)$, since it is of the form "$x$ is round and $b$ is not square," and of $f(x, y)$, since it is of the form "$x$ is round and $y$ is not square"; and it is, of course, also an instance of $f(x) . g(y)$ and of $f(x) . \sim g(y)$. What distinguishes the functions dealt with in this chapter from elementary functions is that here we introduce variables such as $f$ and $x$ which can denote constituents of propositions that are not themselves propositions, whereas in elementary functions only propositional variables occur. It is commonly supposed that variables like $f$ and $x$ cannot denote propositions; but we shall see, later on, that they can, and that they differ from $p$, $q$, ... only in having a wider range of variation. This is why the present theory is more general, and includes functions involving propositional variables as a special case.

Now, let us take the proposition $(\exists p) . p$, i.e., "There is at least one true proposition," and let us replace $p$ by $f(x)$, so that we shall have $(\exists f(x)) . f(x)$, which will mean "There is at least one true proposition of the form $f(x)$" or "At least one value of $f(x)$ is true." It is not customary in such a case to use the symbol $(\exists f(x))$ as a prefix, however; we write instead $(\exists f, x) . f(x)$, which is to be read: "For at least one value of $f$ and at least one value of $x$, $f(x)$ is true," or "There are values of $f$ and $x$ such that $f(x)$ is true." And it is clear that we can here say equally well, "Some value of $f$ is such that there is a value of $x$ for which $f(x)$ is true," and write $(\exists f) : (\exists x) . f(x)$, which expresses a proposition about $(\exists x) . f(x)$ to the effect that, for at least one value of $f$, $(\exists x) . f(x)$ is true. The proposition $(\exists f) : (\exists x) . f(x)$ is to be conceived as built up by means of two successive generalizations: we first take $f(x)$ and generalize with respect to $x$, so that we have $(\exists x) . f(x)$, where $f$ remains undetermined, and then we generalize this latter with respect to $f$.

It is to be observed that whereas $(\exists f) : (\exists x) . f(x)$ expresses a proposition, $(\exists x) . f(x)$ expresses a propositional function, which will give rise to a proposition when a value is assigned to $f$; so that, for instance, if we specify $f$ as meaning 'is round,' we shall have the proposition "$(\exists x) . x$ is round," i.e., "There is at least one round thing," as a value of the function. $(\exists x) . f(x)$ belongs to a new kind of propositional functions, which we shall call general functions because they involve generalization. They are to be contrasted with such functions as $f(x)$ and $p \vee q$, which do not involve generalization, and which we may call *matrices*.[1] In particular, we shall refer to $(\exists x) . f(x)$ as a *singly-general* function, since it involves only a single generalization.

[1] See *Principia Mathematica*, ∗12.

If we have a function of the form $f(x)$, where $f$ is constant, such as "$x$ is round," there are two assertions that can be made by way of generalizing $x$: we can say "$f(x)$ has a true value" and write $(\exists x) . f(x)$, or we can say "$f(x)$ does not have a true value" and write $\sim(\exists x) . f(x)$; and there are, accordingly, two fundamental sorts of singly-general propositions—those like "$(\exists x) . x$ is round," which are particular propositions, and those like "$\sim(\exists x) . x$ is round," which are universal ones. But since $f(x)$ is associated with its negative, $\sim f(x)$, it will be convenient to consider, together with $(\exists x) . f(x)$ and $\sim(\exists x) . f(x)$, the functions $(\exists x) . \sim f(x)$ and $\sim(\exists x) . \sim f(x)$, which are identical with the first ones except that they result from generalization on $\sim f(x)$ rather than on $f(x)$. These four expressions provide us with a means of rendering any proposition that can be said to be constructed on a function $f(x)$ in terms of $(\exists x)$ and $\sim$. A proposition of the form $(\exists x) . f(x)$ means that for some value or other of $x$, $f(x)$ is true; one of the form $\sim(\exists x) . f(x)$ means that all values of $f(x)$ are false; one of the form $(\exists x) . \sim f(x)$ means that for some value or other of $x$, $f(x)$ is false; whereas, one of the form $\sim(\exists x) . \sim f(x)$ means that there does not exist a value of $x$ for which $f(x)$ is false, or, in other words, that all values of $f(x)$ are true.

The logical relations which hold among these four functions are very simple: $(\exists x) . f(x)$ and $\sim(\exists x) . f(x)$ are, of course, contradictories, as are $(\exists x) . \sim f(x)$ and $\sim(\exists x) . \sim f(x)$; and $(\exists x) . f(x)$ is logically consistent with $(\exists x) . \sim f(x)$, as is $\sim(\exists x) . f(x)$ with $\sim(\exists x) . \sim f(x)$. This latter relation, however, is likely to lead to confusion. We might suppose that if $\sim(\exists x) . f(x)$ held, that is, that if $f(x)$ had no true values, then $(\exists x) . \sim f(x)$ would necessarily hold, and $\sim(\exists x) . \sim f(x)$ would have to be false. But if these expressions are interpreted carefully, this will be seen to be not the case: $\sim(\exists x) . f(x)$ simply denies that there is a true value of $f(x)$, whereas $\sim(\exists x) . \sim f(x)$ denies that there is a false one; so that if both were true, it would follow merely that there were no values of $f(x)$ at all; and this is logically possible. For the same reason, $(\exists x) . f(x)$ is not a logical consequence of $\sim(\exists x) . \sim f(x)$; though, of course, if we know that there is at least one value within the range of significance of $x$, this knowledge, together with $\sim(\exists x) . \sim f(x)$, will enable us to infer $(\exists x) . f(x)$. All that needs to be emphasized here is that $(\exists x) . f(x)$ does not follow from $\sim(\exists x) . \sim f(x)$ alone.

Now, just as we replace $\sim(\exists p) . \sim$ by $(p)$, so we may replace $\sim(\exists x) . \sim$ by $(x)$; so that we may write $(x) . f(x)$, and say "For every value of $x$, $f(x)$ is true," where $(x) . f(x)$ is simply another way of expressing $\sim(\exists x) . \sim f(x)$. This will give rise to a number of redundant, though convenient, expressions. We shall have $(x) . \sim f(x)$, which is equivalent to $\sim(\exists x) . f(x)$; $\sim(x) . f(x)$, which is equivalent to $(\exists x) . \sim f(x)$; and $\sim(x) . \sim f(x)$, which is equivalent to $(\exists x) . f(x)$. And in view of these equivalences, it is easy to see that $(x) . f(x)$ is contradicted by $(\exists x) . \sim f(x)$, and $(x) . \sim f(x)$ by $(\exists x) . f(x)$.

We are here interpreting universal propositions as being purely negative, inasmuch as we are defining them as denials of particular, existential propositions. And, indeed, when a universal proposition is examined, this is seen to be its essential import. Take, for instance, the universal "Everything is extended," which we should write

$$\sim(\exists x) . x \text{ is not extended,}$$
or
$$(x) . x \text{ is extended.}$$

It is clear that, in making this assertion, we are not saying what things do exist; what we are in fact doing is *denying* the existence of unextended things; we are saying, with regard to the function "$x$ is unextended," that there is nothing to which it applies. It would, of course, be possible so to interpret "Everything is extended" that it would imply, not only that there were no unextended things, but also that there were, say, at least two things that were extended, or at least one; and it is quite possible that such a meaning is often, if not always, attached to these words in ordinary discourse. But this means merely that these words are commonly used to express a compound proposition like

$$\sim(\exists x) . x \text{ is not extended} : (\exists x) . x \text{ is extended,}$$

where the left-hand expression in the conjunction does not imply that there are any things at all. We shall always interpret a universal proposition as merely denying the existence of anything of a certain kind, and thus as being without existential import.

It will be clear, then, that the foregoing functions all take as values propositions which either assert or deny the existence of entities of a certain sort. There are, however, other functions that can be constructed on $f(x)$ which take as values propositions of an entirely different kind. Let us consider the function $(\exists x) . f(x)$, and assign to $f(x)$ the meaning "$x$ is round," so that we shall have the proposition "There are round things." If we write

$$\sim\Diamond(\exists x) . x \text{ is round},$$

we shall be expressing the false proposition "It is impossible that there should exist a thing that was round," and if we deny this proposition, by writing

$$\Diamond(\exists x) . x \text{ is round},$$

we shall be saying, not that there *are* round things, but simply that there might be, i.e., that round things are logically possible. Of course, it is true both that there are round things and that there might be; but let us assign to $f(x)$ the meaning "$x$ is a centaur." Then we have the false proposition,

$$(\exists x) . x \text{ is a centaur},$$

i.e., "Centaurs exist," and the true one,

$$\Diamond(\exists x) . x \text{ is a centaur},$$

i.e., "It is logically possible that centaurs should exist." Again, if we assign to $f(x)$ the meaning "$x$ is both round and square," we can write the true propositions:

$$\sim(\exists x) . x \text{ is both round and square},$$

$$\text{and} \quad \sim\Diamond(\exists x) . x \text{ is both round and square}.$$

If, however, we give to $f(x)$ the meaning "$x$ is both human and immortal," we shall have the true proposition,

$$\sim(\exists x) . x \text{ is both human and immortal},$$

i.e., "Immortal men do not exist," and the false one,

$$\sim\Diamond(\exists x) . x \text{ is both human and immortal},$$

i.e., "Immortal men are not logically possible."

Thus, in addition to functions of the forms $(\exists x) . f(x)$ and $\sim(\exists x) . f(x)$, we must take account of those of the forms $\Diamond(\exists x) . f(x)$ and $\sim\Diamond(\exists x) . f(x)$. These latter are said to be *intensional* functions, whose values are propositions in intension, whereas the former are said to be *extensional* functions, whose values are propositions in extension. Now, it will be clear, in view of the foregoing examples, that from a proposition of the form $(\exists x) . f(x)$ a corresponding proposition of the form $\Diamond(\exists x) . f(x)$ follows, but that the converse does not hold; from the existence of an entity of a certain sort, we can infer the possibility of its existence, but from the mere logical possibility that there should be things of a given sort we cannot infer that such things actually occur. It will be clear, also, that from a proposition of the form $\sim\Diamond(\exists x) . f(x)$ a corresponding proposition of the form $\sim(\exists x) . f(x)$ follows, but not conversely; if we know that things of a certain kind are logically impossible, we can know that no such things exist, but we cannot know that such-and-such things are logically impossible by knowing that there are no such things.

We are here introducing propositions which express categorical possibility, as contrasted with those which express possibility only hypothetically. That is to say, in place of propositions of the form $\Diamond p \prec \Diamond q$, we have those of the form $\Diamond p$, where the scope of $\Diamond$ is the whole expression in question. Such propositions result from the substitution of values for $p$ in $\Diamond p$ and similar functions. And although the propositions of this kind which have been so far formulated are material rather than logical, we shall see presently that analogous strictly logical propositions are to be asserted. There are, clearly, purely logical truths to be expressed in the form of statements of categorical possibility. A proposition will be a logical truth if it is both constructed wholly in logical terms and certifiable on logical grounds, *a priori*. Thus, it can be seen *a priori* that $\Diamond(\exists p) . p$ is true, and this proposition contains nothing other than logical constants and variables. It will therefore be a purely logical truth expressing categorical possibility. Such propositions are essential in proofs of logical independence and non-deducibility, as we shall see later on. But when they are introduced, a deductive development of theorems from a few selected premises does not seem possible, because, in such a deductive development, we proceed by substituting more specific expressions for more generic ones, and that process is valid only where we have functions that are universally true in which to substitute.

We may now observe how purely logical propositions are to be constructed. All propositions whatever can be derived from logical matrices, such as $f(x)$, $p \vee q$, and $f(x) \vee {\sim}f(x)$, a matrix being a function which involves no generalized variables. There are two ways in which a variable in a matrix may be transformed, in the process of deriving a proposition from the matrix: we may specify the variable by assigning a value to it, or we may generalize the variable. When each of the variables in a logical matrix has been either generalized or specified, a proposition, true or false, results; but so long as at least one variable remains free, we have a propositional function. Thus, if we take the matrix $f(x)$, and specify $f$ as being 'is round,' we have the function "$x$ is round," involving the free variable $x$; but if we then go on to specify $x$ as being an assigned thing $a$, we have the proposition "$a$ is round." If, on the other hand, we generalize $x$, in place of assigning a value to it, by writing, say, "$(\exists x) . x$ is round," we have the general proposition "There are round things." If, again, we take the matrix $f(x)$, and assign to $x$ the value $a$, so that we have the function $f(a)$, and then generalize $f$ by writing, say, $(\exists f) . f(a)$, we have the proposition "$a$ has some property." If, finally, we generalize both $f$ and $x$ by writing, say, $(x) : (\exists f) . f(x)$, we have the proposition "Everything has some property or other." Now, each of the first three propositions here derived involves one or both of the material constituents $a$ and 'being round,' and for this reason is not purely logical; but the fourth proposition, which results from generalization with respect to both $f$ and $x$, involves only logical factors. A purely logical proposition is one that can be derived from some logical matrix without the assignment of a value to any variable in the matrix.

In connection with more complex matrices, we can, of course, construct functions involving generalization which are similar to those we have been considering: we have $(x) . f(x) \vee {\sim}f(x)$;

$\sim(\exists x) . \sim f(x) . f(x)$; $\sim(x) . \sim f(x) . f(x)$; etc. The function $(x) . f(x) \vee \sim f(x)$ is, by definition, the same as $\sim(\exists x) . \sim[f(x) \vee \sim f(x)]$, and since $\sim[f(x) \vee \sim f(x)]$ is equivalent to $\sim f(x) . f(x)$, we have $\sim(\exists x) . \sim f(x) . f(x)$; so that the functions

$$(x) . f(x) \vee \sim f(x) \quad \text{and} \quad (\exists x) . \sim f(x) . f(x)$$

are mutually contradictory, in the sense that, when a value is assigned to $f$, the resulting propositions will be mutually contradictory. Again, $\sim(x) . \sim f(x) . f(x)$ means what is meant by $(\exists x) . \sim[\sim f(x) . f(x)]$, where the matrix involved in the latter expression is equivalent to $f(x) \vee \sim f(x)$; so that we have

$$(\exists x) . f(x) \vee \sim f(x) \quad \text{and} \quad (x) . \sim f(x) . f(x)$$

as contradictory functions.

Now, it is clear that whatever value we may assign to $f$, the function $(x) . f(x) \vee \sim f(x)$ must, of necessity, give rise to a true proposition; that is to say, from the mere fact that a proposition was an instance of the function here in question, it would follow that the proposition was true; so that we may write the purely logical proposition:

$$\sim\Diamond(\exists f) : \sim(x) . f(x) \vee \sim f(x)$$
$$\text{or} \quad \sim\Diamond(\exists f) : (\exists x) . \sim[f(x) \vee \sim f(x)],$$

i.e., "It is impossible that there should be a value of $f$ such that some value of $f(x) \vee \sim f(x)$ was false." This is a specific form of the principle of excluded middle, the general form being $\sim\Diamond(\exists p) . \sim(p \vee \sim p)$, i.e., "It is impossible that there should be a proposition which was neither true nor false." Again, it is clear that from the mere circumstance that a proposition was an instance of the function $(\exists x) . \sim f(x) . f(x)$, we should be able to infer that it was false; so that we have

$$\sim\Diamond(\exists f) : (\exists x) . \sim f(x) . f(x),$$

i.e., "It is impossible that there should be values of $f$ and $x$ such that $\sim f(x) . f(x)$ was true." This is a specific form of the principle of contradiction, the general form being $\sim\Diamond(\exists p) . \sim p . p$, i.e., "It is impossible that there should be a proposition which was both true and false."

Corresponding to each of the foregoing propositions, which are in intension, we have, of course, a proposition in extension, since a universal in intension always implies a corresponding extensional universal. Thus, we have

$$\sim(\exists f) : (\exists x) . \sim f(x) . f(x),$$

which expresses the fact, not that there could not be values of $f$ and $x$ such that $\sim f(x) . f(x)$ was true, but merely that there are no such values.

Let us take now the function $(\exists x) . f(x)$. It is easily seen that, from the mere circumstance that a proposition was an instance of this function, we should not be able to infer that the proposition was true; so that we may write

$$\Diamond(\exists f) : \sim(\exists x) . f(x),$$

i.e., "It is possible that there should be a value of $f$ such that $(\exists x) . f(x)$ was false." It is equally clear, on the other hand, that a proposition of the form $(\exists x) . f(x)$ might, possibly, be true; so that we have the correlative proposition

$$\Diamond(\exists f) : (\exists x) . f(x).$$

And, obviously, we can write also:

$$\Diamond(\exists f) : (x) . f(x) \quad \text{and} \quad \Diamond(\exists f) : \sim(x) . f(x).$$

We have seen how from such a proposition as $\sim\Diamond(\exists p) . p . \sim p$ we can infer a proposition like $\sim\Diamond(\exists f, x) . f(x) . \sim f(x)$, on the ground that if the more generic function, $p . \sim p$, could not have a true value, the more specific one, $f(x) . \sim f(x)$, could not, the values of the more specific function being necessarily among those of the more generic. In the case of propositions expressing possibility rather than impossibility, however, such an inference would be invalid. Consider, for example, the true proposition $\Diamond(\exists p, q) . p . q$, i.e., "It is possible that there should be a true proposition of the form $p . q$," where, if we replace $p$ by $f(x)$, and $q$ by $\sim f(x)$, we get the falsehood $\Diamond(\exists f, x) . f(x) . \sim f(x)$. On the other hand, the converse implication holds in such a case: from a proposition about a more specific function we can infer a proposition about a less specific one. Thus, from $\Diamond(\exists f, x) . f(x)$

we can infer $\Diamond(\exists p) . p$, on the ground that any true value of $f(x)$ would necessarily be a true value of $p$.

It will be observed, with regard to each of the propositions so far considered, that each prefix has within its scope the entire matrix on which the proposition is constructed. If, however, we substitute $(\exists x) . f(x)$ for $p$ in the matrix $p \vee \sim p$, we shall have $(\exists x) . f(x) . \vee . \sim(\exists x) . f(x)$, where the two prefixes apply to separate subordinate matrices. This is a disjunctive function of two singly-general functions. And since $\sim(\exists x) . f(x)$ is equivalent to $(x) . \sim f(x)$, we can write the function in question in the form $(\exists x) . f(x) . \vee . (x) . \sim f(x)$ and say "Either there is a value of $x$ for which $f(x)$ is true, or else every value of $x$ is such that $f(x)$ is false." In the same way, we may substitute $(\exists x) . f(x)$ for $p$ in $\sim(p . \sim p)$, and obtain $\sim[(\exists x) . f(x) : (x) . \sim f(x)]$, which may be read "It is not the case both that some value of $x$ is such that $f(x)$ is true and that every value of $x$ is such that $f(x)$ is false." Since these propositions result from substitution in $p \vee \sim p$ and $\sim(p . \sim p)$, respectively, where both $\sim\Diamond(\exists p) . \sim(p \vee \sim p)$ and $\sim\Diamond(\exists p) . p . \sim p$ hold, we have the two theorems:

$$\sim\Diamond(\exists f) . \sim[(\exists x) . f(x) . \vee . (x) . \sim f(x)],$$
$$\text{and} \quad \sim\Diamond(\exists f) : (\exists x) . f(x) : (x) . \sim f(x),$$

as well as two corresponding propositions in extension, where $\sim\Diamond$ is replaced by $\sim$. And we have also, of course, both

$$\Diamond(\exists f) : (\exists x) . f(x) . \vee . (x) . \sim f(x)$$
$$\text{and} \quad \Diamond(\exists f) . \sim[(\exists x) . f(x) : (x) . \sim f(x)].$$

These are singly-general propositions constructed on disjunctions and conjunctions of singly-general functions.

It will, perhaps, be of interest to make some comparison at this point between the theory of propositions so far developed and the theory involved in the traditional Aristotelian logic. Traditional formal logic was concerned mainly with four fundamental propositional functions, or types of propositions, which were expressed, respectively, by "All *a*'s are *b*'s," "No *a*'s are *b*'s," "Some *a*'s are *b*'s," and "Some *a*'s are not *b*'s." Let us first express these functions in symbolic form. A class *a* is to be understood as being determined by a defining function, $f(x)$; so that we may replace $a$ by $f(x)$, and $b$ by $g(x)$, and write the function "All $a$'s are $b$'s" in the form:

$$\text{(A)} \qquad (x) \,.\, f(x) \supset g(x),$$

i.e., "For every value of $x$, $f(x)$ is false or $g(x)$ is true." Again, the function "No $a$'s are $b$'s" is to be written in the form:

$$\text{(E)} \qquad \sim(\exists x) \,.\, f(x) \,.\, g(x),$$

i.e., "There is nothing which satisfies both $f(x)$ and $g(x)$." And the function "Some $a$'s are $b$'s" is to be written:

$$\text{(I)} \qquad (\exists x) \,.\, f(x) \,.\, g(x),$$

i.e., "There exists at least one thing satisfying both $f(x)$ and $g(x)$." Whereas, "Some $a$'s are not $b$'s" is to be written:

$$\text{(O)} \qquad (\exists x) \,.\, f(x) \,.\, \sim g(x),$$

i.e., "There is something which satisfies $f(x)$ and fails to satisfy $g(x)$."

Now, according to the traditional doctrine, (A) and (O) were contradictory functions, as were (E) and (I); (I) was implied by (A), and (O) by (E); while (A) and (E) were incompatible. It is easy to see that (A) and (O) are, in fact, contradictories, since $(x) \,.\, f(x) \supset g(x)$ is equivalent to $\sim(\exists x) \,.\, \sim[\sim f(x) \vee g(x)]$, which is equivalent to $\sim(\exists x) \,.\, f(x) \,.\, \sim g(x)$; and, of course, (E) is contradictory to (I). But we cannot admit the view that (A) implies (I), or that (E) implies (O). Suppose we have a value assigned to $f$ such that $\sim(\exists x) \,.\, f(x)$ holds. Then, of course, (I) will be false, whatever meaning $g$ may have, since there will not exist a value of $x$ such that $f(x)$ and $g(x)$. Thus, let $f(x)$ mean "$x$ is a centaur," and $g(x)$ mean "$x$ lives upon the earth"; then $(x) \,.\, f(x) \supset g(x)$ will be true, because $\sim(\exists x) \,.\, f(x) \,.\, \sim g(x)$ will be, while $(\exists x) \,.\, f(x) \,.\, g(x)$ will be false. We have, then, contrary to the traditional doctrine,

$$\Diamond(\exists f, g) : (x) \,.\, f(x) \supset g(x) : \sim(\exists x) \,.\, f(x) \,.\, g(x),$$

from which it follows that

$$\sim(f, g) : (x) \,.\, f(x) \supset g(x) \,.\, \prec \,.\, (\exists x) \,.\, f(x) \,.\, g(x).$$

And note that, in the first of these expressions, the right-hand member of the matrix, $\sim(\exists x) . f(x) . g(x)$, is a function of the type (E); so that we must deny that (A) and (E) are incompatible. Again, if $f$ and $g$ take the values just assigned to them, function (O) will become a false proposition, while (E) will, as we have just seen, become a true one; so that we must write

$$\Diamond(\exists f, g) : \sim(\exists x) . f(x) . g(x) : \sim(\exists x) . f(x) . \sim g(x),$$

and deny that (O) follows from (E).

Now it is of course true that, in the traditional interpretation of expressions of the forms "All $a$'s are $b$'s" and "No $a$'s are $b$'s," existential import was assigned; and in this interpretation, we should have:

(A′) $\sim(\exists x) . f(x) . \sim g(x) : (\exists x) . f(x) : (\exists x) . \sim g(x)$;

(E′) $\sim(\exists x) . f(x) . g(x) : (\exists x) . f(x) : (\exists x) . g(x)$;

(I′) $(\exists x) . f(x) . g(x)$;

(O′) $(\exists x) . f(x) . \sim g(x)$.

Here, of course, (A′) and (E′) are incompatible; (I′) follows from (A′), and (O′) from (E′). But the relationship of contradictories breaks down, as may be seen if we allow $f(x)$ to mean "$x$ is a centaur" and $g(x)$ to mean "$x$ lives upon the earth." In this case, all four expressions (A′)–(O′) become falsehoods; and two contradictory propositions cannot both be false.

We must, then, emend the traditional scheme either by denying that "All $a$'s are $b$'s" implies "Some $a$'s are $b$'s," and that "No $a$'s are $b$'s" implies "Some $a$'s are not $b$'s," or by denying that "All $a$'s are $b$'s" contradicts "Some $a$'s are not $b$'s," and that "No $a$'s are $b$'s" contradicts "Some $a$'s are $b$'s." And there can be little doubt which emendation ought to be adopted: if we interpret these expressions by means of functions (A′)–(O′), thus allowing them all to imply existence, we shall have a scheme of propositions such that, if $p$ belongs to the scheme, $\sim p$ does not.

The four fundamental propositional forms of the traditional logic might, of course, be interpreted in intension. In place of "All $a$'s are $b$'s" we might say "Anything that was an $a$ would necessarily be a $b$" or "It is impossible that there should be an *a* that was not also a *b*." And we might interpret the remaining types of propositions, respectively, by "It is impossible that there should be anything that was both an *a* and a *b*"; "It is possible that there should be something that was both an *a* and a *b*"; and "It is possible that there should be a thing that was an *a* and not a *b*." In this interpretation, we should have the four fundamental functions:

(A″) $\sim\Diamond(\exists x) \,.\, f(x) \,.\, \sim g(x);$

(E″) $\sim\Diamond(\exists x) \,.\, f(x) \,.\, g(x);$

(I″) $\Diamond(\exists x) \,.\, f(x) \,.\, g(x);$

(O″) $\Diamond(\exists x) \,.\, f(x) \,.\, \sim g(x).$

It is, of course, clear that the range of values satisfying the first two of these intensional functions is narrower than that satisfying the corresponding extensional ones, (A), (E), and that the range of values satisfying the last two is wider than that satisfying the corresponding extensional functions, (I), (O). Thus, let $f(x)$ mean "$x$ is a man" and $g(x)$ mean "$x$ lives on the earth." Then $(x) \,.\, f(x) \supset g(x)$ will mean "All men live on the earth" and so will be true, while $\sim\Diamond(\exists x) \,.\, f(x) \,.\, \sim g(x)$ will mean "It is not possible that there should be a man who did not live on the earth" and so will be false; whereas, $(\exists x) \,.\, f(x) \,.\, \sim g(x)$ will mean "There is at least one man who does not live on the earth" and so will be false, while $\Diamond(\exists x) \,.\, f(x) \,.\, \sim g(x)$ will mean "It is possible that there should be a man who did not live on the earth" and so will be true. As we have said, an intensional universal implies a corresponding extensional universal, but not conversely; whereas an extensional particular implies a corresponding intensional particular, but not conversely.

Now, in connection with this intensional interpretation, difficulties arise with regard to the traditional doctrine which are exactly analogous to those which arise in connection with the extensional interpretation: (A″) does not imply (I″); (E″) does not imply (O″); and (A″) is compatible with (E″). Thus, let $f(x)$ mean "$x$ is both round and square" and $g(x)$ mean "$x$ is colored." Then $\sim\Diamond(\exists x) \,.\, f(x) \,.\, \sim g(x)$ will be true, since it will mean "It is not possible that there should be anything that was round, square, and not colored," whereas $\Diamond(\exists x) . f(x) . g(x)$ will be false, since it will mean "It is possible that there should be a thing that was round, square, and colored." And if we attempt to rectify this situation by changing (A″) to

$$\sim\Diamond(\exists x) . f(x) . \sim g(x) : \Diamond(\exists x) . f(x) . g(x),$$

then (I″) will, indeed, follow, but the relationship of contradictories will be destroyed. Thus, if we allow $f(x)$ and $g(x)$ to retain the meanings just assigned to them, the expression here given will mean "It is impossible that there should be anything which was round, square, and not colored, and possible that there should be a thing which was round, square, and colored," whereas

$$\Diamond(\exists x) . f(x) . \sim g(x)$$

will mean "It is possible that there should be a thing which was round, square, and not colored"; so that these two propositions will both be false, and will, therefore, not be contradictories.

Let us form now an expression for the syllogistic proposition " 'All $a$'s are $b$'s, and all $b$'s are $c$'s' implies 'All $a$'s are $c$'s.' " Consider the three functions:

$$(x) . f(x) \supset g(x), \qquad (x) . g(x) \supset h(x), \qquad (\exists x) . f(x) . \sim h(x).$$

Clearly, there cannot be values of $f$, $g$, and $h$ for which all three of these functions give rise to true propositions; so that we may write

$$\sim\Diamond(\exists f, g, h) : \sim(\exists x) . f(x) . \sim g(x) : \sim(\exists x) . g(x) . \sim h(x) : (\exists x) . f(x) . \sim h(x),$$

from which we have, as an immediate consequence,

$$(f, g, h) :. (x) . f(x) \supset g(x) : (x) . g(x) \supset h(x) : \prec . (x) . f(x) \supset h(x).$$

And it is to be noted that from this same incompatible triad of functions we have the two further syllogistic propositions:

$$(f, g, h) :. (x) . f(x) \supset g(x) : (\exists x) . f(x) . \sim h(x) : \prec . (\exists x) . g(x) . \sim h(x),$$

and $(f, g, h) :. (x) . g(x) \supset h(x) : (\exists x) . f(x) . \sim h(x) : \prec . (\exists x) . f(x) . \sim g(x).$

Moreover, we have also:

$$\sim\Diamond(\exists f, g, h) : \sim\Diamond(\exists x) \,.\, f(x) \,.\, \sim g(x) : \sim\Diamond(\exists x) \,.\, g(x) \,.\, \sim h(x) : \Diamond(\exists x) \,.\, f(x) \,.\, \sim h(x),$$

from which follow the three consequences:

$$(f, g, h) :. (x) \,.\, f(x) \prec g(x) : (x) \,.\, g(x) \prec h(x) : \prec . (x) \,.\, f(x) \prec h(x),$$

$$(f, g, h) :. (x) \,.\, f(x) \prec g(x) : \Diamond(\exists x) \,.\, f(x) \,.\, \sim h(x) : \prec . \Diamond(\exists x) \,.\, g(x) \,.\, \sim h(x),$$

and $(f, g, h) :. (x) \,.\, g(x) \prec h(x) :$

$$\Diamond(\exists x) \,.\, f(x) \,.\, \sim h(x) : \prec . \Diamond(\exists x) \,.\, f(x) \,.\, \sim g(x),$$

in which $\prec$ occurs in subordinate positions in the matrix.

Let us form an expression for the syllogistic proposition

"All $a$'s are $b$'s, and $x$ is an $a$" implies "$x$ is a $b$,"

where we have the incompatible triad

$$(y) \,.\, f(y) \supset g(y), \qquad f(x), \qquad \sim g(x).$$

It will be noted here that $f$, $g$, and $x$ are free variables, and that we must write:

$$\sim\Diamond(\exists f, g, x) : (y) \,.\, f(y) \supset g(y) : f(x) : \sim g(x),$$

from which we shall have, as an immediate consequence,

$$(f, g, x) : (y) \,.\, f(y) \supset g(y) \,.\, f(x) \,.\prec .\, g(x),$$

as well as the two further propositions:

$$(f, g, x) : (y) \,.\, f(y) \supset g(y) \,.\, \sim g(x) \,.\prec .\, \sim f(x),$$

and $(f, g, x) : f(x) \,.\, \sim g(x) \,.\prec .\, (\exists y) \,.\, f(y) \,.\, \sim g(y).$

There are certain syllogistic arguments occurring in the traditional logic, however, which we shall have to disallow. In particular, it must be denied that from "All $a$'s are $b$'s" and "All $b$'s are $c$'s" we can infer "Some $a$'s are $c$'s." Here we have the three functions,

$$(x) \,.\, f(x) \supset g(x), \qquad (x) \,.\, g(x) \supset h(x), \qquad (x) \,.\, f(x) \supset \sim h(x),$$

which do not constitute an incompatible triad; so that we must write:

$$\Diamond(\exists f, g, h) : \sim(\exists x) . f(x) . \sim g(x) : \sim(\exists x) . g(x) . \sim h(x) : \sim(\exists x) . f(x) . h(x).$$

This expression states a fact to the effect that certain functions are independent of others, and that therefore certain propositions do not follow from certain others. It is ordinary practice in such a case simply to say on the side, and in English, that such-and-such implications do not hold. But it is plain that facts like these about non-implication and independence are coördinate in every way with facts about implication and dependence, and ought, therefore, to be given a coördinate status.

So far, in discussing singly-general functions, we have dealt only with those in one generalized variable, such as $(\exists x) . f(x)$ and $(x) . f(x)$; but it is easy to see that there are singly-general functions involving any number of variables, since all that is required in such a case is that only one generalization shall occur. Thus, we can write

$$(\exists x, y) . f(x, y) \text{ and } (x, y) . f(x, y),$$

which are singly-general functions in two generalized variables and one free variable; and we can write

$$(\exists x_1, \ldots, x_n) . f(x_1, \ldots, x_n) \text{ and } (x_1, \ldots, x_n) . f(x_1, \ldots, x_n),$$

which involve $n$ generalized variables, where $n$ is any finite number. So long as we are confined to a single generalization, however, the formal properties of functions in $n$ variables are the same as those of functions in one; so that a detailed treatment of functions in more than one variable will not be necessary. We have such propositions as:

$$\Diamond(\exists f) : (\exists x_1, \ldots, x_n) . f(x_1, \ldots, x_n),$$

$$\Diamond(\exists f) : (x_1, \ldots, x_n) . f(x_1, \ldots, x_n),$$

$$(f) : (x_1, \ldots, x_n) . f(x_1, \ldots, x_n) . \prec . \sim(\exists x_1, \ldots, x_n) . \sim f(x_1, \ldots, x_n),$$

and $$\sim\Diamond(\exists f) : (x_1, \ldots, x_n) . f(x_1, \ldots, x_n) : (\exists x_1, \ldots, x_n) . \sim f(x_1, \ldots, x_n),$$

of which the corresponding theorems for functions in one generalized variable are special cases.

We turn now to doubly-general functions. It will be clear that $(\exists x, y) \centerdot f(x, y)$ is equivalent to $(\exists x) : (\exists y) \centerdot f(x, y)$, that is, that we have

$$(f) :. (\exists x, y) \centerdot f(x, y) \centerdot = : (\exists x) : (\exists y) \centerdot f(x, y);$$

and that we have also

$$(f) :. (x, y) \centerdot f(x, y) \centerdot = : (x) : (y) \centerdot f(x, y).$$

The right-hand function in each of these equivalences is doubly general, since it involves two occurrences of $\exists$; and although, in each case, we have an equivalent singly-general function, doubly-general functions usually involve new logical force, in that equivalent functions of a lower degree of generality do not exist. Thus, in connection with $(\exists x) : (y) \centerdot f(x, y)$, and with $(x) : (\exists y) \centerdot f(x, y)$, there are no equivalent singly-general functions. The first of these expressions may be read "There is a value of $x$ such that for every value of $y$, $f(x, y)$ is true" or, more strictly, "There is a value of $x$ such that no value of $y$ exists for which $f(x, y)$ is false," i.e., $(\exists x) : \sim(\exists y) \centerdot \sim f(x, y)$; and the second may be read "Every value of $x$ is such that a value of $y$ exists for which $f(x, y)$ is true" or, more strictly, "It is false that a value of $x$ exists for which there is no value of $y$ such that $f(x, y)$ is true," i.e., $\sim(\exists x) : \sim(\exists y) \centerdot f(x, y)$. On the other hand, $(\exists x) : (\exists y) \centerdot f(x, y)$ means "Some value of $x$ is such that there exists a value of $y$ for which $f(x, y)$ is true"; and this can, as we have just seen, be expressed in terms of a single occurrence of $\exists$: "$x$ and $y$ exist such that $f(x, y)$ is true." Functions like this one, which can be expressed in equivalent form by means of functions of a lower degree of generality, will be said to be *reducible;* whereas those like $(x) : (\exists y) \centerdot f(x, y)$, which are not equivalent to any function of a lower degree, will be said to be *irreducible.* And it is clear that a function will be reducible, in this sense, if and only if, when it is expressed in terms of $\exists$ and $\sim$, two occurrences of $\exists$ are juxtaposed, without the intervention of $\sim$. Thus, $(x) : (y) \centerdot f(x, y)$ is equivalent to

$\sim(\exists x) : \sim \sim(\exists y) . \sim f(x, y)$, which is equivalent to $\sim(\exists x) : (\exists y) . \sim f(x, y)$, which is equivalent to $\sim(\exists x, y) . \sim f(x, y)$.

On a function $f(x)$, where $x$ is to be generalized and $f$ is to remain free, there are, as was pointed out above, four general functions that can be constructed by the use of $\exists$ and $\sim$. On a function $f(x, y)$, where $x$ and $y$ are to be generalized and $f$ is to remain free, there are sixteen such functions that can be constructed:

| | | | |
|---|---|---|---|
| [1] | $(\exists x) : (\exists y) . f(x, y)$; | [9] | $(\exists y) : (\exists x) . f(x, y)$; |
| [2] | $\sim(\exists x) : (\exists y) . f(x, y)$; | [10] | $\sim(\exists y) : (\exists x) . f(x, y)$; |
| [3] | $(\exists x) : \sim(\exists y) . f(x, y)$; | [11] | $(\exists y) : \sim(\exists x) . f(x, y)$; |
| [4] | $(\exists x) : (\exists y) . \sim f(x, y)$; | [12] | $(\exists y) : (\exists x) . \sim f(x, y)$; |
| [5] | $\sim(\exists x) : \sim(\exists y) . f(x, y)$; | [13] | $\sim(\exists y) : \sim(\exists x) . f(x, y)$; |
| [6] | $\sim(\exists x) : (\exists y) . \sim f(x, y)$; | [14] | $\sim(\exists y) : (\exists x) . \sim f(x, y)$; |
| [7] | $(\exists x) : \sim(\exists y) . \sim f(x, y)$; | [15] | $(\exists y) : \sim(\exists x) . \sim f(x, y)$; |
| [8] | $\sim(\exists x) : \sim(\exists y) . \sim f(x, y)$; | [16] | $\sim(\exists y) : \sim(\exists x) . \sim f(x, y)$. |

Some of these functions are, however, equivalent to others. And it will be seen that all those that are, are also reducible: [1] is equivalent to [9], and to $(\exists x, y) . f(x, y)$; [2] is equivalent to [10], and to $\sim(\exists x, y) . f(x, y)$; [4] is equivalent to [12], and to $(\exists x, y) . \sim f(x, y)$; [6] is equivalent to [14], and to $\sim(\exists x, y) . \sim f(x, y)$. There are, then, four pairs of these functions that are equivalent and reducible; they correspond to the four functions that can be constructed on $f(x)$, and there are no other equivalent pairs, as will become clear presently.

Let us write [5] in the form $(x) : (\exists y) . f(x, y)$, and [15] in the form $(\exists y) : (x) . f(x, y)$, and inquire how these functions are related. The first expression is to be read "Every value of $x$ is such that for some value of $y$, $f(x, y)$ is true," whereas the second is to be read "Some value of $y$ is such that for every value of $x$, $f(x, y)$ is true." These two readings, though likely to be confused, differ in important respects, as may be seen if we take an example. Let $f(x, y)$ be interpreted to mean "$x$ is in contact with $y$." Then $(x) : (\exists y) . f(x, y)$ says "Each thing is in contact with something or other," whereas $(\exists y) : (x) . f(x, y)$ says "Some one and the same thing is such that everything is in contact with it." Obviously, the first of these propositions might be true while the second was false; so that we have

$$\Diamond(\exists f) :. (x) : (\exists y) . f(x, y) :. \sim(\exists y) : (x) . f(x, y).$$

On the other hand, the first proposition does follow from the second: if there were one thing that was in contact with everything, then, of course, everything would be in contact with something or other. And such an implication can be seen to hold quite generally; so that we have

$$(f) :. (\exists y) : (x) . f(x, y) : \prec : (x) : (\exists y) . f(x, y).$$

Whenever the prefix attaching to a given variable comes before the one attaching to another, the first variable is said to have a wider scope than the second: in $(\exists y) : (x) . f(x, y)$, the scope of $y$ is wider than that of $x$, whereas in $(x) : (\exists y) . f(x, y)$, it is narrower. In the position of wider scope, the prefix $\exists$ has the force of 'some one and the same,' while in the position of narrower scope, it has the force of 'some one or other.'

We have, of course,

$$(f) :. (x) : (\exists y) . f(x, y) : \vee : (\exists x) : (y) . \sim f(x, y),$$

since the two functions here involved are contradictories. And it will be seen that, in order to get the contradictory of a function expressed in terms of $(\exists x)$ and $(x)$, we must change each occurrence of $(\exists x)$ to $(x)$, and each occurrence of $(x)$ to $(\exists x)$, and take the negative of the matrix. Thus, again, we have

$$(f) :. (x) : (y) . f(x, y) : \vee : (\exists x) : (\exists y) . \sim f(x, y),$$

where the two alternatives are contradictories.

There are one or two points regarding the way in which functions are related to the propositions that are their values or instances which we must endeavor to make clear. We have called $(x) . f(x)$ a singly-general function, and $(x) : (\exists y) . f(x, y)$ a doubly-general one; and these same terms may be applied to the propositions which are instances of these functions. But it will be convenient to use the terms in connection with propositions in a slightly different sense, owing to the following circumstance. Let us take the proposition "Everything is in contact with something." If we assign the meaning "$x$ is in contact with something" to $f(x)$, this proposition is seen to be an instance of the function $(x) . f(x)$, and therefore ought presumably to be called singly general. But we have seen that the proposition so expressed involves a further element of generality: it says that everything is in contact with something or other, and so can be written in the form "$(x) : (\exists y) . x$ is in contact with $y$." Thus it might seem to be at most doubly general; but if we carried the analysis further, another element of generality might be found. We might find that "$x$ is in contact with $y$" meant "$x$ has contact of some specific sort or other with $y$" and was therefore of the form $(\exists \phi) . \phi(x, y)$; so that the original proposition would be of the form $(x) :. (\exists y) : (\exists \phi) . F(\phi, x, y)$.[2] For this reason, and for the reason that a logical matrix may take as values propositions involving any number of generalizations, we are going to say that a proposition is singly general if it involves at least one generalization, that it is doubly general if it involves at least two, etc. In connection with purely logical functions, on the other hand, our terminology indicates the exact number of generalizations that occur. This usage is justified by the fact that all generalizations in a logical function are necessarily explicit. It is, of course, true that, for instance, $(x) : (\exists y) . f'(x, y)$ is a species of $(x) . f(x)$, in the sense that we can derive the first of these functions from the second by replacing $f(x)$ by $(\exists y) . f'(x, y)$; but such a specific function is not identical with the function from which it is derived, the possibility of the derivation being simply dependent upon the fact that every value of $(x) : (\exists y) . f'(x, y)$ is also a value of $(x) . f(x)$. It is true, also, that there may be concealed general-

[2] This point in the analysis of propositions, to which we shall refer several times later on, is due to Professor G. E. Moore. See *Proc. Arist. Soc.*, Sup. Vol. VII, pp. 171 ff. Professor Moore holds, in effect, that whenever we assert "$a$ has $R$ to $b$," where $R$ is a generic relation, what is said can be expressed equivalently by "$a$ has to $b$ some relation of the kind $R$," where any relation of the kind in question will be an absolutely specific one. It is to be noted, however, that he does not suppose this second expression to be necessarily identical in meaning with the first. In the paper here referred to, he shows quite clearly that there may be genuinely distinct propositions which are yet logically equivalent—by showing that there are pairs of equivalent propositions one of which contains a concept not contained in the other. We give an example of this at the beginning of Chapter XI.

izations in a non-logical function, and that all generalizations in a purely logical proposition must be explicit; but the fact that a logical proposition will, according to our conventions, be of only one degree of generality does not matter, and we shall be concerned with non-logical functions only as they enter non-logical propositions. All that it is necessary to bear in mind is that when material factors enter a proposition or a function, implicit elements of generality may exist.

Having discussed propositions constructed on singly and doubly general functions, we are in a position to see something of what the limitations of the traditional formal logic of propositions are and to see how that logic is related to more modern developments. The main point of difference is extremely simple; it consists simply in this, that the traditional logic is confined to functions involving a single generalization, while the modern logic of propositions deals with functions involving many generalizations. Thus, the typical expression "All *a*'s are *b*'s," i.e., $(x) . f(x) \supset g(x)$, is seen to be a function constructed on the matrix $f(x) \supset g(x)$ by means of the single generalization expressed by $(x)$; and this is as far as we can go in accordance with the traditional procedure. Consider, however, such a proposition as "Every man has a father," which is, in English, explicitly doubly general. This proposition can be analyzed in part in terms of the traditional scheme: we can let *a* stand for the class of men, and *b* stand for beings that have fathers, and write "Everything that is an *a* is also a *b*"; and we can, correspondingly, let $f(x)$ mean "$x$ is a man" and $g(x)$ mean "$x$ has a father," and write $(x) . f(x) \supset g(x)$. But this effects an analysis of the proposition only in respect of its first generalization. In order to represent it as being doubly general, we shall have to proceed as follows. Let $f(x)$ mean "$x$ is a man" and $g(x, y)$ mean "$y$ is father of $x$." Then we have

$$(x) : (\exists y) . f(x) \supset g(x, y),$$

$$\text{or} \quad (x) : f(x) . \supset . (\exists y) . g(x, y),$$

i.e., "For every $x$, either $x$ is not a man or there is a $y$ such that $y$ is father of $x$." It is plain that such propositions and functions cannot be expressed in Aristotelian terms. They are, however, as we shall see, essential to any development of types of order and mathematical systems. Of course, modern logic differs also from the traditional scheme in the degree to which it pushes its analyses. Thus, such an expression as "Some $a$'s are $b$'s," which remains in effect unanalyzed in the traditional account, turns out to be complex, and to be of the form $(\exists x) . f(x) . g(x)$, where the more general expression would be $(\exists x) . F(x)$, of which the other was a specific determination. But these are minor differences as compared with the chief one here pointed out.

We come now to triply-general functions. A detailed treatment of these functions will not be necessary, however, owing to the fact that they are related to doubly-general functions in the way in which these latter are related to functions that are singly general.

Note that

$$(f) :: (\exists x) :. (\exists y) : (z) . f(x, y, z) :. \prec :. (\exists x) :. (z) : (\exists y) . f(x, y, z),$$

and that

$$(f) :: (\exists x) :. (z) : (\exists y) . f(x, y, z) :. \prec :. (z) :. (\exists x) : (\exists y) . f(x, y, z),$$

but that we have both

$$\Diamond(\exists f) :: (\exists x) :. (z) : (\exists y) . f(x, y, z) :: {\sim}(\exists x) :. (\exists y) : (z) . f(x, y, z)$$

and

$$\Diamond(\exists f) :: (z) :. (\exists x) : (\exists y) . f(x, y, z) :: {\sim}(\exists x) :. (z) : (\exists y) . f(x, y, z).$$

And we have, of course,

$$(f) :: (\exists x) :. (y) : (\exists z) . f(x, y, z) :. \vee :. (x) :. (\exists y) : (z) . {\sim}f(x, y, z),$$

which involves a disjunction of contradictory functions.

If we are given a matrix $f(x, y, z)$, where $f$ is to remain free and $x, y, z$ are to be generalized, there are ninety-six triply-general extensional functions that can be constructed, as may be seen from the following consideration. Take

$$(\exists x) : . (\exists y) : (\exists z) . f(x, y, z),$$

and consider the number of functions that must arise in virtue of the presence or absence of ~ before each prefix and before the matrix $f(x, y, z)$. There are, in all, $2^4$ cases. Then, in virtue of the fact that the three prefixes can be arranged in 3! different orders, we have $3! \times 2^4$ functions that can be constructed. Some of these will, however, be reducible, and will therefore not involve new logical force over and above that which can be expressed by means of functions of a lower degree of generality. Thus

$$(\exists x) : . (\exists y) : \sim(\exists z) . f(x, y, z)$$

is equivalent to

$$(\exists x, y) : \sim(\exists z) . f(x, y, z)$$

and is thus reducible to a doubly-general function, but is not further reducible; whereas

$$\sim(\exists x) : . (\exists y) : (\exists z) . \sim f(x, y, z)$$

reduces immediately to the singly-general function

$$\sim(\exists x, y, z) . \sim f(x, y, z).$$

Now, a function will be irreducible if, and only if, ~ appears between any two occurrences of $\exists$; so that, among the ninety-six functions that can be constructed on $f(x, y, z)$, there will be $4 \times 3!$ or twenty-four which involve new logical force. In the same way, on the matrix $f(x, y, z, w)$, there will be in all $4! \times 2^5$ or 768 quadruply-general functions that can be constructed; and among these, there will be $4 \times 4!$ or ninety-six which are irreducible. And, in general, on a matrix $f(x_1, \ldots, x_n)$, there will be altogether $n! \times 2^{n+1}$ $n$-tuply general extensional functions that can be constructed, and there will be $4 \times n!$ irreducible ones.

We have seen that any singly-general extensional function has one of the forms

$$(x_1, \ldots, x_n) . f(x_1, \ldots, x_n) \text{ or } (\exists x_1, \ldots, x_n) . f(x_1, \ldots, x_n),$$

and that any irreducible doubly-general extensional function has one of the forms

$$(x_1, \ldots, x_m) : (\exists y_1, \ldots, y_n) . f(x_1, \ldots, x_m; y_1, \ldots, y_n)$$
$$\text{or } (\exists x_1, \ldots, x_m) : (y_1, \ldots, y_n) . f(x_1, \ldots, x_m; y_1, \ldots, y_n).$$

It will be easy to see, in general, that there are two forms of irreducible multiply-general functions which involve a single prefix applied to a matrix, namely,

$$(\alpha) \quad (x_1, \ldots, x_m) :. (\exists y_1, \ldots, y_n) : \ldots f(x_1, \ldots, x_m; y_1, \ldots, y_n; \ldots)$$

and

$$(\beta) \quad (\exists x_1, \ldots, x_m) :. (y_1, \ldots, y_n) : \ldots f(x_1, \ldots, x_m; y_1, \ldots, y_n; \ldots).$$

Note that the contradictory of $(\alpha)$ is

$$(\exists x_1, \ldots, x_m) :. (y_1, \ldots, y_n) : \ldots \sim f(x_1, \ldots, x_m; y_1, \ldots, y_n; \ldots),$$

and that that of $(\beta)$ is

$$(x_1, \ldots, x_m) :. (\exists y_1, \ldots, y_n) : \ldots \sim f(x_1, \ldots, x_m; y_1, \ldots, y_n; \ldots);$$

so that if we wish to express the contradictory of a function involving a single complex prefix in 'some' and 'every,' we have simply to replace each occurrence of 'some' by 'every,' and each occurrence of 'every' by 'some,' and apply $\sim$ to the matrix. Of course, $(\alpha)$ can be written in the form

$$\sim(\exists x_1, \ldots, x_m) :. \sim(\exists y_1, \ldots, y_n) : \ldots f(x_1, \ldots, x_m; y_1, \ldots, y_n; \ldots),$$

where the contradictory is obtained when the first occurrence of $\sim$ is dropped; and it can be written in the form

$$(x_1, \ldots, x_m) :. \sim(y_1, \ldots, y_n) : \ldots f(x_1, \ldots, x_m; y_1, \ldots, y_n; \ldots),$$

where the contradictory arises through the application of $\sim$ to the entire function.

We may now return to singly-general functions in order to develop some theorems connecting them with functions of a higher degree of generality. Let us take a function $(\exists x) . f(x)$, and another function $p$, and form the disjunctive expression $p . \vee . (\exists x) . f(x)$, which may be read "$p$ is true, or $f(x)$ is true for at least one value of $x$." Clearly this will hold when and only when $(\exists x) . p \vee f(x)$ holds, that is, when and only when there is at least one value of $x$ such that $p \vee f(x)$ is true; so that we may write:

(I) $(p, f) :. p . \vee . (\exists x) . f(x) : \equiv . (\exists x) . p \vee f(x)$.

Again, it will be seen that $p : (\exists x) . f(x)$, i.e., "$p$ is true, and there is at least one value of $x$ for which $f(x)$ is true," will hold when and only when $(\exists x) . p . f(x)$ holds; so that we have

(II) $(p, f) :. p : (\exists x) . f(x) : \equiv . (\exists x) . p . f(x)$.

And in the same way, we have:

(III) $(p, f) :. p . \vee . (x) . f(x) : \equiv . (x) . p \vee f(x)$,
and
(IV) $(p, f) :. p : (x) . f(x) : \equiv . (x) . p . f(x)$.[3]

Let us take the function $(\exists x) . f(x) . \vee . (y) . g(y)$, which may be read "$f(x)$ is true for some value of $x$, or $g(y)$ is true for all values of $y$." It is easy to see that the force of this reading can be given by "Every value of $y$ is such that $(\exists x) . f(x) . \vee . g(y)$ is true," that is, by

$$(y) : (\exists x) . f(x) . \vee . g(y),$$

where the scope of $(y)$ is the whole expression, while that of $(\exists x)$ is limited to $f(x)$. This latter reading is, however, plainly equivalent to "Every value of $y$ is such that for some value of $x$, $f(x) \vee g(y)$ is true"; so that we have, from (I) and (III),

(1) $(f, g) :. (\exists x) . f(x) . \vee . (y) . g(y) : \equiv : (y) : (\exists x) . f(x) \vee g(y)$,

where the left-hand expression is the disjunction of two singly-general functions, while the right-hand one is a doubly-general function constructed on a matrix. It is to be noted here that we can, of course, replace $f(x)$ and $g(y)$ in this proposition by functions of any degree of generality, just as we are able to substitute any function for $p$. We can, for instance, replace

[3] Compare with these propositions the definitions given in *Principia Mathematica*, ∗9.

$f(x)$ by $(z) . f'(x, z)$, and $g(y)$ by $(\exists z) . g'(y, z)$, and so derive, as a logical consequence of (1),

$$(f', g') :: (\exists x) : (z) . f'(x, z) : \vee : (y) : (\exists z) . g'(y, z) :. \equiv :. (y) :. (\exists x) : (z) . f'(x, z) . \vee . (\exists z) . g'(y, z).$$

Let us consider the function $(x) . f(x) . \vee . (y) . g(y)$, which may be rendered "Either $f(x)$ is true for all values of $x$, or $g(y)$ is true for all values of $y$." Plainly, the force of this assertion can be given by "For all values of $x$, $f(x) . \vee . (y) . g(y)$ is true," and also by "For every $x$, every $y$ is such that $f(x) \vee g(y)$ is true"; so that we have, from (III),

(2) $(f, g) :. (x) . f(x) . \vee . (y) . g(y) : \equiv : (x) : (y) . f(x) \vee g(y).$

And in the same way, we have, from (I),

(3) $(f, g) :. (\exists x) . f(x) . \vee . (\exists y) . g(y) : \equiv : (\exists x) : (\exists y) . f(x) \vee g(y).$

Again, consider the function $(x) . f(x) : (\exists y) . g(y)$, the force of which can be expressed by "All values of $f(x)$ are true, and at least one value of $g(y)$ is true." Here we can say "$(x) . f(x) : g(y)$ is true for at least one value of $y$" or write $(\exists y) : (x) . f(x) : g(y)$; and we can say "Some value of $y$ is such that for all values of $x$, $f(x) . g(y)$ is true"; so that we have, from (II) and (IV),

(4) $(f, g) :. (x) . f(x) : (\exists y) . g(y) : \equiv : (\exists y) : (x) . f(x) . g(y).$

And, similarly, we can write:

(5) $(f, g) :. (x) . f(x) : (y) . g(y) : \equiv : (x) : (y) . f(x) . g(y),$

and

(6) $(f, g) :. (\exists x) . f(x) : (\exists y) . g(y) : \equiv : (\exists x) : (\exists y) . f(x) . g(y).$

There is one point, having to do with a refinement of theory, which must be noted with regard to propositions (I)–(IV) and (1)–(6). It will be seen that the equivalences expressed in these propositions are all material rather than strict. The reason we have stated them in this way is that in general the corresponding strict equivalences do not hold, owing to the fact that one of the two functions involved implies existence in a respect in which the other does not. There are only two exceptions to this, namely, propositions (2) and (6). In each of the other cases, however, we can obtain a strict equivalence either by confining $x$ and $y$ to the same range of variation or by inserting appropriate existence-conditions.

Let us take proposition (I), and consider the import of the function $p . \vee . (\exists x) . f(x)$; and let us suppose $p$ to be so chosen that it is a proposition without existential import. However $f$ may be chosen, $(\exists x) . f(x)$ can be true only if there is at least one value within the range of significance of $x$; but since $p$ does not imply existence, $p . \vee . (\exists x) . f(x)$ will not imply the existence of anything at all, because it will be true if $p$ is true and $(\exists x) . f(x)$ is false. But then consider the import of $(\exists x) . p \vee f(x)$. This function cannot be satisfied unless there is at least one value within the range of significance of $x$, although of course such a value need not satisfy $f(x)$. Now, it is plainly a logical possibility that $f$ should be so chosen that there would be no values within the range of $x$; and since this is so, the equivalence in (I) cannot be strict, although in fact there may always be values either satisfying or failing to satisfy $f(x)$ for any arbitrarily chosen value of $f$.

In the case of proposition (1), similarly, we have no corresponding strict equivalence. Suppose that meanings were assigned to $f$ and $g$ such that there were no values within the range of $x$, but such that there were values within the range of $y$, and $(y) . g(y)$ held. Then the left-hand member of the equivalence would be true; but the right-hand member,

$$\sim(\exists y) : \sim(\exists x) . f(x) \vee g(y),$$

would be false, since it would mean that there was no value $a$ such that

$$\sim(\exists x) . f(x) \vee g(a)$$

was true, and this latter would mean that there was no value of $x$ such that $f(x) \vee g(a)$ was true. In such a case, there would be values of $y$ not associated with values of $x$ which satisfied $f(x) \vee g(y)$, inasmuch as there would be nothing within the range of $x$ and something within that of $y$.

A similar situation arises in connection with proposition (3). Suppose that $f$ and $g$ are so chosen that $x$ and $y$ can never take the same value, and that, further, there are no values within the range of $y$. Then if $(\exists x) . f(x)$ is true, the left-hand expression will be true; but the right-hand expression says that there is a value of $x$ to which there corresponds a value of $y$ such that $f(x) \vee g(y)$ is true, and this cannot be so unless there is at least one value of $y$ satisfying or failing to satisfy $g$.

Let us take proposition (4), and consider the following possibility. Suppose that $x$ and $y$ could not take values in common, and that no values existed within the range of $x$, while there were only such within the range of $y$ as failed to satisfy $g$. Then although the left-hand side of the equivalence would be false, the right-hand side would be true. For

$$(\exists y) : \sim(\exists x) . \sim f(x) \vee \sim g(y)$$

means that there is a value $a$ such that

$$\sim(\exists x) . \sim f(x) \vee \sim g(a)$$

is true, while this latter means that no value of $x$ exists which makes $\sim f(x) \vee \sim g(a)$ true; and if no values of $x$ existed at all, there could be nothing which transformed this matrix into a true proposition. Moreover, with regard to proposition (5), it will be seen that under these same conditions, the left-hand member of the equivalence would be false while the right-hand member would be true.

In virtue of propositions (I)–(IV), it is possible to express any complex function involving prefixes of restricted scope in an equivalent form in which there occurs only a single complex prefix applied to a matrix. In particular, any function can be so expressed as to have one of the forms:

$$(x_1, \ldots, x_m) :. (\exists y_1, \ldots, y_n) : \ldots f(x_1, \ldots, x_m; y_1, \ldots, y_n; \ldots)$$

or

$$(\exists x_1, \ldots, x_m) :. (y_1, \ldots, y_n) : \ldots f(x_1, \ldots, x_m; y_1, \ldots, y_n; \ldots).$$

In order to find an equivalent form in the case of a given function, we must first so express the function that the sign of negation ~ never has a prefix within its scope; and this can always be done by means of the following equivalences:

$$\sim(\exists x) \,.\, f(x) \,.\, = \,.\, (x) \,.\, \sim f(x);$$
$$\sim(x) \,.\, f(x) \,.\, = \,.\, (\exists x) \,.\, \sim f(x);$$
$$\sim(p \vee q) \,.\, = \,.\, \sim p \,.\, \sim q;$$
$$\sim(p \,.\, q) \,.\, = \,.\, \sim p \vee \sim q.$$

The function will then be built up in terms of $\vee$, ., $(\exists x)$, and $(x)$ on certain expressions not involving generalization; and by referring to propositions (I)–(IV), we can develop a single complex prefix applied to a matrix.

Take, for example, the function

$$\sim[(\exists x) : (y) \,.\, f(x, y) :. \sim(\exists z) : (w) \,.\, g(z, w)].$$

Removing ~ from before prefixes, we have

$$(x) : (\exists y) \,.\, \sim f(x, y) : \vee : (\exists z) : (w) \,.\, g(z, w).$$

Then, by (III), we have

$$(x) :. (\exists y) \,.\, \sim f(x, y) \,.\, \vee : (\exists z) : (w) \,.\, g(z, w);$$

by (I)

$$(x) :: (\exists y) :. \sim f(x, y) \,.\, \vee : (\exists z) : (w) \,.\, g(z, w);$$

by (I) again

$$(x) :: (\exists y) :. (\exists z) : \sim f(x, y) \,.\, \vee \,.\, (w) \,.\, g(z, w);$$

and by (III)

$$(x) :: (\exists y) :. (\exists z) : (w) \,.\, \sim f(x, y) \vee g(z, w).$$

We must now discuss in detail some points with regard to a question which has been heretofore almost entirely neglected, namely, that having to do with the range of significance of the functions and variables with which we have been concerned. We began by allowing $p$ to denote any proposition, and then we replaced $p$ by such functions as $f(x)$ and $f(x, y)$, which, as was indicated, denote propositions in virtue of some analysis of which the propositions admit. Now, in functions constructed on $f(x, y)$, the variables $x, y$ have been generalized, while $f$ has not; and it might therefore be supposed that $f$ was to be understood as occupying some special position in the function, different in point of syntax from that of $x$ and $y$. This, however, is not the case; $f(x, y)$ is, in fact, a function of three variables, and could be written equally well as $(f, x, y)$, where $f$, $x$, and $y$ would denote factors into which a proposition was analyzable, and $(f, x, y)$ the whole proposition. We have used the expression $f(x, y)$ merely with a view to suggesting a distinction between those variables that were to be generalized in the construction of general functions and those that were not; whereas the only necessary distinction here is that between the whole function, which denotes propositions, and the variables in the function, which denote factors in propositions. Thus, suppose that $a$ and $b$ are names of assigned things, such that "$a$ is to the right of $b$" expresses a proposition, true or false. The function $(f, x, y)$ will denote this proposition if $x$ corresponds to $a$, and $y$ to $b$, while $f$ corresponds to 'being to the right of'; it will denote the proposition if $x$ corresponds to $b$, $y$ to $a$, and $f$ to 'being to the right of'; but it will equally well denote the proposition if $f$ corresponds to $a$, and $x$ to $b$, while $y$ corresponds to 'being to the right of.' Of course, if $(f, x, y)$ denotes the proposition "$a$ is to the right of $b$" where $x$ corresponds to $a$, $y$ to $b$, and $f$ to 'being to the right of,' then, correlatively, $(f, y, x)$ must denote "$b$ is to the right of $a$," and $(x, f, y)$ cannot denote anything at all; but initially, it does not matter how the correspondence is established.

The point here in question has an important bearing upon the notion of the range of significance of functions and variables. A variable is not an independent entity, but is merely an item of syntax in a function; so that those entities which may be said to be values of an assigned variable are determined by the propositions to which the function involving the variable applies. A function, when it is the whole function on which a proposition is constructed, always has a determinate range of application; it applies to all propositions possessing its form; and when this class of values is fixed, as it always is by the nature of the function, the values of the variables in the function are determined as all those factors in the members of this class of propositions to which the variables may correspond. Let us take, for instance, a function in two variables, which we may write $(x, y)$. This function, which is purely logical, will denote any proposition that can be analyzed into two factors, and $x$ and $y$ will correspond in each case to these factors. It must not be supposed, however, that if $x$ can take a certain value in connection with an assigned value of $y$, it can take that value in connection with any arbitrarily chosen value of $y$. Thus, the proposition "*a* is round" is denoted by $(x, y)$ when, say, $x$ corresponds to 'being round' and $y$ to $a$; and the proposition "*c* is larger than *d*" is denoted by this function when, say, $x$ is taken as denoting $c$, and $y$ as denoting 'being larger than *d*.' But the value 'being round,' taken by $x$ in conjunction with $a$ as value of $y$, cannot be taken by $x$ in conjunction with 'being larger than *d*' as value of $y$, because there is no such proposition. This means that a variable has no preassigned range of variation. We cannot designate a class of entities and say that the variable $x$, in $(x, y)$, can be assigned as a value any member of that class, no matter what value $y$ may have; and we must therefore distinguish between the values that $x$ can take in conjunction with some value or other of $y$, i.e., with at least one value of $y$, and those that it can take in conjunction with an assigned value.

Now, it may be thought that if we attempt to allow a function to have a range of application as wide as the one just indicated, we shall encounter difficulties in formulating general propositions and general functions; for we are saying that, as a rule, it is not possible to speak of *all* values of a variable $x$ irrespective of what values variables associated with $x$ may have; and yet in saying, for instance, that for every value of $x$, every value of $y$ is such that $f(x, y)$ is true, we seem to be presupposing an independent range of variation for both $x$ and $y$. It will be recalled, however, that 'every' has been defined in terms of 'some' and 'not': "All values of $x$ and $y$ are such that $f(x, y)$ is true" means what is meant by "It is not the case that $x$ and $y$ exist such that $f(x, y)$ is false." And it is clear that we can assert, or deny, "For some $x$, $y$, $f(x, y)$ is false" irrespective of whether there are values that $x$ can take in conjunction with some values of $y$ and not in conjunction with others. Again, consider $(x) : (\exists y) . f(x, y)$ or $\sim(\exists x) : \sim(\exists y) . f(x, y)$, which means "There is no value of $x$ not associated with a value of $y$ such that $f(x, y)$ is true." For an assigned value of $f$ there will be a class of propositions denoted by $f(x, y)$, and the values that $x$ can take, with that value of $f$, will be all those factors in these propositions to which $x$ corresponds. And we can assert, or deny, that a value of $x$ exists such that there never corresponds a value of $y$ making $f(x, y)$ true. When, in $f(x, y)$, where $f$ is constant, we assign a value to $x$, there will then be a class of values that $y$ can take with that value of $x$, this class being determined by the values of $f(x, y)$ in which that value of $x$ occurs, whereas, for another value of $x$, there may be a different class of values that $y$ can take.

Let us consider the function $f(x, y)$, with $f$ variable, and take three propositions denoted by it: "$a$ is larger than $b$"; "$c$ is both round and colored"; and "$d$ is round or $e$ is square." With regard to the first proposition, let a value be assigned to $f$ such that $f(x, y)$ becomes "$x$ is larger than $y$," and let $x$ be replaced by $a$, and $y$ by $b$; with regard to the second proposition, let $f$ be assigned a value such that $f(x, y)$ becomes "$c$ is both $x$ and $y$," and let 'round' be substituted for $x$, and 'colored' for $y$; with regard to the third proposition, let $f$ be so determined that $f(x, y)$ becomes "$x$ or $y$," and let $x$ be replaced by "$d$ is round," and $y$ by "$e$ is square." In the first case, after $f$ has been determined, $x$ and $y$ are restricted to denoting particular things; in the second case, they are restricted to denoting properties; whereas in the third they must of necessity denote propositions. But it is *only* after $f$ has been assigned a value that the denotations of $x$ and $y$ are so restricted. It will be seen, too, in view of the third example, that $f(p, q)$ is simply a more specific function than $f(x, y)$, limiting $x$ and $y$ to propositions, and thus restricting the range of $f$.

Consider the general logical principle:

$$(f) : (x, y) \,.\, f(x, y) \,.\vee.\, (\exists x, y) \,.\, {\sim}f(x, y).$$

From this principle, we can derive

$$(x, y) \,.\, x \text{ is larger than } y \,.\vee.\, (\exists x, y) \,.\, x \text{ is not larger than } y,$$

where the variables are confined to such entities as can significantly be said to be one larger than the other. We can derive, also,

$$(x, y) \,.\, c \text{ is both } x \text{ and } y \,.\vee.\, (\exists x, y) \,.\, c \text{ is not both } x \text{ and } y,$$

where $x$ and $y$ are plainly confined to properties. And we can derive

$$(x, y) \,.\, x \vee y \,.\vee.\, (\exists x, y) \,.\, {\sim}x \,.\, {\sim}y,$$

where the two variables must be restricted to propositions.

A further point is to be noted with regard to the range of significance of functions. Suppose that, in place of dealing with a single function, we are concerned with two related ones, say $f(x)$ and $g(x)$, which involve a variable in common. If we substitute a value for $x$ in $f(x)$, then of course that value must be substituted in $g(x)$ also, and this will restrict the values that $g$ can take. Suppose, again, that $f$ and $g$ were assigned values, so that we had $f_1(x)$ and $g_1(x)$. It might happen in such a case that there were values that $f_1(x)$ alone could take which were such that $g_1(x)$ could not, so that the range of application of $f_1(x)$ would be restricted. To say that these two functions are connected or taken together, however, means simply that we have to consider some function into which they both enter as constituents, such as $f_1(x) \,.\, g_1(x)$; and it is this expression which determines the range of application of the subordinate functions. These subordinate functions must be regarded as variables which enter the compound expression, and the values they can take as being determined by reference to it. Similarly, in the case of $f_1(x) \vee g_1(x)$, we cannot determine the values of the disjunction by determining separately those of the constituent functions, but must proceed the other way round. And in general, in the case of any complex function, it is the whole function that determines, and often restricts, the ranges of the subordinate functions. Of course, two functions can have a variable in common only if they occur as factors in the same complex function, and ultimately in the same proposition.

We shall be able to develop further the points here in question if we consider an alternative conception of the way in which general propositions and functions are to be analyzed. Throughout the foregoing discussion, general propositions in extension are conceived in the usual way as being those propositions which arise from matrices by generalization, this generalization being effected by the attachment of a prefix to each variable constituent of the matrix; and general propositional functions are thought of as being those functions which arise from matrices by generalization with respect to some but not all variables. It is possible to analyze these propositions and functions in a slightly different way, and this alternative analysis has some advantages as against the ordinary one. We have seen that a singly-general proposition is always concerned in effect with the applicability or non-applicability of some propositional function, and that in the simplest case this reduces to an assertion to the effect that a matrix $f(x)$ has a true instance or does not have a true instance. But in attaching prefixes to the variables in a matrix, we do not seem to be making an assertion of precisely this kind; we are saying "For some value of $f$ and some value of $x$, $f(x)$ is true," and not applying the prefix 'some' to the entire matrix $f(x)$, as we should be doing if we said "Some value of $f(x)$ is true." No doubt there appears to be good reason for applying prefixes to variables rather than to functions; for when we come to multiply-general propositions, it is not immediately clear how we can attach prefixes to functions, as we can in the case of propositions that are singly general. It seems, however, that there is a way of doing this, and it will be of interest to see how this alternative procedure is to be carried out.

In this connection, it is important to have a clear conception of what we have called the 'scope' of an apparent variable; and since this notion is the same as the mathematical one of what we may call the 'order' of a parameter, we can bring out the import of the conception by considering parameters of various orders. A comparison here between the scope of a variable and the order of a parameter is of interest because, in the parameter, we have the notion of scope dissociated from the prefixes 'some' and 'every.' Roughly, the order of a parameter in a function is the 'degree of fixity' of the parameter as a variable constituent of the function. To take a simple illustration, consider the equation $y = kx$, which is that of a line through the origin of coördinates in the Cartesian plane, and in which $k$ is a parameter of the first order with respect to $x$ and $y$ as ordinary variables. We tend to express the relation of $k$ to $x$ and $y$ by saying that $k$ is a constant, or represents a constant; though of course $k$ is in fact no more a constant than $x$ is. But there is, nevertheless, an important difference between $y = kx$ and $y = zx$, where $z$ is an ordinary variable; and this difference becomes clear when we consider typical values of these two expressions. The equation $y = zx$ is a propositional function, which denotes such propositions as $6 = 2 \cdot 3$; whereas $y = kx$ does not denote arithmetical propositions; it denotes such equations as $y = 2x$, which in turn denote propositions like $6 = 2 \cdot 3$. Thus $y = kx$ is one step removed from propositions; it collects together a class of propositional functions, and each of these functions collects together a class of arithmetical propositions. Hence it is easy to see why we say that $k$ represents a constant; in $y = kx$ it denotes constants, whereas it is only in such expressions as $y = 2x$ that $x$ and $y$ denote constants. And this is, of course, why $y = kx$ determines lines in the plane; each value of $k$ is such that the values of $x$ and $y$ which give rise to true propositions for that value of $k$ fall along one and the same straight line. If it were not for a convention with regard to the parametric orders of these variable constituents, the expression $y = kx$ would be ambiguous; and, indeed, ambiguity does arise in other cases—as in $y = kx + l$. In this case, the relative orders of $k$ and $l$ are not given, but they may be designated by the use of subscripts. We may, for example, write $y_0 = k_2x_0 + l_1$, where the highest subscript indicates the parameter of highest order, and the lowest subscripts the parameters of lowest order, or the variables; and, of course, we may here omit the lowest subscripts without incurring ambiguity. Now, $y = k_2x + l_1$ denotes such expressions as $y = 2x + l_1$, which in turn denote such expressions as $y = 2x + 3$, which in turn denote such propositions as $11 = 2 \cdot 4 + 3$; and this means that $y = k_2x + l_1$ determines systems of parallel lines in the plane. On the other hand, $y = k_1x + l_2$ denotes $y = k_1x + 3$, which denotes $y = 2x + 3$, which denotes $11 = 2 \cdot 4 + 3$; that is, this expression determines pencils of lines on points on the $y$-axis. But $y = k_1x + l_1$ denotes $y = 2x + 3$

directly; that is to say, it determines, not systems of lines, but simply any line in the plane.

We have here a hierarchy of denoting; and it is a hierarchy of this sort that is involved in multiply-general propositions and functions. Consider, for example, a function of the form $f(x, y)$, in which $f$ is constant, and attach subscripts to $x$ and $y$—as in $f(x_0, y_1)$. This expression collects together all functions that can be obtained by the assignment of a value to $y$, and each of these latter, in turn, collects together all propositions that result from the assignment of a value to $x$; and when, for instance, we write $(y) : (\exists x) \, . \, f(x, y)$, we are saying in effect that any value of $f(x, y)$, say $f(x, b)$, resulting from a determination of $y$ has at least one value $f(a, b)$ which is true, where the values that $y$ can take are determined by the propositions to which $f(x, y)$ applies, and those that $x$ can take are in turn determined by the range of values of $f(x, b)$. In virtue of the significance of the subscripts, such an expression as $(\exists x) : (y) \, . \, f(x_0, y_1)$ is meaningless; parameters of highest order correspond to variables of widest scope; and it is therefore unnecessary to employ subscripts together with a prefix of this kind. But a prefix involves generalization as well as scope: $(x) : (\exists y) \, . \, f(x, y)$ and $(\exists x) : (y) \, . \, f(x, y)$ involve precisely the same determination of scope; and when it is desirable to determine scope and leave generalization undetermined, the use of subscripts or some similar usage is necessary.

We are now in a position to see how multiply-general propositions in which each prefix attaches to an entire function, rather than to a variable in a function, are to be constructed. If we take $f(x_0, y_1)$, where $f$ is constant, we can say "Some value of every value of $f(x_0, y_1)$ is true" or write

$$(f(x_0, y_1)) : (\exists f(x_0, y_0)) \, . \, f(x_0, y_0),$$

which would be expressed in ordinary notation by $(y) : (\exists x) \, . \, f(x, y)$. Again, let us take the proposition "$a$ gives $b$ to $c$." It is a value of $f(x, y, z)$ if this function is regarded as denoting propositions directly; but without such an understanding, the function is ambiguous as regards the parametric order of its variables. We may have $f_1(x_0, y_0, z_0)$, which will denote the function "$x_0$ gives $y_0$ to $z_0$," which will denote "$a$ gives $b$ to $c$"; or we may have $f_0(x_1, y_1, z_1)$, which will denote $f_0(a, b, c)$, which will denote "$a$ gives $b$ to $c$." Omitting the lowest subscripts as a matter of convenience, we have in connection with this function such propositions as

$$(\exists f_1(x, y, z)) : (f(x, y, z)) \,.\, f(x, y, z),$$

which corresponds to $(\exists f) : (x, y, z) \,.\, f(x, y, z)$ in ordinary notation; and

$$(\exists f(x_1, y_1, z_1)) : (f(x, y, z)) \,.\, f(x, y, z),$$

which corresponds to $(\exists x, y, z) : (f) \,.\, f(x, y, z)$.

We can now see more clearly how the range of variation of each variable in a function is to be determined. Let us take again the function $(x) : (\exists y) \,.\, f(x, y)$, where, in accordance with the order of generalization determined by the prefix together with the free variable $f$, the variables must take values in the order represented by $f_2(x_1, y_0)$. Consider first the range of application of $f(x, y)$, which will be all those propositions that can be analyzed, in any way whatever, into three factors that can be replaced by variables. In each proposition of this class, there will be a constituent corresponding to $f$, and since, in $(x) : (\exists y) \,.\, f(x, y)$, $f$ has the widest scope, and will therefore take values first, it can take any one of these constituents as a value—and, of course, nothing else. Let $\phi$ be one of these constituents, and let it be assigned as a value to $f$, so that we have the proposition $(x) : (\exists y) \,.\, \phi(x, y)$. The propositions to which $\phi(x, y)$ applies will be all those among the values of $f(x, y)$ in which $\phi$ occurs; and this subclass will involve all the values that $x$ and $y$ can take in conjunction with the given value of $f$. In $\phi(x, y)$, $x$ is the variable of widest scope, and for each value of this function there will be a value that $x$ can take. If $a$ is one of these values, then we have $\phi(a, y)$, which determines a subclass of the values of $\phi(x, y)$; and corresponding to each member of this subclass, there will be a value that $y$ can take in conjunction with the assigned values of $f$ and $x$.

The variables in such functions as $f(x, y)$ are, then, not restricted by anything except the values of the functions into which they enter. But there are certain relative restrictions which can be placed upon the values that a variable may take, and these are often important, owing to the fact that many propositions depend for their validity upon them. Just as we indicate by $f(x, x)$ the condition that both occurrences of a variable within the parentheses must take the same value, so we may indicate by $f(x, x')$ that a value taken by one variable shall be of the same kind as a value taken by the other. And what is meant here by "of the same kind" can be specified in the following way. Suppose that $a$ and $b$ are such that $f(a, b)$ is significant for a given value of $f$; then they are values of the same kind if, and only if, $f(b, a)$ is significant for that value of $f$. Thus, $f(x, x')$ has as a value the proposition "$a$ is larger than $b$," where $f$ corresponds to 'being larger than,' $x$ to $a$, and $x'$ to $b$, because, owing to the fact that "$b$ is larger than $a$" is significant, $a$ and $b$ are of the same kind. The function $f(x, y)$, on the other hand, in addition to applying to each of these propositions, has as a value "$a$ is characterized by $\psi$," where $\psi$ is an assigned character; but in this case, "$\psi$ is characterized by $a$" is not significant, so that $f(x, x')$ does not have "$a$ is characterized by $\psi$" as a value. If we wish to make the definition of $f(x, x')$ formal, we can say that it means what is meant by

$$f(x, y) \,.\, f(y, x) \vee {\sim} f(y, x),$$

since this conjunctive expression will not be significant unless the values of $x$ and $y$ are, in the sense intended, of the same kind.

We may employ $x, x', x'', \ldots$ to stand for variables taking values of the same kind, and may employ $y, y', y'', \ldots$ and $f, f', f'', \ldots$ similarly. Of course, it is possible that $y, y', y'',$ $\ldots$ should take the same values as those taken by $x, x', x'', \ldots$ and $f, f', f'', \ldots$, the distinction in question being simply that they need not. Accordingly, all values of $f(x, x')$ are values of $f(x, y)$, just as all of $f(x, x)$ are values of $f(x, x')$; so that from a proposition of the form $(x, y) \,.\, f(x, y)$ we can infer one of the form $(x, x') \,.\, f(x, x')$, provided $f(y, x)$ is significant; and, again, from a proposition of the form $(\exists x, x') \,.\, f(x, x')$ we can infer one of the form $(\exists x, y) \,.\, f(x, y)$. It will, of course, be clear that we do not mean to restrict $x, x', x'', \ldots$ to one particular kind of entities, but only to entities of the *same* kind:

$f(x, x')$ has as a value the proposition "*Red* is a species of *color*," as well as the proposition "*a* is larger than *b*"; but *a* and "*red*" are of different kinds, since "*Red* is *a*" is nonsense.

We have said that all the propositions with which we have so far been concerned are valid without explicit restriction of any of the variables involved to the same range of variation. Take, for example,

$$(f) :. (x) : (y) . f(x, y) \vee \sim f(x, y).$$

In this and similar propositions, it is plain that $x$ and $y$ need not take values of the same kind, i.e., values such that $f(y, x)$ will be significant. There are, however, a few propositions that have been stated where certain variables will of necessity, and without an explicit condition, take values in common. Consider, for instance,

$$(f) : (\exists x) . f(x) . \vee . (y) . \sim f(y),$$

where the occurrences of $x$ and $y$ are, of course, independent; and take the two functions $f(x)$ and $g(y)$. By themselves, these functions have the same range of application, since each denotes any proposition that can be analyzed into two factors. And, obviously, when $f$ and $g$ are given the same value, the values that can be taken by $x$ and $y$ will be the same. Again, take the proposition

$$(f) :. (x) : (\exists y) . f(x, y) : \vee : (\exists z) : (w) . \sim f(z, w).$$

Here $f(x, y)$ and $f(z, w)$ will necessarily have the same range; and it is clear that $x$ and $z$ can always take the same values (if $y$ and $w$ remain undetermined); also that when they do, $y$ and $w$ can take the same values. Hence the pairs of values taken by $x$, $y$ will be identical with those taken by $z$, $w$; although, of course, neither $x$ and $y$ nor $z$ and $w$ need take values of the same kind. Again, consider the proposition

$$(f) :. (x) . f(x, x) . \prec : (x) : (\exists y) . f(x, y).$$

This holds because $y$ can always be assigned any value taken by $x$. And here an explicit condition to the effect that $x$ and $y$ shall take values of the same kind is unnecessary, owing to the fact that $f(x, x)$ must be significant.

We shall formulate a few propositions that require such an explicit restriction. We have, in the first place,

$$(f) :. (x) : (x') . f(x, x') : \prec : (x) : (\exists x') . f(x, x'),$$
$$\text{and } (f) :. (\exists x) : (x') . f(x, x') : \prec : (\exists x) : (\exists x') . f(x, x'),$$

because $x'$ can always be assigned any value taken by $x$.

It is to be noted here that $(x) : (x') . f(x, x')$ would be satisfied if there were not at least one value within the range of $x$ and $x'$, since a proposition of this form means "It is false that there is a value of $x$ not associated with a value of $x'$ such that $f(x, x')$ fails," and thus that $(\exists x) : (x') . f(x, x')$ is not strictly implied. In general, in the case of any proposition, we can derive a logical consequence by turning a universal variable into a particular if there is in the proposition some other generalized variable of the same kind and of wider scope. In particular, however, if we have, for example, the proposition $(p) . p \vee {\sim}p$, where the variable can denote propositions only, we can infer $(\exists p) . p \vee {\sim}p$, because a value of $p$ can be constructed out of purely logical materials.

We can, if we like, reformulate the foregoing propositions without using the variables $x$ and $x'$ by putting in a condition that can be satisfied only if the two variables are of the same kind. Thus, the first proposition can be written

$$(f) :. (x) : (y) . f(x, y) . f(y, x) \vee {\sim}f(y, x) : \prec : (x) : (\exists y) . f(x, y),$$

where the significance of $f(y, x) \vee {\sim}f(y, x)$ ensures a common range.

It was remarked above with regard to the proposition

$$(f, g) :. (\exists x) . f(x) . \vee . (\exists y) . g(y) : \equiv : (\exists x) : (\exists y) . f(x) \vee g(y)$$

that we did not have, without special conditions, a corresponding strict equivalence. This was because, if $f$ and $g$ were so chosen that $x$ and $y$ did not have the same range of variation, the right-hand expression would demand at least two entities, one significant as a value of $f(x)$ and the other as a value of $g(y)$, whereas the left-hand expression would demand the existence of at most one entity. We have, however,

$$(f, g) :. (\exists x) . f(x) . \vee . (\exists x') . g(x') : = : (\exists x) : (\exists x') . f(x) \vee g(x'),$$

because the right-hand expression in this case demands, at most, one value within the range of $x$ and $x'$.

In formulating general propositions, we have so far introduced only two prefixes, $(x)$ and $(\exists x)$, which correspond to the force of 'every' and 'some,' respectively; but it is possible to define two further prefixes, either or both of which may be employed for the purposes of generalization. There are, in the traditional treatment of singly-general propositions, four generalizations of a function $f(x)$, namely, "*Every* $x$ is such that $f(x)$," "*Some* $x$ is such that $f(x)$," "*No* $x$ is such that $f(x)$," and "*Not-every* $x$ is such that $f(x)$"; and it is the last two of these that we have not symbolized explicitly. The force of "No $x$ is such that $f(x)$" has been expressed by $\sim(\exists x) . f(x)$, or by $(x) . \sim f(x)$; and what we are going to do is to replace the compound symbol $\sim(\exists x)$ by $[x]$, so that we shall have $[x] . f(x)$. Again, the force of "Not-every $x$ is such that $f(x)$" has been expressed by $\sim(x) . f(x)$ or by $(\exists x) . \sim f(x)$; so that we may replace $\sim(x)$ by $\{x\}$, and write $\{x\} . f(x)$. It will appear that certain advantages, as regards symmetry and the like, result from the use of $[x]$ and $\{x\}$ in place of $(x)$ and $(\exists x)$; but there can be no doubt that these new symbols are, nevertheless, generally less convenient than the ordinary ones.[4]

Unlike $(x)$ and $(\exists x)$, the force of $[x]$ depends upon its position in a complex prefix. Taken alone, $[x]$ is of course negative in effect, but if a complex prefix is made up of two occurrences of it, the force of the second occurrence is affirmative, owing to the fact that it is affected by the first occurrence. Thus, the import of

$$(x) : (\exists y) . f(x, y), \text{ or } \sim(\exists x) : \sim(\exists y) . f(x, y),$$

is given by

$$[x] : [y] . f(x, y),$$

that is, by "No $x$ is such that no $y$ is such that $f(x, y)$" or "There is no value of $x$ without a value of $y$ such that $f(x, y)$."

[4] The prefix $\{x\}$, as correlative with $[x]$, was suggested to us by Professor H. M. Sheffer. See *Bull. Amer. Math. Soc.*, XXXII (1926), 694. The prefixes are analogues of Sheffer's stroke-function $p | q$ in its two interpretations.

In exactly the same way,

$$(x) :. (\exists y) : (z) . f(x, y, z)$$

is equivalent to

$$[x] :. [y] : [z] . \sim f(x, y, z),$$

where the force of the first generalization is negative, that of the second affirmative, and that of the third negative. And it is to be observed, in this connection, that when we express in terms of $[x]$ a function of the form

$$(x_1)(\exists x_2) \ldots (x_n) . f(x_1, x_2, \ldots, x_n),$$

where $n$ is odd, we have

$$[x_1][x_2] \ldots [x_n] . \sim f(x_1, x_2, \ldots, x_n);$$

whereas, when we express in this way a function of the form

$$(x_1)(\exists x_2) \ldots (\exists x_n) . f(x_1, x_2, \ldots, x_n),$$

where $n$ is even, we have

$$[x_1][x_2] \ldots [x_n] . f(x_1, x_2, \ldots, x_n).$$

That is, $f$ does or does not become $\sim f$ according as the degree of generality of the function is or is not odd.

Since the force of $[x]$ depends upon its position in the prefix, the import of $[x, y] . f(x, y)$ is very different from that of $[x] : [y] . f(x, y)$, the first of these expressions being equivalent to $(x, y) . \sim f(x, y)$, and the second, as we have seen, to $(x) : (\exists y) . f(x, y)$. This brings out an important fact with regard to functions in terms of $[x]$, namely, that they must be in reduced form; and there will therefore usually be many different functions in terms of $(x)$, or in terms of $(\exists x)$, corresponding to one and only one in $[x]$. Thus,

$$(x) :. (y) : (z) . f(x, y, z), \qquad (x, y) : (z) . f(x, y, z),$$
$$(x) : (y, z) . f(x, y, z), \qquad (x, y, z) . f(x, y, z),$$

are all equivalent, and each is equivalent to

$$[x, y, z] . \sim f(x, y, z),$$

there being no other equivalent expression in $[x]$.

By virtue of the fact that any proposition in a single complex prefix whose variables of widest scope are universal can be expressed in the form

$$\sim(\exists x_1, \ldots, x_m) :. \sim(\exists y_1, \ldots, y_n) : \ldots$$
$$f(x_1, \ldots, x_m; y_1, \ldots, y_n; \ldots),$$

any such proposition can be written:

$$[x_1, \ldots, x_m] :. [y_1, \ldots, y_n] : \ldots f(x_1, \ldots, x_m; y_1, \ldots, y_n; \ldots).$$

The fact that irreducible multiply-general propositions can be expressed in this way by the use of $[x]$ alone distinguishes this prefix both from $(x)$ and from $(\exists x)$.

The properties of functions in terms of $\{x\}$ are analogous to those of functions in $[x]$. But in contrast to $[x]$, the prefix $\{x\}$ is affirmative in import when it occurs in functions of the form $\{x\} . f(x)$; and when we have a function involving more than one occurrence, the import of the first occurrence is affirmative, that of the second negative, and so on. Thus,

$$(\exists x) : (y) . f(x, y)$$

is equivalent to

$$\{x\} : \{y\} . f(x, y);$$

and

$$(\exists x) :. (y) : (\exists z) . f(x, y, z)$$

is equivalent to

$$\{x\} :. \{y\} : \{z\} . \sim f(x, y, z).$$

It will be seen that $f$ changes to $\sim f$ in the second case, but not in the first; and generally that, in expressing a function in $(x)$ and $(\exists x)$ in terms of $\{x\}$, we must apply $\sim$ to the matrix if, and only if, the degree of generality of the function is odd.

As in the case of $[x]$, functions in terms of $\{x\}$ are always in reduced form; so that although $(\exists x) : (\exists y) . f(x, y)$ and $(\exists x, y) . f(x, y)$ are equivalent expressions in $(\exists x)$, there is just one corresponding function in $\{x\}$, namely $\{x, y\} . \sim f(x, y)$. And just as any proposition in a single prefix whose variables of widest scope are universal can be expressed in terms of $[x]$ alone, so any proposition of this sort whose variables of widest scope are particular can be expressed in the form

$$\{x_1, \ldots, x_m\} :. \{y_1, \ldots, y_n\} : \ldots f(x_1, \ldots, x_m; y_1, \ldots, y_n; \ldots).$$

When the functions with which we are concerned are not given in terms of a single prefix applied to a matrix, their formulation by means of $[x]$ and $\{x\}$ is usually less convenient than it is in the ordinary notation. In this connection we have the following equivalences, which relate conjunctions and disjunctions of general functions to functions constructed on matrices:

$$[x] . f(x) . \vee . [y] . g(y) : \equiv . [x, y] . f(x) . g(y);$$
$$[x] . f(x) : [y] . g(y) : \equiv . [x, y] . f(x) \vee g(y);$$
$$\{x\} . f(x) . \vee . \{y\} . g(y) : \equiv . \{x, y\} . f(x) . g(y);$$
$$\{x\} . f(x) : \{y\} . g(y) : \equiv . \{x, y\} . f(x) \vee g(y);$$
$$[x] . f(x) . \vee . \{y\} . g(y) : \equiv : [x] : [y] . {\sim}f(x) \vee {\sim}g(y);$$
$$\{x\} . f(x) : [y] . g(y) : \equiv : \{x\} : \{y\} . {\sim}f(x) . {\sim}g(y).$$

# CHAPTER X

## PROPOSITIONS OF ORDINARY DISCOURSE

The purely formal theory of general propositions as developed in the preceding chapter would be incomplete without a somewhat detailed account of the way in which propositions of ordinary discourse are to be interpreted in terms of it; so, in order to supplement this formal treatment, we are going to discuss in the present chapter some points regarding the analysis of ordinary judgments. This will consist mainly in an endeavor to make explicit what is implicit in judgments of unanalyzed discourse, and in an attempt to show how the resulting analyzed judgments are to be formulated by means of the technical apparatus employed in the abstract theory of propositions. We shall examine samples of judgments of different kinds and shall try to show what their logical forms are, what are the logical constants and variables involved in them, and how they are to be classified. In doing this, however, we shall be led occasionally to adopt certain views, as against others, with regard to the way such judgments are to be interpreted in respects that are not purely logical. This is inevitable, because the form that a proposition is to be understood to have will depend upon its import in other respects; but where such non-logical interpretation is necessary, the points to be illustrated will not in general depend upon the correctness of the particular view adopted, owing to the fact that, with appropriate alterations, these points could be brought out equally well if some other view were taken. We are interested primarily in showing how the analysis of ordinary judgments is to be developed in accordance with our theory of general propositions, and only secondarily in defending particular views regarding the way in which judgments that are not purely logical are to be analyzed in respect of their non-logical features.

We may, to begin with, consider some points regarding the nature of ordinary words, and the way they are connected with their meanings. It has often been pointed out that a word, strictly so called, is not one single entity, but is rather a class or collection of entities which resemble one another in certain respects. It may be said that, in the ordinary sense of the term, there is only one word 'man' in the English language; but if we look over a page of print, we may find this written symbol occurring several different times. Clearly, in one sense, there is not simply a single symbol 'man,' but a multiplicity of such symbols. We shall have to distinguish here between a word, as a generic entity, and the several occurrences of the word, just as we distinguish between a piece of music and its several renditions, or a book and the different copies of the book. The word 'man' has many different instances, written or spoken, and the word itself cannot be identified with any one of these instances, but must be regarded either as the class made up of them all or as an abstract entity after the fashion of a universal. And in the same way we shall have to distinguish between any verbal phrase and an occurrence of that phrase, as well as between a complete sentence and an occurrence of the sentence.

It is plain that instances of spoken words or sentences are particular sounds, which are auditory events. But it is to be observed that written words, similarly, when they function symbolically, are visual events; for it is, of course, the word as read, the visual impression received, which actually arouses in the mind of the reader a corresponding meaning, and it is only when a mark or set of marks actually gives rise to meaning that it is operating as a symbol. It is to be noted, too, that any sign or symbol, taken merely as an object, is of great complexity, but that it is only certain features of signs which are symbolically significant. Take again the word 'man.' It does not matter how large or how small this word is written, or what the color of the ink is, and there may also be a good deal of difference in the shapes of the letters, as in the handwriting of different persons. All these features, and many others, are symbolically irrelevant; although they might of course be given meaning in some usage—in maps and in bookkeeping, for example, color often has notational significance. There will, however, in the case of any symbol, always be an enormous variety of aspects which are to be neglected, and only a small number selected to represent what is to be meant by the symbol.

Now, with regard to the relation of words to what they stand for (when they stand by themselves for anything at all), we can easily distinguish two quite different kinds. Take, for example, the words "That is a table," which, when read, give us a particular instance of a sentence. As here given, no proposition is conveyed by this expression, not because the part "is a table" fails to arouse a definite meaning, but because "That" is without other than syntactical significance. Consider, however, two instances of this sentence or, as we may say, two different occasions of its use. On one of these occasions one proposition may be expressed, and on the other another proposition, owing to the fact that the two occurrences of "That" correspond to different things. Clearly, we may distinguish between demonstrative words, like 'this' and 'that,' whose several instances have many different meanings, and adjectival words, like 'table' and 'round,' whose instances have, ideally, the same meaning. Of course, the precise meaning of an adjectival word often varies from instance to instance; but that results from a defect in the language, whereas the variation in meaning among the instances of a demonstrative word is essential to the language.

We can, if we like, speak less accurately in this connection, and say that a demonstrative word has many different meanings, while an adjectival word has only one, although strictly it is only instances of words that function symbolically and correspond to meanings. If this were not so, the use of demonstrative terms in the ordinary way would be impossible. Thus we could not say, on a given occasion, "This is red" without expressing the proposition that everything was red, because different instances of the word 'this,' and therefore the word itself, may be applied to anything whatever. And with regard to adjectival terms, it seems clear that it is the particular sound or particular visual impression which gives rise to an understood meaning, and not the class of such sounds or visual impressions.

There are some words which carry both adjectival and demonstrative significance; and these, of course, have different meanings on different occasions of their use, owing to the presence of a demonstrative factor. It appears to be always possible, however, to replace the single word in such a case by an equivalent verbal phrase in such a way that some of the words in the phrase are purely demonstrative and others purely adjectival. Take, for instance, the word 'here,' which means 'this place,' or 'this, which is a place,' with some preposition usually understood. We can say "He came to this place," where "this" is purely demonstrative and "came to . . . place" purely adjectival. And in the same way, 'now' has the force of 'this time,' 'to-day' of 'this day,' etc.; so that a separation of adjectival from demonstrative factors would seem to be always possible.[1]

All or nearly all the propositions that we are accustomed to express in ordinary discourse turn out upon analysis to be much more complex than we are at first sight inclined to suppose them to be. Let us take an example which is as simple as any that we should in practice have frequent occasion to use—a proposition, say, which can be expressed by the words "That table is square." Grammatically, we have here a subject-predicate expression; but it is easy enough to see that, when we make a judgment expressible in these words, we are not in fact simply assigning a single predicate to a given subject. We are at the least assigning two predicates; for we are saying, with regard to the entity in question, both that it is a table and that it is square. It is, of course, possible to be mistaken in such a judgment on the ground that the thing is not a table, even if it is square. So, in place of saying "That table is square," we can express the proposition in equivalent form by the words "That square thing is a table," or by the words "That is a table and it is square." Which of these three expressions we use on a given occasion will very likely depend upon what we wish to emphasize and what we suppose our hearer already to understand. The last is, of course, the most explicit: we have a proposition that involves conjunction; but it will be seen presently that this analysis is very far indeed from being a complete one, in the sense of revealing

[1] It must not be supposed that demonstrative words correspond to or stand for particular 'things,' as commonly understood; the presumption is that they never do; but that is a matter to be discussed later on.

the complete logical structure of the proposition under consideration. The point to be noted now is that when a proposition involves two or more terms having adjectival significance, whether these terms are given in the verbal expression as common nouns or as adjectives, it can always be shown to be a logical function of simpler expressions. Let us take as a further example a proposition that can be expressed by the words "This piece of cloth is either blue or green." Here we can write, in accordance with the interpretation just given, "This is a piece of cloth, and it is either blue or green"; so that we have at least a proposition involving conjunction. But it is clear that 'being either blue or green' is not a simple property, and that the proposition "This is either blue or green" can be expressed in equivalent form by "This is blue or it is green"; so that the force of the original proposition can be given by "This is a piece of cloth, and it is blue or it is green," which appears to be an expression of the form $p \centerdot q \vee r$. Again, take the proposition "This book is larger than that one." We have here the two propositions "This is a book" and "That is a book" expressed by parts of the complex expression, and we may therefore write, as a partial interpretation of what is meant by the whole expression, "This is a book and that is a book, and this is larger than that," which would seem to be of the form $f(x) \centerdot f(y) \centerdot g(x, y)$.[2]

Let us turn now to propositions which are in ordinary discourse explicitly general, in that their expression involves a use of the prefixes 'some' and 'all,' or equivalent applicatives. The simplest examples are found in such statements as "I saw a large house," where the article "a" has the force of 'some.' This statement can plainly be rendered otherwise in the words "There was a large house which I saw," and is therefore of the form $(\exists x) \centerdot \phi(x)$. But in virtue of what has just been said about expressions containing several adjectival terms, we can also write "$(\exists x) \centerdot x$ was seen by me, $x$ was a house, and $x$ was large"; so that there results a proposition of the form

$$(\exists x) \centerdot f(x) \centerdot f'(x) \centerdot f''(x).$$

[2] It is not to be held that this is in fact the form of the proposition in question, because it will be seen upon further analysis that the proposition is really a general one, which is constructed on a function of this form and which contains prefixes covering the entire function.

This does not give us a complete representation of the formal structure of the proposition, however; for it is plain that to use a past tense and say "*I saw* so-and-so" is to make a judgment about the time at which the statement is made, and also about some past time. Saying on one occasion "*I saw* so-and-so" may express what is true, and on another occasion what is false, since it plainly involves 'now' as an essential part of its meaning and implies that there was some other occasion of a certain sort prior to the one in question.[3] Let $f(x, t)$ mean "I saw $x$ at $t$," $f'(x, t)$ mean "$x$ was a house at $t$," $f''(x, t)$ mean "$x$ was large at $t$"; and let $g(t, t_1)$ mean "$t$ is a time earlier than $t_1$." Then we have

$$(\exists x) : (\exists t) \,.\, f(x, t) \,.\, f'(x, t) \,.\, f''(x, t) \,.\, g(t, t_1),$$

where $t_1$ is the particular time at which the statement is made. Still, there is no assurance that the expression here given represents all the details of the formal structure of the original proposition; it would, indeed, be easy to suggest elements of generality not yet made explicit; but this is as far as we need carry the analysis in the present instance, since it indicates sufficiently the complexity of any judgment of the kind in question.[4]

Let us take, as a further example, the proposition "There are no books on that table." This statement must be carefully interpreted, because it appears at first sight to be negative and of the form $\sim(\exists x) \,.\, \phi(x)$, but is in fact a conjunctive statement, one part of which is of this form and the other existential. The proposition is plainly equivalent to "That is a table, and there are no books on it"; so that if we allow $f(y)$ to mean "$y$ is a table," $f'(x)$ to mean "$x$ is a book," and $g(x, y)$ to mean "$x$ is on $y$," and if "That" is replaced by $a$, we have, as a partial interpretation,

$$f(a) : \sim(\exists x) \,.\, f'(x) \,.\, g(x, a).$$

[3] Cf. G. E. Moore, *Proc. Arist. Soc.*, Sup. Vol. VII, p. 185.

[4] There is no reason in formal logic why a proposition should have a complete analysis. If it turned out that interpretation could be continued indefinitely in some or in all cases, that would not affect ordinary logical procedures. We denote a proposition in virtue of some aspect of its logical form, which is represented by the function through which it is denoted; but this form may be more or less specific and need not embody the complete logical structure of the proposition denoted; nor is there any presupposition that a most specific form exists, though there may be grounds upon which it can be shown that one must exist.

Suppose, however, that we changed the statement to "That is not a table with books on it." In the most natural understanding of this expression, there is no implication that the object in question is a table, since everything that is said would ordinarily be taken to fall within the scope of the negation, and we should have

$$\sim(\exists x) \cdot f(a) \cdot f'(x) \cdot g(x, a).$$

One is tempted to try to interpret general propositions like those here considered as conjunctions and disjunctions of their values—or rather, of the values of the matrices on which they are constructed. But, in fact, such an interpretation cannot be carried out. Let us take, as a simple example, the proposition "Everything is extended," and represent it by $(x) \cdot f(x)$. We are inclined to say that this is really a shorthand way of stating a long conjunction, $f(x_1) \cdot f(x_2) \cdot \ldots$, where $x_1$, $x_2$, ... either name or uniquely describe particular things. And similarly, there is a temptation to say that $(\exists x) \cdot f(x)$ means what is meant by $f(x_1) \vee f(x_2) \vee \ldots$. Consider, however, the exact import of the proposition "Everything is extended," and suppose some one to be knowing this proposition. All that he will be knowing is that, whatever things there may happen to be, they are extended. But if he were knowing the proposition represented by $f(x_1) \cdot f(x_2) \cdot \ldots$, he would have to be aware of what things there were which were named or described by $x_1$, $x_2$, .... Clearly, the existence of those particular things is not implied by the proposition "Everything is extended," which is in fact not existential at all, but of the form $\sim(\exists x) \cdot \sim f(x)$. And the same will be true of $f(x_1) \vee f(x_2) \vee \ldots$ as contrasted with $(\exists x) \cdot f(x)$. We can know that something is extended by making a particular observation, but we cannot know a proposition of this disjunctive form without knowing about the existence of each of the things represented by $x_1$, $x_2$, ....

It might be supposed, however, that such conjunctions and disjunctions were stronger statements, from which propositions like $(x) \cdot f(x)$ and $(\exists x) \cdot f(x)$, respectively, followed. This is true in the second case; but it is not true in the first, as may be seen from the following consideration. Suppose we knew a proposition of the form $f(x_1) . f(x_2) . . . .$ to the effect that each of the things $x_1, x_2, \ldots$ was extended, and suppose that it was in fact the case that these were all the things that existed. Nevertheless, we should not, merely by knowing that these things were all extended, be able to infer that unextended things did not exist, since the proposition itself does not imply this. Let us take a simpler example, which, although it is not strictly analogous to this one, will perhaps bring out the point more clearly. There are just three things, $a$, $b$, $c$, on this table, and each of them is rectangular; so that if we allow $f(x)$ to mean "$x$ is on the table," and $g(x)$ to mean "$x$ is rectangular," we shall have

$$(x) . f(x) \supset g(x),$$

as well as

$$f(a) . g(a) : f(b) . g(b) : f(c) . g(c).$$

Obviously, by merely knowing this second proposition, we cannot know the first, because we are not able to infer that $a$, $b$, and $c$ are all the things on the table; the proposition would be equally true if a fourth thing, $d$, satisfied the condition $f(x)$ and failed to satisfy $g(x)$. And since we are plainly not able to know the second proposition by knowing the first, so far from having here two equivalent propositions, one of which could be taken as an interpretation of the other, we have two propositions which are in fact independent, in that neither is a logical consequence of the other.

The sense of the term 'exists,' as it is asserted in existential propositions and denied in universal ones, is especially difficult to analyze; but there are certain points with regard to it which seem clear enough. In all the ordinary uses of this term, it is predicated of concepts or descriptions, and not of particular things.[5] If you say "Men exist," you are making a judgment about the property 'being a man,' to the effect that that property applies to something, or, in other words, is realized, where 'to exist,' 'to apply,' and 'to be realized' all have the same meaning. The subject of your judgment is not any particular man, nor all men together, but simply the concept or description which you

[5] This is Russell's view, as explained, for instance, in his *Introduction to Mathematical Philosophy*, Ch .XVI.

have in mind. If this were not so, you could not make significantly such judgments as "Ghosts exist," since there would then be nothing whatever which was the subject of your judgment; nor could you make true judgments like "Ghosts do not exist." In point of fact, we never talk about concrete particular things except through concepts, and the question whether these concepts apply to anything, or 'exist,' is always an open one. This is true even in the case of judgments of perception, where we judge, say, with regard to some object 'seen' that it exists. In such a case, as is shown by illusions and hallucinations, as well as by direct inspection, the object in question, if there is one, is not bodily present in the judgment, but is given only indirectly by way of a conceptual complex which is integrated with a sensory appearance. When, for example, we judge with regard to an object apprehended in this way "That is a book," we are judging that the conceptual complex in question, which contains a datum of sense as a factor, is exemplified or realized or 'exists.' [6]

So far as this account goes, it would seem to be satisfactory; but it by no means provides answers to all the questions that one would wish to raise. There is in the view a suggestion to the effect that we are to think simply of a dyadic relation as holding between an idea and some particular thing to which the idea applies; and so far as contemporary things are concerned, this might seem to be unobjectionable. We might say, for instance, that the words 'the King of England' stood for a descriptive idea, and that there was a substantival person whose existence satisfied this description. But it is also true that Cæsar existed, and yet there is nothing whatever which answers to the notion for which the term 'Cæsar' stands; so that there can be no relation between an idea and a particular thing in this case. Whatever may be the nature of facts about the past, they are

[6] The reason why 'exists' is put in quotes here is not that it is being employed in an unusual sense, but that it is being employed in an unusual context. For in saying "the conceptual complex in question exists," we should naturally be understood to mean, not that the idea 'this book' exists, i.e., is realized, but that a description of this idea, namely 'the conceptual complex in question,' exists or is realized; and although this is true enough, what we wish to say is not that the description 'the conceptual complex in question' applies to something, but that what it applies to applies to something.

all present facts; it is a present fact that Cæsar did exist, and also a present one that Zeus did not; but inasmuch as there is no substantival past, there can no more be a particular thing to which the description 'Cæsar' applies than there can be one to which the description 'Zeus' applies. Plainly, existential assertions about the future are in the same case. If a man says "I am going to build a house," we cannot understand him to mean "There *is* a house which I am going to build," but must render his assertion by "There will be a house which I shall have built," that is, by "$(\exists x) . x$ will be a house, and I shall have built $x$."

It is a curious circumstance that in English certain non-existential statements have exactly the same grammatical form as certain existential ones, and that some expressions can be employed either as implying or as not implying existence. Take, for example, the statement "I am looking at a house." In any proper sense, this statement cannot possibly be true unless there does exist a house which the speaker is seeing; if he is suffering from an illusion, he must be speaking falsely. Consider, however, the statement "I am thinking of a house." This is ambiguous, since it may mean "There is a house of which I am thinking" and thus be existential, or may mean "I am entertaining a conception of such a kind that, if it did apply to anything, that thing would be a house," from which it does not follow that there is anything to which the conception so described applies. Take the statement "I am thinking of a centaur." If these words are to be used truly, their import must be, in effect, "I am conceiving an idea which is such that, whether it applies to anything or not, if it should do so, what it applied to would be a centaur."[7] Again, suppose some one to say "I wish to build a house." Then, clearly, we cannot draw the absurd consequence, "There is a house which I wish to build"; though it does look as if the drawing of just this consequence were responsible for the common view that a desire must have an 'object.' Nor will it help matters, so far as finding an object for the desire in such a case is concerned, to say that what is really meant is "I desire that the building of a house by me should

[7] Cf. G. E. Moore, *Philosophical Studies*, pp. 216 ff.

be realized," although this is plainly true. The words 'the building of a house by me' stand merely for a descriptive idea, and inasmuch as this idea is not realized, there is nothing which can properly be called the object of the desire in question. What one is doing is, of course, desiring by way of or through this description, which is capable of being the medium of a desire irrespective of whether it ever will in fact be realized.

We come now to certain propositions which occur with great frequency in ordinary discourse. An analysis of propositions of this kind, in the respects here to be considered, is of importance both on its own account and in virtue of its bearing on other points with which we shall be concerned presently. Following the usage of Mr. Russell, to whom the interpretation of these propositions is due, we shall say that they are such as involve *definite descriptions*.[8] Consider the import of the propositional function "$x$ is a man whom you met yesterday," and contrast its import with that of "$x$ is *the* man you met yesterday." Each of these functions is descriptive, the first being an indefinite description and the second a definite one. And the difference between them is clearly this: if you met two men yesterday, the first will describe each man, whereas the second will describe neither, since neither will satisfy the condition of being *the* man whom you met. If we allow $f(x)$ to mean "$x$ is a man whom you met yesterday," then the force of the second function is given by

$$f(x) : (y) \,.\, {\sim}f(y) \vee (y = x),$$

which will be satisfied if, and only if, there is just one person of the sort in question. Thus, 'the' in the singular means 'an only,' as in "I have *an only* brother."

Let us examine a proposition in which a definite description occurs. Suppose some one to say "I have been reading the book which I have in my hands." There are three circumstances under which such a proposition might be false: it might of course be the case that the person in question had one and only one book in his hands, but had not been reading it; it might be the case that he had in his hands no book whatever; or it might be

[8] *Loc. cit.*, and *Principia Mathematica*, ✳14.

the case that he had more than one. And, clearly, what any one who made such an assertion would be saying is "I have a book in my hands, one and only one, and I have been reading it"; so that if we allow $f(x)$ to mean "$x$ is a book in my hands" and $g(x)$ to mean "I have been reading $x$," we can express the proposition here in question by

$$(\exists x) : f(x) : (y) . \sim f(y) \vee (y = x) : g(x)$$

or by $$(\exists x) . f(x) . g(x) : \sim(\exists y, z) . f(y) . f(z) . \sim(y = z),$$

that is, "There is a book in my hands which I have been reading, and it is not the case that there are two books in my hands." Note that although in the first expression the words "the book which I have in my hands" correspond to the part $f(x) : (y) . \sim f(y) \vee (y = x)$, which is equivalent to $(y) . f(y) \equiv (y = x)$, in the second expression there is no part to which these words can be said to correspond, owing to the limited scope of $(\exists x)$. If, however, we put two dots after this prefix, thus bringing the whole expression within its scope, an equivalent rendering of the proposition will result, and we can then say that the phrase "the book which I have in my hands" corresponds to $f(x) : \sim(\exists y, z) . f(y) . f(z) . \sim(y = z)$.

Take the proposition "The satellite of the earth is uninhabited." The truth of this proposition depends upon the fact that there is at least one satellite of the earth, that there is at most one, and that there does not exist a satellite of the earth which is inhabited; so that if we allow $f(x)$ to mean "$x$ is a satellite of the earth" and $g(x)$ to mean "$x$ is uninhabited," the import of the statement will be given by

$$(\exists x) . f(x) : \sim(\exists x, y) . f(x) . f(y) . \sim(x = y) : (x) . f(x) \supset g(x).$$

Thus, "The square root of four is two" is a false proposition, not because two is not a square root, but because it is not the only one; we can say truly "The positive square root of four is two" or "The negative square root of four is minus two." Again, let us take "The book on that table is the one you gave me." This proposition may be rendered "There is an $x$ which is both a book on that table and a book you gave me, and if $y$ is either a book on that table or a book you gave me, then $y$ is identical with $x$."

So, if $f(x)$ means "$x$ is a book on that table" and $g(x)$ means "$x$ is a book you gave me," we can write either

$$(\exists x) :. f(x) . g(x) :. (y) : \sim f(y) . \sim g(y) . \vee . (y = x)$$

or $$(\exists x, z) :. f(x) : (y) . \sim f(y) \vee (y = x) :. g(z) : (y) . \sim g(y) \vee (y = z) :. (x = z).$$

Although propositions like this one are such as imply that there is at least and at most one entity of the kind in question, it is not to be supposed that all assertions in which definite descriptions occur will have existential import in this way; that will depend upon the position of the description in the complex expression and upon the force of the whole assertion. If some one should say "The book on that table is not mine," he would actually be saying, in part, that there was one and only one book on that table; but if he should say "It is false that the book on that table is mine," his words would be open to another interpretation: we might understand him to mean "Either there is not just one book on that table, or else there is just one and it does not belong to me." The distinction depends, of course, upon whether negation is to be understood as applying to the whole proposition or only to a part of it; so that if we allow $f(x)$ to mean "$x$ is a book on that table" and $g(x)$ to mean "$x$ belongs to me," we can express the first proposition by

$$(\exists x) : f(x) : (y) . f(y) \supset (y = x) : \sim g(x),$$

and the second by

$$\sim(\exists x) : f(x) : (y) . f(y) \supset (y = x) : g(x).$$

There is an ambiguity of another sort, as between extension and intension, which may arise in connection with propositions involving definite descriptions, and which may be responsible for doubt whether a proposition does or does not have existential import. Suppose some one to say "The President of the United States commands the Army and the Navy." He may mean simply "There is one and only one person who is President of the United States, and he is in command of the Army and the Navy." But it is also true that a man would not, by legal definition, be President unless he were in command of the Army and the Navy; so that the speaker may mean to express a proposition in intension: "From the fact with regard to anybody whatever that he was the President of the United States, it would follow that he was in command of the Army and the Navy." If we allow $f(x)$ to mean "$x$ is President of the United States" and $g(x)$ to mean "$x$ commands the Army and the Navy," then we can express this latter proposition by writing

$$\sim\Diamond(\exists x) : f(x) : (y) \,.\, f(y) \supset (y = x) : \sim g(x),$$

or by writing

$$(x) :. f(x) : (y) \,.\, f(y) \supset (y = x) : \prec \,.\, g(x),$$

the corresponding proposition in extension being

$$(\exists x) : f(x) : (y) \,.\, f(y) \supset (y = x) : g(x).$$

In intension there is no implication that a President exists, although the rendering of the definite description "the President of the United States" by $f(x) : (y) \,.\, f(y) \supset (y = x)$ is the same in each case. A change from extension to intension never alters in any way the interpretation to be put upon a phrase of the form 'the so-and-so.'

An exactly similar ambiguity occurs in connection with certain apparently tautological propositions. Take, for instance, the expression "The integer between three and four is the integer between three and four." Interpreted in extension, this expression may be understood to mean: "There is one and only one entity $x$ having the property of being an integer between three and four; there is one and only one entity $y$ having this same property; and $x$ is identical with $y$," which is, of course, a false proposition. In intension, however, we have a true proposition: "If anything had the property of being the only integer between three and four, then it would have that property." So, if $f(x)$ means "$x$ is an integer between three and four," we have, in intension,

$$(x) :. f(x) : (y) \,.\, f(y) \supset (y = x) : \prec : f(x) : (y) \,.\, f(y) \supset (y = x).$$

It will be seen, too, that $\prec$ might be replaced by $\supset$, and the statement interpreted to mean "If anything is the only integer between three and four, then it is the only one," although this would hardly be a natural rendering. On the other hand, "The present King of France is the present King of France" might quite naturally be understood as being of this form, and therefore as being true. Or we might write

$$(\exists x) : f(x) : (y) \,.\, f(y) \supset (y = x) : \supset :$$
$$(\exists z) : f(z) : (y) \,.\, f(y) \supset (y = z),$$

and interpret the statement to mean "If something has the property of being the present King of France, then something has that property."

The theory of definite descriptions enables us to interpret certain propositions dealt with above in respects which have so far been left unanalyzed. It will be recalled that we considered the proposition "That table is square," and said merely that it appeared to be conjunctive and of the form "That is a table and it is square." However, let us take simply "That is a table," which is part of what is being expressed, and consider the exact significance of this part. We have seen that the import of 'that' is purely demonstrative, with no admixture of adjectival significance. And it is plain that the entity designated by this demonstrative term, whatever it may be, is the primary subject of the judgment we are making when we judge, on a given occasion, "That is a table." At first sight, we are inclined to say that the subject of such a judgment, which corresponds to the demonstrative term, is the concrete thing which we are at the time perceiving, and which we are asserting to be a table. But there are certain considerations which make it impossible to hold such a view. We cannot say that the subject of a judgment of this kind is the table or other object which we are at the moment perceiving, because it sometimes happens that there is no object at all that is being perceived, as in mirror-images, dreams, and waking hallucinations. In these cases, it is plain that we can and do judge such things as "That is a table"; and even if such judgments are false, they are significant and must have subjects. Moreover, it is obvious that if physical things cannot be the subjects of hallucinatory judgments, they cannot be the subjects in veridical instances either; for there is no intrinsic difference between the two cases. If there were, we could tell whether a judgment was veridical or not by mere inspection, which we cannot do. It is, indeed, obvious that what the words in the verbal expression of a judgment stand for will be the same whether the judgment is true or false, and that therefore we must not suppose an entity to be a constituent of a judgment, whether as subject or as some other factor, which is not essential to the significance of the judgment.

We are going to say, quite simply, that the logical subject of a judgment of perception is the given datum which is sensed when the proposition is asserted. There must of course always be such a datum, even when we are judging falsely, as may be seen by reference to illusory cases. On any occasion on which there was no such sense-datum, a significant judgment, true or false, would be impossible. When we judge "That is a table," the sense-datum corresponding to "That" seems to be a part of the surface of a table; in an illusory instance it of course cannot be, and there are reasons for believing that it cannot be even in a veridical instance; but it is in any case the immediate subject of the judgment, upon which an interpretation is placed, truly or falsely.[9]

If this is so, however, we shall have to be very careful in rendering the import of the words "is a table"; for it looks at first sight as if we were asserting the entity corresponding to "That" to be a table. But in point of fact, we are not dealing here with a simple subject-predicate proposition; we are saying something like "That is an appearance of one and only one table" or "That is a manifestation of one and only one table" or "That discloses one and only one table," where the relation expressed by "appearance of," "manifestation of," and "discloses" remains to be analyzed. How such a relation is to be interpreted will, of course, depend upon what view is to be taken concerning the nature of physical objects and their connections with data of sense, and we are not here concerned to maintain any particular theory with regard to this matter. All we wish to do is to point out that judgments about physical objects are

[9] The account of judgments of perception as here given is due to Professor G. E. Moore. See his *Philosophical Studies*, pp. 220 ff.

not simple subject-predicate ones and to indicate what, in certain respects, their logical form seems to be. If $f(x)$ means "$x$ is a table" and if "That" is replaced by $a$ and if "$a$ is an appearance of $x$" is expressed by $h(a, x)$, then the proposition under consideration can be rendered by

$$(\exists x) : h(a, x) : (y) \,.\, h(a, y) \supset (y = x) : f(x),$$

which may be read "There is an $x$ which is *the* $x$ of which $a$ is an appearance, and that $x$ is a table." It will be seen, too, that the proposition with which we began, namely, "That table is square," will be of the form

$$(\exists x) : h(a, x) : (y) \,.\, h(a, y) \supset (y = x) : f(x) \,.\, g(x).$$

Let us take, finally, the statement "That piece of cloth is either blue or green," which was considered above. If $f(x)$ is understood to mean "$x$ is a piece of cloth," $g(x)$ to mean "$x$ is blue," and $g'(x)$ to mean "$x$ is green," then we have, as an interpretation of the proposition in question,

$$(\exists x) : f(x) \,.\, g(x) \vee g'(x) \,.\, h(a, x) : (y) \,.\, h(a, y) \supset (y = x).$$

If this is a right account, so far as it goes, of judgments about physical objects, then one important consequence follows with regard to the communicability of such judgments. Suppose that one person, A, endeavors to communicate such a judgment to another, B; suppose A says "That is a table," where "That" corresponds to a given datum $a$ and where the judgment is to be analyzed in the manner indicated. B will not be apprehending the datum apprehended by A; he will be led to judge "That is a table" where the demonstrative term will correspond to one of his data $b$. And A will have succeeded in communicating his judgment, in so far as it can be communicated, if the datum $b$ is, in point of fact, an appearance of the same object as that of which the datum $a$ is an appearance; although, strictly, B will not succeed in apprehending the exact proposition apprehended by A, owing to this difference in respect of a single factor. It is to be noted, too, that this same consideration presumably applies to two successive judgments made by the same person: if A says, on two successive occasions, "That is a table," then, according to most theories of the nature of data of sense at least, the immediate subject of his judgment on the first occasion will be distinct from the immediate subject on the second.

The theory of definite descriptions supplies an explanation of so-called proper names. Let us take, for instance, the name 'Lincoln' as it would be understood in a proposition expressed by the words "Lincoln was assassinated." It might seem at first sight as if "Lincoln" were a purely demonstrative term, which was employed as a sort of sign in the designation of a particular person; but obviously such a view is quite impossible, owing to the fact that there is no person who is so designated. There did exist a certain man who bore that name, but all that we have now is the fact that there was such a person; and it therefore seems necessary that we interpret the term "Lincoln" as standing for a definite description, in such a way that the proposition "Lincoln was assassinated" will be of the form "The person having such-and-such characteristics was assassinated." We may say, "There was such-and-such a person, one and only one, who was known as Lincoln, and who was assassinated." It is true that different speakers may have in mind different descriptive complexes when they use this name, and may therefore be asserting different propositions; but this means merely that sentences containing proper names are more likely to be ambiguous than those which involve explicitly a phrase of the form 'the so-and-so.' Such ambiguity will, however, be of no practical importance if the description that the hearer is led to conceive is, in point of fact, such as would apply to the same thing as the one conceived by the speaker. If, for instance, by "Lincoln" one person understands 'the President of the United States during the Civil War' while another understands 'the President who signed the Proclamation of Emancipation,' there will be sufficient agreement for most purposes; though there will, of course, be two genuinely distinct propositions that are in question. Moreover, even when a proper name is applied to an existing person, it is clear that the name must have descriptive significance, because the person, in such a case, is never directly apprehended. If we say, for instance, "John Smith is ill," the words "John Smith" will stand for some description like 'the person whom we call John Smith.' And even when, on seeing the person, we say "That person is John Smith," we are saying something like "That is an appearance of one and only one person, who is the one we know as John Smith." The only proper names, strictly so called, are demonstrative pronouns and demonstrative adjectives.

We turn now to certain propositions of ordinary discourse which involve numerical factors—such, for instance, as "There are *three* books on this table." Roughly speaking, we may say that a natural number is an adjective which can be predicated significantly of classes or collections.[10] To say that there are three books on this table is tantamount to saying that the collection of books on the table has the number 'three,' or is characterized by that number. The adjective 'three' will, of course, apply to many different collections; it will apply to the three chairs in this room as well as to the three books in question, just as the adjective 'red' applies to this book and also to that piece of cloth.

If any conception of an ordinary natural number is to be an adequate one, it must enable us to say what is meant by the sum of two numbers, as well as by the sum of instances of two numbers. And the rough conception here suggested does enable us to do this. If *a*, *b*, *c* are the books on this table, we can form the collection whose only member is *a* as well as the collection whose members are *b*, *c*, and say that this *one* book together with these *two* is a collection of *three* books. This will mean that since the class of which *a* is the only member is 'one,' and that of which *b* and *c* are the only members is 'two,' there will be a single collection each of whose members belongs to one or the other of these, and this collection will be 'three.' This formulation is not quite adequate, however, because there must be a condition to the effect that the two classes shall not overlap. If we take the class whose members are *a*, *b*, and the one whose members are *b*, *c*, we shall have two classes of two members each; but their sum is not four, and indeed they do not have a numerical sum, owing to the fact that they do not satisfy the condition of having

[10] Cf. W. E. Johnson, *Logic*, Pt. I, pp. 126 ff.

no members in common. In the abstract case, we can say that the statement $1 + 2 = 3$ is to be interpreted as follows: "If there were a class of one member, and another of two, and if there were nothing which belonged to both, there would be a class made up of the members of these two, and that class would have three members." In this formulation it will be seen that an arithmetical statement is interpreted as being strictly hypothetical and that the statement would therefore be true even if no classes of the kind in question existed. This is obviously a necessary condition for any correct interpretation of purely arithmetical statements, since they plainly do not depend for their significance or validity upon the existence of corresponding classes.

So far as this account goes it would seem to be a satisfactory one, but it does not go very far. It tells us nothing about the structure of a numerical adjective, which must at least be somewhat different from that of an adjective like 'red,' because it has to do with classes or collections and not with individual things. Moreover, the account suggests a naïve and untenable view of the nature of a class. In most cases in which this notion is employed, it cannot possibly be understood as referring to a group or aggregate of particular things, but must be given some more complex interpretation. Thus we may say that the class of Presidents of the United States up to the present time comprises some thirty members. But there cannot possibly be any such group or collection of particular persons; nor, of course, was there ever a time at which such a concrete group or aggregate existed. We shall have to revise this crude conception of the class of the Presidents; and perhaps the following will serve this purpose as well as anything else. It is a fact that there was a President satisfying the description 'Lincoln,' and it is also a fact that there was a President satisfying the description 'Washington,' etc.; and since the number of facts of this kind is the number we want, they can be held to be what we are counting when we enumerate the Presidents. Indeed, it is pretty evident that this is what we actually do; we say, "Washington was President, Adams was President, . . . ," and thus actually count the facts of this kind.

Let us see how a natural number is to be understood as being an adjective or property, and how such properties differ from more ordinary ones. A property is always represented by a propositional function. Thus "$x$ is red" will be satisfied for certain values of $x$, and to say that these values satisfy the function or give rise to true propositions when substituted for $x$ is of course tantamount to saying that they possess the property of being red. To say that a number is a property is therefore equivalent to saying that it is a propositional function.

Consider, then, the following function, which contains only one free variable, $f$:

$$(\exists x) \,.\, f(x) : \sim(\exists x, y) \,.\, f(x) \,.\, f(y) \,.\, \sim(x = y).$$

We shall say that this function defines, or is, the cardinal number 1. If this is a correct definition, it must of course enable us to count. In particular, it happens to be a fact that there is just one table in this room; and if the definition is right, it must be possible to state this fact. This is easily done. For if, by way of applying the definition to the particular case, we interpret $f(x)$ to mean "$x$ is a table in this room," we have "There is a value of $x$ such that $x$ is a table in this room, and it is false that there are distinct values of $x$ such that this is true." Again, the moon is the only satellite of the earth; and if we assign to $f(x)$ the meaning "$x$ is a satellite of the earth," a statement of the fact that the earth has one satellite results. The number 'one' is of the form "$f$ is one," just as the property 'red' is of the form "$x$ is red."

It will be seen that the notion of a class can be dispensed with altogether in this connection and can be replaced by any property which would, in the ordinary manner of speaking, be said to determine the class. We can say that the property 'being a satellite of the earth' has or corresponds to or is associated with the number 'one.' But it must be noted that the number which a given property has is an extrinsic and not an intrinsic characteristic of that property. So far as the intrinsic nature of the property 'being a satellite of the earth' is concerned, it might just as well have been associated with 'two' as with 'one.'

This is why we cannot tell what the number of a property is by merely inspecting the property.

It is easy to see how the number 2 can be defined according to the plan followed in defining 1:

$$(\exists x, y) \centerdot g(x) \centerdot g(y) \centerdot \sim(x = y) : \\ \sim(\exists x, y, z) \centerdot g(x) \centerdot g(y) \centerdot g(z) \centerdot \sim(x = y \vee x = z \vee y = z).$$

If, for example, we wish to say "The earth and the moon are two," we have simply to interpret $g(x)$ to mean "$x$ is either the earth or the moon" and read the result. Similarly, it is possible to define 0 according to this plan, by writing

$$\sim(\exists x) \centerdot h(x).$$

Thus, the moon has no satellites; and if we wish to say that the number of its satellites is zero, we have merely to replace $h(x)$ by "$x$ is a satellite of the moon." [11]

It will be clear what is to be meant by the assertion that a given collection of two things is equal in number to another collection of two things; it is simply that they both satisfy the definition. There are two books on that chair, and also two windows in this room; so that if, in the definition of 2, $g$ is interpreted to mean 'a book on that chair,' and again to mean 'a window in this room,' the function will be satisfied in each case. Equality between the sum of two numbers and a single number may be understood in a corresponding sense. Let us consider, for example, what is to be meant by $1 + 1 = 2$, and how this proposition is to be proved. In the definition of 1, we may replace $f$ by the independent variable $f'$, so that there will result the same function of $f'$ as of $f$. Then $1 + 1$ may be defined by

$$(\exists x) : f(x) : (y) \centerdot f(y) \supset (y = x) : \centerdot \\ (\exists x) : f'(x) : (y) \centerdot f'(y) \supset (y = x) : \centerdot \sim(\exists x) \centerdot f(x) \centerdot f'(x),$$

which is, literally, 'one and one, but not the same one.' By simple logical transformations, it can be shown that this function

[11] We are not attempting to follow at all closely the procedure of *Principia Mathematica* in dealing with cardinal numbers. The technique developed by the authors of *Principia* is much too elaborate to be considered here and is really not necessary to a fairly clear understanding of the way particular numbers occur in ordinary judgments.

implies

$$(\exists x, y) :. f(x) \vee f'(x) . f(y) \vee f'(y) . \sim(x = y) :. \quad (z) : f(z) \vee f'(z) . \supset . (z = x) \vee (z = y),$$

which results from the definition of 2 when $g(x)$ is replaced by $f(x) \vee f'(x)$, and $g(y)$ by $f(y) \vee f'(y)$. Thus, anything that is a case of $1 + 1$ will also be a case of 2. It does not matter that the definition of $1 + 1$ is a more specific function, which implies but is not implied by the general definition of 2; for to say that $1 + 1$ equals 2 is merely to say that any value satisfying either function must have the same number as any value satisfying the other. And similarly, to say that $1 + 4$ equals $2 + 3$ is to say that if we had an instance of the first of these functions, and also an instance of the second, each would be an instance of one and the same number.

We come, finally, to certain verbal expressions of ordinary discourse which, although they are complete sentences, seem to express propositional functions rather than propositions. It has been pointed out that all ordinary propositions involve functions as factors or constituents. Thus, the proposition "*a* is round" involves in its structure the function "*x* is round," and so does "Something is round," since it is of the form $(\exists x) . \phi(x)$. But an interrogative expression would seem itself to stand for a function, and not for a proposition.[12] Suppose some one to say "What time is it?" Then he would seem to be merely stating the function "*x* is the time"; and a correct answer to his question would seem to be given when a value of *x* was supplied which transformed this function into a true proposition—one might say, in response, "Ten o'clock is the time." According to this view, the interrogative 'what' of ordinary discourse will be a variable. And it seems pretty clear that the force of any other interrogative word can be given in terms of 'what.' Thus, 'who' means 'what person,' 'when' means 'what time,' 'where' means 'what place,' etc.; so that, for example, the question "Who is the present King of England?" will be identical in import with the function "*x* is the person who is the present King of England."

[12] Cf. a paper by F. S. Cohen, in *The Monist*, XXXIX (1929), 350.

It will be seen that if this is a correct view of the nature of interrogative expressions, there can be no question without a true answer, and therefore, strictly speaking, no such thing as a 'false question'; for a propositional function can always be transformed into a true proposition either by specification or by generalization. If some one asks "Who is the present King of France?" we may say, "$\sim(\exists x) . x$ is the person who is the present King of France," and thus transform the function or question into a true proposition by generalization. It is to be noted, too, that there may be questions which contain more than one free variable. Thus, "What shall we do when?" and "Who said what when?" are questions that have been known to be asked, the first being of the form "$x$ is the thing we shall do at time $y$" and the second of the form "$x$ is the person who said $y$ at time $z$."

On the view here suggested, it is not so easy to deal with questions of the yes-no variety, because they seem, at first sight, to be propositions, true or false. Take, for example, the simple question "Is it raining?" This looks like an inverted form of the proposition "It is raining," and there can be no doubt that the question either is identical with this proposition or involves it as a constituent. It seems plausible, however, to adopt the latter alternative, and to say that the question is a function constructed on the proposition, and means "It is raining is $x$," where there are only two values that $x$ can take, true and false. If this is right, then every yes-no question can, in a strict sense, be answered by a plain 'yes' or 'no,' because every proposition is either true or false; although, of course, this is not to say that such an answer may not in certain circumstances be misleading. Thus, suppose some one to ask "Has it stopped raining?" on an occasion on which it has not been raining. The proposition "It has stopped raining" may be false on two different grounds: it may have begun to rain and be continuing to do so, or it may not have begun. And in a large majority of cases (possibly in every case) when this proposition is denied, it is on the presumption that rain continues; so that a hearer, in ordinary circumstances, will immediately judge that this is why the proposition is denied, despite the fact that what the reason may happen to be is no part of what is being expressed.

It is sometimes suggested that questions are simply propositions which express desires or wishes on the part of a speaker to know so-and-so. Thus, it may be held that the words "What time is it?" mean what could be expressed otherwise by "I should like to know what the time is" and will therefore be true if the speaker does in fact wish to know the time, and false if he does not. According to this view, a question will not itself be a function, but will always be a proposition about one, to the effect that the speaker desires to know how the function is to be transformed into a true proposition. And it is of course the case that people do often convey questions which they have in mind in this way. But when we ask what precisely it is in such a case that the speaker wishes to know, it becomes clear that his whole statement does not express the question to which an answer is desired. To say "I wish to know what the time is" is tantamount to saying "I should like to know the answer to the question 'What is the time?'" Merely because a speaker who expresses a question usually wishes to be given an answer it is not to be supposed that the statement of the question actually expresses this desire. We must distinguish between the logical import of a question and the fact that so-and-so asks it. His act of asking the question will of course be an event, which a hearer will perceive; and it is almost inevitable, under ordinary circumstances, that the hearer should conclude, from the observed fact that the speaker thought it worth while to ask the question, that an answer is desired. But this act of asking the question can hardly be taken to fall within the import of the statement itself, because, if it did, no two persons could ask the same question.

# CHAPTER XI

## POSTULATIONAL TECHNIQUE: DEDUCTION

### SECTION 1. INTRODUCTION

We have seen that no proposition can be true merely by itself, since each one is so related to others that, under any conceivable circumstances under which it would be true, the others would necessarily be true also. These are the logical consequences of an assigned proposition; they are, as we have seen, related to the proposition of which they are consequences in such a way that we can by knowing it know them also, without further appeal to empirical fact. This is the circumstance out of which deduction arises. We may take a given proposition and ask what, if it were known to be true, could be known about the truth or falsity of other propositions by reasoning alone and without additional empirical information. Let us take, for instance, the proposition "This table is brown" and ask what must necessarily be true solely in virtue of the fact that it is true. Clearly, we have here the following logical consequences, among many others: "There exists at least one table"; "There exists at least one physical object"; "This table is colored"; "There are colored things"; "There is at least one thing that is not a chair"; "If any one were to believe tables not to exist, he would believe falsely"; "If any one were to judge this table to be brown, he would judge truly." Each of these propositions is such that, if it were false, then "This table is brown" would of necessity be false too. But in general the converse implication does not hold: it might be false that this table was brown, and yet be true that there was at least one physical object, that there was at least one table, that this table was colored, that if any one were to believe tables not to exist, he would believe falsely, etc.

There is, however, one exception to this in the list of consequences given, which we may note in passing. From the fact that, were any one to judge this table to be brown, he would judge truly, it does follow that this table is brown; these propositions imply each other or, in other words, are logically equivalent. But it must not be supposed that, since they are equivalent and thus would under any conceivable circumstances be true together or false together, they are really one and the same proposition expressed in different words. That we have here two genuinely distinct propositions which are nevertheless logically equivalent can be seen from the fact that one of them involves the concept of a person, the concept of judging, and the concept of being true, while the other does not.

Now, these same considerations will apply equally when we are concerned with a collection or set of propositions the members of which are to be employed as premises. Let us take, for instance, the following set of three propositions, with a view to examining the logical consequences entailed:

There are just five books on this table.
Each of these books has been read by at least one person.
Nobody has read more than one of them.

The implications of these propositions may be divided into those which follow from one of the set, by itself, those which follow from two, without the third, and those which require all three, jointly. Thus, "There are tables" and "This is a table" are logical consequences of the first proposition; whereas "There is a book on this table which has been read by some one" is a proposition which does not follow from any one of the three alone, but requires the first and second together; while the proposition "There is a book on this table which has been read by just one person" is one the falsity of which is compatible with the truth of any two of the three premises given, but not with that of all three.

We speak of the logical consequences of a set or collection of propositions; but in order to be quite accurate, we should say that these consequences, which are said to follow from the set, really follow from one single proposition, which is the conjunction of the several members of the set. In strict accuracy, two or more propositions as a mere collection do not have logical consequences jointly, though they do separately; it is the proposition that results when they are connected by 'and' which really has the implications commonly spoken of as being those of the set. If $r$ must be true in virtue of the fact that $p$ and $q$ are true, then what $r$ follows from is the proposition "Both $p$ and $q$" or $p \cdot q$; if $r$ is false, then what implies it must be false, and the mere collection $p, q$ has no truth-value. When we speak of a proposition as following from several others, we really mean, then, that it follows from the conjunctive proposition determined by these others; but in order to avoid tiresome circumlocution, we shall adhere for the most part to the more usual way of putting the matter.

It will be seen that the foregoing set of three propositions enables us to define a class made up of all the logical consequences of the set. This class is said to be *determined* by the three propositions. And, of course, since a proposition always implies itself, the members of the set themselves belong to the class they determine. The set constitutes, as it were, a logical warrant for all the propositions belonging to this class; if the members of the set are true, then the truth of each proposition belonging to the class can be inferred.

Suppose, now, that we add to this set the further proposition "Each of these books has more than 200 pages." Then we can deduce further consequences, not implied by the original set; we can, for instance, infer that at least one person has read a book of more than 200 pages; hence the class of propositions determined by the new set will be wider than that determined by the original one. Suppose, however, that we add to the original set the proposition "There are tables," which is itself a logical consequence of the set. Then, of course, in accordance with the principle that, if $p$ implies $q$ and $q$ implies $r$, then $p$ implies $r$, the class of logical consequences of the set will not be widened. Moreover, in the set so reconstituted, we have a redundancy, in the sense that one member can be dropped without any resultant weakening of the logical force of the whole.

So, in general, if we have a set of $n$ propositions and if one of them is a logical consequence of the remaining $n - 1$, that one will be redundant with the remainder and may be discarded from the set. When no further reduction of this sort is possible, the propositions of the set are said to be 'independent.' This term 'independent,' as applied to a set of propositions no one of which follows from the others, is in common use, and we shall adopt it; but we must here point out a possible source of ambiguity connected with the term. Even if two propositions $p$, $q$ are independent in the sense in question, it may still happen that $p$ implies $\sim q$, and that $q$ implies $\sim p$; so that there may, in fact, be a good deal of mutual dependence. All that is meant, however, in the special sense of this term here intended, is that if $p$ is true, $q$ may be false, and if $q$ is true, $p$ may be false.

Suppose, now, that to the set of three propositions given above we add "There are no tables." Then the set becomes inconsistent with itself, in the sense that it is impossible for the several propositions to be true jointly. And it is clearly an important question regarding any set of propositions in which we may be interested whether they are possibly all true—that is, whether they are compatible both with themselves and with one another. This is the question of *consistency*. We often say of two propositions which are incompatible that they contradict each other, and this is, in fact, a fairly accurate way of putting the matter. Take, for example, the two propositions "$A$ is red" and "$A$ is green": the first implies "$A$ is not green," and so contradicts the second, while the second implies "$A$ is not red," thus contradicting the first. It will be seen, however, that two propositions $p$, $q$ might form an inconsistent set owing to the fact that $p$ implied $\sim p$, or that $q$ implied $\sim q$. Or it might happen that, although both $p$ and $q$ were self-consistent, and although $p$ did not imply $\sim q$ and $q$ did not imply $\sim p$, the two propositions jointly would imply $\sim p$ or imply $\sim q$. And even if none of these things happened, the propositions might still imply $\sim p \vee \sim q$, which is the contradictory of $p \cdot q$. A set of propositions may be said to be consistent, or the members of the set to be compossible, if and only if the set does not imply a contradiction.

When we have several propositions which are not in fact all true (such as the set of three we have been considering), it is often possible to see that they *might* all be true; and if this can be seen, we can of course infer that they do not imply a contradiction. Often, however, we have to do with a set of true propositions; and from the fact that several propositions are all true, it follows that they are consistent. This circumstance sometimes furnishes us with a test of consistency, because we can sometimes be quite sure that each proposition of a set is true where we cannot be nearly so sure of the consistency of the set on other grounds. Let us take, as an example, a set which has some degree of intrinsic importance, and with regard to which it is especially easy to see that each proposition is true:

$$(p) : p \vee p \,.\supset.\, p,$$
$$(p, q) : q \,.\supset.\, p \vee q,$$
$$(p, q) : p \vee q \,.\supset.\, q \vee p,$$
$$(p, q, r) :. p \,.\vee.\, q \vee r :\supset: q \,.\vee.\, p \vee r,$$
$$(p, q, r) :. q \supset r \,.\supset: p \vee q \,.\supset.\, p \vee r.$$ [1]

From this set, any proposition in extension of the theory of elementary functions follows; and since all five propositions are plainly true, we can infer that they do not lead to contradiction. However, since this argument from truth to consistency can be employed only when we are concerned with a set of true propositions, the criterion it supplies is merely a sufficient condition of consistency, not a necessary one.

We have so far been discussing propositions; but in fact in the theory of deduction it is not propositions with which we are primarily concerned, because they involve more specificity than is actually required. We can just as well deal with sets of propositional functions, and can in so doing attain a degree of generality that is not possible in connection with propositions. This can be illustrated by a simple example. Suppose we take a proposition about a particular given thing $A$ which can be expressed by the words "$A$ is red," and consider its logical consequences. We can infer that $A$ is colored, that it is not green, that it is extended, that it has a shape, that if any one were to

[1] These are the formal premises for elementary functions as given in *Principia Mathematica*. It may be noted that they are not independent, although this fact is not relevant to our illustration. The third is really a consequence of $(p) \,.\, p \supset p$, and therefore of the remainder of the set, because two propositions have only one disjunction, the order in which $p$ and $q$ are written in $p \vee q$ being a non-significant feature of the symbol. See *Bull. Amer. Math. Soc.*, XXXVI (1930), 23. Moreover, it has been shown that the fourth proposition can be derived from the others. See Hilbert and Ackermann, *Grundzüge der theoretischen Logik*, p. 27.

judge $A$ to be not red, he would judge falsely, etc. But all this is obviously more restricted than necessary: not only does "$A$ is red" imply "$A$ is colored," "$A$ is not green," etc., but "$B$ is red" implies "$B$ is colored," "$B$ is not green," etc.; so that we may replace $A$ by a variable $x$ and say that any proposition of the kind "$x$ is red" implies a corresponding proposition of the kind "$x$ is colored." One proposition implies another in virtue of its logical form or in virtue of its conceptual content, and any proposition of the same form or conceptual content will imply a corresponding proposition.

Let us take another example, which is less simple and of more intrinsic importance. Suppose we have a collection of pieces of metal, no two of which have the same weight, and suppose we compare these objects with respect to the relation 'heavier than.' Then the following propositions can be seen to be plainly true:

If $x$ is a member of the collection, then it is not heavier than itself.

If $x$ and $y$ belong to the collection, and are distinct, then either $x$ is heavier than $y$ or $y$ is heavier than $x$.

If $x$ and $y$ belong to the collection, and are distinct, then either $x$ is not heavier than $y$ or $y$ is not heavier than $x$.

If $x$, $y$, $z$ are distinct things belonging to the collection, and if $x$ is heavier than $y$, and $y$ than $z$, then $x$ is heavier than $z$.

It will be easy to see that, in virtue of the truth of these propositions, the weights of the class fall into a series with respect to the relation 'heavier than'; as connected by this relation, they constitute an instance of Serial Order. And, of course, the set of propositions here in question implies many different consequences; we can, for instance, infer the proposition "If $x$ and $y$ belong to the collection, and if $x$ is not heavier than $y$, and $y$ not heavier than $x$, then they are identical."

Now, we may rewrite the foregoing propositions in the following way. Let $f(x)$ mean "$x$ belongs to the collection," and let $g(x, y)$ mean "$x$ is heavier than $y$"; then we have:

(a) $(x) . f(x) \supset \sim g(x, x)$.

(b) $(x, y) : f(x) . f(y) . \sim(x = y) . \supset . g(x, y) \vee g(y, x)$.

(c) $(x, y) : f(x) . f(y) . \sim(x = y) . \supset . \sim g(x, y) \vee \sim g(y, x).$

(d) $(x, y, z) : f(x) . f(y) . f(z) . d(x, y, z) . g(x, y) . g(y, z) . \supset . g(x, z).$[2]

The logical consequence of this set just indicated will then be expressed in the form

$$(x, y) : f(x) . f(y) . \sim g(x, y) . \sim g(y, x) . \supset . x = y;$$

that is, "For all values of $x$ and $y$, either it is not the case that $x$ and $y$ both belong to the collection, and that $x$ is not heavier than $y$, and $y$ not heavier than $x$, or else $x$ and $y$ are identical." It will readily appear, however, that in drawing inferences from (a)–(d), it is not really essential that we allow $f(x)$ and $g(x, y)$ to have the meanings assigned to them, or any other specified meanings. We can understand these expressions as representing functions rather than propositions, and can draw inferences applicable to any values that may be given to the functions. Not only does the theorem just cited follow in the case of the particular meanings assigned to $f$ and $g$, but corresponding theorems follow for all meanings whatever.

But, now, just as a set of propositions is really one compound proposition, so this set of functions, which results when the values of $f$ and $g$ are discarded, is one compound function. And the only free variables that occur are $f$ and $g$; so that the set is really a function, $\Phi(f, g)$, of these variables, such that when values are assigned to them, a compound proposition, true or false, results. If we allow $P$ to represent the compound proposition which results when $f(x)$ and $g(x, y)$ are assigned the meanings "$x$ is a member of the collection" and "$x$ is heavier than $y$" respectively, and allow $Q$ to represent the logical consequence given above, then, in saying that this consequence follows, we are asserting the proposition $P \prec Q$ or $\sim\Diamond(P . \sim Q)$. But if we drop these meanings and represent the compound propositional function by $\Phi(f, g)$ and the function that is said to follow by $\Psi(f, g)$, then, in saying that this consequence follows, we are

[2] The expression $d(x, y, z)$ is to be understood to mean "$x$, $y$, and $z$ are all distinct," i.e., $\sim(x = y) . \sim(x = z) . \sim(y = z)$; $d$ will be subsequently employed in the same sense as applied to any number of variables.

asserting the proposition

$$(f, g) \cdot \Phi(f, g) \prec \Psi(f, g),$$

$$\text{or } \sim\Diamond(\exists f, g) \cdot \Phi(f, g) \cdot \sim\Psi(f, g),$$

i.e., "It is impossible that there should be values of $f$ and $g$ such that $\Phi(f, g)$ would be true and $\Psi(f, g)$ false."

When we speak of one function as being implied by another, we mean, then, that the implication holds for all values of the variables. It is in this sense that we can speak of the class of all functions that follow from the set (a)–(d), or from the function $\Phi(f, g)$, just as we speak of the class of all propositions that follow from an assigned proposition. For any values of $f$ and $g$ whatever which transform the functions (a)–(d) into a set of propositions, there will be a corresponding class of propositions; and if all the functions of the set are transformed into true propositions by the assignment of a pair of values to $f$ and $g$, then all the functions that are implied by (a)–(d) will be transformed into true propositions by that same pair of values.

A set of propositions resulting from the assignment of values to $f$ and $g$ in the functions (a)–(d) is called an *interpretation* of these functions; and if, in such a case, all the propositions are true ones, we are said to have an interpretation *satisfying* the functions, or a *true* interpretation. It will be clear, however, that in general an arbitrarily chosen interpretation will not transform all the functions into true propositions. If, for instance, we take a collection of sticks of wood of varying lengths, which are, however, such that at least two of them have the same length, and if we allow $f(x)$ to mean "$x$ belongs to the collection" and $g(x, y)$ to mean "$x$ is longer than $y$," then we have, as an interpretation of the functions (a)–(d), the following propositions:

If $x$ is a stick belonging to the collection, then $x$ is not longer than itself.

If $x$ and $y$ belong to the collection, and are distinct, then either $x$ is longer than $y$ or $y$ is longer than $x$.

If $x$ and $y$ are distinct members of the collection, then $x$ is not longer than $y$, or $y$ not longer than $x$.

If $x$, $y$, $z$ are distinct members of the collection, and if $x$ is longer than $y$, and $y$ longer than $z$, then $x$ is longer than $z$.

Although the first, third, and fourth of these propositions will be true, the second will be false. On the other hand, it can easily be verified that each of the following interpretations transforms all the functions (a)–(d) into true propositions:

Let $f(x)$ mean "$x$ is a cardinal number" and $g(x, y)$ mean "$x$ is greater than $y$."

Let $f(x)$ mean "$x$ is a cardinal number" and $g(x, y)$ mean "$x$ is less than $y$."

Let $f(x)$ mean "$x$ is one of the forty-eight States comprised in the United States" and $g(x, y)$ mean "$x$ has more inhabitants than $y$" (or, alternatively, "$x$ has fewer inhabitants than $y$").

Let $f(x)$ mean "$x$ is a planet revolving about the sun" and $g(x, y)$ mean "$x$ is nearer the sun than $y$."

Let $f(x)$ mean "$x$ is a sentence on this page" and $g(x, y)$ mean "$x$ comes before $y$."

We shall have a definition of independence for sets of propositional functions which is quite similar to that given in connection with sets of propositions. We may say that the functions (a)–(d) are independent if, and only if, no one of them is implied by the remaining three, in the special sense of 'implied' understood in connection with functions. In this sense, to say, for instance, that (a) is not implied by (b) is to assert the proposition

$$\Diamond(\exists f, g) :. (x, y) : f(x) . f(y) . \sim(x = y) . \supset . g(x, y) \vee g(y, x) :. (\exists x) . f(x) . g(x, x),$$

that is, "It is possible that there should be values of $f$ and $g$ such that, for those values, (*b*) would be true and (a) false."

It is not to be supposed, however, that because two functions are independent, two propositions which are true interpretations of the functions will be, and thus that any interpretation satisfying (a)–(d) will be an independent set of propositions if these functions are independent. Let us take, for example, the two simple functions $\phi(x)$ and $\psi(x)$, which do not contain any generalized variables, and let us first interpret them to mean "$A$ is red" and "$A$ is round," respectively. The two functions are independent, since

$$\Diamond(\exists\phi, \psi) . \phi(x) . \sim\psi(x) \quad \text{and} \quad \Diamond(\exists\phi, \psi) . \psi(x) . \sim\phi(x)$$

hold; and the two propositions are, since it is not impossible that *A* should be red and not round, and not impossible that it should be round and not red. But let us leave the interpretation of $\phi(x)$ unchanged, and allow $\psi(x)$ to mean "*A* is colored." Then, although the two functions are independent, the propositions resulting from this interpretation are not. It will be clear, in general, that values of functions may be more determinate in logical or conceptual form than are the functions from which they are derived, and thus that there may be implications holding among the propositions which do not hold among the functions. If we know that a set of functions is independent, all we know is that the set *may* have independent interpretations. If, on the other hand, we know that a set of functions is not an independent one, we know that it cannot possibly have an independent interpretation, and that there will inevitably be some point of redundancy; for if one function follows from another, any value of the one must follow from a corresponding value of the other.

Now this fact, that a non-independent set of functions cannot possibly have an independent interpretation, gives us a criterion by which we can often determine that a set involves only independent functions. In order to illustrate this criterion, let us take again the two functions $\phi(x)$ and $\psi(x)$, with a view to showing that $\phi(x)$ neither implies nor is implied by $\psi(x)$. This is obvious and trivial, of course; but we wish to prove it by the method in question. To show that $\psi(x)$ does not follow from $\phi(x)$, we must find an interpretation which transforms $\phi(x)$ into a true proposition and $\psi(x)$ into a false one. This page of print is a rectangular, black-and-white pattern of color, which we may call *S*; and we may allow $\phi(x)$ to mean "*S* is black-and-white" and $\psi(x)$ to mean "*S* is circular," the first proposition being true and the second false. So, $\phi(x)$ cannot imply $\psi(x)$, since, if it did, "*S* is black-and-white" would have to imply "*S* is circular," and no true proposition can imply a false one. Again, a certain fountain-pen, which we may call *T*, is green and cylindrical; so that we may interpret $\phi(x)$ to mean "*T* is red" and $\psi(x)$ to mean "*T* is cylindrical," thus giving $\psi(x)$ a true and $\phi(x)$ a false interpretation. But let us take two functions which are not in fact independent—$(x, y) . g(x, y)$ and $(x) . g(x, x)$, for example—

where, of course, $x$ and $y$ in the first function are independent variables, taking the same or different values. We can find an interpretation making $(x, y) . g(x, y)$ false and $(x) . g(x, x)$ true: if $g(x, y)$ is understood to mean "$x$ is identical with $y$," the first function becomes "For every $x$, $y$, $x$ is identical with $y$," and the second becomes "For every $x$, $x$ is identical with $x$." Hence the first cannot be implied by the second. But it is plainly quite impossible to make $(x, y) . g(x, y)$ true without making $(x) . g(x, x)$ true.

We may now apply this procedure to showing that the four functions (a)–(d) form an independent set. In the first place, in order to see that (a) does not follow from (b), (c), and (d), we must find meanings for the variables $f$ and $g$ which make (a) false and (b), (c), (d) all true; and the following interpretation will be seen to do this. Let $f(x)$ mean "$x$ is a natural number," and let $g(x, y)$ mean "$x$ is not larger than $y$." Then $\sim g(x, x)$ will mean "$x$ is larger than itself," and (a) will become "If anything is a natural number, then it is larger than itself," while all the other functions will be transformed into true propositions. Second, to see that (b) does not follow from (a), (c), and (d), interpret $f(x)$ to mean "$x$ is a human being" and $g(x, y)$ to mean "$x$ is an ancestor of $y$." Then (a) is satisfied, since nobody is his own ancestor; (c) is satisfied, since no two persons can be ancestors of each other; and (d) is satisfied, since if one person is an ancestor of another, and the other of a third, the first is an ancestor of the third; but (b) fails, owing to the fact that there are persons between whom the ancestral relation does not hold either way. In the third place, to show that (c) does not follow from (a), (b), (d), let $f(x)$ mean "$x$ is a degree of temperature" and $g(x, y)$ mean "$x$ is either higher or lower than $y$." Here (c) will fail, since it will mean "If $x$ and $y$ are distinct degrees of temperature, then it is not the case that $x$ is higher or lower than $y$, or not the case that $y$ is higher or lower than $x$"; whereas all the other functions are easily seen to be transformed into true propositions. Note that (d) would become false with this interpretation if it were not for the condition in that function that $x$, $y$, and $z$ shall all be distinct, since from $g(x, y)$ and $g(y, x)$ we should have $g(x, x)$. Finally, that

(d) does not follow from (a), (b), and (c) may be seen from the following interpretation. Take a circle, and three points on it, $l$, $m$, $n$; let $f(x)$ mean "$x$ is identical with $l$, $m$, or $n$," and let $g(x, y)$ mean "$y$ comes next after $x$ in the clockwise direction." Then, clearly, (a), (b), and (c) are satisfied, but the relation 'coming next after' is not transmitted in the manner required by (d), since, for example, we may have $g(l, m)$ and $g(m, n)$ together with $g(n, l)$ rather than $g(l, n)$.

The procedure here in question is known as the Interpretational Method for proving the independence of a set of functions. It is dependent upon the fact that we can often observe with more certainty that certain propositions are true and others false than we can that a given function is or is not implied by others. But the situation is, of course, entirely relative; it might happen in a particular case that we could see more clearly how a function did not follow from certain others than we could see that corresponding propositions were true and false, respectively. Moreover, this method gives us merely a sufficient condition of independence, not a necessary one: if interpretations of an appropriate sort exist, then the functions of the set are independent; but if none do, it does not follow that they are not independent. We might quite well have a function that was not deducible from certain others, and yet no interpretation which would make it false and the others true. It may, indeed, be the case that for any independent set of functions, there exist, in point of fact, appropriate interpretations showing it to be so, but that is hardly a matter open to logical demonstration.

We may now turn to the question of consistency as it arises in connection with functions. We shall say that a set is consistent if, and only if, there does not exist a function $F$ such that the set implies both $F$ and $\sim F$. So, if a set is not consistent, it will imply a function of the form $F . \sim F$, which cannot have a true value. And from the fact that a set of true propositions cannot imply a false consequence, it follows that an inconsistent set of functions cannot have a true interpretation; so that we may define a consistent set, alternatively, as one that *might* be interpreted truly. In view of this latter definition, it is clear that we can adopt an interpretational procedure in proving consistency; for if we can show that a set of functions *does* have a true interpretation, we can, of course, infer that it *might* have, on the ground that what is actual is possible. And it is easy to see, by means of a true interpretation, that the set of functions (a)–(d) is consistent; any of the five true ones given above will do. Here, however, as in the case of proofs of independence, we cannot infer from the mere fact that a set does not have a true interpretation, that it is not consistent; truth is a sufficient condition of consistency, not a necessary one.

But, now, there is a feature of the functions (a)–(d) in virtue of which we can see that they must be consistent, without resort to particular interpretations: they are all universal functions, which are negative in effect; and no purely negative function can be inconsistent either with itself or with another purely negative function. Thus, in the case of function (a), we have $\sim(\exists x) \centerdot f(x) \centerdot g(x, x)$, which merely denies the existence of a thing of a certain kind; and the only functions that can be inconsistent with this one are those with existential import. It sometimes happens that when a negative function is interpreted, the resulting proposition is true because there do not exist things sufficient to fulfil its hypothesis; and when this is the case, we say that the function is satisfied 'vacuously.' Thus, let $f(x)$ mean "$x$ is either the earth or the moon" and $g(x, y)$ mean "$x$ is larger than $y$." Then (a), (b), and (c) are plainly satisfied; but so is (d), since all it says is that *if* there are three distinct things in the class determined by $f(x)$, then they will satisfy such-and-such a condition; that is to say, either there are not at least three things of the kind in question or else the consequence holds. Again, let $f(x)$ mean "$x$ is a satellite of the earth" and $g(x, y)$ mean "$x$ is larger than $y$." Then (a) is satisfied in the ordinary way, while (b), (c), and (d) are satisfied vacuously. Thus, (b) says that either there are not two distinct things, $x$, $y$, in the class determined by $f(x)$ or else one of the two functions $g(x, y)$ and $g(y, x)$ holds; and so for the other cases. Finally, let $f(x)$ mean "$x$ is a satellite of the moon" and $g(x, y)$ mean "$x$ is larger than $y$" or, for that matter, anything else whatever; then all four functions are satisfied vacuously. It is, then, a characteristic of universal or negative propositions that they would all be true if nothing whatever existed. And this brings out precisely the conditions under which a negative proposition is true as contrasted with those under which an affirmative one is: an affirmative proposition will be true if and only if something makes it so; a negative proposition will be true if and only if nothing makes it false; it does not require anything to make it true.

There is one further notion relevant to sets of functions which we must endeavor to explain. It has been pointed out that the only free variables occurring in the set (a)–(d) are $f$ and $g$, and that each of the four expressions is constructed on $f(x)$ and $g(x, y)$, in the sense that no further functions are involved, the other factors introduced being logical constants. The two functions $f(x)$ and $g(x, y)$ are said to constitute the 'base' of the set, it being understood that $f$ and $g$ are to remain free, and that the other variables are to be generalized. Now, we can speak of other functions as being constructed on this same base, and of still others as constructed on different bases. Thus, the function $(\exists x) . f(x) . g(x, x)$ is on the base $f(x), g(x, y)$; but if $g'(x, y)$ is another matrix, which can take values independently, then the expressions $(\exists x) . f(x) . g'(x, x)$ and $(x, y) . g'(x, y)$ will not be on this base. It is to be noted, too, that a function on the base of the set (a)–(d) need not involve both $f(x)$ and $g(x, y)$; all that is necessary is that it should not involve matrices other than these two. Thus, $(\exists x) . f(x)$ is on the base in question, as is $(x, y) . g(x, y)$. And there is one further circumstance that must be taken account of here. We sometimes define functions in terms of others, in the sense of giving a purely verbal definition. We can, for instance, define $h(x, y, z)$ as meaning $g(x, y) . g(y, z)$; and if this is done, then, of course, $(x, y, z) . h(x, y, z)$ will be on the base $f(x), g(x, y)$, since it will simply mean what is meant by $(x, y, z) . g(x, y) . g(y, z)$.

The importance of the notion of the base of a set of functions can be seen from the following considerations. From a set, consequences may be deduced which are on the base of the set, and we may consider the class of all consequences that are on that base. It might be supposed that any theorem which followed from a set would be on the same base as the set, and there is a sense in which all 'important' theorems are; but strictly speaking, in the case of any set of functions, there are many implications containing variables which do not appear in the functions of the set. This arises from the circumstance that if $p$ implies $q$, then it implies $q \vee r$, and also $q \cdot r \vee {\sim}r$, no matter what $r$ may be. Thus, from conditions (a)–(d), we have

$$\sim(\exists x, y) \cdot g(x, y) \cdot g(y, x) \cdot f(x) \cdot f(y) \cdot \sim(x = y),$$

and so we have

$$\sim(\exists x, y) \cdot g(x, y) \cdot g(y, x) \cdot g'(x, y) \cdot f(x) \cdot f(y) \cdot \sim(x = y),$$

which contains the new variable $g'$.

In this connection there is one further important notion, which is that of *all* functions that can be constructed on the base $f(x)$,$g(x, y)$. This will be a wider class than that of all functions on the base in question which are deducible from (a)–(d), since, for one thing, it will include the contradictories of all such functions. Thus,

$$(x, y) : \sim f(x) \vee \sim f(y) \,.\vee.\, g(x, y) \supset \sim g(y, x)$$

is a logical consequence of (a)–(d), and its contradictory,

$$(\exists x, y) \cdot f(x) \cdot f(y) \cdot g(x, y) \cdot g(y, x),$$

is, of course, on the same base. So, if a set of properties is consistent, i.e., never implies both $F$ and ${\sim}F$, the class of all functions that can be constructed on the base of the set will be at least twice as large as that of all those following from the set. In general, however, it will be a still wider class; for only in exceptional cases does a set of properties imply one or the other of every pair of mutually contradictory functions that can be constructed on the base of the set. Thus, in the case of the set (a)–(d), neither the function $(\exists x) \cdot f(x)$ nor its contradictory, $(x) \cdot \sim f(x)$, is implied; and, again, neither

$$(x) :. (\exists y) : f(x) \,.\supset.\, f(y) \cdot g(x, y)$$

nor

$$(\exists x) : (y) \cdot f(x) \cdot \sim f(y) \vee \sim g(x, y)$$

is implied.

The proof that these functions do not follow from the set is, of course, like the proofs of independence given above: we find an interpretation satisfying (a)–(d) and failing to satisfy the function that is to be shown not to follow. Let $f(x)$ mean "$x$ is a satellite of the moon" and $g(x, y)$ mean "$x$ revolves about $y$." Then (a)–(d) are satisfied vacuously, while $(\exists x) . f(x)$ fails. Let $f(x)$ mean "$x$ is a satellite of the earth" and $g(x, y)$ mean "$x$ is not identical with $y$." Then (a)–(d) are satisfied (the last three vacuously), while $(x) . \sim f(x)$ fails. Again, if we allow $f(x)$ to mean "$x$ is one of the numbers 1, 2, . . ., 9" and $g(x, y)$ to mean "$x$ is less than $y$," then (a)–(d) are satisfied, and the first one of the other pair of contradictory functions fails. And, finally, if we allow $f(x)$ to mean "$x$ is one of the numbers 1, 2, 3, . . ." and $g(x, y)$ to mean "$x$ is less than $y$," then the second function of this pair fails, while (a)–(d) are satisfied.

If we denote by $\alpha$ the class of all functions that can be constructed on the base $f(x), g(x, y)$, we can say that $\alpha$ falls into three mutually exclusive and jointly exhaustive subclasses, $\alpha_1$, $\alpha_2$, $\alpha_3$, where $\alpha_1$ is the class of all functions that follow from (a)–(d), $\alpha_2$ the class of all contradictories of these functions, and $\alpha_3$ the class of all those functions such that neither they nor their contradictories follow from the set. Here, it is to be noted that the members of $\alpha_2$ are no more independent of the set than are those of $\alpha_1$; if an interpretation makes (a)–(d) true, then all the members of $\alpha_1$ will be transformed into true propositions, and all those of $\alpha_2$ into false ones; so that we may combine $\alpha_1$ and $\alpha_2$ into one class, $\alpha_{12}$, and say that (a)–(d) determine the truth-value of every member of this class. If we add to the set (a)–(d) a function from the class $\alpha_{12}$, we shall get either a contradiction or a redundancy, whereas if we add a member of $\alpha_3$, the new set will be self-consistent—although it may not be an independent set, owing to the fact that the new condition, either alone or together with some of the original ones, may imply others of the original set. Now, of course, this new set will have a wider range of implications; $\alpha_{12}$ will be increased, and $\alpha_3$ correspondingly diminished. So, we may continue to add functions to (a)–(d) until the class $\alpha_3$ vanishes altogether; and when this occurs, the set obtained is said to be *categorical* or *complete*.

A set is complete if, and only if, it determines the truth-value of every function that can be constructed on its base. In the case of such a set, one of every pair of mutually contradictory functions is implied, and the other is, of course, incompatible with the set. The problem of completeness is a difficult one, and we shall not deal with it in this chapter, except by way of showing that certain sets are not complete—as has already been done with (a)–(d). In the next chapter, however, we shall take up this problem with reference to certain particular examples, and under a restricted form, in connection with the general problem of deducibility.

For the purpose of illustrating how deductions are to be made from the functions (a)–(d), we may now show that the following miscellaneous theorems are logical consequences of this set.

(1) $(\exists x) . f(x) . \supset . (\exists x) . \sim g(x, x).$

That is, if there is at least one thing satisfying $f$, then there is an $x$ such that $g(x, x)$ fails. This follows immediately from (*a*), since, according to that condition, either a thing does not satisfy $f$ or else it is such that $\sim g(x, x)$.

(2) $(\exists x, y) . f(x) . f(y) . \sim(x = y) . \supset .$
$$(\exists x, y) . g(x, y) \equiv \sim g(y, x).$$

That is, if there are at least two things satisfying $f$, then there will be two things $x$, $y$ such that $g(x, y)$ has a truth-value opposite to that of $g(y, x)$. This follows from (b) and (c), since, according to (*b*), there will in such a case exist two things $x$, $y$ such that $g(x, y)$ holds, and, according to (c), no two things satisfying $f$ can be such that both $g(x, y)$ and $g(y, x)$ hold.

(3) $(\exists x, y, z) . f(x) . f(y) . f(z) . \sim(x = y) . \sim(x = z) .$
$$\sim(y = z) . \supset . (\exists x, y, z) . g(x, y) . g(y, z) . g(x, z).$$

From (b), if $x$ and $y$ satisfy $f$, then either $g(x, y)$ or $g(y, x)$ holds, and since these two cases are distinguishable only relatively to each other, we may say that $g(x, y)$ holds, without loss of generality. Using (b) again, we have $g(y, z)$ or $g(z, y)$, where $z$ is taken to be another thing satisfying $f$. If $g(y, z)$ holds, we have, by (d), $g(x, z)$, and the theorem is satisfied; so that we may suppose $g(z, y)$ to hold. Then there are two further possibilities, $g(x, z)$ and $g(z, x)$; but if $g(x, z)$ holds, the theorem is satisfied, since we shall have $g(x, z) . g(z, y) . g(x, y)$; and if $g(z, x)$ holds, we shall have $g(z, x) . g(x, y) . g(z, y)$.

It is to be noted that the three theorems here established do not have existential import, despite the fact that the symbol $\exists$ occurs in their formulation. This symbol occurs only as governing subordinate constituents of the expressions, and it must do so in connection with any function deducible from conditions (a)–(d), since they are non-existential.

(4) $(x, y) : f(x) . f(y) . \sim g(x, y) . \sim g(y, x) . \supset . x = y.$

From (*b*), if $x$ and $y$ were distinct, either $g(x, y)$ or $g(y, x)$ would hold.

(5) $(x, y) : g(x, y) . g(y, x) . \supset . \sim f(x) \vee \sim f(y).$

From (*c*), if both $x$ and $y$ satisfied $f$ and were distinct, either $g(x, y)$ or $g(y, x)$ would fail; and from (a), if they satisfied $f$ and were not distinct, $g$ would not be satisfied.

(6) $(x) . g(x, x) \supset \sim f(x).$

Note that this theorem is really identical with (a). Replacing $\supset$ by its definition, we have $(x) . \sim g(x, x) \vee \sim f(x)$; and since the order of the alternatives is not symbolically relevant, we may write $(x) . \sim f(x) \vee \sim g(x, x)$.

(7) $(x, y, z) : f(x) . f(y) . f(z) . g(x, y) . g(y, z) . \supset . \sim g(z, x).$

This follows from (a), (c), and (d). If $g(x, y)$ and $g(y, z)$ hold, then, by (a), $x$ is distinct from $y$, and $y$ from $z$; but $x$ is also distinct from $z$, since, if it were not, we should have both $g(x, y)$ and $g(y, x)$, contrary to (c); so that from $g(x, y)$ and $g(y, z)$ we have, by (d), $g(x, z)$, which implies $\sim g(z, x)$, by (c).

It will be seen that we cannot deduce from conditions (a)–(d) functions like

$$(x) . \sim f(x) \supset g(x, x)$$

$$\text{and } (x, y) : \sim f(x) \vee \sim f(y) . \supset . \sim g(x, y),$$

as could easily be established by reference to appropriate interpretations. This fact is connected with a general feature of the set (a)–(d), namely, that it places no restrictions upon things not satisfying the function $f$, that is, not belonging to the class determined by this function. In connection with any interpretation of the set, we are interested merely in relationships among those things belonging to the class determined by the interpretation put upon $f$; this class constitutes, as it were, the 'universe of discourse.' If, for instance, we allow $f(x)$ to mean "$x$ is a planet," and $g(x, y)$ to mean "$x$ is larger than $y$," we are concerned solely with size among planets. Nevertheless, the propositions resulting from this interpretation will be significant for other things, and will always be satisfied by them. All other things satisfy the conditions by failing to satisfy their hypotheses.

Among all the functions that can be deduced from conditions (a)–(d), there are certain selections from which (a)–(d) in turn follow. Any such selection will be a set of conditions which is equivalent to the set (a)–(d); it will be one which has exactly the same logical force, and which determines, accordingly, the same class of theorems. Let us take, as an example, the following selection of three functions, with a view to showing that it implies and is implied by (a)–(d):

($\alpha$) $(x, y) : f(x) . f(y) . g(x, y) . \supset . \sim(x = y)$.

($\beta$) $(x, y) : f(x) . f(y) . \sim(x = y) . \sim g(x, y) . \supset . g(y, x)$.

($\gamma$) $(x, y, z) : f(x) . f(y) . f(z) . g(x, y) . g(y, z) . \supset . g(x, z)$.[3]

Note that ($\gamma$) differs from (d) merely in respect of the fact that the condition of distinctness among $x$, $y$, $z$ is omitted in the one case and not in the other. In order to show that the two sets are equivalent, we must show that each function of either set follows when the other set is assumed. And we may begin by showing that ($\alpha$), ($\beta$), and ($\gamma$) are consequences of (a)–(d).

($\alpha$) follows from (a), since, according to (a), $g(x, x)$ cannot hold if $x$ satisfies $f$.

($\beta$) follows from (b), since, according to (b), if $\sim g(x, y)$, where $x$ and $y$ are distinct, then $g(y, x)$.

($\gamma$) follows from (a), (c), and (d): If $g(x, y)$ and $g(y, z)$ hold, then, by (a), $x$ and $y$ are distinct, as are $y$ and $z$; but it is also

[3] This set is given by E. V. Huntington, in *The Continuum*, p. 10.

true that $x$ is distinct from $z$, since otherwise we should have both $g(x, y)$ and $g(y, x)$, contrary to (c); and so, by (d), $g(x, z)$ holds.

It will be seen that in these deductions each of the conditions (a)–(d) is used at least once. If this were not so, the two sets could not be equivalent, because, if the functions ($\alpha$)–($\gamma$) followed, say, from (a), (b), and (c), they could not imply (d), owing to the fact that it does not follow from (a), (b), (c). That the functions (a)–(d) are logical consequences of ($\alpha$)–($\gamma$) may be seen as follows:

(a) is an immediate consequence of ($\alpha$), and (b) of ($\beta$). (c) is a consequence of ($\alpha$) and ($\gamma$); for, if both $g(x, y)$ and $g(y, x)$ hold, then, by ($\gamma$), $g(x, x)$, contrary to ($\alpha$). And (d) follows immediately from ($\gamma$).

In view of these deductions, it will be observed that ($\alpha$) and ($\beta$) are equivalent to (a) and (b), respectively; so that in the set (a)–(d), we can replace (c) and (d) by the single function ($\gamma$), without altering the force of the set. It will be seen, too, that since ($\alpha$)–($\gamma$) and (a)–(d) are equivalent, and since the latter is consistent, the former must be; any interpretation satisfying the one must satisfy the other also. And it can be shown, by means of appropriate examples, that conditions ($\alpha$)–($\gamma$) make up an independent set. If $f(x)$ is interpreted to mean "$x$ is a day of the week" and $g(x, y)$ to mean "$x$ does not come before $y$," then ($\alpha$) fails, while ($\beta$) and ($\gamma$) are satisfied. If $f(x)$ is interpreted to mean "$x$ is a President of the United States" and $g(x, y)$ to mean "$x$ is an ancestor of $y$," then ($\beta$) fails, while ($\alpha$) and ($\gamma$) are satisfied. If $f(x)$ is interpreted to mean "$x$ is a thing" and $g(x, y)$ to mean "$x$ is other than $y$," then ($\gamma$) fails, since from $g(x, y)$ and $g(y, x)$ we shall have $g(x, x)$.

The sets of postulates dealt with in this and in the next chapter are chosen for the purpose of illustrating how the formal logical theory of propositions is to be applied to problems arising in connection with types of order and deductive systems, and also to show how this logical theory may be developed in the direction of mathematics. The examples selected are very simple, and are designed rather to exhibit principles of logical procedure than to be of mathematical interest on their own account. These two aims, however, are not clearly separable, and it will be seen that the theorems established in the next chapter are not without strictly mathematical significance.

The postulates themselves are, of course, simply premises or 'definitions,' and the theorems logical consequences of them. Thus, as has been pointed out above, if we show that $(x) . f(x, x)$ follows from $(x, y) . f(x, y)$, we are establishing the logical proposition

$$(f) : (x, y) . f(x, y) . \prec . (x) . f(x, x).$$

It is possible in such a case to refer the proposition in question back to simpler logical 'principles' by way of proof. Indeed, it would seem to be possible, by the use of certain assumptions which are themselves purely logical truths, to refer all such propositions back to a small finite number of principles. But it is to be noted that no such reference is necessary to a strict proof, because all propositions like the one here cited are as much logical principles as anything else is. That is to say, if $(x, y) . f(x, y)$ implies $(x) . f(x, x)$, it is in virtue of an internal relationship in which these functions stand, and no appeal beyond that fact is necessary. The method of proving logical propositions by basing them on a limited set of primitive assumptions is an important one, because it shows that the propositions dealt with, however complex, can be derived from and established in terms of certain very simple ideas. But this method does not seem to be adequate to propositions expressing possibility, which are involved in proofs of independence. Thus, it can be observed that $(x) . f(x, x)$ does not imply $(x, y) . f(x, y)$, and this is, like the observation that the converse implication does hold, a matter of strictly logical insight; so that we have

$$\Diamond(\exists f) : (x) . f(x, x) : (\exists x, y) . \sim f(x, y).$$

It seems evident that there must be uniform analytic procedures by which any such proposition could be established, but it is doubtful whether this could be done by deduction from any restricted set of propositions.

## Section 2. Types of Serial Order

In virtue of the fact that functions (a)–(d) do not form a categorical set, we are able to determine specific kinds of serial order by adding further conditions to these four. We may, for instance, add the condition $(\exists x) . f(x)$, which demands that there shall be at least one thing satisfying $f$. In that case, the set will no longer be satisfied when $f(x)$ is given such interpretations as "$x$ is a satellite of the moon," however $g(x, y)$ may be interpreted. Or we may add the function $(\exists x, y) . f(x) . f(y) . \sim(x = y)$, which demands that there shall be at least two things in the class determined by $f$; and in that case the set will not be satisfied when, for example, $f(x)$ is interpreted to mean "$x$ is a satellite of the earth." There is, of course, no upper limit to the number of things which can belong to the class determined by $f$ in either of these cases; nor is it customary to restrict this class so as to make it finite in number, since that gives rise to relatively trivial situations. It is, however, quite easy to impose such restrictions. Suppose, for example, that in addition to the requirement that there shall be at least two things satisfying $f$, we demand that there shall be at most two:

$$\sim(\exists x, y, z) . f(x) . f(y) . f(z) . \sim(x = y) . \sim(x = z) . \sim(y = z).$$

Then the set can be satisfied only when $f(x)$ is given such a meaning as "$x$ is either the earth or the moon." It will be seen, too, that with this further restriction function (d) becomes redundant, since it follows immediately from the requirement that there shall not be as many as three things which satisfy $f$. A condition that is not implied by a set may itself imply some member, or may do so in conjunction with other members of the set.

We shall get an interesting case if to the functions (a)–(d) we add the following two:

(e) $(\exists x, y) . f(x) . f(y) . \sim(x = y)$.

(f) $(x, y) :. (\exists z) : f(x) . f(y) . g(x, y) . \supset . f(z) . g(x, z) . g(z, y)$.

The second of these expressions may be rendered "If $x$ and $y$ satisfy $f$, and are such that $g(x, y)$ holds, then there exists at least one thing $z$ which satisfies $f$, and which is such that both $g(x, z)$ and $g(z, y)$ hold." In order to make clear the force of this condition, we may take a true interpretation of properties (a)–(f). Consider an assigned straight line running from left to right, and let $f(x)$ mean "$x$ is a point on the line" and $g(x, y)$ mean "$x$ is to the left of $y$." Then, what (f) tells us is, that if $x$ and $y$ are points on the line such that $x$ is to the left of $y$, there will exist a point $z$ which is to the right of $x$ and to the left of $y$. So we can express what this really comes to by saying "Between any two points there is a third." And condition (e) tells us that there are at least two points. Without this condition we could not prove that there were points on the line at all. With it, however, we can prove that the number of points cannot be finite; for if there are two distinct points, $x$, $y$, there must be a third, $z$, between $x$ and $y$, and, again, a fourth, $z'$, between $x$ and $z$, etc., and it is easy to see that none of the points so derived can be identical with any of the others. This, of course, does not show that there are, in fact, a non-finite number of points on a given line, but only that *if*, as we supposed, a line affords a true interpretation of postulates (a)–(f), there must be. Any true interpretation of these functions is called a 'dense series.'

With only one existential condition in the list, then, and that one satisfied by the existence of a class of just two members, we have here framed a set which can be satisfied only by a non-finite class. This shows how the joint force of several conditions may be vastly different from that of the several conditions separately, and suggests a conception which might be called the 'fertility' of a set of properties. Suppose we have a condition $p$, with consequences $q, r, \ldots$, and another $p'$, with consequences $q', r', \ldots$. Then, of course, $p \cdot p'$ will imply all these consequences, and therefore the conjunction of any of them. But if these two functions constitute a fertile set, they will entail some consequence $s$ which cannot be analyzed as a mere conjunction, or any other truth-function, of implications derivable from $p$ and $p'$ separately. Thus, if $p$ is the conjunction of conditions (a)–(e), and $p'$ is the single function (f), from $p \cdot p'$ we can infer that there are, say, at least ten things involved in any true interpretation, whereas from $p$ alone we can infer at most that there are two things, while from $p'$ alone we are not able to infer that there are any things at all.

It may be of interest to observe how conditions (a)–(f) are to be classified, with respect to their degrees of generality and the like. The first four of these functions are, as has been pointed out, non-existential, and all four are singly general, the first being a function in one variable, the second and third in two, and the fourth in three; (e) is a singly-general existential function in two variables, while (f) is a doubly-general non-existential function in three variables. Moreover, (f) is irreducible, as of course the other functions are, since they are singly general. When the members of a set of functions are not irreducible, the mere fact that they are of certain degrees of generality is of no special significance, since any function in $n$ generalized variables can be so expressed as to be $n$-tuply general.

We may be reasonably assured that conditions (a)–(f) are independent by reference to the following interpretations, the first example failing on (a), the second on (b), etc.:

(A) Take a line running from left to right, and interpret $f(x)$ to mean "$x$ is a point on the line" and $g(x, y)$ to mean "$x$ is not to the left of $y$."

Here (f) will be satisfied when $x$, $y$, and $z$ all denote the same point, as well as in other cases.

(B) Take two parallel lines running from left to right, and let $f(x)$ mean "$x$ is a point on one of these lines" and $g(x, y)$ mean "$x$ is to the left of $y$."

(C) Interpret $f(x)$ to mean "$x$ is a number" and $g(x, y)$ to mean "$x$ is distinct from $y$."

(D) Consider the circumference of a circle drawn on this page. Let $f(x)$ mean "$x$ is a point on the circumference," and assign to $g(x, y)$ the following meaning: "It is less than 180°, but not a zero distance, in the clockwise direction from $x$ to $y$, or else it is exactly 180° in that direction to $y$, and $x$ is higher up on the page than $y$, or else it is just that far in that direction to $y$, and $x$ is at the same height and also to the left of $y$."

Thus, if $x$ and $y$ are distinct points not at opposite ends of a diameter, and it is nearer from $x$ to $y$ clockwise than from $y$ to

$x$, $g(x, y)$ holds; if they are at opposite ends of a diameter that is not the horizontal one, and $x$ is above $y$, $g(x, y)$ holds; if they are the end-points of the horizontal diameter, and $x$ is to the left of $y$, $g(x, y)$ holds; and in each of these cases, $g(y, x)$ fails; so that conditions (b) and (c) are satisfied. But so is (a), since a point is not less than 180° clockwise from itself, nor above, nor to the left of itself. Moreover, (f) is clearly satisfied if $x$ and $y$ are not on a diameter; and if they are, and $g(x, y)$ holds, then when we go clockwise from $x$ to $y$, each point between will be less than 180° from either. However, condition (d) fails for sets of three points $x, y, z$ where $g(x, y)$ and $g(y, z)$ hold, but where it is more than 180° from $x$ to $z$ clockwise, as well as in certain other cases.

(E) Let $f(x)$ mean "$x$ is this table" and $g(x, y)$ mean "$x$ is not identical with $y$."

(F) Let $f(x)$ mean "$x$ is a rational number not falling between 1 and 2" and $g(x, y)$ mean "$x$ is greater than $y$."

Here (f) fails when $x$ takes the value 2 and $y$ the value 1.

In the set (a)–(f), we can replace function (f) by the following condition, without altering the logical force of the set:

$$(\mathrm{f}_1) \quad (x, y) :: (\exists z) :. f(x) . f(y) . \sim(x = y) . \supset : \\ f(z) : g(x, z) . g(z, y) . \vee . g(y, z) . g(z, x).$$

When this substitution is made, however, condition (b) becomes redundant with the remainder of the set; for if, in the case of every pair of distinct terms $x$, $y$, either $g(x, z) . g(z, y)$ or $g(y, z) . g(z, x)$ holds for some term $z$, then, by (a), $z$ must be distinct from both $x$ and $y$, so that, by (d), we have $g(x, y)$ or $g(y, x)$. And in virtue of the fact that (b) may here be discarded, a set of four conditions that will be equivalent to (a)–(f) can be made up in the following way. We have seen that conditions ($\alpha$)–($\gamma$) are equivalent to (a)–(d), where (a) is equivalent to ($\alpha$) and (b) to ($\beta$), and where, therefore, ($\gamma$) supplies the force of (c) and (d) jointly. So, to begin with, we have (a), (b), ($\gamma$), (e), ($\mathrm{f}_1$) equivalent to (a)–(f). But we have just seen that (b) follows from (a), (d), ($\mathrm{f}_1$), and since ($\gamma$) is stronger than (d), (b) will, of course, follow when ($\gamma$) is substituted; so that we have (a), ($\gamma$), (e), ($\mathrm{f}_1$).

We may now consider the following logical consequences of (a)–(f), each of which expresses a property that is possessed in common by all dense series:

(1) $(\exists x, y, z) . f(x) . f(y) . f(z) . \sim(x = y) . \sim(x = z) . \sim(y = z)$.

By (b) and (e), there are at least two elements $x$, $y$ such that $g(x, y)$ holds; and so, by (f), there will be an element $z$ which is such that $f(z)$, $g(x, z)$, and $g(z, y)$ all hold, and which, by (a), must be distinct from $x$ and $y$.

(2) $(x, y) :. g(x, y) : (z) . \sim g(x, z) \vee z = y :\supset . \sim f(x) \vee \sim f(y)$.

That is, if $g(x, y)$ holds, and if we have $\sim g(x, z)$ except when $z$ is identical with $y$, then $f$ cannot be satisfied by both $x$ and $y$. This follows from conditions (a) and (f).

(3) $(x) :. (\exists y, z) : f(x) . \supset . g(x, y) \vee g(z, x)$.

That is, if $x$ satisfies $f$, then there is some term $y$ such that $g(x, y)$ holds, or some term $z$ such that $g(z, x)$ holds. This follows from (b) and (e). By (e), there are at least two terms satisfying $f$, and so, if $x$ is any such term, there will be at least one other, $x'$, such that, by (b), $g(x, x')$ or $g(x', x)$ will hold.

(4) $(x) :. (\exists y, z) : f(x) . \supset . \sim g(x, y) \vee \sim g(z, x)$.

This follows from (c) and (e), or from (a).

(5) $(x, y) :. (\exists z) : f(x) . f(y) . \sim(x = y)$
$. \sim g(x, y) . \supset . g(y, z) . g(z, x)$.

By (*b*), if $x$ and $y$ are distinct, $\sim g(x, y)$ implies $g(y, x)$, and so, by (f), there exists a $z$ such that $g(y, z)$ and $g(z, x)$ hold.

(6) $(\exists x, y, z) . g(x, y) . g(y, z) . g(x, z)$.

By theorem (1), there are three distinct elements, $x$, $y$, $z$, which satisfy $f$; by (b), $g(x, y)$ or $g(y, x)$, and $g(y, z)$ or $g(z, y)$, and $g(x, z)$ or $g(z, x)$ all hold; but any combination of these possibilities that is compatible with (d) satisfies the theorem.

Let us consider now certain functions which cannot be deduced from (a)–(f), and which show that this set is incomplete in an important respect. In the first place, it cannot be proved that there is a term $x$, which satisfies $f$, such that for every other term $y$, satisfying $f$, $g(x, y)$ holds, and it cannot be proved that there is no such term. In other words, if we represent conditions (a)–(f), which are functions of the free variables $f$ and $g$, by $\Phi(f, g)$, then we have the two theorems

$$\Diamond(\exists f, g) :: \Phi(f, g) :. (x) : \sim f(x) . \vee . (\exists y) . f(y) . \sim(y = x) . \sim g(x, y),$$

and $$\Diamond(\exists f, g) ::. \Phi(f, g) :: (\exists x) :. f(x) :. (y) : f(y) . \sim(y = x) . \supset . g(x, y).$$

These theorems are established by the following examples: Let $f(x)$ mean "$x$ is a rational number between 1 and 2" and $g(x, y)$ mean "$x$ is less than $y$."

Let $f(x)$ mean "$x$ is a rational number less than 2 but not less than 1" and $g(x, y)$ mean "$x$ is less than $y$."

We may express this situation with regard to functions (a)–(f) by saying that these conditions are compatible with the absence as well as with the presence of a 'first' term in any series which satisfies them. And they are, of course, compatible with the absence, and with the presence, of a 'last' term in any such series. Thus there appear to be four possibilities with regard to a further determination of (a)–(f); we may add

(g) $(x) :. (\exists y) : f(x) . \supset . f(y) . g(y, x)$,

(h) $(x) :. (\exists y) : f(x) . \supset . f(y) . g(x, y)$,

or

(g′) $(\exists x) :: (y) :. f(x) : f(y) . \sim(y = x) . \supset . g(x, y)$,

(h′) $(\exists x) :: (y) :. f(x) : f(y) . \sim(y = x) . \supset . g(y, x)$,

or (g), (h′), or (g′), (h). Conditions (a)–(f),(g),(h) define a dense series with no extreme elements, while conditions (a)–(f), (g′),(h′) define a dense series with two extreme elements.

Now, it looks as if we had here four types of dense series; but there are good reasons for holding that this is not in fact the case, and that the set expressed by (a)–(f),(g′),(h) is really identical with the one expressed by (a)–(f),(g),(h′). There does not appear to be any formal distinction involved in demanding a 'first' and no 'last' element as against a 'last' and no 'first.' Whether this is so, however, will depend upon whether every true interpretation in the one case will be a true interpretation in the other, and conversely.

Let us consider this situation somewhat in detail, since it is one with regard to which confusion may easily arise. And let us begin by considering a very simple example. Take the two expressions $h(x, y)$ and $h(y, x)$. Plainly, these are simply two ways of representing one and the same function, since every admissible meaning of either of them will also be an admissible meaning of the other. Suppose, however, that we bring them into conjunction by writing $h(x, y) \cdot h(y, x)$. Still there are not two functions entering into this conjunction, but only one, the conjunction itself being a function constructed on this single one and demanding two values of this one function related in the way it specifies. That is to say, the conjunction demands for its satisfaction two values of the function $h(t, t')$ so related that they will be of the form $h(x, y) \cdot h(y, x)$. Let us take, as a further example, the expressions $(x) : (\exists y) \cdot h(x, y)$ and $(y) : (\exists x) \cdot h(x, y)$. If these two expressions do not enter the same context, they differ merely in respect of a trivial point of notation and not at all in what they mean. With regard to the first, if $h(x, y)$ is interpreted to mean "$x$ is smaller than $y$," we shall have "Everything is smaller than something or other." But with regard to the second, if $h(x, y)$ is interpreted to mean "$y$ is smaller than $x$," we shall have the same thing. If the two expressions occur together in one context, however, that context will demand two different values of the one function which is represented by either expression separately, and will specify by the two representations the way in which these values are to be related. If one of the two values of this function should be "Everything is smaller than something," the other would have to be "Everything is such that something is smaller than it."

In view of these considerations, it will be clear that the conjunctive expressions (g′) . (h) and (g) . (h′) represent the same function. But it does not follow from this alone that (a)–(f), (g′),(h) and (a)–(f),(g),(h′) stand for the same set of conditions, because one and the same function may enter a set in different ways. To take a simple example, let us consider the two symbolizations of the function $h(t, t')$ given by $h(x, y)$ and $h(y, z)$, and let us conjoin them in order with $j(z, z)$, so that we have $h(x, y) \cdot j(z, z)$ and $h(y, z) \cdot j(z, z)$. Plainly, these conjunctive expressions stand for different functions, since there will be true values of the first which are not true values of the second. However, (g′) . (h) and (g) . (h′) seem, as a matter of fact, to be conjoined with (a)–(f) in exactly the same way. If, in connection with (a)–(f),(g′),(h), we allow $f(x)$ to mean "$x$ is a positive rational number or zero" and $g(x, y)$ to mean "$x$ is less than $y$," the set will be satisfied. But it is also true that if, in connection with (a)–(f),(g),(h′), we allow $f(x)$ to have the same meaning, and interpret $g(x, y)$ to mean "$y$ is less than $x$," we shall have a true interpretation. It is, indeed, easy to see quite generally that every true interpretation in either case must be a true interpretation in the other; all we have to do is to assign to $g(x, y)$ in the one case the meaning assigned to $g(y, x)$ in the other.

It is to be observed that we can weaken condition (e) of the set (a)–(f),(g),(h) by substituting for it the function $(\exists x) \cdot f(x)$, since both (g) and (h) imply that if there is one element in the class determined by $f(x)$, there will be another. Moreover, in the set (a)–(f),(g),(h′), condition (e) is redundant, and may be dropped altogether. For (h′) implies that there will be at least one element satisfying $f$, and it follows from (g) that there will be two. Here, however, we can, if we like, replace (h′) by the condition

$$(\exists x) :. (y) : f(y) \cdot \sim(y = x) . \supset . f(x) \cdot g(y, x),$$

which does not imply that there is at least one element satisfying $f$; and then (e) cannot be discarded altogether, but can be weakened to $(\exists x) \cdot f(x)$. It will be clear, also, that both (g′) and (h′) of the set (a)–(f),(g′),(h′) can be altered in this way. But in the case of that set, whether this change is made or not, condition (e) cannot be weakened.

We may turn now to a consideration of *discrete* series of various kinds. A discrete series is one in which, if $g(x, y)$ holds, then there will always be some term $y'$ such that $g(x, y')$

holds, and such that for every $z$, $g(x, z)$ and $g(z, y')$ are not both true, and some term $x'$ such that $g(x', y)$ holds, and such that for every $z$, $g(x', z)$ and $g(z, y)$ are not both true. In short, a discrete series is one in which, if a term has a successor, it has an immediate successor, and if it has a predecessor, it has an immediate predecessor. So, we may define such a series generically by subjoining to (a)–(e) the condition

$$\text{(f}'\text{)}\quad (x, y) :: f(x) . f(y) . g(x, y) . \supset :. \\ (\exists y') : f(y') . g(x, y') : \sim(\exists z) . f(z) . g(x, z) . g(z, y') :. \\ (\exists x') : f(x') . g(x', y) : \sim(\exists z) . f(z) . g(x', z) . g(z, y).$$

And we may then go on to determine specific sorts of discrete series by placing further restrictions upon this generic definition.[4] Thus, if we subjoin conditions (g′) and (h), above, we shall have a definition of a discrete series with just one extreme element.

Let us consider the following examples, some of which afford true interpretations of the set (a)–(e),(f′),(g′),(h), and others false ones:

(I) Interpret $f(x)$ to mean "$x$ is one of the natural numbers, 1, 2, 3, . . . " and $g(x, y)$ to mean "$x$ is greater than $y$."

(II) Interpret $f(x)$ to mean "$x$ is a natural number" and $g(x, y)$ to mean "$y$ is greater than $x$."

(III) Interpret $f(x)$ to mean "$x$ is one of the numbers 1, . . ., 10" and $g(x, y)$ to mean "$x$ is less than $y$."

(IV) Take a line two inches long, running from left to right, and measure off from the middle of the line, 0, the distances 1, ½, ¼, . . . to the right, and the distances −1, −½, −¼, . . . to the left, in terms of inches, so that there will be a class of points corresponding to these numbers, with a zero point. Then let $f(x)$ mean "$x$ is one of these points" and $g(x, y)$ mean "$x$ is to the left of $y$."

(V) In the example just given, change the meaning of $f(x)$ to "$x$ is one of the points of the class, but not the zero point."

(VI) In the same example, interpret $f(x)$ to mean "$x$ is one of the points 0, . . ., ¼, ½, 1."

[4] Cf. Huntington, *loc. cit.*, p. 19. There one further condition is used in defining a 'discrete series,' but a less specific definition seems desirable in the present connection.

(VII) Let $f(x)$ mean "$x$ is one of the odd numbers 1, 3, 5, . . ." and $g(x, y)$ mean "$x$ is a natural number just less than $y$."

(VIII) Let $f(x)$ mean "$x$ is one of the negative integers $-1$, $-2$, $-3$, . . ." and $g(x, y)$ mean "$x$ is greater than $y$."

(IX) In the same example, change the meaning of $g(x, y)$ to "$x$ is less than $y$."

(X) Let $f(x)$ mean "$x$ is an integer, positive, negative, or zero" and $g(x, y)$ mean "$x$ is less than $y$."

It will be seen that examples (II) and (VIII) satisfy each function of the set (a)–(e),(f′),(g′),(h) and that the other examples fail to satisfy one or more of these conditions. The first example fails to satisfy (g′), because this condition, with the interpretation in question, requires that there should be a greatest natural number; and it fails to satisfy (h) because there is a least natural number. Example (III) satisfies (g′), but it fails on (h), owing to the fact that 10 has no successor belonging to the class determined by $f(x)$. (IV) fails on (h), and also on (f′), in that there is no point immediately to the right of the zero point, and none immediately to the left. In the next example, however, where the zero point is omitted, (f′) is satisfied, while (h) fails; whereas in example (VI), (f′) fails, since there is no term coming next after 0, while (g′) holds. Note that (VII) fails on conditions (b), (g′), (h) and satisfies the other conditions. And finally, it will be seen that (IX) differs from (VIII) in having a greatest but no least element, and thus in failing on both (g′) and (h), whereas (X) differs from (VIII) in having no least element, and thus in failing on (g′).

Let us consider now the set (a)–(e),(f′),(g′),(h) together with the two other sets which result from replacing (g′), (h) by (g), (h) and by (g′), (h′). It is to be observed that there is an important respect in which each of these sets is incomplete and therefore open to further determination. This point of incompleteness can be brought out by contrasting examples (III) and (V), each of which satisfies the third set, where the existence of both extreme elements is demanded. In example (III) the number of terms of the series which fall between any two is finite, whereas in (V), between any positive and any negative point, the number of terms is non-finite; and thus there can be nothing in the conditions imposed by the set which decides whether or not, in the case of a true interpretation, any term of the series can be reached from any other by a finite number of steps. We might therefore impose the further condition "If $x$ and $y$ satisfy $f$, and are distinct, then not more than a finite number of terms fall between $x$ and $y$," which fails on examples (IV), (V), (VI) and is satisfied by each of the others.

The importance of this condition lies in the fact that unless it holds, arguments by 'mathematical induction' are not valid. Suppose we have the series of numbers 1, ½, ¼, . . ., where each term is one-half its immediate predecessor, and wish to show that every member of the series is a positive number. To do this, we show, in the first place, that when any member of the series is a positive number, its immediate successor, if it has one, is positive, and then we show that the first member of the series is positive. If there were terms in the series which were not positive, there would have to be a first term of this kind, which would necessarily have an immediate predecessor, since 1 is positive; and thus the condition that positive terms can have only positive successors would be violated. We can convince ourselves of the necessity of the condition that there should not be more than a finite number of terms between any two by considering the series 1, ½, ¼, . . ., . . ., −¼, −½, −1. Here the condition that positive members of the series cannot have other than positive immediate successors is satisfied, as well as the condition that the first term should be positive; but the trouble is that certain terms cannot be reached step by step from 1.

Whenever a property is such that, if it belongs to a given member of a series having an immediate successor, it belongs to the successor, the property may be said to be 'hereditary' in the series with respect to the relation 'being an immediate predecessor of,' as defined in terms of the ordering relation of the series.[5] Thus, in 1, ½, ¼, . . ., "$x$ comes just before $y$" means "$x$ is twice as great as $y$," and the property 'being a positive number' is transmitted by the relation 'being twice as great as.' Let us take the series of positive integers 1, 2, 3, . . . and consider some properties which are hereditary with respect to the

[5] Cf. Russell, *Introduction to Mathematical Philosophy*, Ch. III.

relation 'being one less than.' Of course, the property 'being greater than 0' is hereditary in this series; and since it belongs to 1, it belongs to every member, owing to the fact that any positive integer can be reached step by step from 1. In general, however, hereditary properties do not belong to every member of a series. Thus, 'being greater than 10' is hereditary in the series of positive integers, because, once it gets into the series, it does not come out. Moreover, it is not at all necessary that an hereditary property should belong to at least one member of a series, as may be seen if we take the property 'being less than 0' in connection with the positive integers. This property is said to be transmitted, because there is no term possessing the property whose immediate successor lacks it. And perhaps it will be well, in view of this example, to reformulate the definition of an hereditary property in the following way: "A property $\phi$ is hereditary in a series with respect to a relation $\psi(x, y)$ if, and only if, there is no pair of terms $a$, $b$ such that $\psi(a, b)$, $\phi(a)$, and $\sim\phi(b)$ are all true." One final example will bring out further the exact force of this definition. Let us take the series of positive integers from 1 to 9, and consider the property 'being less than 10.' This property is hereditary with respect to the relation 'being one less than,' because it nowhere comes out of the series. It is only when there is some pair of terms between which a property leaves the series that it is not hereditary.

We may say that two terms of a discrete series are an 'inductive distance' apart if, and only if, any hereditary property belonging to either of them is transmitted to the other by an appropriate relation. This is, as we have seen, tantamount to saying that either of the terms can be reached from the other step by step, and thus that not more than a finite number of elements fall between the two. And what we wish to do is to frame a condition, in terms of the theory of general propositions heretofore developed, which will hold if and only if any two terms of a discrete series satisfying the condition in question are at most an inductive distance apart. We shall consider three ways of doing this, two of which seem to be satisfactory and one not.

It will be observed that if an inductive series like that of the numbers 1, 2, 3, . . . is separated into two parts in such a way that every element of one part comes before every element of the other, there will be a last element of the one part and a first element of the other. In the case of a non-inductive series like $-1, -\frac{1}{2}, -\frac{1}{4}, \ldots, \ldots, \frac{1}{4}, \frac{1}{2}, 1$, however, if we separate all the negative terms from all the positive ones, there will be neither a last element of the one part nor a first element of the other. We might try imposing the following condition: "If $K$ is any non-empty subclass of the elements of the series, such that at least one element of the series does not belong to $K$, and such that if $x$ belongs to $K$ and $y$ does not, $g(x, y)$ holds, then there will be an element $x'$, in $K$, such that for every other element $x$, in $K$, $g(x, x')$ holds; and there will be an element $y'$, not in $K$, such that for every other element $y$, not in $K$, $g(y', y)$ holds." Suppose that $x$ and $y$ are any two terms of a discrete series of this kind such that $g(x, y)$ holds, and suppose that $\phi$ is an hereditary property belonging to $x$. If $\phi$ does not belong to $y$, it cannot belong to the immediate predecessor of $y$, nor to the second term preceding $y$, etc., so that there will be an infinite sequence of terms, $\ldots, y_2, y_1, y$, with no first member; and this sequence cannot include $x$, since $\phi$ belongs to it. Hence we may let $K$ be the class of all those terms which precede every member of this sequence. Then the sequence of all terms not belonging to $K$ will have no first element, contrary to the condition in question. This condition is, then, sufficient; and we can, if we like, weaken it slightly. It is not necessary to say that there shall be both a last term belonging to $K$ and a first not belonging to $K$; we can say that there shall be either a last term in $K$ or a first not in $K$, because in a discrete series every term has an immediate predecessor and an immediate successor, and therefore if a first or a last term exists, both must exist.[6]

We may consider, then, how this condition is to be expressed formally. In the first place, in order to say that $K$ is a sub-

[6] This is Dedekind's postulate; it is used by Veblen and by Huntington in defining an inductive series. See *Trans. Amer. Math. Soc.*, VI (1905), 165, and Huntington, *loc. cit.*

class of the class determined by $f(x)$, we may write

$$(x) \cdot \phi(x) \supset f(x),$$

where $\phi$ is a determining function of $K$. But since we wish to say that the class determined by $\phi(x)$ has members, and is yet not the whole of the class determined by $f(x)$, we shall have to add:

$$(\exists x) \cdot \phi(x) : (\exists x) \cdot f(x) \cdot \sim\phi(x).$$

We wish to say, further, that each element in the class determined by $\phi(x)$ precedes each one in the class determined by $f(x) \cdot \sim\phi(x)$:

$$(x, y) : \phi(x) \cdot f(y) \cdot \sim\phi(y) \cdot \supset \cdot g(x, y).$$

It will be convenient if we abbreviate the conjunction of these three expressions, each of which is a function of two or more of the free variables $\phi$, $f$, and $g$, by writing $H(\phi, f, g)$. This is the hypothesis of the required condition; and the conclusion is, that there will be either a last term in the class determined by $\phi(x)$ or a first in the one determined by $f(x) \cdot \sim\phi(x)$, that is, that

$$(\exists x') :. (x) : \phi(x) \cdot \sim(x = x') \cdot \supset \cdot \phi(x') \cdot g(x, x') :. \vee :.$$
$$(\exists y') :. (y) : f(y) \cdot \sim\phi(y) \cdot \sim(y = y') \cdot \supset \cdot f(y') \cdot \sim\phi(y') \cdot g(y', y),$$

which may be shortened to $I(\phi, f, g)$. We can, then, express the condition in question by writing

$$(\phi) \cdot H(\phi, f, g) \supset I(\phi, f, g).$$

It will be observed that this condition contains the new variable $\phi$, and might therefore be thought to be not on the same base as the other conditions. In one sense of the term 'base,' and that the one we have heretofore understood, this is true. By 'a function on the base $f(x)$,$g(x, y)$' we have meant one which involves no matrices other than $f(x)$ and $g(x, y)$, and in which $f$ and $g$ are not generalized, while $x$ and $y$ are, these latter variables being understood to have a common range of variation. But there is an important sense of this term in which the function here introduced is on the base of the other conditions. We can say that the base of a set is made up of all the free variables contained in the set, that is, of all the variables to which values must be assigned in arriving at an interpretation; and in this sense the condition under consideration, like the other conditions, is on the base comprising only $f$ and $g$, since the variable $\phi$ is generalized. When we wish to refer to the base in question in the first of these senses, we may write $f(x)$, $g(x, y)$, and when we wish to refer to it in the second and weaker sense, we may write $f$, $g$.

It has been held that an inductive series can be defined simply by imposing the condition that any two elements $x$, $y$ of the series shall be such that every hereditary property which belongs to $x$ belongs also to $y$.[7] A property $\phi$ is hereditary if, and only if,

$$(z, z') :. f(z) . f(z') . g(z, z') . \phi(z) : \\ \sim(\exists z'') . f(z'') . g(z, z'') . g(z'', z') :\supset . \phi(z'),$$

which may be written $J(\phi, f, g)$. And we wish to say that if $g(x, y)$ holds, then every property of the sort here in question which is possessed by $x$ is possessed also by $y$:

$$(x, y) :. f(x) . f(y) . g(x, y) . \supset : (\phi) : J(\phi, f, g) . \phi(x) . \supset . \phi(y).$$

Let us take, for example, the series 1, ½, ¼, . . ., 0, where we have an inductive sequence followed by the single term 0. Here every hereditary property belonging to 1, such for instance as that of being a positive number, must belong to every term except 0. It is true that certain hereditary properties possessed by 1, such as that of being a number, are possessed also by 0; but the presumption is that if $x$ and $y$ are any two terms of a series which are more than an inductive distance apart, there will always be some property belonging to $x$ which does not belong to $y$.

This presumption, however, is one that raises doubts concerning the adequacy of the condition here given. In the case of the example just cited, we know that there is at least one hereditary property belonging to 1 which does not belong to 0, since an instance can be produced; but it is by no means easy to see that this will necessarily be true in general. It would seem that there might be two terms $x$, $y$ of a discrete series which were not an inductive distance apart, but which were

[7] See *Principia Mathematica*, I, 543 f.

yet such that every hereditary property possessed by $x$ was, in point of fact, possessed also by $y$; and if this were so, then the condition would not be sufficient. If $\phi$ is any hereditary property belonging to $x$, and if not more than an inductive distance separates $x$ from $y$, we can *prove*, from that alone, that $\phi$ belongs to $y$. If, on the other hand, $x$ and $y$ are more than an inductive distance apart, it may *happen* that $\phi$ always belongs to $y$, although from the mere fact that $\phi$ belongs to $x$ and is transmitted in the series, we cannot infer that it belongs to $y$. Clearly, the condition we want here is not that every hereditary property possessed by $x$ is also in fact possessed by $y$, but that every one must necessarily be. To this objection it has been replied that, for the proof of inductive properties in a series of the form 1, 2, 3, ..., it does not matter if entities other than members of the series possess all hereditary properties belonging to 1, since in such a case any inductive argument will still be valid. This reply is correct, but it does not meet the point of the objection. We wish to be able to give a definition that will be satisfied by a series of this form and by nothing else; and if other entities could possess all hereditary properties belonging to 1, series of other sorts would satisfy the definition. Moreover, even if it so happened that nothing else possessed all these hereditary properties, and thus that inductive series were uniquely selected, that would be a 'material' accident, and would not mean that our analysis was correct.

What we have to do is to make the main implication of our condition strict rather than material. We wish to say, in effect, that in an inductive series, from the fact that an hereditary property belongs to $x$, we can *infer* that the property belongs to $y$. We do not wish to say, however, that this consequence follows solely from the fact that the property belongs to $x$, but from this fact together with the general definition of an inductive series. If the set (a)–(e),(f′) is represented by $F(f, g)$, the required condition can be written as follows:

$$(x, y) :. f(x) . f(y) . g(x, y) . F(f, g) . \prec :$$
$$(\phi) : J(\phi, f, g) . \phi(x) . \supset . \phi(y).$$

### Section 3. Definition of 'Betweenness'

Heretofore we have been dealing with sets of properties constructed on a function $f(x)$, whose values determine classes, and a function $g(x, y)$, whose values are dyadic relations. In this section, we shall replace $g(x, y)$ by the function $g(x_1, x_2, x_3)$, which gives rise to a triadic relation when a value is assigned to $g$. Thus, $f(x)$ may be interpreted to mean "$x$ is either a person or a thing" and $g(x_1, x_2, x_3)$ to mean "$x_1$ gives $x_2$ to $x_3$," where we have to do with the triadic relation of 'donation.' Or we may take a line $l$, and allow $f(x)$ to mean "$x$ is a point on $l$" and $g(x_1, x_2, x_3)$ to mean "$x_2$ is between $x_1$ and $x_3$," where we are concerned with the relation of 'betweenness' in connection with points on a line. It is interpretations like this latter one which are here of interest. We shall construct a set of functions on the base $f(x)$,$g(x_1, x_2, x_3)$ which are such that, whenever $f(x)$ and $g(x_1, x_2, x_3)$ are given an interpretation of this kind, all the functions will be transformed into true propositions. Any interpretation satisfying these functions will be said to be a case of Betweenness.

Let us consider the particular example of points on a line, in order to list certain properties which every one will recognize as essential to the relation in question. In the first place, if $x_1$, $x_2$, $x_3$ are points such that $x_2$ is between $x_1$ and $x_3$, it must be true that $x_2$ is between $x_3$ and $x_1$; so that we must have, either explicitly or by implication, a condition to the effect that whenever $g(x_1, x_2, x_3)$ holds, so does $g(x_3, x_2, x_1)$. It will be clear, too, that if $x_1$, $x_2$, $x_3$ are distinct points on a line, one of them must be between the other two; so that we must have a condition to the effect that $g(x_1, x_2, x_3)$ holds or $g(x_2, x_3, x_1)$ holds or, etc. Moreover, if $g(x_1, x_2, x_3)$ is true, it cannot be the case that $g(x_1, x_3, x_2)$ is true also; so that we must say, or be able to prove, that $g(x_1, x_2, x_3)$ implies $\sim g(x_1, x_3, x_2)$. Again, if $x_2$ is between $x_1$ and $x_3$, it cannot be identical with either, nor can they be identical with each other; and we must therefore be able to show that whenever $g(x_1, x_2, x_3)$ holds, $x_1$, $x_2$, and $x_3$ are all distinct. Finally, suppose we have $g(x_1, x_2, x_3)$, and that $x_4$ is any fourth point; then we must have either $g(x_1, x_2, x_4)$

or $g(x_4, x_2, x_3)$. These five conditions, which we shall take as defining Betweenness, may be formulated more exactly as follows:

(1) $(x_1, x_2, x_3) : f(x_1) . f(x_2) . f(x_3) . g(x_1, x_2, x_3) . \supset . g(x_3, x_2, x_1)$.

(2) $(x_1, x_2, x_3) : f(x_1) . f(x_2) . f(x_3) . d(x_1, x_2, x_3) . \supset .$
$g(x_1, x_2, x_3) \vee g(x_2, x_3, x_1) \vee g(x_3, x_1, x_2) \vee$
$g(x_3, x_2, x_1) \vee g(x_1, x_3, x_2) \vee g(x_2, x_1, x_3)$.

(3) $(x_1, x_2, x_3) : f(x_1) . f(x_2) . f(x_3) . d(x_1, x_2, x_3) . \supset .$
$\sim g(x_1, x_2, x_3) \vee \sim g(x_1, x_3, x_2)$.

(4) $(x_1, x_2, x_3) : f(x_1) . f(x_2) . f(x_3) . g(x_1, x_2, x_3) . \supset . d(x_1, x_2, x_3)$.

(5) $(x_1, x_2, x_3, x_4) : f(x_1) . f(x_2) . f(x_3) . f(x_4) . g(x_1, x_2, x_3)$
$. \sim(x_4 = x_1 \vee x_4 = x_2 \vee x_4 = x_3) . \supset . g(x_1, x_2, x_4) \vee g(x_4, x_2, x_3)$.[8]

There are two senses in which this set might be said to constitute a definition of Betweenness. The first is that of merely verbal definition. We might say of any interpretation satisfying these conditions that it was a case of Betweenness, irrespective of whether or not this usage accorded with the ordinary understanding of the term. The second sense is that of a correct analysis of this ordinary meaning. We might try to show that these properties could be satisfied if and only if we had a case of Betweenness in a sense closely similar to the ordinary one. It can be seen by inspection that any interpretation failing to satisfy one or more of these conditions will not accord with the ordinary notion (as exemplified, for instance, by the points on a line); but it is not clear that properties (1)–(5) are sufficient. Indeed, there is one respect in which they are certainly not. It will be seen that these conditions are all non-existential, and would thus hold for an interpretation in which nothing satisfied $f$, or in which just one thing or two things did, while it is clear that common usage would require at least three things for a case of Betweenness. Thus, we shall have to add

(6) $(\exists x_1, x_2, x_3) . f(x_1) . f(x_2) . f(x_3) . d(x_1, x_2, x_3)$.

It still remains possible, however, that some essential non-

[8] These postulates are due to Huntington, and so are the theorems to which we shall come presently. See *Trans. Amer. Math. Soc.*, XXVI (1924), 257.

existential property has been overlooked, and the only way we have at present of obtaining evidence that this is not so is to deduce any property that we can think of which might seem to be essential. Later on, we shall be able to supply positive proof that the conditions here given are sufficient. This will be done in the following way. It is clear that any property involved in the general notion of Betweenness, as exemplified by the series of whole numbers in order of magnitude, or the letters of the English alphabet in their conventional order of occurrence, can be expressed by means of a singly-general function; and we can see that, aside from the existential condition just given, all these properties can be expressed by means of universal functions like those in the list (1)–(5). So, it must be shown that, in an appropriate sense, no singly-general universal function of this kind can be both consistent with and independent of the set (1)–(6). With this result, which will be established in the next chapter, we can argue that since conditions (1)–(6) are necessary, they must also be sufficient.

The independence of these six properties can be seen from the following interpretations, where the first example fails on (1), the second on (2), etc.:

(I) Let $f(x)$ mean "$x$ is a natural number" and $g(x_1, x_2, x_3)$ mean "$x_1$ is less than $x_2$, and $x_2$ less than $x_3$."

(II) Take three points $a$, $b$, $c$ not on a straight line, and let $f(x)$ mean "$x$ is $a$, $b$, or $c$" and $g(x_1, x_2, x_3)$ mean "$x_2$ is between $x_1$ and $x_3$."

(III) Consider a plane, and let $f(x)$ mean "$x$ is a point in the plane" and $g(x_1, x_2, x_3)$ mean "$x_1$, $x_2$, and $x_3$ are all distinct."

(IV) Consider a line $l$ and intervals determined by pairs of distinct points, the end-points of an interval being understood to belong to it. Let $f(x)$ mean "$x$ is a point on $l$" and $g(x_1, x_2, x_3)$ mean "$x_2$ belongs to the interval determined by $x_1$ and $x_3$."

(V) Take a circle in which two perpendicular diameters have been drawn, and consider the four quadrants. Let $f(x)$ mean "$x$ is one of these quadrants" and $g(x_1, x_2, x_3)$ mean "$x_1$ and $x_3$ are contiguous to $x_2$ on opposite sides."

In this case, if the quadrants are lettered in order, $a$, $b$, $c$, $d$, we shall have $g(a, b, c)$, but neither $g(a, b, d)$ nor $g(d, b, c)$, so that condition (5) will fail. And note that if we had not said "on opposite sides," (4) would have failed also.

(VI) Take two points $a$, $b$ on a line, and let $f(x)$ mean "$x$ is either $a$ or $b$" and $g(x_1, x_2, x_3)$ mean "$x_2$ is between $x_1$ and $x_3$."

We may now consider some theorems deducible from conditions (1)–(5). If the reader will draw a line and mark off points upon it in accordance with the hypotheses of the theorems, he will see that what is to be proved in each case is immediately obvious from the interpretation. Of course, this by itself has no tendency to show that the theorems are deducible from the postulates; all it can show is that what is to be proved is self-consistent and, since the points on a line are a true interpretation of the set (1)–(5), that the theorems are consistent with the set. In these theorems, all the variables are to take distinct values, as well as to satisfy $f$, and it will be convenient if we omit the explicit insertion of these conditions. The variables are also always generalized universally, so that the prefix in each case may be dropped.

(7) $g(x_1, x_2, x_3) . g(x_2, x_3, x_4) .\supset. g(x_1, x_2, x_4)$.

By condition (5), $g(x_1, x_2, x_3)$ implies $g(x_1, x_2, x_4)$ or $g(x_4, x_2, x_3)$; but $g(x_2, x_3, x_4)$ implies $g(x_4, x_3, x_2)$, by (1), which is incompatible with $g(x_4, x_2, x_3)$, by (3). The theorem follows, then, from (1), (3), and (5).

(8) $g(x_1, x_2, x_3) . g(x_2, x_4, x_3) .\supset. g(x_1, x_2, x_4)$.

This also follows from (1), (3), and (5). By (1), $g(x_2, x_4, x_3)$ implies $g(x_3, x_4, x_2)$; and, by (5), $g(x_1, x_2, x_3)$ implies $g(x_1, x_2, x_4)$ or $g(x_4, x_2, x_3)$; but this latter implies $g(x_3, x_2, x_4)$, which is incompatible with $g(x_3, x_4, x_2)$, by (3).

(9) $g(x_1, x_2, x_3) . g(x_2, x_4, x_3) .\supset. g(x_1, x_4, x_3)$.

Here, again, we employ (1), (3), and (5). By (5), $g(x_1, x_2, x_3)$ implies $g(x_1, x_2, x_4)$ or $g(x_4, x_2, x_3)$, this latter being equivalent to $g(x_3, x_2, x_4)$; and $g(x_2, x_4, x_3)$ implies $g(x_2, x_4, x_1)$ or $g(x_1, x_4, x_3)$. But $g(x_2, x_4, x_3)$ is equivalent to $g(x_3, x_4, x_2)$, contrary to $g(x_3, x_2, x_4)$, by (3); so that we have $g(x_1, x_2, x_4)$. If $g(x_2, x_4, x_1)$

holds, then $g(x_1, x_4, x_2)$ holds, and the latter is incompatible with $g(x_1, x_2, x_4)$; so that we have $g(x_1, x_4, x_3)$.

(10) $g(x_1, x_2, x_4) \,.\, g(x_1, x_3, x_4) \,.\supset.\, g(x_1, x_2, x_3) \vee g(x_1, x_3, x_2)$.

By (5), $g(x_1, x_2, x_4)$ implies $g(x_1, x_2, x_3)$ or $g(x_3, x_2, x_4)$, and $g(x_1, x_3, x_4)$ implies $g(x_1, x_3, x_2)$ or $g(x_2, x_3, x_4)$; but, by (1) and (3), $g(x_2, x_3, x_4)$ and $g(x_3, x_2, x_4)$ will not both be true; so that we shall have either $g(x_1, x_2, x_3)$ or $g(x_1, x_3, x_2)$.

(11) $g(x_1, x_2, x_4) \,.\, g(x_1, x_3, x_4) \,.\supset.\, g(x_1, x_2, x_3) \vee g(x_3, x_2, x_4)$.

Here the hypothesis is simply stronger than that of (5), and the conclusion is the same.

(12) $g(x_1, x_3, x_4) \,.\, g(x_2, x_3, x_4) \,.\supset.\, g(x_1, x_2, x_4) \vee g(x_2, x_1, x_4)$.

By (1) and (2), $g(x_1, x_2, x_4)$ or $g(x_2, x_1, x_4)$ or $g(x_1, x_4, x_2)$. But if $g(x_1, x_4, x_2)$ holds, then $g(x_1, x_4, x_3)$ or $g(x_3, x_4, x_2)$ holds, by (5), the first being incompatible with $g(x_1, x_3, x_4)$ and the second with $g(x_2, x_3, x_4)$.

(13) $g(x_1, x_3, x_4) \,.\, g(x_2, x_3, x_4) \,.\supset.\, g(x_1, x_2, x_3) \vee g(x_2, x_1, x_3)$.

By (12), the hypothesis here implies $g(x_1, x_2, x_4)$ or $g(x_2, x_1, x_4)$. If $g(x_1, x_2, x_4)$ holds, then, by (5), $g(x_1, x_2, x_3)$ or $g(x_3, x_2, x_4)$ will hold, and the latter is incompatible with $g(x_2, x_3, x_4)$. If $g(x_2, x_1, x_4)$ holds, then $g(x_2, x_1, x_3)$ or $g(x_3, x_1, x_4)$ will hold, and the latter is incompatible with $g(x_1, x_3, x_4)$.

(14) $g(x_1, x_3, x_4) \,.\, g(x_2, x_3, x_4) \,.\supset.\, g(x_1, x_2, x_3) \vee g(x_2, x_1, x_4)$.

By (1) and (2), $g(x_1, x_4, x_2)$ or $g(x_1, x_2, x_4)$ or $g(x_2, x_1, x_4)$ holds. If $g(x_1, x_4, x_2)$ holds, then $g(x_1, x_4, x_3)$ or $g(x_3, x_4, x_2)$ will hold, the first alternative being incompatible with $g(x_1, x_3, x_4)$ and the second with $g(x_2, x_3, x_4)$. If $g(x_1, x_2, x_4)$ holds, then $g(x_1, x_2, x_3)$ or $g(x_3, x_2, x_4)$ will hold, the latter being incompatible with $g(x_2, x_3, x_4)$.

We may now show how new sets of properties which are equivalent to (1)–(5) can be derived, by showing how condition (5) can be replaced by two or more of the functions (7)–(14) without altering the logical force of the set.[9] It will be shown, first, that an equivalent set results when (5) is replaced by (7) and (8). In order to do this, it will, of course, be sufficient to show that (5) follows from (1)–(4),(7),(8), since it has already been shown that (7) and (8) are consequences of (1)–(5).

(5) $g(x_1, x_2, x_3) . \supset . g(x_1, x_2, x_4) \vee g(x_4, x_2, x_3)$.

By (1) and (2), we have $g(x_4, x_2, x_3)$ or $g(x_2, x_3, x_4)$ or $g(x_2, x_4, x_3)$. If $g(x_2, x_3, x_4)$ holds, then since $g(x_1, x_2, x_3)$ holds, we have $g(x_1, x_2, x_4)$, by (7); and if $g(x_2, x_4, x_3)$ holds, then since $g(x_1, x_2, x_3)$ holds, we have $g(x_1, x_2, x_4)$, by (8).

That neither (7) alone nor (8) alone can replace (5) may be seen from the following examples, the first being such as to satisfy (1)–(4),(7) and fail on (5), and the second such as to satisfy (1)–(4),(8) and fail on (5):

Take a right triangle *abc*, with right angle at *b*, and draw from *b* a perpendicular, *bo*, to the side *ac*. Then let $f(x)$ mean "$x$ is one of the points *a*, *b*, *c*, *o*" and $g(x_1, x_2, x_3)$ mean "$x_1x_2x_3$ is either a right or a straight angle." Here (7) holds, because its hypothesis $g(x_1, x_2, x_3) . g(x_2, x_3, x_4)$ is never satisfied; but (5) fails, as, for instance, when we take $g(a, b, c)$ and have both $\sim g(a, b, o)$ and $\sim g(o, b, c)$.

Take a square, and draw the two diagonals *ac* and *bd*. Then let $f(x)$ mean "$x$ is one of the points *a*, *b*, *c*, *d*" and $g(x_1, x_2, x_3)$ mean "$x_1x_2x_3$ is a right angle." Here (8) is satisfied, owing to the fact that its hypothesis always fails; but if we take $g(a, b, c)$, we have both $\sim g(a, b, d)$ and $\sim g(d, b, c)$, contrary to (5).

In order to see that the set (1)–(4),(7),(8) is an independent one, we may observe, in the first place, that (8) cannot follow from (1)–(4),(7), since these conditions would then be equivalent to (1)–(5), and that, similarly, (7) cannot follow from (1)–(4), (8). In the second place, if we take any one of the conditions (1)–(4), we can, of course, find an example for which it fails

[9] These equivalent sets are selected from among a number given by Huntington. See the paper just referred to, pp. 267 ff. We are also indebted to Professor Huntington for the convenient expression 'vacuously satisfied' as used in this chapter. See "The Fundamental Propositions of Algebra," in *Monographs on Modern Mathematics* (edited by J. W. A. Young), pp. 187, 193.

and the other three hold, and in which there are only three elements in the class determined by $f$, (7) and (8) thus being satisfied vacuously.

A set of properties equivalent to (1)–(5) can be derived by replacing (5) by (7) and (11), since condition (5) can be shown to follow from (1)–(4),(7),(11):

By (1) and (2), $g(x_1, x_2, x_4)$ or $g(x_2, x_1, x_4)$ or $g(x_1, x_4, x_2)$ holds, and $g(x_4, x_2, x_3)$ or $g(x_2, x_3, x_4)$ or $g(x_2, x_4, x_3)$ also holds, where the first alternative in each case satisfies the theorem. Now, $g(x_1, x_2, x_3)$ is equivalent to $g(x_3, x_2, x_1)$; and, by (7), this latter together with $g(x_2, x_1, x_4)$ implies $g(x_3, x_2, x_4)$, which implies $g(x_4, x_2, x_3)$; and, again, $g(x_1, x_2, x_3)$ together with $g(x_2, x_3, x_4)$ implies $g(x_1, x_2, x_4)$. It might be the case, however, that $g(x_1, x_4, x_2)$ and $g(x_2, x_4, x_3)$ were both true. We have, by (1) and (2), $g(x_1, x_3, x_4)$ or $g(x_3, x_1, x_4)$ or $g(x_3, x_4, x_1)$; $g(x_1, x_3, x_4)$ and $g(x_3, x_4, x_2)$ imply $g(x_1, x_3, x_2)$, by (7), and this is incompatible with $g(x_1, x_2, x_3)$; $g(x_3, x_1, x_4)$ and $g(x_1, x_4, x_2)$ imply $g(x_3, x_1, x_2)$, which is incompatible with $g(x_1, x_2, x_3)$; $g(x_3, x_2, x_1)$ and $g(x_3, x_4, x_1)$ imply $g(x_3, x_2, x_4)$ or $g(x_4, x_2, x_1)$, by (11); and, therefore, $g(x_1, x_2, x_4)$ or $g(x_4, x_2, x_3)$ holds.

That (5) cannot be replaced by condition (11) alone in the formation of a set equivalent to (1)–(5) may be seen from the following example:

Take the letters $a$, $b$, $c$, $d$, and form the eight ordered triads *abc, adb, bcd, bda, cad, cba, dac, dcb*. Then let $f(x)$ mean "$x$ is one of the letters $a$, $b$, $c$, $d$," and let $g(x_1, x_2, x_3)$ mean "$x_1x_2x_3$ is some one of these eight triads." Here (1)–(4) are satisfied, and so is (11), in that its hypothesis is never fulfilled; but since we have $g(a, b, c)$ together with $\sim g(a, b, d)$ and $\sim g(d, b, c)$, (5) fails.

Inasmuch as properties (1)–(5) follow neither from (1)–(4), (7) nor from (1)–(4),(11), and yet do follow when (7) and (11) are both included, it must be true that (7) is not a consequence of (1)–(4),(11), and also that (11) is not a consequence of (1)–(4),(7). Moreover, we can easily find an example where just three things satisfy $f$ which will fail to satisfy any chosen one of the properties (1)–(4) while satisfying the others; and such an example will, of course, satisfy (7) and (11) vacuously.

A set of properties equivalent to (1)–(5) results when (5) is replaced by (7) and (12), as may be seen from the fact that (5) is a logical consequence of (1)–(4),(7),(12):

By (1) and (2), $g(x_1, x_2, x_4)$ or $g(x_1, x_4, x_2)$ or $g(x_2, x_1, x_4)$ holds, and $g(x_4, x_2, x_3)$ or $g(x_2, x_3, x_4)$ or $g(x_2, x_4, x_3)$ also holds, where the first member of each triad of alternatives satisfies the theorem. By (7), $g(x_1, x_2, x_3)$ and $g(x_2, x_3, x_4)$ imply $g(x_1, x_2, x_4)$; so that only one alternative of the second triad remains to be considered. Suppose both $g(x_1, x_4, x_2)$ and $g(x_2, x_4, x_3)$ to hold. We have $g(x_3, x_4, x_2)$, and so, by (12), $g(x_1, x_3, x_2)$ or $g(x_3, x_1, x_2)$, both of which are incompatible with $g(x_1, x_2, x_3)$. Suppose $g(x_2, x_1, x_4)$ and $g(x_2, x_4, x_3)$. From $g(x_4, x_1, x_2)$ and $g(x_1, x_2, x_3)$, we have $g(x_4, x_1, x_3)$, by (7); and, by (12), $g(x_2, x_1, x_4)$ and $g(x_3, x_1, x_4)$ imply $g(x_2, x_3, x_4)$ or $g(x_3, x_2, x_4)$, both of which are incompatible with $g(x_2, x_4, x_3)$.

That (12) alone cannot replace (5) can be seen in the following way. Suppose we had a class of just four things *a*, *b*, *c*, *d* which satisfied *f*, and suppose that $g(x_1, x_2, x_3)$ was satisfied by each of the eight ordered triads *abc*, *adc*, *bad*, *cba*, *cbd*, *cda*, *dab*, *dbc*, and by no others. Then conditions (1)–(4),(12) would hold, but since we should have $g(a, d, c)$ together with $\sim g(a, d, b)$ and $\sim g(b, d, c)$, (5) would fail.

It is to be observed that we have here a general method for constructing examples satisfying or failing to satisfy given conditions. We do not need to take an actual interpretation, it being sufficient to consider abstractly the notion of an interpretation which should involve, say, four elements *a*, *b*, *c*, *d* satisfying $f(x)$, and to indicate all those ordered triads for which *g* is to be thought of as holding, and all those for which it is to be thought of as failing. Any combination of holding and failing among distinct ordered triads is, of course, logically possible; so that if some combination can be specified which would, if realized, satisfy one condition and fail to satisfy another, we can know that the second condition does not follow from the first; and if we can specify some combination that would satisfy both conditions, we can know that they are consistent. It is to be noted, however, that except where one or more general rules can be given by which ordered selections of elements are to be listed, this procedure is applicable only to cases in which a finite interpretation is sufficient. If, for instance, we should add to properties (1)–(6), above, the condition that between any two elements there must exist a third, no finite interpretation would do, and no list of ordered triads for which $g$ was to hold could be arbitrarily specified, although such a list might be given by some appropriate rule.

The so-called interpretational method is, then, frequently not interpretational at all, but involves a quite different procedure, which is really analytic. It will be recalled that the method of interpretation in proofs of consistency rests on the fact that truth implies consistency. To say that a set of properties is not inconsistent is to say that it might, conceivably, have a true interpretation; and if the set does have, then of course the possibility follows. But, now, suppose we have two functions $F$, $G$, which are such that $F$ implies $G$, and suppose that $F$ is known to be self-consistent. To say that $F$ implies $G$ is to say that any true interpretation of $F$ will also, of necessity, be a true interpretation of $G$; and since no self-consistent function can imply an inconsistent one, from the fact that $F$ is self-consistent, we can conclude that $G$ is, without resorting to interpretations. This is what is done in many cases. We have a function $G$ which is to be shown to be self-consistent, and we set about finding a function $F$ which implies $G$, and which can be seen by inspection or in some other way to admit of true values.

Of course, this same procedure is valid in proofs of independence; for to show that $p$ and $q$ do not imply $r$ is merely to show that $p . q . {\sim}r$ is self-consistent. Let us take the set of properties (a)–(d), which is given in the first section of this chapter, and show that (a), (b) do not imply (c). It must be shown that the function

$$(x) . f(x) \supset {\sim}g(x, x) :.$$
$$(x, y) : f(x) . f(y) . {\sim}(x = y) . \supset . g(x, y) \vee g(y, x) :.$$
$$(\exists x, y) . f(x) . f(y) . {\sim}(x = y) . g(x, y) . g(y, x),$$

which we may call $G(f, g)$, is self-consistent. Let us construct a function $F(f, g)$ which will imply this one and which can be seen to be logically possible:

$$(\exists x, y) \cdot f(x) \cdot f(y) \cdot \sim(x = y) \cdot g(x, y) \cdot g(y, x) \cdot \sim g(x, x) \cdot \sim g(y, y) : \sim(\exists x, y, z) \cdot f(x) \cdot f(y) \cdot f(z) \cdot d(x, y, z).$$

Here, each of the pairs $x, y; y, x; x, x; y, y$ enters only once, and in such a way that no contradiction can arise. It can be seen that $\Diamond(\exists f, g) \cdot F(f, g)$, and also that $\sim\Diamond(\exists f, g) \cdot F(f, g) \cdot \sim G(f, g)$, from which it can be concluded that $\Diamond(\exists f, g) \cdot G(f, g)$. When we take, supposititiously, four things $a$, $b$, $c$, $d$ that shall be said to satisfy $f$, and then list a set of ordered triads for which $g$ is supposed to hold, we are really constructing a function $F(f, g)$ which can be seen by inspection to be self-consistent.

## Section 4. Definition of Betweenness in Terms of Serial Order: Equivalent Definitions on Different Bases

We can begin with a definition of Serial Order, and then define on the base $f(x), g(x, y)$ a triadic relation having all the formal properties of the relation of Betweenness as given on the base $f(x), g(x, y, z)$. Let us take the properties (a)–(d), which are used in Section 1 to define Serial Order, and, in order to avoid trivial cases, let us add:

(e) $(\exists x, y, z) \cdot f(x) \cdot f(y) \cdot f(z) \cdot d(x, y, z).$

If we consider an interpretation of this set in terms of the points on a line running from left to right, where $g(x, y)$ means "$x$ is to the left of $y$," it will be clear how "$y$ is between $x$ and $z$" is to be defined. $y$ will be between $x$ and $z$ if either $g(x, y) \cdot g(y, z)$ holds or $g(z, y) \cdot g(y, x)$ holds; so that we may define a triadic relation $g(x, y, z)$ by writing

$$g(x, y) \cdot g(y, z) \cdot \vee \cdot g(z, y) \cdot g(y, x).$$

This is, of course, to be understood as a purely verbal definition, in the sense that the expression $g(x, y, z)$ is merely an abbreviation for the more complex expression which is its definition.

In order to see that the triadic relation so specified has all the formal properties of Betweenness as defined in Section 3, it will be sufficient to prove as theorems from the set (a)–(e) all the properties (1)–(6), of that section, with the definition here given substituted for $g(x, y, z)$.

(1) $g(x, y, z) \supset g(z, y, x)$.[10]

Note that this theorem does not require any of the premises (a)–(e), but is merely a logical necessity in virtue of the definition. For, by the definition of $g(x, y, z)$, we have

$$g(x, y) \cdot g(y, z) . \vee . g(z, y) \cdot g(y, x) :\supset: g(z, y) \cdot g(y, x) . \vee . g(x, y) \cdot g(y, z),$$

which is, of course, certifiable on logical grounds alone.

(2) $g(x, y, z) \vee g(y, z, x) \vee g(z, x, y) \vee g(z, y, x) \vee g(y, x, z) \vee g(x, z, y)$.

By (b), $g(x, y)$ or $g(y, x)$ holds, and we may, without loss of generality, say $g(x, y)$. Consider any third element $z$, where we have, by (b), $g(x, z)$ or $g(z, x)$. If $g(z, x)$ holds, then, by definition, $g(z, x, y)$ also holds; so that we may suppose $g(x, z)$ to hold. By (b), we have $g(z, y)$ or $g(y, z)$; if $g(z, y)$ holds, then, by definition, $g(x, z, y)$ also holds; whereas, if $g(y, z)$ holds, then, since $g(x, y)$ holds, $g(x, y, z)$ will also hold.

(3) $\sim g(x, y, z) \vee \sim g(x, z, y)$.

This follows immediately from (c) and (d), since we have either $\sim g(y, z)$ or $\sim g(z, y)$.

(4) $g(x, y, z) \supset d(x, y, z)$.

We have, by definition, either $g(x, y) \cdot g(y, z)$ or $g(z, y) \cdot g(y, x)$, and we may suppose the first without loss of generality. By (a), $y$ is distinct from both $x$ and $z$; but $x$ and $z$ are distinct from each other, since otherwise we should have $g(x, y) \cdot g(y, x)$, contrary to (c).

(5) $g(x, y, z) . \supset . g(x, y, t) \vee g(t, y, z)$.

We may suppose $g(x, y)$ and $g(y, z)$ without loss of generality. By theorem (4), $x$, $y$, $z$ must all be distinct; and if $t$ is

[10] In these theorems, the universal prefix and the conditions that the variables shall take distinct values and satisfy $f$ are omitted.

any fourth element, we have $g(y, t)$ or $g(t, y)$. If $g(y, t)$ holds, then $g(x, y, t)$ will hold, and if $g(t, y)$, then $g(t, y, z)$.

From these theorems, together with the fact that conditions (6) and (e) are identical, it can be seen that the function $g(x, y, z)$ has all the formal properties of Betweenness, and thus that wherever the conditions for Serial Order are fulfilled, a sub-system possessing properties (1)–(6) must exist. If, for instance, we take a set of concentric circles of varying radii, and interpret $g(x, y)$ to mean "$x$ is within $y$," we shall have an interpretation of conditions (1)–(6) where $g(x, y, z)$ means "$x$ is within $y$, which is within $z$, or $z$ is within $y$, which is within $x$." And, again, if we take the system of positive integers, 1, 2, $\cdots$, and let $g(x, y)$ mean "$x$ is less than $y$," we have an interpretation of (1)–(6) in which $g(x, y, z)$ means "$x$ is less than $y$, which is less than $z$, or $z$ is less than $y$, which is less than $x$." In such interpretations, however, condition (1) will, as we have seen, reduce to a logical principle, and so may be omitted from the definition.

Now, if we could reverse the process here carried out, defining a dyadic relation, $g(x, y)$, in terms of the triadic one on which Betweenness has been defined, and then deducing all the properties of Serial Order from those of Betweenness, the two sets of properties (a)–(e) and (1)–(6) would be equivalent, in the sense that wherever a true interpretation of either was found, a true interpretation of the other would be uniquely determined. But it seems pretty clear upon inspection that this cannot be done, owing to the fact that, in Serial Order, 'direction' can be distinguished, whereas the conditions for Betweenness do not enable us to make such a distinction. Suppose we give an interpretation to the set (a)–(e) where $f(x)$ means "$x$ is a number" and $g(x, y)$ means "$x$ is less than $y$." Then the corresponding interpretation of the set (1)–(6) will be one such that $g(x, y, z)$ means what is meant by $g(x, y) \cdot g(y, z) \cdot \vee \cdot g(z, y) \cdot g(y, x)$. But if we interpret $g(x, y)$ to mean "$y$ is less than $x$," the corresponding interpretation of (1)–(6) will be exactly the same. It is clear, in such a case, that whereas we shall have two different interpretations of conditions (a)–(e), there will be only one interpretation of (1)–(6). If, therefore, we begin initially with an interpretation of conditions (1)–(6), in which $f(x)$ means "$x$ is a number" and $g(x, y, z)$ means "$y$ is between $x$ and $z$," and try to define $g(x, y)$ so that all the properties of Serial Order will be demonstrable, the question arises whether $g(x, y)$ will mean "$x$ is less than $y$" or mean "$y$ is less than $x$." Since the meaning assigned to $g(x, y, z)$ corresponds to both of these, it is clear that neither interpretation of the set (a)–(e) can be uniquely determined, and thus that Serial Order cannot be defined in terms of the conditions for Betweenness.

Another way of seeing that the definition of Serial Order is stronger than that of Betweenness, in the sense that any interpretation of the former will determine uniquely a corresponding interpretation of the latter, but not conversely, is to exhibit an example satisfying conditions (1)–(6) and failing to satisfy (a)–(e). Let us take a class of four persons $A$, $B$, $C$, $D$, where $f(x)$ is to mean "$x$ is one of these persons" and $g(x, y, z)$ is to mean "$x$ and $z$ are both admirers of $y$"; and let us suppose it to be in fact the case that the following relationships and their converses are all that hold:

$$g(A, B, C),\quad g(A, B, D),\quad g(A, C, D),\quad g(B, C, D).$$

Of the twenty-four ordered triads that can be formed, we have eight for which $g$ holds and sixteen for which it fails; and although this interpretation satisfies conditions (1)–(6), it seems plainly impossible to define in terms of the interpretation here assigned to $g(x, y, z)$ a meaning for $g(x, y)$ which will satisfy conditions (a)–(e).

It is possible, however, to write two sets of postulates, one on a dyadic relation and the other on a triadic, which shall be such that any interpretation of the one will give rise to a corresponding interpretation of the other, and conversely. It is possible, in particular, to construct a set of conditions on the base $f(x)$,$g(x, y, z)$ which are such that the conditions for Serial Order on $f(x)$,$g(x, y)$ can be defined and proved in terms of them, and such that, conversely, they can be defined and proved in terms of the conditions for Serial Order. Consider the following set of four properties on $f(x), g(x, y, z)$:

(a′) $f(x) . f(y) . f(z) . g(x, y, z) . \supset . d(x, y, z)$.

(b′) $f(x) . f(y) . f(z) . d(x, y, z) . \supset .$
$g(x, y, z) \vee g(y, z, x) \vee g(z, x, y) \vee g(z, y, x) \vee g(y, x, z) \vee g(x, z, y)$.

(c′) $f(x) . f(y) . \sim(x = y) . \supset :.$
$(z) : f(z) . \supset . \sim g(x, y, z) . \sim g(x, z, y) . \sim g(z, x, y) : \vee :$
$(z) : f(z) . \supset . \sim g(y, x, z) . \sim g(y, z, x) . \sim g(z, y, x)$.

(e′) $(\exists x, y, z) . f(x) . f(y) . f(z) . d(x, y, z)$.

We shall first define $g(x, y, z)$ in terms of $g(x, y)$ and prove properties (a′)–(e′) from (a)–(e).

Let $g(x, y, z)$ mean, by definition, $g(x, y) . g(y, z) . g(x, z)$.

Then (a′) follows immediately from (a).

(b′) follows from (b) and (d).

For if $x, y, z$ are any three distinct elements satisfying $f$, we have $g(x, y)$ or $g(y, x)$, and $g(x, z)$ or $g(z, x)$, and $g(y, z)$ or $g(z, y)$, by (b); and we may, without loss of generality, suppose $g(x, y)$ to hold. If $g(z, x)$ holds, then we have, by (d), $g(z, y)$, and thus $g(z, x, y)$; so that we may suppose $g(x, z)$ to hold. If $g(y, z)$ holds, then $g(x, y) . g(y, z) . g(x, z)$ will hold, and this is $g(x, y, z)$; if $g(z, y)$ holds, then $g(x, z) . g(z, y) . g(x, y)$ will hold, and this is $g(x, z, y)$.

(c′) follows immediately from (c), while (e′) is identical with (e).

It must be shown, in the second place, how $g(x, y)$ is to be defined in terms of the base $f(x), g(x, y, z)$, and how the properties (a)–(e) follow, in accordance with the definition, from (a′)–(e′).

Let $g(x, y)$ mean, by definition,

$$(\exists z) . f(z) . g(x, y, z) \vee g(x, z, y) \vee g(z, x, y).$$

Then (a) follows from (a′) and (e′).

For (a) is logically equivalent to

$$f(x) . f(y) . g(x, y) . \supset . \sim(x = y),$$

which, when the definition of $g(x, y)$ is substituted, becomes

$$f(x) \,.\, f(y) : (\exists z) \,.\, f(z) \,.\, g(x, y, z) \vee g(x, z, y) \vee g(z, x, y) :\supset. \sim(x = y).$$

Now, by (e′), there must always be an element $z$ satisfying the existence-demand here; and, by (a′), $x$, $y$, $z$ must all be distinct.

(b) follows from (b′) and (e′).

For, when $g(x, y)$ and $g(y, x)$ in (b) are replaced in accordance with the definition, we have

$$f(x) \,.\, f(y) \,.\, \sim(x = y) \,.\supset: (\exists z) \,.\, f(z) \,.\, g(x, y, z) \vee g(x, z, y) \vee g(z, x, y) \,.\vee.\, (\exists z) \,.\, f(z) \,.\, g(y, x, z) \vee g(y, z, x) \vee g(z, y, x).$$

But, by (e′), if $x$ and $y$ are any two elements satisfying $f$, there will always be a third, $z$, and, by (b′), $g$ will hold for some one of the six permutations of $x$, $y$, $z$.

When the definition is substituted in (c), we have (c′).

When it is substituted in (d), we have

$$f(x) \,.\, f(y) \,.\, f(z) \,.\, d(x, y, z) : (\exists t) \,.\, f(t) \,.\, g(x, y, t) \vee g(x, t, y) \vee g(t, x, y) : (\exists t) \,.\, f(t) \,.\, g(y, z, t) \vee g(y, t, z) \vee g(t, y, z) :\supset. (\exists t) \,.\, f(t) \,.\, g(x, z, t) \vee g(x, t, z) \vee g(t, x, z),$$

which follows from (b′) and (c′). For these conditions imply that if $g(x, y, t) \vee g(x, t, y) \vee g(t, x, y)$ holds for some value of $t$, it holds for every value which is distinct from $x$ and $y$; and so in the other case. Hence $g(x, y, z)$ is the only possibility, so that $(\exists t) \,.\, g(x, t, z)$.

Thus we have two sets of properties, one on the base $f(x)$, $g(x, y)$ and the other on the base $f(x), g(x, y, z)$, which are such that any interpretation of the one determines uniquely a corresponding interpretation of the other, and conversely. They are equivalent sets of postulates. And since such a set is simply a compound propositional function, we have here two equivalent functions; whenever either of them has a true value, the other must have a true value also.

Two things have been shown, then, with regard to sets of postulates on different bases, namely, that (1) it is sometimes possible to define a set on a given base in terms of another on a different base where the converse possibility of definition does not exist, and that (2) it is sometimes possible to define equivalent sets on different bases. But here, when the converse definition is not possible and the sets are therefore not equivalent, we must observe carefully what exactly the logical situation is. When we define Betweenness in terms of Serial Order, the 'Betweenness' so defined is not that of the ordinary definition, because, as has been shown, there will be interpretations of the set given by the ordinary definition that are not interpretations of the one given in terms of Serial Order. This latter definition is stronger than the independent one, and therefore we have not succeeded in defining the general meaning in terms of Serial Order. The set given on the base for Serial Order may be called 'Betweenness' because all its interpretations will satisfy the definition independently given, but there will be cases of the latter kind which are not cases of the former. The relationship is that of implication rather than that of equivalence.

It is sometimes suggested that, when a set of properties is defined on a dyadic relation, we can always replace the relation employed by a truth-function constructed out of simple predicates and can formulate the set of properties on these predicates, thus avoiding the use of dyadic relations. This suggestion usually takes the following form. Suppose we have a set of properties constructed on the matrix $g(x, y)$; then we may define $g(x, y)$ in terms of two functions in one variable each, $f'(x)$ and $f''(y)$, in such a way that it will mean $f'(x) \cdot f''(y)$ and will therefore be a conjunctive function of predicates. It is important to see that no such definition is possible in general, and thus that dyadic relations cannot be analyzed as conjunctions of predicates.

The fact that such definitions cannot in general be given rests on the following property of truth-functions. Consider the doubly-general function

$$(x) : (\exists y) \cdot g(x, y),$$

and compare it with

$$(x) : (\exists y) . f'(x) . f''(y).$$

We have seen that from the first of these the function

$$(\exists y) : (x) . g(x, y)$$

does not follow, even where we have appropriate existence-conditions; but it is easy to see that, with the existence of at least one value within the range of $x$ and $y$,

$$(\exists y) : (x) . f'(x) . f''(y)$$

does follow from the second; so that the force of the first function cannot be given on $f'(x) . f''(y)$.

Consider the set of properties which was given above as defining a dense series with a first but no last element. In this definition, we have the condition

$$(x) :. (\exists y) : f(x) . \supset . f(y) . g(x, y),$$

which, together with the other conditions, is incompatible with

$$(\exists y) :. (x) : f(x) . \supset . f(y) . g(x, y).$$

And here, if $g(x, y)$ were equivalent to a truth-function of the form $f'(x) . f''(y)$, the set defining a series without a last element would be self-contradictory.

## SECTION 5. DEFINITION OF CYCLIC ORDER

We turn now to a set of properties which resembles closely the set defining Betweenness. A typical interpretation of these properties is given by the order of points on a closed curve as we proceed in an assigned direction. Take a circle, and let $a$, $b$, $c$ be any three points such that, if we start at $a$, we can proceed clockwise to $b$ and then to $c$. If $g(a, b, c)$ means that the three points stand in the relation so defined, then it will be clear that the following propositions are all true:

If $a$, $b$, $c$ are distinct points, and $g(a, b, c)$ is true, then $g(b, c, a)$ will be true.

If $a$, $b$, $c$ are distinct points, then for at least one permutation of $a$, $b$, and $c$, $g$ will hold.

If $a$, $b$, $c$ are distinct points, then $g(a, b, c)$ and $g(a, c, b)$ will not both be true.

If $a$, $b$, $c$ are points on the circle, and $g(a, b, c)$ is true, then they are distinct.

If $a$, $b$, $c$, $d$ are distinct points, and $g(a, b, c)$ is true, then either $g(a, b, d)$ or $g(d, b, c)$ will be true.

When the meaning here assigned to $g$ is dropped, and the notion of being a point on the circle is replaced by $f(x)$, we have the following set of functions on the base $f(x), g(x_1, x_2, x_3)$:

(1) $f(x_1) . f(x_2) . f(x_3) . d(x_1, x_2, x_3) . g(x_1, x_2, x_3) . \supset . g(x_2, x_3, x_1)$.

(2) $f(x_1) . f(x_2) . f(x_3) . d(x_1, x_2, x_3) . \supset .$
$g(x_1, x_2, x_3) \vee g(x_2, x_3, x_1) \vee g(x_3, x_1, x_2) \vee$
$g(x_3, x_2, x_1) \vee g(x_2, x_1, x_3) \vee g(x_1, x_3, x_2)$.

(3) $f(x_1) . f(x_2) . f(x_3) . d(x_1, x_2, x_3) . \supset .$
$\sim g(x_1, x_2, x_3) \vee \sim g(x_1, x_3, x_2)$.

(4) $f(x_1) . f(x_2) . f(x_3) . g(x_1, x_2, x_3) . \supset . d(x_1, x_2, x_3)$.

(5) $f(x_1) . f(x_2) . f(x_3) . f(x_4) . d(x_1, x_2, x_3, x_4) . g(x_1, x_2, x_3) . \supset .$
$g(x_1, x_2, x_4) \vee g(x_4, x_2, x_3)$.

We shall take this set of postulates as defining Cyclic Order. Whether it does in fact (if we add an existence-condition) involve all that is essential to the ordinary notion of directed order on a closed curve is a question which we are not now in a position to answer; we shall show in the next chapter that it does, but we must here simply assume the proofs there given, or, perhaps better, take the definition of Cyclic Order as merely verbal, the connotation of this term being arbitrarily assigned.

In order to bring out the import of properties (1)–(5), we may consider the following examples, each of which satisfies all five conditions:

Let $f(x)$ mean "$x$ is a number on the face of a clock" and $g(x_1, x_2, x_3)$ mean "The hour-hand moves from $x_1$ to $x_2$ and then to $x_3$, without passing through $x_1$."

Take a square with vertices $a$, $b$, $c$, $d$, and let $f(x)$ mean "$x$ is $a$, $b$, $c$, or $d$" and $g(x_1, x_2, x_3)$ mean "$x_1$, $x_2$, $x_3$ are vertices in clockwise order."

Let $f(x)$ mean "$x$ is one of the natural numbers, 1, 2, 3, ..." and let $g(x_1, x_2, x_3)$ mean "$x_1 < x_2 < x_3$ or $x_2 < x_3 < x_1$ or $x_3 < x_1 < x_2$." Note that this example satisfies condition (1) by definition, since, in accordance with the interpretation, $g(x_1, x_2, x_3)$, $g(x_2, x_3, x_1)$, and $g(x_3, x_1, x_2)$ all have the same meaning. Of course, the basic relation, $x_1 < x_2 < x_3$, of which $g$ is a disjunctive function, does not satisfy this condition; but it will be seen that the four remaining conditions are satisfied when $g(x_1, x_2, x_3)$ is interpreted to mean $x_1 < x_2 < x_3$, and thus that condition (1) differentiates Cyclic from Serial Order.

To see that properties (1)–(5) are independent, we may consider the following examples, the first of which fails on (1), the second on (2), etc.:

Let $f(x)$ mean "$x$ is a natural number," and let $g(x_1, x_2, x_3)$ mean $x_1 < x_2 < x_3$.

Let $f(x)$ mean "$x$ is a natural number" and $g(x_1, x_2, x_3)$ mean "$x_1 < x_2 < x_3$ and $x_3 < x_2 < x_1$." Here $g(x_1, x_2, x_3)$ never holds, so that condition (2) is falsified; (3) holds, of course, owing to the fact that $\sim g(x_1, x_2, x_3)$ is always true, and the remaining conditions are satisfied because their hypotheses are never fulfilled.

Let $f(x)$ mean "$x$ is a thing," and let $g(x_1, x_2, x_3)$ mean "$x_1$, $x_2$, and $x_3$ are all distinct."

Let $f(x)$ mean "$x$ is one of the numbers 1, 2, 3, 4," and let $g(x_1, x_2, x_3)$ mean "$x_1 \leqq x_2 \leqq x_3$ or $x_2 \leqq x_3 \leqq x_1$ or $x_3 \leqq x_1 \leqq x_2$." Here we have, for example, $g(2, 1, 1)$ holding, which falsifies condition (4); and (3) holds, owing to the fact that its hypothesis requires that $x_1$, $x_2$, and $x_3$ shall all be distinct.

Let $f(x)$ mean "$x$ is one of the letters $a$, $b$, $c$, $d$" and $g(x_1, x_2, x_3)$ mean "The ordered triad $x_1x_2x_3$ occurs in the following list: *abc*, *cab*, *bca*, *acd*, *dac*, *cda*, *bdc*, *cbd*, *dcb*, *dba*, *adb*, *bad*." Here conditions (1)–(4) are seen to be satisfied; but we have $g(a, b, c)$ together with both $\sim g(a, b, d)$ and $\sim g(d, b, c)$.

We shall now show that the following two properties are logical consequences of the definition of Cyclic Order.

(6) $f(x_1) \cdot f(x_2) \cdot f(x_3) \cdot f(x_4) \cdot d(x_1, x_2, x_3, x_4) \cdot$
$g(x_1, x_2, x_4) \cdot g(x_2, x_3, x_4) \cdot \supset \cdot g(x_1, x_2, x_3)$.

We have, by (1), $g(x_4, x_2, x_3)$ from $g(x_2, x_3, x_4)$; and we have from $g(x_1, x_2, x_4)$ either $g(x_1, x_2, x_3)$ or $g(x_3, x_2, x_4)$; but if we have the latter, then $g(x_4, x_3, x_2)$ holds, contrary to $g(x_4, x_2, x_3)$.

$$(7)\ f(x_1) \,.\, f(x_2) \,.\, f(x_3) \,.\, f(x_4) \,.\, d(x_1, x_2, x_3, x_4) \,. \\ g(x_1, x_2, x_4) \,.\, g(x_2, x_3, x_4) \,.\!\supset\!.\, g(x_1, x_3, x_4).$$

We have, by (1), $g(x_2, x_4, x_1)$ from $g(x_1, x_2, x_4)$; and, by (5), $g(x_2, x_4, x_1)$ implies $g(x_2, x_4, x_3)$ or $g(x_3, x_4, x_1)$. But $g(x_2, x_4, x_3)$ is incompatible with $g(x_2, x_3, x_4)$, by (3); so that we have $g(x_3, x_4, x_1)$, which implies $g(x_1, x_3, x_4)$.

To see that (6) can replace (5) in the definition of Cyclic Order, it will now be sufficient to see that (5) follows from (1)–(4) together with (6). We wish to show that if $g(x_1, x_2, x_3)$ holds, then we have either $g(x_1, x_2, x_4)$ or $g(x_4, x_2, x_3)$. From $g(x_1, x_2, x_3)$ we have, by (1), $g(x_2, x_3, x_1)$; and, by (1) and (2), we have either $g(x_1, x_2, x_4)$ or $g(x_4, x_2, x_1)$. But, by (6), from $g(x_4, x_2, x_1)$ and $g(x_2, x_3, x_1)$, we have $g(x_4, x_2, x_3)$; so that $g(x_1, x_2, x_4)$ or $g(x_4, x_2, x_3)$ must hold.

In order to see that (7) can replace (5), we must show that (5) follows from (1)–(4) together with (7). By (1), we have $g(x_3, x_1, x_2)$ from $g(x_1, x_2, x_3)$; and, by (1) and (2), either $g(x_1, x_2, x_4)$ or $g(x_1, x_4, x_2)$ must hold. But, by (7), from $g(x_3, x_1, x_2)$ and $g(x_1, x_4, x_2)$ we have $g(x_3, x_4, x_2)$, and hence, by (1), $g(x_4, x_2, x_3)$; so that either $g(x_1, x_2, x_4)$ or $g(x_4, x_2, x_3)$ must hold.

We have, then, three sets of postulates defining Cyclic Order, namely, (1)–(4),(5), (1)–(4),(6), and (1)–(4),(7).[11] And it has been shown that the first is made up of independent conditions. The following five examples show that the second set is also an independent one, the first example failing on (1) and satisfying all the other conditions, the second failing on (2), etc.:

Take a straight line running from left to right, and let $f(x)$ mean "$x$ is a point on the line" and $g(x_1, x_2, x_3)$ mean "$x_1$, $x_2$, and $x_3$ are in the order $x_1x_2x_3$ from left to right." Here, if

[11] These sets are due to Huntington. See *Proc. Nat. Acad. Sci.*, X (1924), 74.

$g(x_1, x_2, x_3)$ holds, we have always $\sim g(x_2, x_3, x_1)$, contrary to condition (1).

Let $f(x)$ mean "$x$ is a number," and let $g(x_1, x_2, x_3)$ mean $(x_1 = x_2 = x_3) \cdot \sim(x_1 = x_2 = x_3)$.

Let $f(x)$ mean "$x$ is a number" and $g(x_1, x_2, x_3)$ mean "$x_1$, $x_2$, and $x_3$ are all distinct."

Take a circle, and let $f(x)$ mean "$x$ is a point on the circle," and let $g(x_1, x_2, x_3)$ mean "either $x_1$, $x_2$, and $x_3$ are in the order $x_1x_2x_3$, clockwise, or $x_2$ is identical with $x_3$."

Let $f(x)$ mean "$x$ is $a$, $b$, $c$, or $d$," and let $g(x_1, x_2, x_3)$ mean "$x_1x_2x_3$ is one of the following ordered triads: *cba, bac, acb; abd, bda, dab; dca, cad, adc; bcd, cdb, dbc*." Here we have both $g(a, b, d)$ and $g(b, c, d)$, but not $g(a, b, c)$, contrary to condition (6).

With regard to the independence of postulates (1)–(4),(7), it will be seen that we can use the five examples just given; the first example fails on (1) and satisfies the other conditions, the second fails on (2), etc. In the case of condition (7), which fails on the last example, we have $g(a, b, d)$ and $g(b, c, d)$ together with $\sim g(a, c, d)$.

We may now consider a set of four properties which exhibit the structure of Cyclic Order in more explicit form than do the foregoing sets. In order to formulate these properties briefly, we shall require some preliminary definitions. First, let $R(x_1, x_2, x_3)$ mean that

$$g(x_1, x_2, x_3), \quad g(x_2, x_3, x_1), \quad g(x_3, x_1, x_2)$$

hold, and that $g$ fails for each of the three remaining permutations of these variables. Second, let $R(x_1, x_2, x_3, x_4)$ mean

$$R(x_1, x_2, x_3) \cdot R(x_1, x_2, x_4) \cdot R(x_1, x_3, x_4) \cdot R(x_2, x_3, x_4).$$

And finally, consider the twenty-four permutations of the variables $x_1, x_2, x_3, x_4$, and form the disjunctive function

$$R(x_1, x_2, x_3, x_4) \vee R(x_4, x_1, x_2, x_3) \vee \ldots,$$

which involves all these permutations, and which may be written $S(x_1, x_2, x_3, x_4)$.

Then it will be clear that the following four properties all characterize any system of Cyclic Order:

(A) $f(x) \supset \sim g(x, x, x)$.

(B) $f(x_1) . f(x_2) . \sim(x_1 = x_2) . \supset . \sim g(x_1, x_1, x_2) . \sim g(x_1, x_2, x_1) . \sim g(x_2, x_1, x_1)$.

(C) $f(x_1) . f(x_2) . f(x_3) . d(x_1, x_2, x_3) . \supset . R(x_1, x_2, x_3) \vee R(x_3, x_2, x_1)$.

(D) $f(x_1) . f(x_2) . f(x_3) . f(x_4) . d(x_1, x_2, x_3, x_4) . \supset . S(x_1, x_2, x_3, x_4)$.

It will be seen that if there are not exactly three elements satisfying $f$, (C) becomes redundant with (D) and follows from it. For if there are less than three elements, (C) is satisfied vacuously, and if there are at least four, (C) follows in accordance with the definition of $S$. Thus, if we add the condition

(E) $(\exists x_1, x_2, x_3, x_4) . f(x_1) . f(x_2) . f(x_3) . f(x_4) . d(x_1, x_2, x_3, x_4)$,

(C) may be discarded from the set without loss of logical force.

It will be seen, too, that conditions (A)–(D) imply and are implied by (1)–(5). Conditions (1), (2), and (3) follow immediately from (C); (4) follows from (A) and (B), while (5) follows from (D). Conversely, (A) and (B) follow from (4); (C) follows from (1), (2), and (3); and (D) follows from (1), (2), (3), and (5).

## Section 6. Separation of Point-Pairs

We turn now to a type of order which, like the type just examined, is best exemplified by the class of points on a closed curve. In the case of Cyclic Order, however, we had to do with 'direction' on a closed curve, whereas here we are concerned with order irrespective of direction. Consider four points on a circle, $a, b, c, d$, which occur in the order mentioned. If we take any three of these points, say $a, b, c$, we can go from $a$ to $c$ without passing through $b$, and, in fact, from any one to any other without passing through the third, provided it is permissible to choose the direction of movement; but if we take all four points, then it is impossible to go from $a$ to $c$ without passing either through $b$ or through $d$. When this is so, $a$ and $c$ are said to be separated by $b$ and $d$. And it will be clear that the following properties, having to do with this relation of separation, are all true of tetrads of points on a circle:

If $x_1$, $x_2$, $x_3$, $x_4$ are points on the circle and if $x_1$ and $x_3$ are separated by $x_2$ and $x_4$, then the points are all distinct.

If $x_1$, $x_2$, $x_3$, $x_4$ are distinct points, then at least one of them is separated from at least one of the others by the remaining pair.

If $x_1$, $x_2$, $x_3$, $x_4$ are points on the circle, and if $x_1$ is separated from $x_3$ by $x_2$ and $x_4$, then $x_2$ is separated from $x_4$ by $x_3$ and $x_1$.

If $x_1$, $x_2$, $x_3$, $x_4$ are points on the circle, and if $x_1$ is separated from $x_3$ by $x_2$ and $x_4$, then $x_4$ is separated from $x_2$ by $x_3$ and $x_1$.

If $x_1$, $x_2$, $x_3$, $x_4$ are points on the circle, and if $x_1$ is separated from $x_3$ by $x_2$ and $x_4$, then $x_1$ is not separated from $x_4$ by $x_2$ and $x_3$.

If $x_1$, $x_2$, $x_3$, $x_4$, $x_5$ are distinct points, and if $x_1$ is separated from $x_3$ by $x_2$ and $x_4$, then $x_1$ is separated from $x_3$ by $x_5$ and $x_4$ or by $x_2$ and $x_5$.

Let us represent by $P(g, x_1, x_2, x_3, x_4)$ the assertion that $g$ holds for at least one permutation of $x_1$, $x_2$, $x_3$, $x_4$. Then the example just given will be seen to be an interpretation of the following properties, which define Separation of Point-Pairs:[12]

$(x_1, x_2, x_3, x_4, x_5) :. f(x_1) . f(x_2) . f(x_3) . f(x_4) . f(x_5) . \supset :$

(1) $g(x_1, x_2, x_3, x_4) . \supset . d(x_1, x_2, x_3, x_4) :$

(2) $d(x_1, x_2, x_3, x_4) . \supset . P(g, x_1, x_2, x_3, x_4) :$

(3) $g(x_1, x_2, x_3, x_4) . d(x_1, x_2, x_3, x_4) . \supset . g(x_2, x_3, x_4, x_1) :$

(4) $g(x_1, x_2, x_3, x_4) . d(x_1, x_2, x_3, x_4) . \supset . g(x_4, x_3, x_2, x_1) :$

(5) $g(x_1, x_2, x_3, x_4) . d(x_1, x_2, x_3, x_4) . \supset . \sim g(x_1, x_2, x_4, x_3) :$

(6) $g(x_1, x_2, x_3, x_4) . d(x_1, x_2, x_3, x_4, x_5) . \supset .$
$g(x_1, x_5, x_3, x_4) \vee g(x_1, x_2, x_3, x_5).$

As in the case of the other sets of postulates dealt with, we shall not try to prove here that these six properties are in fact a sufficient characterization of what would commonly be understood by reversible order on a closed line. It is evident that they are all necessary, in the sense that they must be present either explicitly or by implication in any adequate definition; and we shall show in the next chapter that they are also sufficient.

[12] This definition is due to Huntington. See *Proc. Nat. Acad. Sci.*, XI (1925), 687, and also *Proc. Amer. Acad. Arts and Sci.*, LXVII (1932), 61.

Here, however, they will be taken as defining Separation of Point-Pairs in a merely verbal sense.

The following interpretations show that the six properties are independent, the first example failing on (1), the second on (2), etc.:

Let $f(x)$ mean "$x$ is $a$, $b$, $c$, or $d$," and let $g(x_1, x_2, x_3, x_4)$ mean "$x_1x_2x_3x_4$ is one of the following ordered tetrads: *aaaa, abcd, bcda, cdab, dabc, dcba, adcb, badc, cbad.*"

With the same meaning for $f(x)$, let $g(x_1, x_2, x_3, x_4)$ mean "$x_1x_2x_3x_4$ is a member of the null class of ordered tetrads constructed out of the letters $a$, $b$, $c$, $d$."

Let $g(x_1, x_2, x_3, x_4)$ mean "$x_1x_2x_3x_4$ is either *abcd* or *dcba*."

Let $g(x_1, x_2, x_3, x_4)$ mean "$x_1x_2x_3x_4$ is one of the tetrads *abcd, bcda, cdab, dabc.*"

Let $g(x_1, x_2, x_3, x_4)$ mean "$x_1x_2x_3x_4$ is one of the ordered tetrads *abcd, bcda, cdab, dabc; dcba, adcb, badc, cbad; abdc, bdca, dcab, cabd; cdba, acdb, bacd, dbac.*"

Let $Q(x_1, x_2, x_3, x_4)$ mean $x_1x_2x_3x_4$, $x_2x_3x_4x_1$, $x_3x_4x_1x_2$, $x_4x_1x_2x_3$; $x_4x_3x_2x_1$, $x_1x_4x_3x_2$, $x_2x_1x_4x_3$, $x_3x_2x_1x_4$. Then let $f(x)$ mean "$x$ is $a$, $b$, $c$, $d$, or $e$" and $g(x_1, x_2, x_3, x_4)$ mean "$x_1x_2x_3x_4$ is one of the ordered tetrads $Q(a, b, c, d)$, $Q(a, b, d, e)$, $Q(a, c, d, e)$, $Q(b, c, d, e)$, $Q(a, b, e, c)$." Here we have $g(a, b, c, d)$ with both $\sim g(a, e, c, d)$ and $\sim g(a, b, c, e)$, so that (6) fails.

We may, of course, add further properties to the set (1)–(6), and thus determine more specific types of order, which involve the general properties of Separation of Point-Pairs. Let us consider, for example, the two further conditions:

(7) $(\exists x_1, x_2) \,.\, f(x_1) \,.\, f(x_2) \,.\, \sim(x_1 = x_2)$.

(8) $(x_1, x_3) :. (\exists x_2, x_4) : f(x_1) \,.\, f(x_3) \,.\, \sim(x_1 = x_2) \,.\supset.$
$f(x_2) \,.\, f(x_4) \,.\, g(x_1, x_2, x_3, x_4)$.

It can be shown that, in any true interpretation of conditions (1)–(8), there must be more than a finite number of elements belonging to the class determined by $f(x)$:

We show, in the first place, that if a set of $n$ elements fails to satisfy condition (8), then a set of $n + 1$ must fail. Suppose that there are $n$ elements $(n \geqq 4)$ in the class determined by

$f(x)$, such that two of them, $a$, $b$, are not separated by any pair of the remaining $n - 2$ elements. Then, by (8), there must exist $x$, $y$ such that $g(a, x, b, y)$ will hold, where at least one of the two, $x$ or $y$, cannot be among the original $n$ elements. But if $z$ is any one of the original elements other than $a$ and $b$, and neither $x$ nor $y$ is an original element, then we have, by (6), $g(a, z, b, y)$ or $g(a, x, b, z)$; and this shows that if the introduction of two further elements will effect a separation between $a$ and $b$, the introduction of one will; so that we may confine attention to the addition of a single element. And here we may assume $g(a, x, b, z)$ to the exclusion of $g(a, z, b, y)$ without loss of generality, since $g(a, z, b, y)$ implies $g(z, b, y, a)$, which implies $g(a, y, b, z)$. Now, with the addition of $x$, we have $n + 1$ elements satisfying $f$; but it can be seen that $a$ and $x$ are not separated by any pair. For $g(a, x, b, z)$ implies $\sim g(a, b, x, z)$, where $z$ is any one of the original $n$ elements other than $a$ and $b$. And if $g(a, z', x, z'')$ holds, where $z'$ and $z''$ are any of the original elements other than $a$ and $b$, then, by (6), $g(a, b, x, z'')$ or $g(a, z', x, b)$ will hold. But $g(a, b, x, z'')$ implies $g(z'', a, b, x)$, while $g(a, x, b, z)$ implies $g(z, a, x, b)$, and these are incompatible, by (5); whereas $g(a, z', x, b)$ is contrary to $g(a, x, b, z)$, since the latter implies $g(a, z, b, x)$. So, if a set of $n$ elements will not satisfy condition (8), a set of $n + 1$ will not; and it is easy to see that four elements will not satisfy the condition.

That properties (1)–(8) constitute a self-consistent set may be seen from the following example:

Take a circle, and let $f(x)$ mean "$x$ is one of its points" and $g(x_1, x_2, x_3, x_4)$ mean "$x_1$ is separated from $x_3$ by $x_2$ and $x_4$."

Here there are an infinite number of elements satisfying $f$, and (8) holds. In the next example, on the other hand, we have only a finite number of elements, and (8) fails, while (1)–(7) are satisfied:

Take a square with vertices $a$, $b$, $c$, $d$, and let $f(x)$ mean "$x$ is a vertex of the square" and $g(x_1, x_2, x_3, x_4)$ mean "$x_1$ is separated from $x_3$ by $x_2$ and $x_4$."

The cycle determined by conditions (1)–(8) is 'dense'; but we can determine a 'discrete' cycle by replacing (8) by the following condition:

$$(8')\quad (x_1) :: (\exists x_3) :. f(x_1) . \supset : f(x_3) . \sim(x_1 = x_3) :$$
$$\sim(\exists x_2, x_4) . f(x_2) . f(x_4) . g(x_1, x_2, x_3, x_4).$$

That is, for each element belonging to the class determined by $f$, there exists another not separated from it by any pair. Conditions (1)–(7),(8′) will be satisfied by the example just given concerning the vertices of a square. But here, too, there may be an interpretation involving an infinite number of elements, as may be seen from the following example:

Take a circle and a point $a$ on it; then move half-way round the circle and determine another point $a_1$; then half of the remaining distance and determine another, $a_2$, etc. Let $f(x)$ mean "$x$ is one of the points so determined" and $g(x_1, x_2, x_3, x_4)$ mean "$x_1$ is separated from $x_3$ by $x_2$ and $x_4$."

# CHAPTER XII

## POSTULATIONAL TECHNIQUE: DEDUCIBILITY

### Section 1. Introduction

We are going to consider in this chapter a problem which, because of its difficulty and complexity, was omitted from the preceding chapter. It was there shown how certain properties were deducible from given premises, and how certain others were incompatible with such premises, this being done by actual deduction of the properties in question, or by deduction of their contradictories. Here, on the other hand, we propose to deal with the logical consequences of a set of premises in another and more general way. We shall write down a set of conditions and then define, in connection with the set, an infinite class of properties, with a view to showing that each member of this infinite class is logically dependent upon the set in question, in the sense that either it or its contradictory is a logical consequence of the set. That is to say, if $\alpha$ is a class of properties, of which $p$ is a member, and $S$ is a set of properties, then we shall show, in certain particular cases, that $p$ always has its truth-value determined by $S$, or, in other words, is not independent of $S$.

The problem here described is a general one, of which that of completeness or categoricalness is a special case; and we may, to begin with, consider this special case somewhat in detail, in order to show how it is related to the general problem. We have seen how the completeness of a set $S$ on a base $B$ is to be defined. We consider the class of all functions that can be constructed on the base $B$, and we find that, in general, these properties fall into three classes, namely, those which follow from $S$, those whose contradictories follow from $S$, and those such that neither they nor their contradictories follow. And $S$ is said to be complete when and only when this third class is null. We have seen also that this definition really contains an ambiguity, owing to the fact that there are two senses in which the term ‘ base ’ may be properly used. Thus, suppose we have a set of functions involving only the free variables $f$ and $g$, which occur in the matrices $f(x)$ and $g(x, y)$. It still remains possible that there should be some other matrix, $h(x, y)$ say, which is a constituent of one or more of the functions, and in which $h$, $x$, and $y$ are all generalized. In one sense, we say that the base of a set is all those free variables that occur in it, and that therefore, even where the matrix $h(x, y)$ occurs, a set may be on the base $f$, $g$, since these may be the only free variables. In another sense, we say that a set is on the base $f(x), g(x, y)$ when no matrices other than such as are constructed out of these two by the use of logical constants occur in the functions of the set, and $f$, $g$ are the only free variables. We shall be confined, in the present chapter, to this second sense of the term 'base,' not because the other sense is an unimportant one, but because all the theorems on deducibility which we shall wish to prove are relative to sets on given bases in this second and narrower sense.

In order to be quite specific, let us take the set (a)–(d), as given above, which was constructed on the base $f(x), g(x, y)$ and used in defining Serial Order. There will be a class of theorems following from this set, each of which will be on the base of the set; and, of course, each of the theorems will have a contradictory on this same base. Then there will be other functions, like $(\exists x) . f(x)$ and $(x, y) . g(x, y) \vee g(y, x)$, which are such that neither they nor their contradictories are logical consequences of the set in question. As has been pointed out, any function belonging to this third group can be added to the set (a)–(d) without contradiction, and when any such function is added, the set will be stronger than it was before, in the sense of having a wider class of logical consequences; although, in such a case, the members of the set may no longer be independent of one another. As more and more conditions are added to the list, the group of logical consequences and their contradictories will become wider and wider, while the class of functions on $f(x), g(x, y)$ which are independent of (a)–(d) will become correspondingly narrower, until finally these independent functions will vanish altogether; and when this occurs, the set (a)–(d), together with all those functions which have been subjoined to it, will be a categorical one, and will be such that, upon the addition of any other function on the same base, there will arise either redundancy or incompatibility.

It must not be supposed that completeness in a set of properties is always a desideratum; indeed, in many cases, it is precisely the point that a set constitutes a generic rather than a specific definition. Thus, in the case of the set (a)–(d), we have a definition of a type of order in general, as against relatively specific sorts, such as dense series, inductive and non-inductive discrete series, dense series with one extreme element, those with both, etc.; and this generic definition enables us to see what these more determinate types of order have in common, and to deal with these common properties all at once. To insist always upon completeness would be like insisting that a geometer be not permitted to prove properties holding for triangles in general (such, for instance, as that the sum of the angles of any triangle is 180°), but must argue only with regard to triangles of some absolutely specific sort.

But, now, even where a set does not imply one or the other of every pair of mutually contradictory functions that can be constructed on its base, and is therefore not categorical, it may still be such as to determine the truth-value of every function belonging to some more restricted class. Let us take the set of functions (a)–(d), with a view to determining its precise logical force in this respect:

(a) $(x) . f(x) \supset {\sim}g(x, x)$.

(b) $(x, y) : f(x) . f(y) . {\sim}(x = y) . \supset . g(x, y) \vee g(y, x)$.

(c) $(x, y) : f(x) . f(y) . {\sim}(x = y) . \supset . {\sim}g(x, y) \vee {\sim}g(y, x)$.

(d) $(x, y, z) : f(x) . f(y) . f(z) . d(x, y, z) . g(x, y) . g(y, z) . \supset . g(x, z)$.[1]

Each function of this set is both singly general and universal. And we have seen that no existential function can be a logical consequence of a set made up wholly of universals, and also that many doubly-general functions, such as $(x) :. (\exists y) :$

[1] For purposes of abbreviation, we are using $d(x, y, z)$ to mean "$x$, $y$, and $z$ are all distinct"; and so in other cases where more than two variables are involved.

$f(x) . \supset . f(y) . g(x, y)$, are independent of the set (a)–(d). We have seen, too, that no condition which places a restriction on elements not belonging to the class determined by $f(x)$ can follow from this set, inasmuch as these functions all involve in their hypotheses the requirement that the elements upon which they place restrictions shall satisfy $f$. Now, the class of all functions constructed on $f(x), g(x, y)$ can be divided into singly-general functions, like $(x, y) . g(x, y)$; doubly-general ones, like $(\exists x) : (y) . g(x, y)$; triply-general ones, etc. Each of these sub-classes can, in turn, be divided into universal functions, such as $(x) : (\exists y) . g(x, y)$ or $(x) . f(x)$, and existential functions, such as $(\exists x) : (y) . g(x, y)$ or $(\exists x) . f(x)$; and what we wish to show is that there is a sense in which conditions (a)–(d) are complete with respect to singly-general universal functions placing restrictions only upon elements belonging to the class determined by $f(x)$. The sense in question is one which enables us to say that, in constructing definitions of any type of serial order, however specific, no singly-general universal functions other than (a)–(d) can be required, and that therefore, in the formulation of such specific definitions, any condition to be added to the set (a)–(d) will be either existential or of a degree of generality higher than the first.

It will be seen that condition (a) is a function in one generalized variable which imposes restrictions only upon elements satisfying $f$. And the first question we have to answer is whether any other independent universal function in one variable which places restrictions only upon elements satisfying $f$ can be added to the list. It is easy to see that none can; for, in accordance with (a), every element $x$, which satisfies $f$, must be such that $\sim g(x, x)$ holds, and this is a completely determinate specification.

Let us see, then, whether any further independent, extensional, universal, singly-general functions in two generalized variables can be added to the list. Consider, in the first place, what must be true of any two elements $x$, $y$ which satisfy $f$, irrespective of postulational conditions: they must be such that

$$g(x, y) . g(y, x) . \vee . \sim g(x, y) . \sim g(y, x) . \vee . \\ g(x, y) . \sim g(y, x) . \vee . \sim g(x, y) . g(y, x),$$

since these alternatives include all the logical possibilities. And condition (b) requires that $x$ and $y$ shall be such that

$$g(x, y) \cdot g(y, x) . \vee . g(x, y) \cdot {\sim}g(y, x) . \vee . {\sim}g(x, y) \cdot g(y, x)$$

is true, thus eliminating the possibility ${\sim}g(x, y) \cdot {\sim}g(y, x)$; whereas condition (c) requires that $x$ and $y$ shall be such that

$${\sim}g(x, y) \cdot {\sim}g(y, x) . \vee . {\sim}g(x, y) \cdot g(y, x) . \vee . g(x, y) \cdot {\sim}g(y, x)$$

holds, thus eliminating the possibility $g(x, y) \cdot g(y, x)$; so that the two conditions together require that we have

$$g(x, y) \cdot {\sim}g(y, x) . \vee . {\sim}g(x, y) \cdot g(y, x).$$

Suppose that we tried to impose a further condition, which would eliminate one of these possibilities. We should then get a contradiction; for if we write, say, " $g(x, y) \cdot {\sim}g(y, x)$ holds for every $x$ and $y$ which satisfy $f$ " and take any two elements $x$, $y$ such that $g(x, y) \cdot {\sim}g(y, x)$ holds, we can, by interchanging $x$ and $y$, get $g(y, x) \cdot {\sim}g(x, y)$. Hence, the two conditions (b) and (c) impose all the restrictions that can be imposed upon pairs of elements satisfying $f$. And if we take this result together with the one just arrived at, we have the following theorem: No further independent universal extensional functions in not more than two generalized variables, which place restrictions only upon elements satisfying $f$, can be added to the set (a)–(d).

This result must, however, be emended in a certain respect. Consider the function that any two elements must satisfy in virtue of (b) and (c): $g(x, y) \cdot {\sim}g(y, x) . \vee . {\sim}g(x, y) \cdot g(y, x)$. If we dropped one of these alternatives, we should not, strictly speaking, get a contradiction, but should get a condition incompatible with the existence of at least two elements satisfying $f$. If every pair of distinct elements which satisfy $f$ must be such that $g(x, y) \cdot {\sim}g(y, x)$, then there cannot be two such elements. So, we shall have to say that no further independent universal extensional functions, etc., *which are compatible with the existence of at least two elements satisfying* $f$ can be added to the list.[2]

[2] The argument here is not entirely rigorous, because we have supposed that a function in two variables which can take identical values can always be analyzed into two functions, one in a single variable and the other in two variables not taking identical values. Later on we shall give proofs in exactly

Let us take, in the next place, three elements satisfying $f$ and consider the logical possibilities, without regard to postulational restrictions. Take the conjunctive function

$$g(x, y) . g(y, z) . g(x, z) . g(y, x) . g(z, y) . g(z, x),$$

together with all functions that can be derived from it by permuting the variables $x$, $y$, and $z$. Then, in the case of each of these conjunctive functions, consider the $2^6$ functions that can be derived by placing or not placing $\sim$ before each of the $g$'s. There will be, in all, $6 \times 2^6$ functions so derived; and if we take the disjunction of all these, we shall have the logical possibilities for three distinct elements. Now, any one of the alternatives of this disjunction which involves two constituents related as are $g(x, y)$ and $g(y, x)$ is excluded by (c); and any one which involves two constituents like $\sim g(x, y)$ and $\sim g(y, x)$ is excluded by (b); while any alternative involving a component of the form $g(x, y) . g(y, z) . \sim g(x, z)$ is excluded by (d). When all these alternatives have been discarded from the original disjunctive function, it will be seen that we have left the alternative

$$g(x, y) . g(y, z) . g(x, z) . \sim g(y, x) . \sim g(z, y) . \sim g(z, x)$$

together with five others of the same form that can be derived from this one by permutation of $x$, $y$, and $z$. If some further condition were added to (a)–(d), which was about any three distinct elements, and which excluded one or more of these alternatives, we should be able to show that there could not be at least three elements in the class determined by $f(x)$; and this, together with the result established above, enables us to put down the following theorem: No further independent universal singly-general functions in not more than three generalized variables, which place restrictions only upon elements satisfying $f$, and which are compatible with the existence of at least three such elements, can be added to the set (a)–(d).

We have now to extend this result, by induction, to functions involving any finite number of generalized variables. Let us

analogous cases which are more rigorous and in which this supposition is not present; but the proof as given is convincing enough, and we wish to make it as simple as possible within this limitation.

represent the function $g(x, y) \cdot g(y, z) \cdot g(x, z) \cdot \sim g(y, x) \cdot \sim g(z, y) \cdot \sim g(z, x)$ by $R(x, y, z)$, and the corresponding function in four variables by $R(x, y, z, t)$; and, in general, let us write $R(x_1, \ldots, x_n)$, where the occurrence of $x_i$, $x_j$ in the order from left to right means $g(x_i, x_j)$ and $\sim g(x_j, x_i)$. Consider $R(x_1, \ldots, x_n)$ together with all the functions that can be derived from it by permutation of $x_1, \ldots, x_n$; form the disjunction of all these functions; and let this disjunction be written $F(x_1, \ldots, x_n)$. We have already shown that any three distinct elements $x$, $y$, $z$ which satisfy $f$ are such that $F(x, y, z)$; and what we wish to show is that for every $n$ distinct elements, $x_1, \ldots, x_n$, $F(x_1, \ldots, x_n)$ holds.

Let us say that $F(x_1, \ldots, x_n)$ holds for an assigned value of $n$ ($\geqq 3$), and that $y$ is a further element satisfying $f$. In the first place, suppose $g(y, x_1)$ to hold. Then if $x_i$ is any one of the elements $x_1, \ldots, x_n$, we have, by (d) and the hypothesis, $g(y, x_i)$; and, by (c), $\sim g(x_i, y)$; so that $F(y, x_1, \ldots, x_n)$ will hold. Second, suppose $g(x_n, y)$ to hold. Then we have $g(x_i, y)$ and $\sim g(y, x_i)$; so that $F(x_1, \ldots, x_n, y)$ will hold. Finally, suppose $y$ to be such that we have both $g(x_1, y)$ and $g(y, x_n)$. In view of conditions (b), (c), (d), it will be seen that there must exist elements $x_i$, $x_j$ such that $F(x_i, y, x_j)$, and such that no element among $x_1, \ldots, x_n$ falls between $x_i$ and $x_j$. Then, if $x_h$ is any element such that $g(x_h, x_i)$ holds, we have $g(x_h, y)$, and if $x_k$ is any element such that $g(x_j, x_k)$ holds, we have $g(y, x_k)$; so that $F(x_1, \ldots, y, \ldots, x_n)$ will hold. In any case, then, $F(x_1, \ldots, x_n)$ implies $F(x_1, \ldots, x_{n+1})$, and we know the hypothesis here to be true when $n$ is 3.

Since we have $F(x_1, \ldots, x_n)$ for every $n$ distinct elements satisfying $f$, it will be easy to see that, were any further condition introduced which would exclude one or more of the alternatives in $F(x_1, \ldots, x_n)$, we should be able to show that there were not at least $n$ elements satisfying $f$; and this, together with the results previously established, enables us to write the following theorem: No further independent universal singly-general functions in $n$ generalized variables ($n \geqq 1$), which place restrictions only upon elements satisfying $f$, and which, in conjunction with (a)–(d), are compatible with the existence of at least $n$ such elements, can be added to the set (a)–(d).

In order to bring out the exact force of this theorem, we must observe that certain functions not involving a single prefix fall within its scope. We have seen that, for instance,

$$(x) . f(x) . \vee . (y) . f(y)$$

is equivalent to the singly-general function

$$(x, y) . f(x) \vee f(y),$$

and that, similarly, any function not involving a single prefix applied to a matrix is equivalent to one that does. So, in general, any function that is equivalent to a universal singly-general function placing restrictions only upon elements satisfying $f$ will have its truth-value determined by conditions (a)–(d). Thus,

$$(x) :: f(x) . \supset :. (y) : f(y) . \sim(y = x) . \supset . g(x, y) \vee g(y, x) :. \\ (z) : f(z) . \sim(z = x) . \supset . \sim g(x, z) \vee \sim g(z, x)$$

is equivalent to

$$(x, y, z) : f(x) . f(y) . f(z) . \sim(x = y) . \sim(x = z) . \supset . \\ g(x, y) \vee g(y, x) . \sim g(x, z) \vee \sim g(z, x),$$

and so falls within the scope of the theorem.[3]

## Section 2. Dense Series

We shall consider in this section several different kinds of dense series, with a view to establishing certain theorems on deducibility in connection with them. We shall, in the first place, deal with properties defining a dense series without extreme elements. It has already been shown how such a series is to be defined; to conditions (a)–(d) the following four

[3] The procedure followed in this section, as well as in Sections 3, 4, and 5, rests very largely on methods developed by Professor H. M. Sheffer in unpublished work. For studies somewhat closely related to the topic of the present chapter, see Hilbert and Ackermann, *Grundzüge der theoretischen Logik*, pp. 72 ff., with references there given, and also F. P. Ramsey, *The Foundations of Mathematics*, Ch. III. With reference to the method of Section 2, see especially Th. Skolem, "Untersuchungen über die Axiome des Klassenkalkuls," *Videnskapsselkapets Skrifter*, I Mat.-nat. Klasse (1919), No. 3.

are to be added:

(e) $(x, y) :. (\exists z) : f(x) . f(y) . g(x, y) . \supset . f(z) . g(x, z) . g(z, y).$

(f) $(x) :. (\exists y) : f(x) . \supset . f(y) . g(x, y).$

(g) $(x) :. (\exists y) : f(x) . \supset . f(y) . g(y, x).$

(h) $(\exists x, y) . f(x) . f(y) . \sim(x = y).$[4]

The first of these conditions is one to the effect that between any two elements of a series of the kind intended there shall be a third; the second condition is one to the effect that there shall be no 'last' element in the series; the third is one to the effect that there shall be no 'first'; while the fourth condition demands that there shall be at least two elements belonging to the series. And what we wish to do is to show that conditions (a)–(h) are sufficient to determine the truth-value of any extensional function, of whatever degree of generality, which can be constructed on the base $f(x)$,$g(x, y)$, and which places restrictions only upon elements satisfying $f$.

It will be easy to see that, in consequence of conditions (a)–(h), there must be more than a finite number of elements belonging to the class determined by $f(x)$. For, by (b) and (h), there are two elements $x$, $y$ such that $g(x, y)$ holds; and, by (e), there must be an element $z$ such that $g(x, z)$ and $g(z, y)$ hold; hence, by (a), $z$ cannot be identical with $x$ or with $y$; and, again, by (e), there must exist $z'$ such that $g(x, z')$ and $g(z', z)$ hold, where $z'$ will be distinct from $x$ and $z$, and also from $y$, since otherwise we should have both $g(y, z)$ and $g(z, y)$, contrary to condition (c); and so on.

Now, among all the functions on the base $f(x)$,$g(x, y)$ which place restrictions only upon elements satisfying $f$, there will be some which involve single complex prefixes applied to matrices and others which involve certain prefixes governing subordinate expressions only. But we have seen that any function of the latter kind is equivalent to some function constructed by generalization on a single matrix, if appropriate existence-conditions

[4] This last property could be weakened to $(\exists x) . f(x)$, but complications that would arise later on will be avoided if it is put in the stronger form, since the demand for a single element is not enough in the corresponding definition of a dense series having both extreme elements.

are present. So that, in virtue of the fact that there must be a non-finite number of elements in the class determined by $f(x)$, any function on $f(x), g(x, y)$ which places restrictions only upon elements satisfying $f$ will be equivalent to some function having one of the two following forms:

$$(\alpha) \quad (x_1, \ldots, x_m) :. (\exists y_1, \ldots, y_n) : \ldots \phi(x_1, \ldots, x_m; y_1, \ldots, y_n; \ldots),$$

$$(\beta) \quad (\exists x_1, \ldots, x_m) :. (y_1, \ldots, y_n) : \ldots \phi(x_1, \ldots, x_m; y_1, \ldots, y_n; \ldots).$$

And this means, of course, that if we show conditions (a)–(h) to be sufficient to determine the truth-value of any function of either of these kinds, we shall have shown, also, that they are sufficient to determine the truth-values of all these equivalent functions; so that we may confine attention in what follows to functions constructed on single matrices.

Let us suppose, now, that we have a function of one of the forms $(\alpha)$ or $(\beta)$, and that it involves only two generalized variables, $x$ and $y$. The matrix in such a case will be a truth-function of one or more of the following elementary expressions, and of nothing else:

$$f(x), f(y), g(x, y), g(y, x), g(x, x), g(y, y), (x = y).$$

And since this is so, we may consider what the initial logical possibilities are, irrespective of postulational conditions. Any elements that $x$ and $y$ may denote will be such that

$$f(x) . f(y) . g(x, y) . \sim g(y, x) . \sim g(x, x) . \sim g(y, y) . \sim(x = y)$$

holds, or such that

$$f(x) . f(y) . \sim g(x, y) . \sim g(y, x) . \sim g(x, x) . \sim g(y, y) . (x = y)$$

holds, etc. In order to get all the logical possibilities, we may form the class of all conjunctive functions like those here given which can be obtained by applying or failing to apply $\sim$ to each constituent. There will be in all $2^7$ such functions; but some of them, such as

$$f(x) . f(y) . g(x, y) . \sim g(y, x) . g(x, x) . \sim g(y, y) . (x = y),$$

will be self-contradictory, and may therefore be discarded from the collection. If we form the disjunction of all the remaining conjunctive functions, we shall have a matrix that will be satisfied by any pair of elements or any single element whatever; and all that any postulational condition can do is, in effect, to demand or reject one or more of the alternatives involved in this disjunction, which is itself a mere tautology, holding universally on logical grounds alone.

We have pointed out how any matrix can be expressed in expanded form with respect to the elementary constituents of which it is a truth-function. When this is done, the matrix becomes a disjunctive function of conjunctive functions of these constituents, where, if $p$ is any elementary constituent, either $p$ or $\sim p$ occurs in each conjunctive function. Let us take, for example, the matrix involved in condition (f), namely $f(x) . \supset . f(y) . g(x, y)$, and write $f(x) = p$, $f(y) = q$, and $g(x, y) = r$. This matrix is of the form $\sim p . \vee . q . r$, and is thus a disjunctive function of $\sim p$ and $q . r$, where in the first alternative $q$ and $r$ do not occur, and in the second $p$ does not. In order to introduce $p$ into all alternatives, we multiply the expression by $p \vee \sim p$, and obtain

$$p . \sim p . \vee . p . q . r . \vee . \sim p . \sim p . \vee . \sim p . q . r,$$

which becomes

$$p . q . r . \vee . \sim p . \vee . \sim p . q . r$$

when the self-contradictory alternative $p . \sim p$ is discarded and $\sim p . \sim p$ is replaced by $\sim p$. This expression is in expanded form with respect to $p$, since either $p$ or $\sim p$ occurs in each alternative; but it is not in expanded form with respect to $q$ and $r$. When we multiply by $q \vee \sim q$, we have

$$p . q . r . \vee . \sim p . q . \vee . \sim p . q . r . \vee . \sim p . \sim q,$$

which involves either $q$ or $\sim q$ in each conjunctive function; and when this latter is multiplied by $r \vee \sim r$, we have

$$p . q . r . \vee . \sim p . q . r . \vee . \sim p . \sim q . r . \vee . \sim p . q . \sim r . \vee . \sim p . \sim q . \sim r.$$

If, now, $p$, $q$, and $r$ are replaced by what they stand for, we have

$$f(x) . f(y) . g(x, y) . \vee . \sim f(x) . f(y) . g(x, y) . \vee . \sim f(x) . \sim f(y) . g(x, y) . \vee . \sim f(x) . f(y) . \sim g(x, y) . \vee . \sim f(x) . \sim f(y) . \sim g(x, y),$$

which is expanded with respect to $f(x)$, $f(y)$, and $g(x, y)$. Of course, we can go on to expand with respect to $g(y, x)$, $g(x, x)$, $g(y, y)$, and $(x = y)$. When this is done, we shall say that the matrix is in expanded form with respect to $f$, $g$, $x$, $y$, and $=$. And it will be clear that, in general, we can expand a matrix involving the variables $x_1, \ldots, x_r$ with respect to $f, g, x_1, \ldots, x_r$, and $=$, or with respect to any selection of the functions that can be constructed out of these constituents.

Although it is not strictly necessary to our argument, it will be conducive to clarity, and perhaps also of some intrinsic interest, if we show to begin with how conditions (a)–(h) determine the truth-value of every singly-general function placing restrictions only upon elements satisfying $f$ which can be constructed on the base $f(x), g(x, y)$. Any singly-general function has either the form $(x_1, \ldots, x_n) . \phi(x_1, \ldots, x_n)$ or the form $(\exists x_1, \ldots, x_n) . \phi(x_1, \ldots, x_n)$. And we have seen that there is a sense in which any function of the first of these two kinds has its truth-value determined by conditions (a)–(h). But this is a special sense, and, in any case, the argument does not cover existential functions; so we shall begin anew and consider both kinds of functions, existential and universal.

Let us take the following function of the $n$ variables $x_1, \ldots, x_n$:

$$\begin{aligned} &g(x_1, x_2) . g(x_1, x_3) . g(x_2, x_3) \ldots g(x_{n-1}, x_n) : \\ &\sim g(x_2, x_1) . \sim g(x_3, x_1) . \sim g(x_3, x_2) \ldots \sim g(x_n, x_{n-1}) : \\ &\sim g(x_1, x_1) . \sim g(x_2, x_2) \ldots \sim g(x_n, x_n) : \\ &\sim(x_1 = x_2) . \sim(x_1 = x_3) . \sim(x_2 = x_3) \ldots \sim(x_{n-1} = x_n), \end{aligned}$$

which, in the case of two variables, reduces to $g(x_1, x_2) . \sim g(x_2, x_1) . \sim g(x_1, x_1) . \sim g(x_2, x_2) . \sim(x_1 = x_2)$, and, in the case of one variable, to $\sim g(x_1, x_1)$. We may form the class made up of this function together with all those that can be derived from it by permutation of the variables $x_1, \ldots, x_n$, and call the class so determined $C$. There will be $n!$ conjunctive functions belonging to $C$, and in each of these functions we shall have, for any two variables $x_i$, $x_j$, the condition $\sim(x_i = x_j)$. Consider now the class of conjunctive functions which can be obtained by replacing each member of $C$ by a set of functions derived in the following way. Take each member of $C$, and derive all those functions that can be got by removing or not removing $\sim$ from before the constitutents of the conjunction of the form $(x_i = x_j)$. To each member of $C$ there will correspond $2^{\frac{n(n-1)}{2}}$ functions; and thus we shall have, in all, $n! \times 2^{\frac{n(n-1)}{2}}$ conjunctive functions in the class so derived, which we may call $C'$. We may now derive a class $C''$, having the same number of members, in the following way. Whenever a member of $C'$ involves a constituent $(x_i = x_j)$ without $\sim$ before it, and involves also $g(x_i, x_j)$ without $\sim$, then this latter is to be replaced by $\sim g(x_i, x_j)$. Some of the members of $C''$ will, of course, be self-contradictory, in that they will contain constituents like $(x_1 = x_2) \,.\, (x_2 = x_3) \,.\, \sim(x_1 = x_3)$, or an expression like $g(x_1, x_2) \,.\, \sim g(x_1, x_3)$ together with $(x_2 = x_3)$; others will be logically equivalent; and we may discard all self-contradictory functions from $C''$, and all but one of each group of equivalent functions, and call the class that remains $C'''$. Let us form, finally, the disjunction of all the members of $C'''$, and denote this disjunction by $S(x_1, \ldots, x_n)$.

Consider the function

(A) $\qquad (x_1, \ldots, x_n) : f(x_1) \ldots f(x_n) \,.\supset .\, S(x_1, \ldots, x_n),$

which, in virtue of the hypothesis, places restrictions only upon elements belonging to the class determined by $f(x)$. It will be seen by reference to the argument of the first section, where we were concerned with deducibility in connection with universal functions only, that conditions (a)–(d) imply the function here given for each value of $n$ ($n \geqq 1$ and finite). It will be seen, also, that any universal singly-general function placing restrictions only upon elements satisfying $f$ can be expressed by

(B) $\qquad (x_1, \ldots, x_n) : f(x_1) \ldots f(x_n) \,.\supset .\, F(x_1, \ldots, x_n),$

the matrix $F$ being in expanded form with respect to $g, x_1, \ldots, x_n$, and $=$. Now, if $F$ involves as an alternative each conjunctive function that occurs in the matrix $S$, then (B) will be implied by (A), and therefore by conditions (a)–(d); if some alternative belonging to $S$ does not occur in $F$, then (B) will, as we have seen, be incompatible with the existence of at least $n$ elements which satisfy $f$; and since we have shown that (a)–(h) imply the existence of a non-finite number of such elements, (B) will be incompatible with these conditions. This shows that conditions (a)–(h) determine the truth-value of every universal singly-general function placing restrictions only upon elements satisfying $f$ which can be constructed on the base $f(x), g(x, y)$, and really completes our argument. For an existential function is always the contradictory of some universal; and if the truth-value of a function is determined, the truth-value of its contradictory is, of course, also determined. Thus, the contradictory of (B) is

$$(\exists x_1, \ldots, x_n) \cdot f(x_1) \ldots f(x_n) \cdot \sim F(x_1, \ldots, x_n).$$[5]

And if we have, say,

$$(\exists x, y) \cdot f(x) \cdot f(y) \cdot \sim(x = y),$$

which does not contain $g$, we can expand the matrix $\sim(x = y)$ with respect to $g(x, y)$, $g(y, x)$, $g(x, x)$, and $g(y, y)$, and so derive an equivalent expression of the form

$$(\exists x, y) \cdot f(x) \cdot f(y) \cdot G(x, y),$$

whose contradictory will be of the form

$$(x, y) : f(x) \cdot f(y) \cdot \supset \cdot \sim G(x, y).$$

Here $\sim G(x, y)$ will lack many alternatives which occur in $S(x, y)$, and the function will, of course, be incompatible with the existence of at least two elements which satisfy $f$.

We may now return to our general theorem, which is to the effect that every extensional function, singly or multiply general,

[5] Note that the negative of the matrix $F$ will be the disjunction of all those and only those conjunctive functions constructed out of $g, x_1, \ldots, x_n$, and $=$ which do not occur in $F$.

which can be constructed on the base $f(x), g(x, y)$, and which places restrictions only upon elements satisfying $f$, either follows from conditions (a)–(h) or is incompatible with these conditions.

Just as we can express any singly-general function constructed on the base $f(x), g(x, y)$ which restricts only elements satisfying $f$ in the form (B) or that of its contradictory, so we can express any doubly-general function of the kind in question in the form

$$(x_1, \ldots, x_m) :. (\exists y_1, \ldots, y_n) : f(x_1) \ldots f(x_m) . \supset . \\ f(y_1) \ldots f(y_n) . F(x_1, \ldots, x_m; y_1, \ldots, y_n)$$

or the form

$$(\exists x_1, \ldots, x_m) :. (y_1, \ldots, y_n) : f(y_1) \ldots f(y_n) . \supset . \\ f(x_1) \ldots f(x_m) . F(x_1, \ldots, x_m; y_1, \ldots, y_n);$$

and, in general, it will be clear that any function, of whatever degree of generality, can be expressed in one of the forms

$$(\alpha') \quad (x_1, \ldots, x_m) :: (\exists y_1, \ldots, y_n) : \ldots : f(x_1) \ldots f(x_m) \ldots . \supset . \\ f(y_1) \ldots f(y_n) \ldots F(x_1, \ldots, x_m; y_1, \ldots, y_n; \ldots)$$

or

$$(\beta') \quad (\exists x_1, \ldots, x_m) :: (y_1, \ldots, y_n) : \ldots : f(y_1) \ldots f(y_n) \ldots . \supset . \\ f(x_1) \ldots f(x_m) \ldots F(x_1, \ldots, x_m; y_1, \ldots, y_n; \ldots),$$

where the condition that the values of a variable shall satisfy $f$ is put before the sign of implication if the variable is generalized universally and after this sign if it is generalized particularly, and where, in each case, the matrix $F$ is in expanded form with respect to $g, x_1, \ldots, x_m, y_1, \ldots, y_n, \ldots$, and $=$.

Let us take now any function on the base $f(x), g(x, y)$, of whatever degree of generality, which restricts only elements satisfying $f$. Let us express this function in one of the forms $(\alpha')$ or $(\beta')$, and consider that part of the matrix of the function represented by

$$F(x_1, \ldots, x_m; y_1, \ldots, y_n; \ldots).$$

We have defined above a disjunctive function $S$, which contains a set of alternatives that any elements substituted for the variables must satisfy, in virtue of (a)–(h), and which is such that it contains every alternative that a given assignment of values can satisfy, in virtue of these conditions. Let us construct, as above, the matrix

$$S(x_1, \ldots, x_m; y_1, \ldots, y_n; \ldots),$$

corresponding to $F$, and compare these two matrices. Since no set of elements substituted for $x_1, \ldots, x_m, y_1, \ldots, y_n, \ldots$ can satisfy an alternative which does not occur in $S$, it is clear that we may discard from $F$ all such alternatives without altering the truth-value of the function in which $F$ occurs. And it follows, therefore, that any function on $f(x), g(x, y)$ which places restrictions only upon elements satisfying $f$ can be expressed equivalently in one of the forms ($\alpha'$) or ($\beta'$) and such that $F$ involves only alternatives among those occurring in the corresponding matrix $S$.

If we show that all functions of this sort have their truth-values determined by conditions (a)–(h), we shall have shown the same thing for all functions whatever which restrict only elements belonging to the class determined by $f(x)$. But the class of functions to be dealt with can be narrowed still further. Any function of the form ($\alpha'$) has a contradictory of the form ($\beta'$), and conversely; so that it will be sufficient to show merely that functions of the form ($\alpha'$), whose variables of widest scope are universal, have their truth-values determined.

There are two theorems by reference to which the remainder of our argument is to be carried out. Let $R(x_1, x_2, \ldots, x_n)$ mean that

$$g(x_1, x_2), \ldots, g(x_1, x_n), \ldots, g(x_2, x_n), \ldots, \ldots, g(x_{n-1}, x_n),$$
$$\sim g(x_1, x_1), \ldots, \sim g(x_n, x_n)$$

all hold, that is, that $g$ holds for any two variables which occur in $R$ in the order from left to right and fails for any single variable, where, in the limiting case, $R(x_1)$ will mean simply $\sim g(x_1, x_1)$. Then it will be clear, in view of conditions (a)–(d), that any $n$ distinct elements satisfying $f$ are such that, for some permutation of these elements substituted in order for $x_1, \ldots, x_n$, $R$ holds, and also that if we have $R(x_1, \ldots, x_n)$, the function resulting when any one of the variables $x_1, \ldots, x_n$ is discarded will hold; so that we shall have:

$$\text{(I)}\quad (x_1, \ldots, x_n) :: f(x_1) \ldots f(x_n) . R(x_1, \ldots, x_n) . \equiv :.$$
$$(y) :. f(y) . \supset : f(x_1) \ldots f(x_n) : R(y, x_1, \ldots, x_n) . \vee .$$
$$R(x_1, y, \ldots, x_n) . \vee . \ldots . \vee . R(x_1, \ldots, x_n, y) . \vee .$$
$$R(x_1, \ldots, x_n) . y = x_1 . \vee . \ldots . \vee . R(x_1, \ldots, x_n) . y = x_n.$$

Again, it will be clear, in view of conditions (e)–(h), that if $R(x_1, \ldots, x_n)$ holds, then there will be some element $y$ such that $R(y, x_1, \ldots, x_n)$ holds, and some element $y$ such that $R(x_1, y, \ldots, x_n)$ holds, etc.; so that we shall have:

$$\text{(II)}\quad (x_1, \ldots, x_n) :. f(x_1) \ldots f(x_n) . \supset : R(x_1, \ldots, x_n) . \equiv .$$
$$(\exists y) . f(y) . R(y, x_1, \ldots, x_n) . \equiv .$$
$$(\exists y) . f(y) . R(x_1, y, \ldots, x_n) . \equiv . \ldots . \equiv .$$
$$(\exists y) . f(y) . R(x_1, \ldots, x_n, y) . \equiv .$$
$$(\exists y) . f(y) . R(x_1, \ldots, x_n) . y = x_1 . \equiv . \ldots . \equiv .$$
$$(\exists y) . f(y) . R(x_1, \ldots, x_n) . y = x_n.$$

In consequence of these two theorems, we can take any function of the form ($\alpha'$) and obtain an equivalent function by discarding the variable of narrowest scope.

Note that ($\alpha'$) can be written in the form

$$(x_1) \ldots (x_m) :: (\exists y_1) \ldots (\exists y_n) :. \ldots : f(x_1) \ldots f(x_m) \ldots . \supset .$$
$$f(y_1) \ldots f(y_n) \ldots F(x_1, \ldots, x_m; y_1, \ldots, y_n; \ldots),$$

where a prefix attaches separately to each variable.

Let us take, then, any function on the base $f(x)$,$g(x, y)$ which places restrictions only upon elements satisfying $f$ and is such that its variables of widest scope are universal, and express it in this form. We may discard from $F(x_1, \ldots, x_m; y_1, \ldots, y_n; \ldots)$ in the function so expressed all those alternatives which do not occur in $S(x_1, \ldots, x_m; y_1, \ldots, y_n; \ldots)$. And we may call the variable of narrowest scope $z_k$. This variable may be generalized either particularly or universally, that is, we may have either $(\exists z_k)$ or $(z_k)$.

If $z_k$ is generalized particularly, then, in virtue of theorem (II), we can obtain an equivalent function, in one fewer variables, by discarding $z_k$. This equivalence is, of course, material and not strict; it means that if conditions (a)–(h) determine the truth-value of either of the two functions, they determine the truth-value of the other.

Suppose, however, that the variable of narrowest scope is generalized universally. For the purpose of finding an equivalent function in which this variable does not occur, we proceed in this case in the following way. Every alternative in $F$ will involve all the variables that occur in the function, and we may consider what conditions of identity and distinctness are imposed upon these variables in the case of each alternative. Let us represent the variables that occur in any alternative by $x_1, \ldots, x_v, z_k$, and consider these variables exclusive of $z_k$. Among the alternatives in $F$, there will be some which involve the same identity-conditions among $x_1, \ldots, x_v$ and others which involve different identity-conditions; and we may, accordingly, collect the alternatives of $F$ into sets, $A_1, A_2$, etc., where those involving the same conditions of identity and distinctness among $x_1, \ldots, x_v$ belong to the same set and those involving different conditions in this respect to different sets. Consider the set $A_1$, and let the variables exclusive of $z_k$ in any alternative be represented by

$$x_1', x_1'' \ldots, x_2', x_2'' \ldots, \ldots, x_t', x_t'' \ldots,$$

where all the $x_i$'s are required to take the same values, while an $x_i$ and an $x_j$ are required to take distinct values. And consider the selection of variables $x_1', x_2', \ldots, x_t'$, where we have always the condition $\sim(x_i = x_j)$. In the case of any given alternative in $A_1$, there must be some permutation of these variables, let us say $x_1', x_2', \ldots, x_t'$, such that we have $R(x_1', x_2', \ldots, x_t')$, whereas in another alternative we may have, say, $R(x_2', x_1', \ldots, x_t')$. And the members of $A_1$ may therefore be collected into sets, $A_{11}, A_{12}$, etc., according as they do or do not involve $R$ as holding for the same permutation of the variables $x_1', \ldots, x_t'$. Take the set $A_{11}$, and say that each of its alternatives asserts, in part, $R(x_1', \ldots, x_t')$. Then consider the functions

$$R(z_k, x_1', \ldots, x_t'), R(x_1', z_k, \ldots, x_t'), \ldots, R(x_1', \ldots, x_t', z_k),$$
$$R(x_1', \ldots, x_t') \,.\, z_k = x_1', \ldots, R(x_1', \ldots, x_t') \,.\, z_k = x_t',$$

and suppose that at least one of these functions is such that no alternative in $A_{11}$ involves it. If we make a substitution of elements for the variables $x_1'$, $x_1''$ ..., $x_2'$, $x_2''$ ..., ..., $x_t'$, $x_t''$ ... such that $R(x_1', x_2', \ldots, x_t')$ holds, our original function cannot hold, with that substitution, for every value of $z_k$, by theorem (II); for we have so defined the set $A_{11}$ that no substitution for the variables exclusive of $z_k$ which will satisfy one of its alternatives can satisfy an alternative of $F$ not belonging to that set. And since this is so, we can discard from $F$ all the alternatives of this set without altering the truth-value of our original function; the resulting function will be equivalent to the original one. In this way, we may test each set, $A_{ij}$, into which the alternatives of $F$ can be divided, and may discard all the alternatives of a given set under the conditions here indicated. We may then obtain an equivalent function, in virtue of theorem (I), by discarding $z_k$ altogether.

It will be seen, therefore, that whether the variable of narrowest scope in a function is particular or universal, an equivalent function in one fewer variables can always be found. It may happen at some stage of this process of reduction, however, that all the alternatives in $F$ vanish, and in that case $F$ is to be represented as a conjunctive function in the following way. Let $p$, $q$, ... be all the alternatives that occur in the original matrix $S$. Then, to indicate that all alternatives fail, we write $\sim p \cdot \sim q \ldots$. And it will be clear that if at any point all alternatives vanish, the function with which we began must be incompatible with conditions (a)–(h); so that further reduction will not be required. If, on the other hand, some alternatives always remain, then when we reach a function in one variable, $F$ will be $\sim g(x_1, x_1)$, and we shall have

$$(x_1) \cdot f(x_1) \supset \sim g(x_1, x_1),$$

which is implied by (a)–(h).

It must be noted what the sense is in which this argument shows conditions (a)–(h) to be categorical. All the functions with which we have been concerned are constructed in terms of the conceptions represented by $\vee$, $.$, $\sim$, and $\exists$; that is to say, they are extensional functions. We have not introduced functions in which the notions denoted by $-\!\!\!3$, $\Diamond$, and the like occur; and it is easy to see that functions involving these intensional constants which are independent of (a)–(h) can be constructed. Moreover, we have employed the term 'base' in the narrower of its two senses: all the functions dealt with are on the base $f(x), g(x, y)$ in the sense that they are all functions of $f(x)$ and $g(x, y)$—one or both—alone.

We turn now to the definition of a dense series having a first but no last element. In order to define a series of this kind, we may replace condition (g) of the set (a)–(h) by

$$\text{(g}'\text{)} \qquad (\exists x) :: (y) :. f(y) . \supset : f(x) . g(x, y) . \vee . x = y,$$

which demands that there shall be a 'first' element $x$ in the series. And what we wish to do is to show that conditions (a)–(f),(g′),(h) either imply or are incompatible with every extensional function, of whatever degree of generality, which can be constructed on the base $f(x), g(x, y)$ and which places restrictions only upon elements belonging to the class determined by $f(x)$.

A part of the argument here is the same as that just given. We may take any function of the kind in question and express it in one of the forms $(\alpha')$ or $(\beta')$; and we may confine attention to functions of the form $(\alpha')$, whose variables of widest scope are universal. Since any set of values substituted for the variables in such a function must, in virtue of conditions (a)–(d), satisfy the matrix

$$S(x_1, \ldots, x_m; y_1, \ldots, y_n; \ldots),$$

we may discard from $F$ all those alternatives which do not occur in $S$. And we may, as above, express any function of this kind in such a way that a separate prefix attaches to each variable.

There are three theorems which will be required in the remainder of the argument. In consequence of condition (g′), there exists a unique element $a$ such that $g(a, y)$ holds for every element $y$ which satisfies $f$ and is distinct from $a$; so that we have immediately:

$$\text{(III)} \quad (\exists a) ::. (x_1, \ldots, x_n) :: f(x_1) \ldots f(x_n) . R(x_1, \ldots, x_n) . \equiv :. f(x_1) \ldots f(x_n) . f(a) :. (z) : f(z) . \sim(z = a) . \supset . g(a, z) :. R(a, x_1, \ldots, x_n) . \vee . R(a, x_2, \ldots, x_n) . x_1 = a.$$

And we shall have two further theorems, which are analogous to (I) and (II), above, and which are easily seen to hold:

(IV) $(a, x_1, \ldots, x_n) :: . f(a) . f(x_1) \ldots f(x_n) : .$
$(z) : f(z) \supset g(a, z) . \vee . z = a : . \supset ::$
$R(a, x_1, \ldots, x_n) . \equiv : . (y) : . f(y) . \supset :$
$R(a, y, x_1, \ldots, x_n) . \vee .$
$R(a, x_1, y, \ldots, x_n) . \vee . \ldots . \vee . R(a, x_1, \ldots, x_n, y) . \vee .$
$R(a, x_1, \ldots, x_n) . y = a . \vee . \ldots . \vee .$
$R(a, x_1, \ldots, x_n) . y = x_n.$

(V) $(x_1, \ldots, x_n) : . f(x_1) \ldots f(x_n) . \supset : R(x_1, \ldots, x_n) . \equiv .$
$(\exists y) . f(y) . R(x_1, y, \ldots, x_n) . \equiv . \ldots . \equiv .$
$(\exists y) . f(y) . R(x_1, \ldots, y, x_n) . \equiv .$
$(\exists y) . f(y) . R(x_1, \ldots, x_n, y) . \equiv .$
$(\exists y) . f(y) . R(x_1, \ldots, x_n) . y = x_1 . \equiv . \ldots . \equiv .$
$(\exists y) . f(y) . R(x_1, \ldots, x_n) . y = x_n.$

Let us take now any function whose variable or variables of widest scope are universal and express it in the form ($\alpha'$); and let us drop from $F$ all those alternatives which do not occur in the corresponding matrix $S$. We may take any alternative in $F$ and subdivide its variables into groups,

$$x_1', x_1'' \ldots, x_2', x_2'' \ldots, \ldots, x_u', x_u'' \ldots,$$

where, if the alternative is to be satisfied, the $x_i$'s must all take the same value and any $x_i$ must take a different value from any $x_j$, owing to the conditions of identity and distinctness involved.

We wish to construct an equivalent function, in accordance with theorem (III), in which every alternative shall involve the variable $a$, upon which the condition $(z) : f(z) . \sim(z = a) . \supset . g(a, z)$ is imposed. In order to do this, we replace each alternative in $F$ by two others. Thus we take an alternative which involves $R(x_1', \ldots, x_u')$, and, in the first place, introduce $a$ in such a way that we have $R(a, x_2', \ldots, x_u') . a = x_1'$. To complete this derived alternative, we conjoin all the conditions required by this identification, such as $(a = x_1'')$, $\sim(a = x_2'')$, $g(a, x_2'')$, and $\sim g(a, x_1')$. Second, $a$ is introduced into the alternative in such a way that we have $R(a, x_1', \ldots, x_u')$. And here, in order to complete the alternative, we must conjoin such conditions as $g(a, x_1'')$, $g(a, x_u'')$, and $\sim(a = x_1')$. In this way, we obtain a new matrix $F'$. And it will be clear, in view of theorem (III), that our original function is equivalent to

$$(\exists a) :::.\ (x_1) \ldots (x_m) ::: (\exists y_1) \ldots (\exists y_n) :: \ldots ::$$
$$f(x_1) \ldots f(x_m) \ldots . \supset :. f(a) :. (z) : f(z) . \sim(z = a) . \supset . g(a, z) :.$$
$$f(y_1) \ldots f(y_n) \ldots F'(a; x_1, \ldots, x_m; y_1, \ldots, y_n; \ldots).$$

Any extensional function on $f(x)$,$g(x, y)$, of whatever degree of generality, which restricts only elements satisfying $f$, and which is such that its variable or variables of widest scope are universal, can be expressed equivalently in this form.

Let us consider any function so expressed, and call the variable of narrowest scope in the main prefix $z_k$. If this variable is generalized particularly, that is, if we have $(\exists z_k)$, then, in virtue of theorem (V), we may discard it, and thus obtain an equivalent function in one fewer variables. If, on the other hand, the variable of narrowest scope is generalized universally, we proceed in the following way. Let us collect the alternatives in $F'$ into sets, $A_1$, $A_2$, ..., in which all those alternatives involving the same conditions of identity and distinctness among the variables exclusive of $z_k$ belong to one and the same set, and all those involving different conditions in this respect belong to different sets. Let us represent the variables exclusive of $z_k$ in an assigned alternative in $A_1$ by

$$a,\ a' \ldots,\ x_1',\ x_1'' \ldots, \ldots,\ x_t',\ x_t'' \ldots,$$

where $a$, $a'$ ... must take the same value, as must $x_1'$, $x_1''$ ..., etc.; and let us suppose that the chosen alternative of $A_1$ asserts, in part, $R(a, x_1', \ldots, x_t')$. Then we may form the sub-set $A_{11}$ of all those alternatives in $A_1$ which involve $R$ as holding for these variables in this order. If one of the functions

$$R(a, z_k, x_1', \ldots, x_t'),\ R(a, x_1', z_k, \ldots, x_t'), \ldots,$$
$$R(a, x_1', \ldots, x_t', z_k),\ R(a, x_1', \ldots, x_t') . z_k = a, \ldots,$$
$$R(a, x_1', \ldots, x_t') . z_k = x_t'$$

fails to occur among the alternatives of $A_{11}$, then we may drop all these alternatives from the matrix $F'$ without altering the truth-value of the function in which $F'$ occurs. And when each of the sub-sets, $A_{11}, A_{12} \ldots, A_{21}, A_{22} \ldots, \ldots$, into which the alternatives of $F'$ are divisible, has been dealt with in this way, we may, in virtue of theorem (IV), obtain an equivalent function in one fewer variables by discarding $z_k$.

If at some point in the process of reducing the number of variables in the function all alternatives vanish, then, clearly, the original function must be incompatible with conditions (a)–(f),(g′),(h). If this does not occur, however, we shall have finally

$$(\exists a) :.\, f(a) :.\, (z) : f(z) \,.\, {\sim}(z = a) \,.\supset.\, g(a, z) :.\, {\sim}g(a, a),$$

where ${\sim}g(a, a)$ is $F'(a)$; and this function is implied by conditions (a)–(f),(g′),(h). Note here that just before this final expression is obtained, we shall have

$$(\exists a) ::.\, (x_1) :: f(x_1) \,.\supset:.\, f(a) :.\, (z) : f(z) \,.\, {\sim}(z = a) \,.\supset.\, g(a, z) :.\, F'(a, x_1),$$

which is equivalent to

$$(\exists a) ::.\, (x_1) :: f(a) :.\, (z) : f(z) \,.\, {\sim}(z = a) \,.\supset.\, g(a, z) :.\, F'(a, x_1) :. \vee .\, {\sim}f(x_1),$$

and that if reduction is possible without the vanishing of all alternatives from $F'$, we have the function just given when $x_1$ is discarded.[6]

We turn finally to the definition of a dense series with both extreme elements. And here we may replace condition (f) of the set (a)–(f),(g′),(h) by

$$\text{(f}'\text{)} \qquad (\exists x) :: (y) :.\, f(y) \,.\supset: f(x) \,.\, g(y, x) \,.\vee.\, x = y,$$

[6] The theorem here established shows that a continuous series with one extreme element (see Huntington, *The Continuum*, Ch. V) cannot be defined on $f(x), g(x, y)$; and, of course, the preceding theorem shows the same thing in the case of a continuous series without extreme elements. For proof of an analogous theorem regarding discrete series having a first but no last element and in which every element but one has an immediate predecessor, see *Annals of Mathematics*, XXVIII (1927), 459. It follows from such a theorem that an inductive series, similarly, cannot be given on $f(x), g(x, y)$, but must involve a further variable $\phi$, as in Section 2 of Chapter XI. In general, whenever it is necessary to speak of all subclasses of the class determined by $f$, the base $f(x), g(x, y)$, in the narrower sense, is not sufficient.

which is a condition to the effect that a 'last' element of the series shall exist. We wish to show, as before, that the set (a)–(e),(f′),(g′),(h) either implies or is incompatible with every extensional function on the base $f(x), g(x, y)$ which places restrictions only upon elements satisfying $f$.

It will be clear that we can, in this case, as in the others, express any function whose variable or variables of widest scope are universal in the form $(\alpha')$, where the matrix $F$ involves only such alternatives as occur in the corresponding matrix $S$. And we shall have here three theorems, which are analogous to those just given, and which are easily seen to be consequences of the conditions defining a dense series with both extreme elements:

(VI) $(\exists a, c) :: . (x_1, \ldots, x_n) :: f(x_1) \ldots f(x_n) .$
$R(x_1, \ldots, x_n) . \equiv : .$
$f(x_1) \ldots f(x_n) . f(a) . f(c) : .$
$(z) : f(z) . \sim(z = a) . \supset . g(a, z) : .$
$(z) : f(z) . \sim(z = c) . \supset . g(z, c) : .$
$R(a, x_1, \ldots, x_n, c) . \vee . R(x_1, \ldots, x_n, c) . a = x_1 . \vee .$
$R(a, x_1, \ldots, x_n) . c = x_n . \vee .$
$R(x_1, \ldots, x_n) . a = x_1 . c = x_n .$

(VII) $(a, c, x_1, \ldots, x_n) :: . f(a) . f(c) . f(x_1) \ldots f(x_n) : .$
$(z) : f(z) . \sim(z = a) . \supset . g(a, z) : .$
$(z) : f(z) . \sim(z = c) . \supset . g(z, c) : . \supset ::$
$R(a, x_1, \ldots, x_n, c) . \equiv : . (y) : . f(y) . \supset :$
$R(a, y, x_1, \ldots, x_n, c) . \vee .$
$R(a, x_1, y, \ldots, x_n, c) . \vee . \ldots . \vee .$
$R(a, x_1, \ldots, x_n, y, c) . \vee .$
$R(a, x_1, \ldots, x_n, c) . y = a . \vee . \ldots . \vee .$
$R(a, x_1, \ldots, x_n, c) . y = c .$

(VIII) $(x_1, \ldots, x_n) : . f(x_1) \ldots f(x_n) . \supset : R(x_1, \ldots, x_n) . \equiv .$
$(\exists y) . f(y) . R(x_1, y, \ldots, x_n) . \equiv . \ldots . \equiv .$
$(\exists y) . f(y) . R(x_1, \ldots, y, x_n) . \equiv .$
$(\exists y) . f(y) . R(x_1, \ldots, x_n) . y = x_1 . \equiv . \ldots . \equiv .$
$(\exists y) . f(y) . R(x_1, \ldots, x_n) . y = x_n .$

In virtue of theorem (VI), any function of the form ($\alpha'$) can be written equivalently in the form:

$$(\exists a, c) :::. (x_1) \ldots (x_m) ::: (\exists y_1) \ldots (\exists y_n) ::\ldots ::$$
$$f(x_1) \ldots f(x_m) \ldots . \supset :. f(a) . f(c) :.$$
$$(z) : f(z) . \sim(z = a) . \supset . g(a, z) :. (z) : f(z) . \sim(z = c) . \supset . g(z, c) :.$$
$$f(y_1) \ldots f(y_n) \ldots F''(a, c; x_1, \ldots, x_m; y_1, \ldots, y_n; \ldots),$$

where $F''$ is derived from $F$ in the following way. Each alternative in $F$ is replaced by four others, in such a way that if

$$x_1', x_1'' \ldots, x_2', x_2'' \ldots, \ldots, x_u', x_u'' \ldots$$

are the variables belonging to a given alternative in $F$, and if we have $R(x_1', \ldots, x_u')$, then we shall have

$$R(a, x_1', \ldots, x_u', c), \qquad R(x_1', \ldots, x_u', c) . x_1' = a,$$
$$R(a, x_1', \ldots, x_u') . x_u' = c, \qquad R(x_1', \ldots, x_u') . x_1' = a . x_u' = c,$$

as determining the substituted alternatives.

If the variable of narrowest scope in the main prefix of this function is particular, then, in virtue of theorem (VIII), we can discard it without altering the truth-value of the function. If the variable of narrowest scope is universal, then we can, as before, divide the alternatives of the matrix $F''$ into sub-sets, $A_{11}, A_{12} \ldots, A_{21}, A_{22} \ldots, \ldots$, according to the conditions of identity and distinctness involved, and according to the permutations of selections of variables taking distinct values for which $R$ holds. We can discard from $F''$ all those sub-sets which do not satisfy theorem (VIII), and can then drop the variable of narrowest scope from the function by applying theorem (VII). If, in the process of reduction, all alternatives vanish from $F''$, the function will be incompatible with conditions (a)–(e),(f′),(g′),(h). If this does not occur, we shall have, finally,

$$(\exists a, c) :. f(a) . f(c) :. (z) : f(z) . \sim(z = a) . \supset . g(a, z) :.$$
$$(z) : f(z) . \sim(z = c) . \supset . g(z, c) :. F''(a, c),$$

where $F''(a, c)$ is $g(a, c) . \sim g(c, a) . \sim g(a, a) . \sim g(c, c) . \sim(a = c)$; and this function is implied by (a)–(e),(f′),(g′),(h).

## SECTION 3. DEDUCIBILITY FROM CONDITIONS FOR BETWEENNESS

We wish to show, in this section, that the conditions defining Betweenness have properties analogous to those already shown to be possessed by the general conditions defining Serial Order. That is to say, we wish to show that any singly-general universal extensional function in $n$ generalized variables on the base $f(x), g(x, y, z)$ which imposes restrictions only upon elements satisfying $f$ either is implied by the conditions for Betweenness or, together with the premise that there are at least $n$ elements satisfying $f$, is incompatible with them. We could not show simply that any such universal function either was implied by the conditions defining Betweenness or else was incompatible with them, because, if there were not enough elements in the class determined by $f(x)$, any universal function would hold, inasmuch as it would be satisfied vacuously.

The definition of Betweenness, which is on the base $f(x)$, $g(x, y, z)$, is as follows:

$$(x_1, x_2, x_3, x_4) : . f(x_1) . f(x_2) . f(x_3) . f(x_4) . \supset :$$

(1) $g(x_1, x_2, x_3) \supset g(x_3, x_2, x_1) :$

(2) $d(x_1, x_2, x_3) \supset P(g, x_1, x_2, x_3) :$ [6]

(3) $d(x_1, x_2, x_3) . \supset . \sim g(x_1, x_2, x_3) \vee \sim g(x_1, x_3, x_2) :$

(4) $g(x_1, x_2, x_3) \supset d(x_1, x_2, x_3) :$

(5) $d(x_1, x_2, x_3, x_4) . g(x_1, x_2, x_3) . \supset . g(x_1, x_2, x_4) \vee g(x_4, x_2, x_3)$.

In consequence of (1) and (2), any three distinct elements which satisfy $f$ are such that for some permutation, say $x_1, x_2, x_3$, both $g(x_1, x_2, x_3)$ and $g(x_3, x_2, x_1)$ hold; and, by (1) and (3), $g$ fails for every other permutation of these elements. Again, by (4), we have always $\sim g(x_1, x_1, x_1)$, $\sim g(x_1, x_2, x_2)$, $\sim g(x_2, x_1, x_2)$, and $\sim g(x_2, x_2, x_1)$.

We may understand $R(x_1, x_2, x_3)$ to mean the conjunction of $g(x_1, x_2, x_3) . g(x_3, x_2, x_1)$ with the negative of each of the other functions of $g, x_1, x_2, x_3$ that can be constructed—such as $\sim g(x_1, x_3, x_2)$, $\sim g(x_1, x_2, x_2)$, and $\sim g(x_1, x_1, x_1)$. We may, simi-

[6] That is, in accordance with the definition of $P$ given above, for at least one of the six permutations of $x_1, x_2, x_3$, $g$ holds.

larly, allow $R(x_1, x_2)$ to stand for the conjunction of the negatives of all functions that can be constructed out of $g$, $x_1$, $x_2$, i.e., for

$$\sim g(x_1, x_2, x_2) \,.\, \sim g(x_2, x_1, x_2) \,.\, \sim g(x_2, x_2, x_1) \,.\, \sim g(x_1, x_1, x_2) \,.$$
$$\sim g(x_1, x_2, x_1) \,.\, \sim g(x_2, x_1, x_1) \,.\, \sim g(x_1, x_1, x_1) \,.\, \sim g(x_2, x_2, x_2),$$

and $R(x_1)$ to stand for $\sim g(x_1, x_1, x_1)$. Again, the function

$$R(x_1, x_2, x_3) \,.\, R(x_1, x_2, x_4) \,.\, R(x_1, x_3, x_4) \,.\, R(x_2, x_3, x_4)$$

may be replaced by $R(x_1, x_2, x_3, x_4)$; and $R(x_1, \ldots, x_n)$ may be similarly understood, as involving $R(x_i, x_j, x_k)$ for any three variables which occur in the order from left to right.

It will be clear, then, that we have

(L) $$g(x_1, x_2, x_3) \equiv R(x_1, x_2, x_3)$$

for any three elements belonging to the class determined by $f(x)$, and that $R(x_1, x_2)$ and $R(x_1)$ always hold. Moreover, in virtue of the definition of $R$, we have

(M) $$R(x_1, x_2, x_3) \equiv R(x_3, x_2, x_1),$$

and

(N) $$R(x_1, x_2, x_3) \,.\!\supset\!.\, \sim R(x_1, x_3, x_2) \,.\, \sim R(x_2, x_1, x_3).$$

We wish to show that some permutation of any $n$ distinct elements satisfying $f$, say $x_1, \ldots, x_n$, is such that $R(x_1, \ldots, x_n)$ holds.

We must show, in the first place, that if $R(x_1, \ldots, x_n)$ holds for an assigned value of $n$ ($\geqq 3$), it will hold for $n + 1$. Let $y$ denote any element in the class determined by $f(x)$ other than those denoted by $x_1, \ldots, x_n$. Then we have, by conditions (1), (2) and theorem (L),

$$R(y, x_1, x_n) \vee R(x_1, x_n, y) \vee R(x_1, y, x_n).$$

Suppose, first, that $R(y, x_1, x_n)$ holds; and let $x_i$, $x_j$ represent any two of the variables $x_1, \ldots, x_n$ which are such that $R(x_1, x_i, x_j)$. By condition (5), $R(y, x_1, x_n)$ implies $R(y, x_1, x_i)$ or $R(x_i, x_1, x_n)$, where the latter is contrary to $R(x_1, x_i, x_n)$, by (N); so that we have $R(y, x_1, x_i)$. Now, from $R(y, x_1, x_n)$ and $R(y, x_1, x_i)$, we have, by definition, $R(y, x_1, x_j)$. Again, by (5), $R(x_1, x_i, x_j)$ implies $R(x_1, x_i, y)$ or $R(y, x_i, x_j)$, where the first implies $R(y, x_i, x_1)$, contrary to $R(y, x_1, x_i)$, by (N); so that we have $R(y, x_i, x_j)$. But $R(y, x_1, x_i)$, $R(y, x_1, x_j)$, $R(y, x_i, x_j)$, and $R(x_1, \ldots, x_n)$ yield $R(y, x_1, \ldots, x_n)$.

Suppose that we have $R(x_1, x_n, y)$. Since $R(x_1, x_n, y)$ is equivalent to $R(y, x_n, x_1)$, and $R(x_1, \ldots, x_n)$ is equivalent to $R(x_n, \ldots, x_1)$, it can be established by the argument just given that $R(y, x_n, \ldots, x_1)$ holds, and therefore that we have $R(x_1, \ldots, x_n, y)$.

Suppose, finally, that $R(x_1, y, x_n)$ holds. Let $x_i$ be any one of the variables $x_1, \ldots, x_n$ other than $x_1$ and $x_n$. Then, by (1), (2), and (L), we have either $R(x_1, x_i, y)$ or $R(x_1, y, x_i)$ or $R(y, x_1, x_i)$. But if $R(y, x_1, x_i)$ holds, then, by (5), $R(y, x_1, x_n)$ or $R(x_n, x_1, x_i)$ will hold, the first being contrary to $R(x_1, y, x_n)$, and the second to $R(x_n, x_i, x_1)$; so that we have

$$R(x_1, x_i, y) \vee R(x_1, y, x_i).$$

Consider the variables $x_{i1}$ such that $R(x_1, x_{i1}, y)$ holds, and the variables $x_{i2}$ such that $R(x_1, y, x_{i2})$ holds. If $x_{i1}$ exists such that $R(x_1, x_{i1}, y)$ holds, then we cannot have $R(x_1, y, x_{i1})$; and if $x_{i2}$ exists such that $R(x_1, y, x_{i2})$ holds, then we cannot have $R(x_1, x_{i2}, y)$, by (N); so that the variables $x_{i1}$ and $x_{i2}$ fall into two non-overlapping classes; though, of course, either or both of these classes may be null. Moreover, every $x_{i1}$ comes before every $x_{i2}$ in $R(x_1, \ldots, x_n)$; for if we have $R(x_1, x_{i2}, x_{i1})$, we shall have, by (5), $R(x_1, x_{i2}, y)$ or $R(y, x_{i2}, x_{i1})$, where the first alternative is contrary to $R(x_1, y, x_{i2})$, and the second to $R(x_{i2}, y, x_{i1})$, which, as will appear immediately, must hold.

Now, since $R(x_1, y, x_{i2})$ holds, then $R(x_1, y, x_{i1})$ or $R(x_{i1}, y, x_{i2})$ holds, by (5), where the first is incompatible with $R(x_1, x_{i1}, y)$, by (N), so that we have $R(x_{i1}, y, x_{i2})$. And in the same way, we have $R(x_{i1}, y, x_n)$. Again, from $R(x_1, x_{i2}, x_n)$ it follows, by (5), that $R(x_1, x_{i2}, y)$ or $R(y, x_{i2}, x_n)$ holds, the first being incompatible with $R(x_1, y, x_{i2})$. We have then, altogether, $R(x_1, y, x_n)$, $R(x_1, x_{i1}, x_n)$, $R(x_1, x_{i2}, x_n)$, $R(x_1, x_{i1}, y)$, $R(x_1, y, x_{i2})$, $R(x_{i1}, y, x_n)$, $R(y, x_{i2}, x_n)$, $R(x_1, x_{i1}, x_{i2})$, and $R(x_{i1}, y, x_{i2})$.

Let $x_{i11}$, $x_{i12}$ represent any two of the variables denoted by $x_{i1}$ which are such that $R(x_{i11}, x_{i12}, x_n)$ holds; and, similarly, let

$x_{i21}$, $x_{i22}$ represent any two of the variables $x_{i2}$ which are such that $R(x_1, x_{i21}, x_{i22})$ holds.[7] By (5), $R(x_{i11}, x_{i12}, x_n)$ implies $R(x_{i11}, x_{i12}, y)$ or $R(y, x_{i12}, x_n)$, where the latter is contrary to $R(x_{i1}, y, x_n)$. And since $R(x_1, \ldots, x_n)$ is equivalent to $R(x_n, \ldots, x_1)$, and $R(x_1, x_{i21}, x_{i22})$ to $R(x_{i22}, x_{i21}, x_1)$, it can be shown in exactly the same way that we have $R(y, x_{i21}, x_{i22})$.

This result, together with the ones obtained above, and with $R(x_1, \ldots, x_n)$, yields $R(x_1, \ldots, y, \ldots, x_n)$. Thus, if $R$ holds for a given value of $n$ ($\geqq 3$), it will hold for $n + 1$; and we have seen that it does hold for $n \leqq 3$.

Consider, now, the function

$$R(x_1, x_2, \ldots, x_n) \centerdot \sim(x_1 = x_2) \centerdot \ldots \centerdot \sim(x_1 = x_n) \centerdot \ldots \centerdot \sim(x_2 = x_n) \centerdot \ldots,$$

where, of course, $R(x_1, x_2, \ldots, x_n)$ is the conjunction of $g(x_1, x_2, x_3)$, $g(x_3, x_2, x_1)$, $\sim g(x_1, x_3, x_2)$, $\sim g(x_1, x_1, x_2)$, etc. Let us form the class made up of this function together with all those that can be derived from it by permutation of $x_1, x_2, \ldots, x_n$, and call this class $C$. Each member of $C$ will, therefore, involve $R$ as holding for some permutation of $x_1, x_2, \ldots, x_n$, and will involve a condition to the effect that each pair of variables shall take distinct values. Again, let us form the class $C'$ by replacing each member of $C$ by functions obtained as follows: take a given member of $C$, and replace it by the $2^{\frac{n(n-1)}{2}}$ functions that can be got by removing or not removing $\sim$ from before its constituents of the form $(x_i = x_j)$. Some of the members of this class will, however, involve self-contradictory identity-conditions, in that they will involve constituents like $(x_1 = x_2) \centerdot (x_2 = x_3) \centerdot \sim(x_1 = x_3)$, and we may drop all such inconsistent members from $C'$. Finally, we may take each one of the remaining members of $C'$ and collect into groups all those variables upon which it imposes a condition of identity, in such a way that variables taking identical values will belong to the same group and those taking distinct values to different groups, and then discard from $R$ all but one of the variables in each group. This

[7] It will be clear that when, in special cases, no elements correspond to the variables introduced, the argument is complete for those cases without the part involving the variables in question.

class, which we may call $C''$, will involve the same number of functions as $C'$. And it is to be noted that in discarding variables from $R$, we must not discard them wholly from the function; all conditions of identity and distinctness remain, and each function contains all the variables $x_1, x_2, \ldots, x_n$. Some members of $C''$ will be redundant with each other in that they will result, for example, from two functions in $C'$ which contain respectively $R(x_1, x_2, \ldots, x_n) . (x_1 = x_2)$ and $R(x_2, x_1, \ldots, x_n) . (x_1 = x_2)$, where all other identity-conditions are the same, and where one of the variables $x_1$ and $x_2$ has been discarded in each case; and we may, of course, drop all but one of each set of redundant functions. We may then form the disjunction of all the members of $C''$, and call this disjunction $S(x_1, \ldots, x_n)$.

In view of the fact that $R$ holds for some permutation of any finite set of elements satisfying $f$, it will be clear that we have, as a logical consequence of conditions (1)–(5),

(A) $\quad (x_1, \ldots, x_n) : f(x_1) \ldots f(x_n) . \supset . S(x_1, \ldots, x_n).$

Consider, then, any singly-general universal function on the base $f(x), g(x, y, z)$ which imposes restrictions only upon elements belonging to the class determined by $f(x)$, and express it in the form

(B) $\quad (x_1, \ldots, x_n) : f(x_1) \ldots f(x_n) . \supset . F(x_1, \ldots, x_n).$

Let $F$ be put in expanded form with respect to $g, x_1, \ldots, x_n$, and $=$; so that we shall have a disjunctive function each of whose alternatives contains all the variables $x_1, \ldots, x_n$. We may, of course, eliminate all self-contradictory alternatives which arise in the process of putting $F$ in expanded form, and all but one of every set of redundant alternatives. And it is to be noted in this connection that $\sim g(x_1, x_1) . (x_1 = x_2)$ is identical with $\sim g(x_1, x_1) . \sim g(x_2, x_2) . (x_1 = x_2)$, although not with $\sim g(x_1, x_1)$, since this last expression does not contain $x_2$, which might appear in some connected function. It is necessary to observe this because, in constructing $S$, we have omitted all redundancies like the one that occurs in the second expression here, whereas $F$ might be so expressed in expanded form as to contain expressions like this second one in place of simpler ones which mean the same thing.

If $F$ involves every alternative that occurs in $S$, then clearly (B) is a logical consequence of (A), and therefore of conditions (1)–(5). Now, $S$ is so constructed that any set of elements substituted in an assigned order for $x_1, \ldots, x_n$ will satisfy one and only one of its alternatives; and, moreover, if we have any set of $n$ elements, we can substitute them or some of them for $x_1, \ldots, x_n$ in such a way that any arbitrarily assigned alternative in $S$ will be satisfied, and therefore in such a way that no other alternative will be satisfied for that substitution; so that, if some alternative in $S$ does not occur in $F$, the function (B), together with the condition that there exist at least $n$ elements in the class determined by $f(x)$, will be incompatible with conditions (1)–(5).

There are several ways in which conditions can be added to the set (1)–(5) so as to secure the existence of a non-finite number of elements in the class determined by $f(x)$. We may consider, in particular, the following two conditions:

(6) $(\exists x_1, x_2) \,.\, f(x_1) \,.\, f(x_2) \,.\, \sim(x_1 = x_2)$.

(7) $(x_1, x_3) :. (\exists x_2) : f(x_1) \,.\, f(x_3) \,.\, \sim(x_1 = x_3) \,.\supset.$
$f(x_2) \,.\, g(x_1, x_2, x_3)$.

It will be easy to see that these two conditions, together with (1)–(5), enable us to infer that there are at least $n$ elements satisfying $f$, where $n$ is any finite number, and that therefore the set (1)–(7) will either imply or be incompatible with any universal singly-general function which can be constructed on $f(x), g(x, y, z)$ and which imposes restrictions only upon elements in the class determined by $f(x)$. But here, since the truth-value of every universal function of the kind in question is categorically determined by the set (1)–(7), we can of course include singly-general existential functions as well, owing to the fact that they are contradictories of corresponding universal functions.

There are, however, many functions of a degree of generality higher than the first which are independent of (1)–(7)—such, for instance, as

(8) $(x_1, x_2) :. (\exists x_3) : f(x_1) \,.\, f(x_2) \,.\, \sim(x_1 = x_2) \,.\supset.$
$f(x_3) \,.\, g(x_1, x_2, x_3)$.

This condition, when subjoined to (1)–(7), excludes the existence of both extreme elements: if we have elements $b$ and $c$, then $d$ must exist such that $g(b, c, d)$ holds, and $a$ must exist such that we shall have $g(c, b, a)$, which implies $g(a, b, c)$. Here it would be interesting to know whether it can be shown, by an argument similar to the one we have used above in dealing with dense series without extreme elements, that conditions (1)–(8) determine the truth-value of every extensional function on $f(x)$, $g(x, y, z)$, of whatever degree of generality, which restricts only elements satisfying $f$.

It was remarked in the preceding chapter that conditions (1)–(5), together with an appropriate existence-condition, presumably constitute a correct analysis of the ordinary notion of Betweenness in general. We were able to see, however, only that the properties put down were necessary to any correct interpretation of this ordinary notion; whereas now, in view of the theorem just established, we can see that these properties are also sufficient, since no other independent general conditions can exist.

## Section 4. Cyclic Order

In this section we shall establish a result exactly analogous to the one just obtained in connection with the properties defining Betweenness. We wish to show that any extensional singly-general universal function in $n$ generalized variables on the base $f(x), g(x, y, z)$ which imposes restrictions only upon elements in the class determined by $f(x)$ either is implied by the set of properties defining Cyclic Order or, in conjunction with the premise that at least $n$ elements satisfying $f$ exist, is incompatible with these properties. The definition of Cyclic Order is as follows:

$$(x_1, x_2, x_3, x_4) :. f(x_1) . f(x_2) . f(x_3) . f(x_4) . \supset :$$

(1) $g(x_1, x_2, x_3) \supset g(x_2, x_3, x_1) :$

(2) $d(x_1, x_2, x_3) \supset P(g, x_1, x_2, x_3) :$

(3) $d(x_1, x_2, x_3) . \supset . \sim g(x_1, x_2, x_3) \vee \sim g(x_1, x_3, x_2) :$

(4) $g(x_1, x_2, x_3) \supset d(x_1, x_2, x_3) :$

(5) $d(x_1, x_2, x_3, x_4) . g(x_1, x_2, x_3) . \supset . g(x_1, x_2, x_4) \vee g(x_4, x_2, x_3)$.

In virtue of conditions (1), (2), (3), and (4), we shall have, for some permutation of any three elements, say $x_1$, $x_2$, $x_3$,

$$g(x_1, x_2, x_3) \cdot g(x_2, x_3, x_1) \cdot g(x_3, x_1, x_2) \cdot \sim g(x_3, x_2, x_1) \cdot \ldots \cdot \sim g(x_1, x_1, x_2) \cdot \sim g(x_1, x_2, x_1) \cdot \ldots \cdot \sim g(x_1, x_1, x_1) \cdot \ldots,$$

and we may allow $R(x_1, x_2, x_3)$ to represent this conjunction, which contains all functions that can be constructed out of $g$, $x_1$, $x_2$, and $x_3$. We may, similarly, allow $R(x_1, x_2)$ to stand for

$$\sim g(x_1, x_1, x_2) \cdot \sim g(x_1, x_2, x_1) \cdot \ldots \cdot \sim g(x_1, x_1, x_1) \cdot \sim g(x_2, x_2, x_2),$$

and $R(x_1)$ to stand for $\sim g(x_1, x_1, x_1)$. Again, we may write $R(x_1, x_2, x_3, x_4)$ in place of

$$R(x_1, x_2, x_3) \cdot R(x_1, x_2, x_4) \cdot R(x_1, x_3, x_4) \cdot R(x_2, x_3, x_4),$$

and we may define $R(x_1, x_2, \ldots, x_n)$ in the same way, as involving $R(x_i, x_j, x_k)$ for any three variables which occur in the order from left to right.

Thus $g(x_1, x_2, x_3) \equiv R(x_1, x_2, x_3)$, and we have, for any two elements $x_1$, $x_2$, $R(x_1, x_2)$, and for any single element $x_1$, $R(x_1)$. Moreover, in virtue of the definition of $R$, we have

$$R(x_1, x_2, x_3) \equiv R(x_2, x_3, x_1) \equiv R(x_3, x_1, x_2).$$

Now, we wish to show that for some permutation of any $n$ elements satisfying $f$, say $x_1, \ldots, x_n$, $R(x_1, \ldots, x_n)$ holds. We know, to begin with, that $R$ holds where $n \leqq 3$, and it will therefore be sufficient to show that if $R$ holds for any assigned value of $n$ ($\geqq 3$), it will hold for $n + 1$.

If $y$ denotes any element other than those denoted by $x_1, \ldots, x_n$, then, by conditions (1) and (2),

$$R(y, x_1, x_n) \vee R(x_1, y, x_n).$$

Suppose, in the first place, that $R(y, x_1, x_n)$ holds. Then, by condition (5), either $R(x_i, x_1, x_n)$ or $R(y, x_1, x_i)$, where $x_i$ is any one of the variables $x_1, \ldots, x_n$ other than $x_1$ and $x_n$. But $R(x_i, x_1, x_n)$ is incompatible with $R(x_1, x_i, x_n)$, by the definition of $R$; so that we have $R(y, x_1, x_i)$. Again, $R(x_1, x_i, x_n)$ implies $R(x_i, x_n, x_1)$, which, by (5), implies $R(y, x_n, x_1)$ or $R(x_i, x_n, y)$; and here the first alternative is incompatible with $R(y, x_1, x_n)$, by definition, so that we have $R(x_i, x_n, y)$, which implies $R(y, x_i, x_n)$. Now, in case the number of the variables $x_1, \ldots, x_n$ is not less than four, we can denote by $x_{i1}$, $x_{i2}$ any two of these variables which are such that $R(x_1, x_{i1}, x_{i2}, x_n)$ holds. And it must be shown that $R(y, x_{i1}, x_{i2})$ holds. $R(x_1, x_{i1}, x_{i2})$ implies $R(x_{i1}, x_{i2}, x_1)$, which, by (5), implies $R(x_{i1}, x_{i2}, y)$ or $R(y, x_{i2}, x_1)$, where the second alternative is incompatible with $R(y, x_1, x_i)$, so that we have $R(x_{i1}, x_{i2}, y)$, which implies $R(y, x_{i1}, x_{i2})$. We have, then, in all, $R(y, x_1, x_n)$, $R(y, x_1, x_i)$, $R(y, x_i, x_n)$, and $R(y, x_{i1}, x_{i2})$, which, together with $R(x_1, \ldots, x_n)$, is $R(y, x_1, \ldots, x_n)$.

Suppose, in the second place, that $R(x_1, y, x_n)$ holds. Then, by conditions (1) and (2), either $R(x_1, x_i, y)$ or $R(x_1, y, x_i)$ will hold. And since no $x_i$ can satisfy both of these alternatives, we may allow $x_{i1}$ to stand for any variable such that $R(x_1, x_{i1}, y)$ holds, and $x_{i2}$ for any such that $R(x_1, y, x_{i2})$ holds, and say that these two classes of variables have no members in common. Now, $R(x_1, y, x_n)$ implies $R(x_{i1}, y, x_n)$ or $R(x_1, y, x_{i1})$, where the second alternative is contrary to $R(x_1, x_{i1}, y)$; so that we have $R(x_{i1}, y, x_n)$. And $R(x_1, x_{i2}, x_n)$ implies $R(y, x_{i2}, x_n)$ or $R(x_1, x_{i2}, y)$, where the second alternative is contrary to $R(x_1, y, x_{i2})$; so that $R(y, x_{i2}, x_n)$ holds. Moreover, $R(x_{i1}, y, x_n)$ implies $R(x_{i2}, y, x_n)$ or $R(x_{i1}, y, x_{i2})$, where the first alternative implies $R(x_n, x_{i2}, y)$, which is incompatible with $R(x_n, y, x_{i2})$; so that we have $R(x_{i1}, y, x_{i2})$. Again, $R(x_{i1}, y, x_n)$ implies $R(y, x_n, x_{i1})$, which implies $R(x_{i2}, x_n, x_{i1})$ or $R(y, x_n, x_{i2})$, where the second alternative is contrary to $R(y, x_{i2}, x_n)$; so that we have $R(x_{i2}, x_n, x_{i1})$, which implies $R(x_{i1}, x_{i2}, x_n)$. Finally, $R(x_1, x_{i1}, x_n)$ implies $R(x_{i2}, x_{i1}, x_n)$ or $R(x_1, x_{i1}, x_{i2})$, where $R(x_{i2}, x_{i1}, x_n)$ implies $R(x_{i1}, x_n, x_{i2})$, which is contrary to $R(x_{i1}, x_{i2}, x_n)$; so that $R(x_1, x_{i1}, x_{i2})$ must hold. So far, then, we have $R(x_1, y, x_n)$, $R(x_1, x_{i1}, y)$, $R(x_{i1}, y, x_n)$, $R(y, x_{i2}, x_n)$, $R(x_{i1}, y, x_{i2})$, $R(x_1, x_{i1}, x_{i2})$, and $R(x_{i1}, x_{i2}, x_n)$.

Let $x_{i11}$, $x_{i12}$ and $x_{i21}$, $x_{i22}$ be variables among the $x_{i1}$'s and $x_{i2}$'s, respectively, such that $R(x_1, x_{i11}, x_{i12}, x_{i21}, x_{i22}, x_n)$ holds. Then it must be shown that we have both $R(x_{i11}, x_{i12}, y)$ and $R(y, x_{i21}, x_{i22})$. $R(x_{i11}, x_{i12}, x_n)$ implies $R(x_{i11}, x_{i12}, y)$ or $R(y, x_{i12}, x_n)$, where the latter is contrary to $R(x_{i1}, y, x_n)$;

$R(x_1, x_{i21}, x_{i22})$ implies $R(y, x_{i21}, x_{i22})$ or $R(x_1, x_{i21}, y)$, where the latter is contrary to $R(x_1, y, x_{i2})$. And this result, in conjunction with the one just obtained and with $R(x_1, \ldots, x_n)$, yields $R(x_1, \ldots, y, \ldots, x_n)$.

The remainder of the argument proceeds exactly as in the preceding section. We consider any function

$$(x_1, \ldots, x_n) : f(x_1) \ldots f(x_n) \,.\supset.\, F(x_1, \ldots, x_n),$$

where $F$ is expanded with respect to $g, x_1, \ldots, x_n$, and $=$. We then construct a matrix $S$ in the following way. Take $R(x_1, \ldots, x_n)$, and form the class made up of this function together with all those which can be derived from it by permutation of $x_1, \ldots, x_n$; replace each function of this class by a set of functions got by conjoining either $(x_i = x_j)$ or $\sim(x_i = x_j)$ to the function in the case of each pair of variables $x_i, x_j$ among $x_1, \ldots, x_n$; discard all functions which involve self-contradictory identity-conditions; take each member of the resulting class, and drop from $R$ all but one of every set of variables that must take the same value; then form the disjunction $S(x_1, \ldots, x_n)$, of all the functions that remain. If $F(x_1, \ldots, x_n)$ contains every alternative that occurs in $S$, we have a logical consequence of the set (1)–(5); if, on the other hand, $F$ lacks some alternative which occurs in $S$, the function in question, together with the condition that there shall be at least $n$ elements in the class determined by $f(x)$, will be incompatible with the set (1)–(5).

If we add to conditions (1)–(5) the following two,

(6) $(\exists x_1, x_2) \,.\, f(x_1) \,.\, f(x_2) \,.\, \sim(x_1 = x_2)$,

(7) $(x_1, x_3) :.\, (\exists x_2) : f(x_1) \,.\, f(x_3) \,.\, \sim(x_1 = x_3) \,.\supset.$
$f(x_2) \,.\, g(x_1, x_2, x_3)$,

we shall have a set which determines categorically the truth-value of every singly-general function, existential as well as universal, which can be constructed on the base $f(x), g(x, y, z)$ and which imposes restrictions only upon elements satisfying $f$; for these conditions ensure that there shall be a non-finite number of elements in the class determined by $f(x)$. It seems likely, too, that the set (1)–(7) determines the truth-value of every function, singly or multiply general, of the kind in question; but we shall not attempt to prove this.

## Section 5. Separation of Point-Pairs

We turn now to the definition of Separation of Point-Pairs, which is as follows:

$$(x_1, x_2, x_3, x_4, x_5) :. f(x_1) . f(x_2) . f(x_3) . f(x_4) . f(x_5) . \supset :$$

(1) $g(x_1, x_2, x_3, x_4) \supset d(x_1, x_2, x_3, x_4) :$

(2) $d(x_1, x_2, x_3, x_4) \supset P(g, x_1, x_2, x_3, x_4) :$[7]

(3) $g(x_1, x_2, x_3, x_4) \supset g(x_2, x_3, x_4, x_1) :$

(4) $g(x_1, x_2, x_3, x_4) \supset \sim g(x_1, x_2, x_4, x_3) :$

(5) $g(x_1, x_2, x_3, x_4) \supset g(x_4, x_3, x_2, x_1) :$

(6) $d(x_1, x_2, x_3, x_4, x_5) . g(x_1, x_2, x_3, x_4) . \supset .$
$g(x_1, x_5, x_3, x_4) \vee g(x_1, x_2, x_3, x_5).$

We wish to show that any extensional singly-general universal function in $n$ generalized variables which is constructed on the base of this set and which restricts only elements belonging to the class determined by $f(x)$ either is implied by these six properties or else, in conjunction with the condition that there shall be at least $n$ elements satisfying $f$, is incompatible with them.[8]

In consequence of conditions (3), (4), and (5), if $g(x_1, x_2, x_3, x_4)$ holds, then

$$g(x_2, x_3, x_4, x_1), g(x_3, x_4, x_1, x_2), g(x_4, x_1, x_2, x_3),$$
$$g(x_4, x_3, x_2, x_1), g(x_3, x_2, x_1, x_4), g(x_2, x_1, x_4, x_3), g(x_1, x_4, x_3, x_2)$$

all hold, and $g$ fails for each of the remaining sixteen permutations of $x_1, x_2, x_3, x_4$. Moreover, in virtue of (1), $g$ fails unless the four variables take distinct values, so that we have $\sim g(x_1, x_2, x_3, x_3)$, $\sim g(x_1, x_1, x_1, x_1)$, etc. We may represent the conjunction of $g(x_1, x_2, x_3, x_4)$ with all these consequences by $R(x_1, x_2, x_3, x_4)$. And we may, similarly, allow $R(x_1, x_2, x_3)$ to stand for the con-

[7] That is, $g$ holds for at least one of the twenty-four permutations of $x_1$, $x_2$, $x_3$, $x_4$.

[8] A more discursive and less rigorous presentation of what is essentially the proof here given will be found in *Trans. Amer. Math. Soc.*, XXIX (1927), 96.

junction of the negatives of all functions that can be formed of $g$, $x_1$, $x_2$, $x_3$, and may employ $R(x_1, x_2)$ and $R(x_1)$ in the same way. Again, let us represent by $R(x_1, x_2, \ldots, x_n)$ the assertion that $R(x_i, x_j, x_k, x_l)$ holds for any four variables which occur in order from left to right. We have, then,

$$g(x_1, x_2, x_3, x_4) \equiv R(x_1, x_2, x_3, x_4),$$

and, in virtue of (2), $g$ holds for some permutation of any four distinct elements. Moreover, we have always $R(x_1, x_2, x_3)$, $R(x_1, x_2)$, and $R(x_1)$; so that for some permutation of any $n$ elements, $n \leqq 4$, $R(x_1, \ldots, x_n)$ holds.

Now, we wish to show that $R$ holds for some permutation of any $n$ elements, where $n$ is any finite number. And it will, of course, be sufficient to show that if $R$ holds for an assigned value of $n$, $\geqq 4$, it holds for $n + 1$.

It has been established in Chapter XI, Section 6, in connection with the definition of Separation of Point-Pairs, that from conditions (1)–(6),

$$g(x_1, x_2, x_3, x_4) \cdot g(x_1, x_2, x_3, x_5) \,.\supset.\, g(x_1, x_2, x_4, x_5) \vee g(x_1, x_2, x_5, x_4)$$

and $g(x_1, x_2, x_3, x_4) \cdot g(x_1, x_2, x_4, x_5) \,.\supset.\, g(x_1, x_2, x_3, x_5)$

follow; and we may therefore employ these theorems in the following argument. Moreover, it will be noted that, in virtue of conditions (3) and (5), if we have $R(x_1, x_2, x_3, x_4)$, then we can permute the variables cyclically and can also reverse this permutation, so that we shall have $R(x_2, x_3, x_4, x_1)$, etc., as well as $R(x_4, x_3, x_2, x_1)$, $R(x_3, x_2, x_1, x_4)$, etc.; and, in general, when we have $R(x_1, x_2, \ldots, x_{n-1}, x_n)$, we shall have $R(x_2, \ldots, x_{n-1}, x_n, x_1)$, etc., and $R(x_n, x_{n-1}, \ldots, x_2, x_1)$, $R(x_{n-1}, \ldots, x_2, x_1, x_n)$, etc., resulting from a cyclic permutation and its reverse.

Suppose, now, that $R$ holds for some permutation of any set of $n$ elements belonging to the class determined by $f(x)$. Any set of $n + 1$ elements has $n + 1$ subclasses of $n$ elements each, and for each subclass the relation $R$ holds for some permutation of its members.

It will be shown, in the first place, that there are at least three members of the set of $n + 1$ elements such that $R(a, b, c, x)$ holds for every element $x$ of the set other than $a$, $b$, and $c$. Take any subclass of $n$ elements, $a, b, c, \ldots$, such that $R(a, b, c, \ldots)$ holds, and call the element of the set of $n + 1$ members which does not belong to this subclass $e$. Now, $R(a, b, c, x)$ holds for every $x$ other than $a$, $b$, and $c$ in the set of $n$ elements; and if $R(a, b, c, e)$, then the requirement is satisfied. Let $z$ be some one of the set of $n + 1$ elements other than $a$, $b$, $c$, and $e$, so that we have $R(a, b, c, z)$. By (6), $R(a, b, c, z)$ implies $R(a, b, c, e)$ or $R(a, e, c, z)$, and we may therefore suppose that the latter holds. $R(a, e, c, z)$ implies $R(e, c, z, a)$, which implies $R(a, z, c, e)$; and $R(a, b, c, z)$ implies $R(b, c, z, a)$, which implies $R(a, z, c, b)$. $R(a, z, c, e)$ and $R(a, z, c, b)$ imply $R(a, z, e, b)$ or $R(a, z, b, e)$, where $R(a, z, e, b)$ implies $R(z, e, b, a)$, which implies $R(a, b, e, z)$, and $R(a, z, b, e)$ implies $R(z, b, e, a)$, which implies $R(a, e, b, z)$; so that we have $R(a, b, e, z)$ or $R(a, e, b, z)$. Suppose, in the first place, that $R(a, b, e, z)$ holds. This implies $R(z, e, b, a)$, which implies $R(e, b, a, z)$, which implies $R(b, a, z, e)$; and $R(a, b, c, z)$ implies $R(z, c, b, a)$, which implies $R(c, b, a, z)$, which implies $R(b, a, z, c)$; whereas $R(b, a, z, e)$ and $R(b, a, z, c)$ imply $R(b, a, e, c)$ or $R(b, a, c, e)$. If $R(b, a, e, c)$ holds, then $R(a, b, c, e)$ will hold, where $a$, $b$, and $c$ satisfy the required condition; if $R(b, a, c, e)$, then $R(a, b, e, c)$, and this together with $R(a, b, c, z)$ implies $R(a, b, e, z)$, where $a$, $b$, and $e$ satisfy the required condition. Suppose, in the second place, that $R(a, e, b, z)$ holds. This implies $R(a, c, b, z)$ or $R(a, e, b, c)$. But $R(a, b, c, z)$ implies $R(z, a, b, c)$, and $R(a, c, b, z)$ implies $R(z, a, c, b)$, which is contrary to $R(z, a, b, c)$; so that we have $R(a, e, b, c)$. And here $a$, $e$, and $b$ satisfy the required condition.

Now, let us take any set of $n + 1$ elements, where, by hypothesis, $R$ holds for some permutation of any $n$ of them, and let us assign these elements severally as values to the variables $x_1, x_2, \ldots, x_{n+1}$. As has just been shown, there will be three elements of the set of $n + 1$, say $x_1, x_2, x_3$, such that $R(x_1, x_2, x_3, x_i)$ holds for every $x_i$ $(i > 3)$. And if we discard $x_3$ from the set, we shall have $R$ holding for some permutation of the remainder. There will be no pair of variables $x_j$, $x_k$ in the set of

$n$ (got by discarding $x_3$) such that $R(x_1, x_j, x_2, x_k)$ holds. For $R(x_1, x_2, x_3, x_j)$ and $R(x_1, x_2, x_3, x_k)$ imply $R(x_1, x_2, x_j, x_k)$ or $R(x_1, x_2, x_k, x_j)$. If $R(x_1, x_2, x_j, x_k)$ holds, then $R(x_k, x_1, x_2, x_j)$ will hold, whereas $R(x_1, x_j, x_2, x_k)$ implies $R(x_k, x_1, x_j, x_2)$, which is contrary to $R(x_k, x_1, x_2, x_j)$; and so in the other case. Thus, in any permutation of the $n$ variables for which $R$ holds, every variable $x_i$, other than $x_1$ and $x_2$, is such that it occurs between $x_1$ and $x_2$ or else no variable is so. We shall have, therefore, $R(x_1, x_2, \ldots)$, $R(x_2, x_1, \ldots)$, $R(\ldots, x_1, x_2)$, $R(\ldots, x_2, x_1)$, $R(x_1, \ldots, x_2)$, or $R(x_2, \ldots, x_1)$. But since, as pointed out above, we can reverse the order of the variables, and permute them cyclically, it is always possible so to choose $R$ that we have $R(x_1, x_2, \ldots)$.

We have, then, $R(x_1, x_2, x_4, \ldots)$ for the $n$ variables among which $x_3$ does not occur. And we wish to show that $R(x_1, x_2, x_3, x_4, \ldots)$ holds, that is, that $x_3$ can be inserted between $x_2$ and $x_4$.

Let $x_i$ be any variable among the $n + 1$ other than $x_1$, $x_2$, and $x_3$; and let $x_{i1}$, $x_{i2}$ be any two of these variables which occur in $R(x_1, x_2, x_4, \ldots)$ in the order $x_{i1}$, $x_{i2}$. Then we have $R(x_1, x_2, x_3, x_i)$ and $R(x_1, x_2, x_{i1}, x_{i2})$. Now, $R(x_1, x_2, x_3, x_{i1})$ implies $R(x_{i1}, x_3, x_2, x_1)$, which implies $R(x_3, x_2, x_1, x_{i1})$; and, similarly, $R(x_1, x_2, x_3, x_{i2})$ implies $R(x_3, x_2, x_1, x_{i2})$. $R(x_3, x_2, x_1, x_{i1})$ and $R(x_3, x_2, x_1, x_{i2})$ imply $R(x_3, x_2, x_{i1}, x_{i2})$ or $R(x_3, x_2, x_{i2}, x_{i1})$, where the first alternative implies $R(x_2, x_{i1}, x_{i2}, x_3)$. $R(x_1, x_2, x_{i1}, x_{i2})$ implies $R(x_2, x_{i1}, x_{i2}, x_1)$; and $R(x_2, x_{i1}, x_{i2}, x_3)$ and $R(x_2, x_{i1}, x_{i2}, x_1)$ imply $R(x_2, x_{i1}, x_1, x_3)$ or $R(x_2, x_{i1}, x_3, x_1)$. Here, however, $R(x_2, x_{i1}, x_1, x_3)$ implies $R(x_{i1}, x_1, x_3, x_2)$, which is contrary to $R(x_{i1}, x_1, x_2, x_3)$; and $R(x_2, x_{i1}, x_3, x_1)$ implies $R(x_1, x_2, x_{i1}, x_3)$, which is contrary to $R(x_1, x_2, x_3, x_{i1})$; so that $R(x_3, x_2, x_{i1}, x_{i2})$ must fail, and $R(x_3, x_2, x_{i2}, x_{i1})$ hold. But this latter implies $R(x_2, x_3, x_{i1}, x_{i2})$. Again, $R(x_1, x_2, x_{i1}, x_{i2})$ implies $R(x_{i2}, x_{i1}, x_2, x_1)$, and $R(x_2, x_3, x_{i1}, x_{i2})$ implies $R(x_{i2}, x_{i1}, x_3, x_2)$; but these, jointly, imply $R(x_{i2}, x_{i1}, x_3, x_1)$, which implies $R(x_1, x_3, x_{i1}, x_{i2})$.

We have now $R(x_1, x_2, x_3, x_i)$, $R(x_1, x_2, x_{i1}, x_{i2})$, $R(x_1, x_3, x_{i1}, x_{i2})$, and $R(x_2, x_3, x_{i1}, x_{i2})$. And we have also $R(x_1, x_{i1}, x_{i2}, x_{i3})$ and $R(x_2, x_{i1}, x_{i2}, x_{i3})$, where $x_{i1}$, $x_{i2}$, $x_{i3}$ are any three variables other than $x_1$, $x_2$ which occur in $R(x_1, x_2, x_4, \ldots)$ in the order given. It remains to be shown, therefore, that $R(x_3, x_{i1}, x_{i2}, x_{i3})$ holds. $R(x_2, x_3, x_{i1}, x_{i2})$ implies $R(x_3, x_{i1}, x_{i2}, x_2)$, which implies $R(x_3, x_{i1}, x_{i2}, x_{i3})$ or $R(x_3, x_{i3}, x_{i2}, x_2)$, where the latter is contrary to $R(x_2, x_3, x_{i2}, x_{i3})$. Hence $R(x_1, x_2, x_3, \ldots, x_{n+1})$ holds.

The remainder of the argument proceeds exactly as in the cases of Betweenness and Cyclic Order.

## CHAPTER XIII

### THE LOGICAL PARADOXES

A paradox arises whenever we seem to have two incompatible propositions both of which, for certain reasons, would, if appearances were correct, be true. We say here "*seem* to have" two true incompatible propositions because, of course, we never do actually have any such state of affairs. A paradox is always a matter of mistaken appearance, and its resolution will consist simply in disclosing the precise character of the mistake involved. When we apparently have two true incompatible propositions, it may be that we do not have two propositions at all, but only two verbal expressions, at least one of which does not express a proposition; or it may be that we have two genuine propositions which are not actually incompatible, or it may be that we have two incompatible propositions at least one of which is false; and the resolution of the difficulty will be effected when any one of these possibilities is shown to be in fact the case. Now, a *logical* paradox arises whenever we seem to have two incompatible propositions true on logical grounds or for logical reasons. And it is with this class of cases that we are here concerned. We shall first examine some examples of paradoxes of different sorts, and shall consider how they are to be classified according to the nature of the difficulties involved; we shall then try to get some notion of the theories that can be advanced by way of explaining their occurrence, as well as of the technique that has been used for the purpose of avoiding them in practice.

Let us take, to begin with, what is perhaps the simplest and best-known example in connection with which we get a logical paradox; namely, that in which we consider what significance the words "I am speaking falsely" or, perhaps better, "This proposition is false" can have, where, if we had a genuine statement, we should have one that was its own subject. In the expression "This proposition is false," the words "This proposition" pretend to designate the whole statement as well as the subject, since these would be the same; and it is clear, therefore, that we can represent the situation in the following way. Let $p$ be the name of a proposition, and let the proposition of which it is the name be "$p$ is false," so that we can write

$$p\colon\ p \text{ is false.}$$

It looks as if these words expressed a genuine statement, and yet, in view of certain considerations, it would seem that this could not possibly be the case; so that we have two incompatible appearances, both claiming assent. If $p$ named a proposition, then it could be replaced by its meaning, and we should have "($p$ is false) is false," that is, "$p$ is true." But if, in turn, $p$ were replaced by its meaning in "$p$ is true," we should have "($p$ is false) is true," that is, "$p$ is false." Thus, not only would $p$ imply its own contradictory, but this contradictory would in turn imply it. That is to say, we should have both $p \prec \sim p$ and $\sim p \prec p$; and this is what is known as a vicious circle. So, if $p$ stood for a proposition, it would have to stand for one that was both true and false; from which it follows, of course, that $p$ does not stand for a proposition at all.

Let us take now a similar form of expression, which, although it does not give rise to a vicious circle, does involve a state of affairs that is equally objectionable. Consider the two expressions

$$p_1\colon\ p_2 \text{ is false,}$$
$$p_2\colon\ p_1 \text{ is false,}$$

where the first has the second as subject and is itself the subject of the second. That no vicious circle arises here may be seen in the following way. Suppose $p_1$ to be true: then, since it says that $p_2$ is false, $p_2$ must be false; but $p_2$ says that $p_1$ is false, and therefore $p_1$ is true, which is the assumption with which we began. Again, suppose that $p_1$ is false: then, since it says that $p_2$ is false, $p_2$ must be true; but $p_2$ says that $p_1$ is false, and therefore $p_1$ is false, which is the assumption with which we began. It is clear that we can assume either of these expressions to be true, or false, as we like, and that tbe other will then merely have to be supposed to take the opposite truth-value. But in this there is, of course, nothing objectionable.

It has sometimes been maintained that because the two verbal expressions here in question do not lead to a vicious circle, there is no objection to regarding them as expressing genuine propositions. This, however, is a mistake. And the mere fact that when we examine them and endeavor to grasp their import, they neither seem to be false nor seem to be true should make us doubtful from the outset whether they can really express propositions. It is, indeed, quite easy to see that they cannot do so. Let us take the expression "$p_2$ is false" and replace $p_2$ by what it stands for, so that we shall have "($p_1$ is false) is false." This does not completely explicate the expression "$p_2$ is false," because $p_1$ remains to be replaced by its meaning. And, of course, when this is done, there will result an expression in which $p_2$ remains to be replaced by its meaning, and so on. We have, that is to say, an infinite sequence of more and more complicated expressions, each of which requires explication before its import can become definite; so that no one of the expressions can be significant unless the sequence terminates, which it does not do. Let us put the matter in another way. We have here two supposedly defined symbols, $p_1$ and $p_2$; and, of course, if they are properly defined, it must be possible to replace them, ultimately, by their undefined equivalents. But when this is attempted, we see that it can never be done, owing to the fact that the sequence of substitutions never ends, and so never ends in any undefined expression. What has happened is, of course, that we have pretended to define $p_1$ and $p_2$ in terms of each other and have therefore not assigned to them any meanings at all. We may call the sequence that develops here a vicious regression.

Consider now the cycle of three expressions,

$$p_1\colon\ p_2 \text{ is false,}$$

$$p_2\colon\ p_3 \text{ is false,}$$

$$p_3\colon\ p_1 \text{ is false,}$$

where $p_1$ is about $p_2$, which is about $p_3$, which, in turn, is about $p_1$. It is easy to see that we are here involved in a vicious circle, as we were in the first case. Suppose that $p_1$ is true: then, since it says that $p_2$ is false, $p_2$ must be false; but $p_2$ says that $p_3$ is false, so that $p_3$ must be true; and $p_3$ says that $p_1$ is false, which is contrary to the initial supposition. Again, suppose that $p_1$ is false: then $p_2$ must be true; and since it says that $p_3$ is false, $p_3$ must be false; but $p_3$ says that $p_1$ is false, and therefore $p_1$ must be true, contrary to the initial supposition.

Anybody who will set up and examine an analogous cycle of four expressions will discover that, in that case, no vicious circle occurs. And it will be seen, in general, that where there is an even number of negations, no vicious circle can be shown, but that where there is an odd number, one always can. It does not matter how many expressions there are in the cycle, but only how many negations there are. Thus,

$$p_1\text{: } p_2 \text{ is false,}$$

$$p_2\text{: } p_3 \text{ is true,}$$

$$p_3\text{: } p_1 \text{ is false,}$$

does not involve a vicious circle, though it does, of course, involve a vicious regression. And we must include in this generalization the case of zero negations, as in

$$p\text{: } p \text{ is true,}$$

where a vicious circle does not arise.

Let us take now, as an example of another well-known type of logical paradox, the proposition "All rules have exceptions." In this case, the question is not whether the words here used express a genuine proposition, but rather what, precisely, the import of the proposition they express is. And the question about the exact significance of these words arises in this way. In using them, we seem to be expressing a rule to the effect that all rules whatever have exceptions, from which it will of course follow that this rule does. But an exception to the rule that all rules have exceptions will be a rule without an exception, from which it will follow that some rules do not have exceptions. Thus, if we suppose that this proposition includes itself within its range of significance, we shall have to say that it is self-contradictory. Now, taken alone, this fact would commonly be held to constitute no good objection to the view that the proposition in question does apply to itself, as one is tempted to suppose it to do; for we apparently cannot, in turn, infer from the proposition "Some rules are without exceptions" that all rules have them, and thus obtain a vicious circle. Nevertheless, there is a genuine difficulty here, because the proposition seems, from one point of view, plainly to apply to itself, and yet, in virtue of other considerations, it seems to be incapable of doing so. We shall examine presently examples of what are apparently exactly analogous cases which, if supposed to be applicable to themselves, give rise to impossible logical situations; and this fact alone might incline one to hold that no proposition of the sort in question can fall within its own range of significance. Here, however, we shall merely examine more closely the exact import of this proposition, with a view to seeing whether the impression that it ought to apply to itself is borne out.

Let us represent by $\phi(x)$ the function "$x$ is a rule" and by $\psi(x)$ the function "$x$ has an exception." We shall then be able to express the proposition "Every rule has an exception" by

$$(x) \centerdot \phi(x) \supset \psi(x),$$

$$\text{or by} \quad \sim(\exists x) \centerdot \phi(x) \centerdot \sim\psi(x).$$

Now, we apparently have $\phi[(x) \centerdot \phi(x) \supset \psi(x)]$, and, therefore, $\psi[(x) \centerdot \phi(x) \supset \psi(x)]$, from which

$$(\exists x) \centerdot \phi(x) \centerdot \sim\psi(x)$$

will follow. The validity of this inference is dependent, however, upon the correctness of the intermediate premise $\phi[(x) \centerdot \phi(x) \supset \psi(x)]$, that is, "(Every rule has an exception) is a rule"; and the correctness of this will depend upon whether "Every rule has an exception" can be understood to be a 'rule' within the significance of that term as it occurs in the general principle. It is surely not easy to decide by direct inspection whether this is so; but some doubt will, perhaps, be thrown upon the correctness of the intermediate premise by the following consideration. The two functions which have been introduced, namely "$x$ is a rule" and "$x$ has an exception," are certainly open to further analysis. Thus, "$x$ has an exception" means, plainly, "$(\exists y) \centerdot y$ is an exception to $x$." And it may well be that, like 'exception,' the term 'rule' is also relational, and that "$x$ is a rule" will mean "$x$ is a rule about so-and-so"; so that we shall really be dealing with the function "$x$ is a rule about $z$," where $z$ is some description that must be satisfied by any value that can be used in transforming the function into a true proposition. If this is so, then, with obvious definitions, the proposition "Every rule has an exception" can be written

$$(x, z) : \phi(x, z) . \supset . (\exists y) . \psi(y, x).$$

And here, in order that the intermediate premise shall be valid, $\phi(x, z)$ must be transformed into a true proposition when "Every rule has an exception" is substituted for both $x$ and $z$. This may not occur. Indeed, the resulting expression may not even make sense; but that is a question of a sort to be discussed later on.

Before we go on to consider other examples of expressions involving paradoxical consequences, it will perhaps be well if we make as clear as possible some points with regard to the significance and nature of 'substitution' in connection with propositions and functions. Of course, when we substitute in an expression, we always get another expression, which results from the first by the act of substituting; and this process of substitution is simply a shorthand way of representing that the proposition expressed by the original expression implies the one expressed by the derived expression. There is, of course, no special efficacy in the act of substitution; it has to be validated solely by reference to the facts which it indirectly represents, and these facts have to be clearly understood before an argument can be carried through by means of it. In logic or mathematics, or any other subject-matter represented through an exact symbolism, talking about the symbols is often more convenient than talking about what they stand for. Thus, if we have the simple algebraic expression $x = y + z$, we may say "Bringing $z$ to the other side of the equation and changing its sign, we have $x - z = y$," and mean to convey, of course, that if $x$ is the sum of $y$ and $z$, then $z$ subtracted from $x$ is $y$. Anybody who listens to a mathematical exposition will discover that the expositor is, more often than not, simply talking about his symbols, and expecting his hearers to understand what this talk indirectly represents. When a difficulty arises, however, direct recourse to the meanings represented is in order.

Now, there are two different grounds upon which a substitution may be validated. Let us take, for example, the expression $(p) \cdot p \vee \sim p$, and substitute $q \vee r$ for $p$, so that we have $(q, r) \cdot (q \vee r) \vee \sim (q \vee r)$. It is often said that we have here replaced $p$ by the value $q \vee r$; but in fact this is not strictly a value of $p$ at all, since a value would be a proposition and $q \vee r$ is simply another function. What we are really doing is replacing the generic expression $p$ by the more specific expression $q \vee r$; and the ground upon which this can be done is, of course, that whatever is true of all propositions of the form $p$ must be true of all of the form $q \vee r$; the operation is valid because the original expression implies the derived one. We may say that this is a case of 'genus-species' substitution. But, now, suppose that instead of replacing $p$ by a more specific function, we replace it by one of its values, such for instance as "Men exist," so that we have "Men either do or do not exist." We have here substituted for $p \vee \sim p$ one of the propositions which it denotes, and we may, accordingly, call this a case of 'genus-instance' substitution. The ground upon which the substitution is to be validated is that whatever holds for all values of $p \vee \sim p$ holds for this particular one. And it is to be noted that here the prefix $(p)$ disappears in consequence of the substitution, but that in the case of a genus-species substitution it does not. A careful distinction between these two sorts of substitution is important, because it appears that paradoxical results arise only in connection with the genus-instance kind.

We may return now to the matter of giving examples of logical paradoxes. Let us consider the following situation, which will be seen to lead, on certain quite natural assumptions, to a logical impossibility. Suppose a person, A, to take a given interval of time (a period of five minutes, say) and during that interval to make only one assertion, namely, "Every proposition asserted by me during this interval is false."[1] Here we are

[1] Cf. Hilbert and Ackermann, *Grundzüge der theoretischen Logik*, p. 94.

inclined to reason in the following way: "If it is true that every proposition asserted by A on the given occasion is false, and if this very proposition falls within the interval in question, then it must be false, so that some proposition expressed by A will be true; but if the only one expressed is the one in question, it must be the one that is true, so that, again, every proposition expressed by A during the interval is false." Apparently, then, we have a vicious circle. In fact, however, we do not have one, although the situation is equally vicious.

Let $\phi(p)$ mean "$p$ is a proposition asserted by A during the interval," so that we shall have $(p) . \phi(p) \supset {\sim}p$; and let us replace this complex expression by $P$. We seem to have $\phi(P)$, from which ${\sim}P$ is to be inferred. But, then, in order to get back to $P$ from ${\sim}P$, we require the premise $\phi(P) : (q) . \phi(q) \supset (q = P)$, that is, "$P$ was asserted by A during the interval, and was the only thing he said"; and each part of this compound premise is a material assumption, which can be denied without contradiction. The situation is this: if the compound assumption is true, then we have both $P$ and ${\sim}P$, so that, by the principle of contradiction, this assumption is impossible. But we can see, by inspection, that the assumption is quite possible, and we have, therefore, both

$$\Diamond[\phi(P) : (q) . \phi(q) \supset (q = P)] \text{ and } {\sim}\Diamond[\phi(P) : (q) . \phi(q) \supset (q = P)].$$

This is the paradox that arises. It is not a vicious circle, because, although from the first of these propositions the second can be inferred, we cannot argue conversely; it is simply that the first can be established on independent grounds and so cannot be allowed to refute itself by implying its contradictory. We have here a state of affairs in accordance with which, if the logical possibility in question were actually realized (as it might easily be), then we could appear to show on logical grounds that there was no realization. That is to say, if A actually did make the assertion in question during a given interval, we should be able to show that he did not do so; and this would involve an incompatibility between logic and fact. There can be little doubt what the resolution of this difficulty must be. We must deny that the statement "Every proposition expressed by A during the given interval is false" could be understood to apply to itself, and must say that it would be true, because there would be no proposition at all of the kind intended.

The next example to be dealt with is analogous to the one here considered, and involves exactly the same difficulty. This is the well-known 'Epimenides,' according to which Epimenides the Cretan said, "All Cretans are liars," and meant, if we are to find anything paradoxical in his assertion, that all statements made by Cretans were false.[2] There is one further condition to be added in order that the difficulty may be properly developed; but note first what happens so far. Obviously, the assertion of Epimenides, if it is to be understood to include itself within its scope, cannot be true, and we shall have consequently "Some statement made by some Cretan is true," unless we are prepared to deny either that Epimenides was a Cretan or that he made the statement. But, now, it is plainly logically possible that all other statements made by Cretans should have been false, as well as that there should have been a Cretan who made the statement in question, and we may suppose all this to be the case. Then the only statement made by a Cretan that can be true is the one made by Epimenides; and it can be true only by being false. Hence, our plain logical possibility that all other assertions should have been false would appear to be impossible. We have here, as in the example just considered, a flat confrontation of a logical possibility with a logical impossibility; and there can be little doubt, in this case also, that we must deny the assumption that Epimenides' assertion can fall within its own range of significance.

Let us take now a simple example of a kind expressible wholly in logical symbols, which resembles in other respects the example given above about 'all rules.' Suppose we write $(p) . \sim p$, that is, "Every proposition is false," and infer from this $(\exists p) . p$, by substituting $\sim(\exists p) . p$ for $p$ in the first expression. Since this result is the contradictory of the proposition from which we purport to derive it, that proposition has been shown to be self-contradictory, provided the substitution is valid. But the initial expression, in any case, expresses what is impossible, and thus

[2] For this and other examples here given, see *Principia Mathematica*, I, 60.

the mere fact that we can show a contradiction in consequence of this substitution is hardly in itself a sufficient reason for holding the substitution to be invalid. And it is not easy to say whether a substitution of this kind can be so interpreted as to be valid. It is an interesting circumstance, however, which we may note in this connection, that whenever we have a proposition of the kind here in question which does not express an impossibility, no contradiction ever results from any substitution that may be made. Thus, let us take the principle of excluded middle as expressed by $(p) . p \vee {\sim}p$, and replace the $p$ in it by the whole expression, so that we shall have

$$(p) . p \vee {\sim}p . \vee . {\sim}(p) . p \vee {\sim}p.$$

On the face of it, this is a case of genus-instance substitution, since the derived proposition appears to be an instance of the matrix of the original one. But it is worth observing that even if, for some reason, this substitution were shown to be inadmissible as such, it could still be validated in another way, inasmuch as the second proposition really is a logical consequence of the first. For $(p) . p \vee {\sim}p$ implies

$$(p) : p \vee {\sim}p . \vee . {\sim}(p \vee {\sim}p),$$

which implies

$$(p) : . (\exists q) : p \vee {\sim}p . \vee . {\sim}(q \vee {\sim}q),$$

which is equivalent to

$$(p) . p \vee {\sim}p . \vee . (\exists q) . {\sim}q . q.$$

It may be well to emphasize again the point that a substitution has no significance in itself and is to be validated solely on the ground that the resulting expression stands for a proposition which can be inferred from the one for which the original expression stands.

We come now to an example which is of considerable importance in logical theory, because it has to do with the question what kinds of things can be significantly said to be members of given classes. It might be supposed that if we had a class comprising a given membership, then we could say of any entity whatever other than each of the members of this class that it was not a member. It might be supposed, in particular, that a class would sometimes be one of its own members and sometimes not; or, at the very least, that we could significantly say of classes that they never were members of themselves. Thus we might be inclined to say that the class of men was not a man, that the class of chairs was not a chair, etc., and therefore that such classes as these were not found within their own membership; but, on the other hand, it might appear that the class of entities was an entity, that the class of classes was a class, etc., and thus that these classes were members of themselves. Consider, however, the following paradoxical situation which arises in this connection. Let us take the class of all classes, $K$. Of each member of this class, we can ask whether it falls within its own membership; so that we can divide $K$ into two mutually exclusive and jointly exhaustive subclasses, $C$ and $\sim C$, where the first comprises all self-membered classes and the second all classes that are not members of themselves, and where, of course, one subclass or the other might conceivably be null. It may then be asked whether $\sim C$ is or is not a self-membered class. If it is, then it must belong to $C$, which contains all self-membered classes; but if it belongs to $C$, it cannot belong to itself, and so cannot be a self-membered class; hence, it must belong to itself and therefore must, again, belong to $C$. That is to say, if $\sim C$ belongs to $C$, then it belongs to $\sim C$, and if it belongs to $\sim C$, then it belongs to $C$.[3] Apparently it cannot be significant to say of classes either that they are or that they are not members of themselves. In enunciating this doctrine, however, we might be thought to be violating it, since we might seem to be presupposing the significance of such an expression as "Classes are never members of themselves." But what is meant is that the concepts 'being a class' and 'being a member of' cannot be synthesized into a genuine proposition in the manner which one would be inclined to represent by "$C$ is a member of $C$"; and this presumably can be significantly said.

The paradox here in question is essentially the same as that about predicates predicable or not predicable of themselves. It is to be supposed that any predicate, say 'being red,' either

[3] *Principia Mathematica*, I, 77.

is or is not predicable of itself—'red' either is or is not red. But, then, when we consider whether the predicate 'not predicable of itself' is or is not predicable of itself, we find that if it is, it cannot be, and if it is not, it must be. The most important form of this paradox occurs in connection with functions. If $F$ is any function, it might be supposed that one of the two, $F(f)$ or $\sim F(f)$, would have to be true, whatever function $f$ might be. But suppose that $F(f)$ means "$f$ is a value which satisfies $f$," so that $\sim F(f)$ will mean "$f$ does not satisfy itself." Then $F(\sim F)$ will mean that $\sim F$ satisfies itself, and we shall have $\sim F(\sim F)$; whereas this latter will mean that $\sim F$ does not satisfy $\sim F$, and must, therefore, satisfy $F$. Thus, $F(\sim F)$ will imply and be implied by $\sim F(\sim F)$.

Finally, we may consider what appears to be a form of this same paradox which arises in connection with the relations of adjective-words to their meanings. Each adjective-word has, of course, an associated adjective, which is its meaning; and it is to be presumed that this meaning will sometimes apply to the word itself, and sometimes not. Thus, 'long' is not a long word, 'bad' is not a bad word, 'big' is not a big word, etc., so that what these words mean does not apply to the words themselves. On the other hand, 'short' is a short word, 'good' is a good word, etc., and each of these does have a meaning which applies to it. We may, accordingly, divide all such words into *autological* adjective-words, which are those whose meanings apply to them, and *heterological* adjective-words, which are those whose meanings do not. But, now, 'autological' and 'heterological' are adjective-words, so that the question may be raised whether 'heterological' is heterological. If it is, it must be autological, since its meaning will apply to it, but if this is so, it must, in turn, be heterological, since that is what it means for this word to be autological.[4]

The foregoing examples would seem to afford a fair sample of the difficulties we are called upon to face, and it will now be in order to raise the question what general solution of these difficulties can be offered. We are going to explain, to begin with, the only thoroughgoing solution which has been advanced,

[4] For a detailed analysis of this paradox, which is due to Weyl, see F. P. Ramsey, *The Foundations of Mathematics*, pp. 27 and 42 ff.

namely, that due to Mr. Bertrand Russell, and known as The Theory of Logical Types.[5] We shall then make some criticisms regarding this doctrine, and suggest certain modifications of it.

Mr. Russell does not attempt to compromise with any of the difficulties that have been brought out by the examples given above, nor does he attempt to explain any of them away as arising merely from minor errors in the use of symbols. He holds, on the contrary, that they all involve serious logical fallacies, which can be overcome only if we recognize that logical entities are not all of one sort, but rather fall into a hierarchy of kinds or types, which are radically distinct among themselves, however similar their verbal symbolization in ordinary language may be. The hierarchy of types which Mr. Russell constructs is not in the first instance a propositional one, although a propositional hierarchy results by implication; his fundamental division of logical entities begins with individuals, or particular things, and goes on up through functions of different kinds; but it will, perhaps, be conducive to clarity in understanding the matter if we begin with propositions, and see first how distinctions of type seem to be forced upon us in connection with them.

We may take the example about 'all rules,' where we say that "All rules have exceptions," and where we seem, at least in many cases, to be making a statement that is not in fact self-contradictory, as we should be doing if the statement fell within its own range of application. Mr. Russell maintains that the sense of the term 'rule' as it occurs in this statement is a very different one from the sense in which the statement itself is a rule. The sense that would ordinarily be intended in the statement made might be expressed roughly by saying that a rule about things was meant, whereas the statement itself is not a rule about things at all, but a rule about rules about things.

There is nothing unusual in this situation, since it often happens that a generic term is used where some unexpressed

[5] See, especially, *Principia Mathematica*, I, Ch. II, pp. 37 ff., and ✳12, pp. 161 ff. Although the references are to *Principia*, we speak throughout of Mr. Russell, because the theory had been previously published by him. See *American Journal of Mathematics*, XXX (1908), 222–262.

restriction is intended; and there can be no doubt that such a sequence of propositions as the one indicated does exist. However, Mr. Russell's main point in this connection has not been explained: he maintains that there is no generic meaning of the term 'rule' which can be specified into 'rule about things,' 'rule about rules about things,' etc. If there were, we could make use of that generic conception, and assert "All rules have exceptions" in a sense in which the statement would apply to itself; and this is what Mr. Russell wishes to deny that we can do. Accordingly, we should write 'rule-about-things' and 'rule-about-rules-about-things' to indicate that it is the whole phrase, in each case, which carries a single meaning, and we should not confuse these phrases with expressions like 'red square thing' and 'red round thing,' where there really is a common subordinate meaning corresponding to the word 'red.'

It has been pointed out above that this example about 'all rules' does not by itself appear to necessitate the construction of a hierarchy, because it does not seem to give rise to a logically impossible state of affairs when the term 'rule' is interpreted univocally. But other examples that we have considered do seem quite clearly to substantiate Mr. Russell's view, since they result in vicious circles or other logical impossibilities. Let us take the case in which A says, during a given interval of time, "All propositions expressed by me during this interval are false" and says nothing else. We can here make the same distinction as before: if A means to say, "All propositions about things expressed by me during this interval are false," then what he means will be true, since there will be no proposition of the kind in question expressed by him. Of course, in this case as in the other, a hierarchy results; but here it seems absolutely necessary to interpret the term 'proposition' equivocally rather than univocally. If we suppose this term to have a generic meaning applicable equally to propositions about things and to those about propositions about things, we shall get the sheer logical nonsense pointed out above in connection with this example. It will be impossible either that the proposition in question should be true or that it should be false.

Consider, now, the so-called principle of excluded middle, as expressed by $(p) . p \vee \sim p$, that is, "Every proposition is either true or false." In accordance with what has already been said, we shall have to begin by interpreting "proposition" here as meaning 'proposition-about-things,' and the principle stated will accordingly be restricted in its range of application, and will not itself fall within that range. But, then, if this is so, we shall require another principle of excluded middle that shall be applicable to the first one and to propositions of its kind; so that we must introduce a new variable $p'$, which will denote propositions denoting propositions about things, and must write $(p') . p' \vee \sim p'$. Of course, this principle will, in turn, be limited in its range of application, and we must have a further principle, $(p'') . p'' \vee \sim p''$; so that an infinite hierarchy will result. Again, consider the expression $(p) . \sim p$, that is, "All propositions are false," from which we got by substitution $(\exists p) . p$. In Mr. Russell's view, the $p$ here must refer to propositions of some one order, and this cannot be the order to which the proposition itself belongs; so that it cannot be a value of its own variable, and the supposed contradiction does not follow. It is true that this proposition does imply a contradiction, since if $P$ is any value falling within the range of $p$, we shall have both $P$ and $\sim P$; but this is to be expected in the case of an impossible proposition and need entail no difficulty.

We seem to be faced, then, with the necessity of conceiving a hierarchy of propositions in each of these cases. But the question arises whether there are separate hierarchies or whether the several cases fit together in such a way that there will be only one, with each proposition falling on some one level. Mr. Russell's view is that the latter is the case, as we have already suggested in speaking of propositions about things, propositions about propositions about things, etc., as if any statement whatever would find a place in such an arrangement. The evidence in favor of this view will be clearer when the hierarchy of functions has been explained, but we may here note two points that will perhaps have some weight. Let us take again the example about 'all rules.' If we had merely to conceive a separate hierarchy made up of the propositions "All rules about things have exceptions," "All rules about rules about things have exceptions," etc., it would seem to be possible to get round the contradiction involved in the generic use of the term 'rule' by saying "All rules have exceptions except this one." But, then, here is a new rule, which will be implied to have an exception unless we make a dispensation in its favor by saying "All rules have exceptions except this one, except this one." Obviously, a vicious regression is entailed. And it seems pretty clear that we cannot conceive a hierarchy which has only one proposition on each level; many other propositions will inevitably have to fall into the scheme. Moreover, we have seen that there must apparently be a hierarchy of principles of excluded middle. But if this is so, then each proposition will have to fall under one and only one of these principles, and that, by itself, will arrange all propositions into one single hierarchy.

We may turn now to the hierarchy of functions and individuals which Mr. Russell constructs, and from which that of propositions results. The reason why a hierarchy of propositions is not sufficient is that propositions are complex entities, and involve constituents which are not interchangeable in a given logical context. Thus, let us take such elementary propositions as "$a$ is round," "$b$ is red," etc., and suppose that we wish to denote them by the function $f(x)$, where $x$ will stand for $a$, $b$, .... The variables $f$ and $x$ cannot be interchanged and cannot take the same range of values, because "round is $a$," "red is red," "$b$ is $b$," etc., do not make sense. If, therefore, we are to avoid nonsense as a consequence of substituting values for the variables in this function, we shall have to proceed in some such way as the following. We may hold that when a value, say that of 'being round,' is assigned to $f$ in the function $f(x)$, we get the function "$x$ is round," which, in turn, gives rise to a proposition when one of the values $a$, $b$, ... is substituted for $x$. Then, since 'being round' cannot be a value of $x$, two types of entities appear, namely, "$x$ is round," "$x$ is red," ..., on the one hand, and $a$, $b$, ..., on the other. And this will, of course, force upon us two classes of variables, $x$, $y$, ..., which denote particular things, and $f$, $g$, ..., which denote properties of the sort here indicated.

It is to be noted also that elementary functions of propositions like "*a* is round" admit of this same analysis. Thus, "~(*a* is round)" and "*a* is round . ∨ . *b* is red" give rise to the functions "~(*x* is round)" and "*x* is round . ∨ . *y* is red," which result from $f(x)$ and $g(x, y)$ when values are assigned to $f$ and $g$. If several propositions are of a given type, then any proposition built up out of them by means of ∨, ., and ~ is of the same type; and if several functions are of a given type, any elementary combination of these functions is of that type.

It will now be in order to explain the principle in accordance with which Mr. Russell constructs his functional hierarchy. There is a distinction here that may be drawn at the outset, namely, that between 'orders' and 'types.' The hierarchy consists first of functions of different orders, and then the functions belonging to a given order subdivide into different types within that order. Thus, functions of different orders are necessarily of different types, whereas functions of the same order may or may not be of the same type.[6] However, not much emphasis is placed upon this difference of type within the same order, and for all practical purposes functions of the same order can be regarded as being of the same type. The reason is that the principle which enables us to avoid reflexive fallacies is fully satisfied if the type of a proposition or function is simply identified with its order, the distinction of type from order being a theoretical matter that can be neglected in practice.

Now, we are concerned with functions only in so far as they fall into different orders, and with the principle in response to which this division is to be made. Mr. Russell formulates this principle as follows: "Whatever involves *all* of a collection must not be one of the collection; or, conversely: If, provided a certain collection had a total, it would have members only definable in terms of that total, then the collection has no total."[7] This is called the 'vicious-circle principle,' because often, though not always, its violation results in the occurrence of a vicious circle.

[6] *Loc. cit.*, ✳9 and ✳12, esp. p. 162.
[7] *Loc. cit.*, p. 37.

It is easy to give examples of the kind of situations this principle is meant to apply to. Thus, take the function "$x$ is round," where $x$ denotes any individual thing. This function itself cannot, according to the principle, be one of the entities denoted by $x$, because that totality is, as it were, already presupposed in the definition of the function; or, to put the matter in another way, since the function in question ranges over the totality of the values of $x$, it cannot itself be a member of that totality. Again, in the case of the assertion "All rules have exceptions," there is a reference to some totality of 'rules,' but the proposition through which that reference is effected cannot be one of the entities referred to. And in the same way, the expression "All propositions are false" must refer to some totality of propositions so restricted that the assertion itself does not fall within the domain of its own reference. In short, no variable can be one of its own values, nor can it take as a value anything that involves it as a constituent.

Consider now the functions "$x$ is near $y$," where $x$ and $y$ are free variables; "$(\exists x) . x$ is near $y$," where $x$ is generalized and $y$ is free; "$x$ is near $a$," where $x$ is free and $a$ is a constant; "$(\exists x) : (\exists z) . y$ is between $x$ and $z$," where $x$ and $z$ are generalized and $y$ is free. These are functions of the 'first order,' a first-order function being one that involves reference to no totality other than that of individuals. And, of course, elementary combinations of functions like these, such as "$x$ is near $y . \vee . x$ is near $a$," as well as such functions as "$\sim(\exists x) : x$ is near $y . \vee . x$ is near $a$," are to be included among first-order functions, since they, too, refer to no totality except that of individuals.

Consider, however, the function $f(x)$, which takes as values propositions like "$a$ is round" and "$(\exists y) . a$ is near $y$." When values are assigned to $f$, first-order functions result, and therefore $f(x)$ cannot, according to the vicious-circle principle, be of the first order. It is said to be of the 'second order,' and so is each of the functions:

$$\sim f(x), \quad f(x) \vee \sim g(x), \quad (x) . f(x) \vee g(x),$$
$$(\exists f, x) . f(x) . g(x), \quad f(x) . \vee . (\exists g, y) . g(y).$$

It will be seen that these functions are constructed wholly of logical constants and variables, and that they differ in this respect from the examples given of first-order functions. Second-order functions sometimes involve non-logical constituents, as in the case of $f(a) \vee g(x)$, where $a$ is a constant; they differ from functions of the first order in that these latter cannot be constructed out of logical materials alone.

Let us consider now the class of all second-order functions. We shall want variables to be used in constructing functions which will give rise to second-order functions when values are assigned to some of the variables, and we cannot, according to the vicious-circle principle, employ $f, g, \ldots$ for this purpose, since they will be constituents of the functions to be denoted. We must, therefore, introduce additional variables, $F, G, \ldots,$ which will appear in a new kind of functions, of which the following are examples:

$$\sim F[f, x], \quad (\exists f) . F[f(x)], \quad (\exists F, f) . F[f(x)], \quad (F, f) . F[f, x],$$
$$F[f(x)] \vee G[g(x)], \quad (\exists F) . F[f, x] . G[g, x].$$

Take the function $f(a)$, where $a$ is a constant, and consider all the propositions that it can be thought of as denoting. Each of these will result from a specification of $f$, and each will be a proposition of which $a$ is a constituent. But we cannot possibly have here every proposition in which $a$ occurs; for we can say $(\exists f) . f(a)$, which arises by generalization and not by specification. In order to denote this proposition, we shall have to write $F(a)$, where $F$ is a variable of higher order than $f$. The point is this: whatever function we may construct, it can denote only those propositions which result when values are assigned to its free variables; but in such a case, it is always possible to get a further proposition by generalizing the free variables.

Let us take an example illustrating the way in which the hierarchy of functions becomes relevant in practice. Suppose we have the following function of the two free variables $x$ and $y$:

$$(f) . f(x) \supset f(y),$$

i.e., "Every function that holds of $x$ holds also of $y$." This is a certain function of $x$, and it is another function of $y$, since $y$ occupies a position in the expression different from the one occupied by $x$. So, if *every* function that holds of $x$ holds of $y$ as well, we shall be able to infer:

$$(f) . f(y) \supset f(y).$$

This is true enough, but the inference is illegitimate according to the vicious-circle principle, since no function involving $f$ as a constituent can result from the assignment of a value to $f$. And the kind of trouble that would arise if this principle were not adhered to can be seen if we take a slightly different illustration. Consider the condition:

$$(f) . f(x) \supset {\sim}f(y),$$

i.e., "Every first-order function that is satisfied by $x$ is such as to be not satisfied by $y$." If we took the second-order function $(\exists f) . f(x)$, which is satisfied for every $x$, as a legitimate value of $f(x)$ resulting from a determination of $f$, we should be able to infer ${\sim}(\exists f) . f(y)$.

Both the hierarchy of functions and that of propositions can be derived from a certain restricted kind of functions, which are called 'matrices.' A matrix is any function that does not involve generalized variables. Matrices may, of course, contain variables of any order, and these variables may take values that involve generalization, but the matrices themselves do not. Thus, "$x$ is round" is a first-order matrix, $f(x) \vee f(y)$ is a second-order matrix, and $F[f(x)]$ is a matrix of the third order. Now, clearly, if we take a matrix of a given order (which is determined by the variable or variables of highest order in it) and generalize some only of the variables, we shall have a function of the same order; and if we generalize all the variables, we shall have a proposition of that order. Thus, from $f(x)$ we can derive $(\exists x) . f(x)$, which still contains the free variable $f$ and is a second-order function; and we can derive $(\exists f) : (x) . f(x)$, which contains no free variables and is a second-order proposition. Again, consider the matrix $p \vee {\sim}p$, which is constructed on the propositional variable $p$. At the very least, this must be of the second order; for if $p$ denotes such propositions as "$a$ is round," it will have the same kind of values as $f(x)$. The simplest proposition that can be found will necessarily contain some constituent which is not an individual, and which will therefore be, in the most favorable case, of the first order. So, $(p) . p \vee \sim p$ will be, at the least, a second-order proposition; and $(\exists q) . p \vee q$ will be a second-order function.

In the introduction to the second edition of *Principia Mathematica,* Mr. Russell gives us a version of the propositional and functional hierarchies which in some respects consists merely in making more specific the original theory, and in other respects introduces modifications of it. At the risk of distorting Mr. Russell's meaning, we must here consider a brief account of these new materials, especially with regard to those parts which supplement the original doctrine, because they throw some light on points not previously made clear.[7]

We begin with what are called 'atomic propositions.' These comprise subject-predicate propositions and relational propositions involving any number of terms, and are to be represented by $R(a)$, $R(a, b)$, $R(a, b, c)$, etc. Mr. Russell suggests the view that there are, and indeed must be, propositions of this kind which are not further analyzable. It seems clear, however, that this is not essential to the logical theory constructed, and that it will be sufficient if the propositions in question simply remain unanalyzed in other respects, whatever their complete analysis may be. Thus, we may take such expressions as "*a* is red," "*a* is larger than *b*," and "*a* is between *b* and *c*" as standing for propositions that are atomic relatively to a given logical context. If it were not possible to treat propositions of this kind as 'atomic,' it would be difficult to find examples of the kind intended; for it is not clear that absolutely atomic propositions can be exhibited. The most favorable case occurs when we say, with regard to some presented datum of sense, such things as "*This* is red." But even here 'red' appears to stand for a kind of characters rather than for a determinate character; and if so, then what we shall be saying is: "This has *some* character of the kind 'red'"; so that the proposition expressed will be of the form $(\exists f) . f(x)$ and will thus involve a generalized variable.

Out of atomic propositions we can build elementary propositions by constructing functions in terms of $\vee$, ., and $\sim$. In this

[7] See Vol. I, Introduction to the Second Edition, and also Appendix A.

connection, Mr. Russell uses Sheffer's stroke-function $p|q$ in one of its two meanings, namely $\sim p \vee \sim q$, rather than using conjunction, disjunction, and negation, but of course the theory is in no way affected by this choice among interdefinable conceptions. So, we can construct elementary propositions having such forms as $R(x) \vee \sim R(x)$, $\sim R'(x, y)$, $R(x) . \sim R'(x, y)$, and the like; and we may denote propositions of this sort by $\varphi(x)$, $\psi(x, y)$, etc. Now, inasmuch as $\varphi(x)$ is a function of $x$, we may, of course, generalize $x$ so as to obtain either $(x) . \varphi(x)$ or $(\exists x) . \varphi(x)$. In these expressions, since $\varphi$ is of wider scope than $x$, it remains relatively constant while $x$ varies, and either expression may be thought of as determining a way of grouping elementary functions so as to form other elementary functions. Thus, $(x) . \varphi(x)$ may be taken as meaning $\varphi(x_1) . \varphi(x_2) . \varphi(x_3) \ldots$, and $(\exists x) . \varphi(x)$ as meaning $\varphi(x_1) \vee \varphi(x_2) \vee \varphi(x_3) \ldots$. When $\varphi$ is fixed, $\varphi(x)$ determines a certain assemblage of elementary propositions, and the difference between $(x) . \varphi(x)$ and $(\exists x) . \varphi(x)$ is simply that the first indicates the conjunction of the members of this assemblage and the second their disjunction.

When we come to functions in two variables, $\psi(x, y)$, a new situation arises. Here, if we hold $x$ constant and vary $y$, and then change $x$ and vary $y$ again, etc., we get an assemblage of assemblages; and if, again, we hold $y$ constant and vary $x$, we get a different assemblage of assemblages. The first case occurs when we write $(\exists x) : (y) . \psi(x, y)$ or $(x) : (\exists y) . \psi(x, y)$, and the second when we write $(\exists y) : (x) . \psi(x, y)$ or $(y) : (\exists x) . \psi(x, y)$, the mode of grouping being determined by the order of generalization, and not by whether the generalizations are universal or particular.

So long as we are confined to classifications obtained by generalizing the variables $x, y, \ldots$, each elementary proposition entering into the grouping will be of the same form as each other one, and the range of the classification will be restricted accordingly. We may denote functions which group elementary propositions in this way by $\varphi_1$, $\psi_1$, etc., and we may take $\varphi(x)$, $\psi(x, y)$, etc., as defined above, to be special cases of these functions, in which there are no generalized variables. $\varphi_1(x)$, $\psi_1(x, y)$, and the like will, then, denote first-order functions of $x, y, \ldots$; their values will not involve any variables, generalized or free, other than those denoting individuals; and they will themselves be second-order functions.

When $\varphi_1$ is varied, however, as in $(\varphi_1) . \varphi_1(x)$ and $(\exists\varphi_1) . \varphi_1(x)$, a much more heterogeneous assemblage of elementary propositions results, which cannot be obtained by variation of $x, y, \ldots$ alone. Thus, if we write $(x) : (\exists\varphi_1) . \varphi_1(x)$, we have a proposition which classifies elementary propositions of all kinds, rather than of one particular kind, and in this way the variable $\varphi_1$ introduces a new sort of generality. Similarly, a variable $\varphi_2$, which will take as values second-order functions, may be introduced. Thus, $\varphi_2(x)$ will denote such second-order functions as $\varphi_1(x)$, $\sim(\varphi_1) . \varphi_1(x)$, and $(x) . \varphi_1(x) \vee \psi_1(x, y)$. It will represent a new method of classifying the ultimate atomic propositions and will introduce a further kind of generality.

In view of this conception of the hierarchy of functions, it will be seen why no variable can take values of its own order, or of any higher order. If we have $\varphi_1(x)$, we cannot take, say, $\sim(\exists\varphi_1) . \varphi_1(x)$ as a value which results from a specification of $\varphi_1$, because the sort of classification of elementary propositions which $\varphi_1$ stands for is not to be found among the values of $\varphi_1$. This variable itself determines a classification of these values, which, in the nature of the case, cannot be found among the materials classified; nor can the classification determined by any variable of the same or a higher order be found.

But although the restrictions with regard to substituting values for variables remain in theory the same, Mr. Russell finds it possible to circumvent some of these restrictions by showing that certain functions of lower order imply corresponding ones of higher order, and that substitutions can be validated on grounds other than that of the relation of a variable to its values. Let us take, for example,

$$(\varphi_1) . \varphi_1(x) \vee \sim\varphi_1(x),$$

which is a second-order function of $x$. Then we have

$$(\varphi_1) : (\exists\psi_1) . \varphi_1(x) \vee \sim\psi_1(x),$$

because $\psi_1$ can take the same values as $\varphi_1$. This implies, however,

$$(\varphi_1) \,.\, \varphi_1(x) \,.\vee.\, \sim(\varphi_1) \,.\, \varphi_1(x),$$

just as if $(\varphi_1) \,.\, \varphi_1(x)$ had been taken as resulting from a determination of $\varphi_1$ in the original expression. Moreover, it can easily be seen that whatever second-order function of $x$ may be substituted for $\varphi_1$ in this original expression, the resulting function will be true for all values of $x$; so that we have, in fact,

$$(\varphi_2) \,.\, \varphi_2(x) \vee \sim\varphi_2(x).$$

The principle involved is this: Whenever a function $F[\varphi_1(x)]$ results from substitution in a universally true elementary function of propositional variables, as $\varphi_1(x) \vee \sim\varphi_1(x)$ results from substitution in $p \vee \sim p$, then $(\varphi_1) \,.\, F[\varphi_1(x)]$ implies $(\varphi_2) \,.\, F[\varphi_2(x)]$, which implies $(\varphi_3) \,.\, F[\varphi_3(x)]$, etc.

It will hardly be necessary to warn the reader that he should not take the foregoing interpretation of Mr. Russell's views as in any way authoritative, but should, in the case of any doubtful point, go directly to the sources cited. Only so much has been given as would afford a notion of the main outlines of the theory and provide a basis for the comments with regard to it to which we now turn.

It will be seen that Mr. Russell's theory demands the existence of an absolute hierarchy of logical propositions and functions, and not merely a relative hierarchical arrangement of functions and functions of functions as they occur within one and the same proposition. That is to say, if we have a function $F(f)$, there must be some one order to which it belongs; $F$ must take values of, say, the $n$th order and $f$ of the order $n - 1$, where $n$ is definitely fixed; and we cannot say merely that if $F$ takes a value of a given kind, $f$ must take values of a subordinate kind. This, Mr. Russell holds, is true in theory; but in practice, he tells us, a relative hierarchy is sufficient. Thus, in one place, he says: "In practice, we never need to know the absolute types of our variables, but only their *relative* types. That is to say, if we prove any proposition on the assumption that one of our variables is an individual, and another is a function of order $n$, the proof will still hold if, in place of an individual, we take a function of order $m$, and in place of our function of order $n$ we take a function of order $n + m$, with corresponding changes for any other variables that may be involved."[8] The reason why only relative typic adjustments are necessary in practice is that symbolic expressions have 'systematic ambiguity.' Thus, the symbol $p \vee \sim p$ can be used to denote propositions of any one order, no matter what order may be decided upon, inasmuch as the form of the symbol required will be the same in any case. But it is only symbols that are susceptible of wandering from type to type in this way; their meanings are not, because, although there may be a systematic analogy between propositions of different types, there will be no generic meaning common to them. If $(f) . f(a) . \vee . \sim(f) . f(a)$ and $f_1(a) \vee \sim f_1(a)$, where $f_1$ is constant and is a value of $f$, look as if both were of the form $p \vee \sim p$, that is really not so, because even the symbols for disjunction and negation are systematically ambiguous, and do not have the same meanings when they occur in expressions for propositions of different orders. One is tempted to suppose that the analogies which occur among functions of different levels are grounded in real generic identities, and that therefore there must be functions which will denote propositions of more than one order. $p \vee \sim p$ might be supposed to be of this kind; and it looks sometimes as if Mr. Russell wished to hold this; but there can be no doubt that his real view is that such functions do not exist.

Now, we must examine the principles or assumptions that have led Mr. Russell to the view here indicated, rather than to what seems to be the more natural view. We know, of course, one of these already, namely, the vicious-circle principle or the principle of illegitimate totalities; but there is another basic assumption in his theory, which is certainly in part responsible for the notion of 'systematic ambiguities' among logical expressions, and which we shall have to consider in detail. A view of the nature of typic relationships among logical functions will be suggested presently, according to which systematic ambiguities vanish altogether, and genuine identity of functions takes their place. If such a view implied any change in the technique and practice of *Principia Mathematica*, it could not be made at all

[8] *Loc. cit.*, p. 165.

plausible as against the view held by Mr. Russell without a thoroughgoing demonstration of the way in which logical analyses were to be carried out in terms of it. But we have just seen that the theory of types demands more than is necessary in practice, because only 'relative' typic adjustments are required; and it will be maintained that a view of the sort we are to consider involves no change in the technique of types, but, on the other hand, simply brings the theory into closer accord with the necessities of practice.

The assumption just referred to, which Mr. Russell makes, and which seems to be fundamental in his view of the hierarchy of types, is one concerned with the range of significance of a variable. We may express it by saying that he supposes every variable to have a preassigned range of variation, or by saying that all variables are 'independent' ones, or, again, by saying that if a variable can take a certain value in a given context, it must be able to take that value in every context in which it can significantly occur. This might be called the principle of independent variability. And there can be no doubt that Mr. Russell adopts such a principle; the theory of types, as he conceives the matter, involves it; and he tells us in several places that this is so. Thus, he says that "a variable may travel through any well-defined totality of values, provided these values are all such that any one can replace any other significantly in any context."[9] And this means, of course, "that two types which have a common member coincide, and that two different types are mutually exclusive," a variable being incapable of taking values beyond the bounds of its own appropriate type.[10]

Now, *prima facie*, such a view would seem to be open to question, as may be seen if we take a simple illustration. Let $p$, $q$, and $r$ be any three variables that denote propositions, and, in order that there may be no question of differences of type, we may say that they denote elementary propositions only. Then let us form the two functions $p \vee q$ and $q \vee r$, and equate the first to $P$ and the second to $R$. The total range of variation of $P$ will, of course, be exactly the same as that of $R$; they will both

[9] *Loc. cit.*, p. xxxv.
[10] *Ibid.*, p. 162.

take as a value any elementary disjunctive proposition. But if we form the function $P.R$, it will be seen that values cannot be assigned arbitrarily to one of the variables in this conjunction irrespective of those assigned to the other variable, because, of course, when $P$ is fixed, the values that $R$ can take will be restricted accordingly, and so for $P$ when $R$ is fixed. It is clear, too, that a violation of these mutual restrictions does not give rise to false results, but to nonsense; it is, for example, mere nonsense to assign "$A$ is red or green" as a value to $P$, and "$B$ is large or heavy" as a value to $R$, and to pretend to get a value of $P.R$, despite the fact that $P$ and $R$ can both take these values in appropriate contexts. Again, although $P$ denotes any elementary disjunctive proposition, and $p$ any elementary proposition whatever, when $p$ is assigned, the range of significance of $P$ is very much limited. This may be compared with Mr. Russell's function $f(x)$, where $x$ is restricted to denoting 'individuals.' There can be nothing which is the totality of 'all functions' of an individual thing; so that once $x$ is restricted, $f$ will be restricted too; and once $f$ is restricted, $F$ in $F[f(x)]$ will also be restricted, and so on; all of which starts from the initial restriction placed upon $x$. Mr. Russell would, no doubt, urge that such an initial restriction was absolutely necessary for the purpose of avoiding nonsense when we come to apply generalization to the variables in a function. We shall consider this view presently, and shall insist that it arises from a misconception of the exact import of generalization, and a consequent application to all variables of the principle of independent variability; but for the moment we are concerned with another aspect of the matter.

It looks as if the restriction of $x$ to denoting individuals, which are one particular kind of objects in the world, involved the introduction of an extra-logical factor into what purports to be a purely logical expression. One might hold that we could take any variables, $x$, $y$, . . ., and say that they were to denote entities of *one and the same* kind, so as to provide for significant interchangeability, without imposing any condition that could not be framed in purely logical terms; but that if we brought in some conception like that of an 'individual,' in the specific sense here intended, and not that of a 'relative individual,' we should have to go outside formal logic to do so, and make our expressions less generic, and therefore of a lesser degree of generality, than the propositions to be expressed actually required. It would, indeed, be possible to compel a restricted interpretation, by putting in an assigned value $a$ and writing $f(a)$; this would start an absolute hierarchy, $f(a)$, $F[f(a)]$, etc.; but it would, of course, involve an extra-logical assignment of values.

Moreover, it is not clear what an 'individual' is to be thought of as being, and how its substitution for a variable $x$ is to be understood. Ordinarily, we think of individuals as being such things as tables, chairs, and coins. But if you take the function "$x$ is a coin" and apply it in a judgment with regard to a particular coin by saying "*This* is a coin," you will not have got that actual coin into your proposition. You will be saying, with regard to a given sensory presentation, something like: "This is an appearance of one and only one thing, and that thing is a coin," where the sensory appearance in question will be the primary subject of your judgment, and where the constituent of the asserted proposition which corresponds to the actual coin will be a definite description.[11] You can, of course, say that "$x$ is a coin" means "$x$ is an appearance of one and only one coin," and that therefore the value substituted for $x$ is a sensory appearance; but if individual variables stand for sensory appearances, they denote entities very different from the ones we commonly suppose them to denote, and our notion of the class of individuals must be radically revised. The fact is that any extra-logical assignment of values to variables often, if not always, involves concealed elements of generality. This is why, in Chapter IX, we introduced the convention that a proposition was to be understood as being, say, doubly general if it involved *at least* two elements of generality, but that a logical function was to be understood as being doubly general if, and only if, it involved *exactly* two. Thus, the logical function $(x) : (\exists y) . f(x, y)$ contains exactly two generalizations, whereas the proposition "$(x) : (\exists y) . x$ gives $y$ to somebody," which is a value of this function, contains two generalizations explicitly and at least one implicitly. It is considerations such as these which start the search for

[11] Cf. G. E. Moore, *Philosophical Studies*, pp. 229 ff.

'atomic' propositions and ultimate simples, despite the initial doubt whether there are any such entities. It must be said, however, that an absolute hierarchy of types does not demand the existence of things that are not further analyzable; the hierarchy could be infinite in both directions and still be absolute, provided we could determine by a unique description, such as that of 'individuals,' some one level as a fixed reference point.

We may return now to the question about the range of variation of the variables in a matrix, and the restrictions which must be placed upon this range in order that, when generalization is applied to these variables, nonsense may not result. We have seen that Mr. Russell's answer to this question is that each variable must have a preassigned range of variation, of such a kind that it can take any value belonging to this range in any context in which it can appear, no matter what values associated variables in the same context may take. However, let us look at the facts anew. And let us take, to begin with, the function $f(x)$, by means of which we wish to denote propositions, and upon which we wish to construct general propositions by generalization. There are three symbols that can be recognized here, two of which are simple and one complex, namely, $f$, $x$, and $f(x)$. But, now, from common usage, as well as from the way $f(x)$ is written, it looks as if $f$ were meant to play a different rôle from that of $x$; and in order to avoid this appearance, we are going to replace $f(x)$ by $(x, y)$, without, however, introducing any presupposition regarding what values $x$ and $y$ can take. The expression $(x, y)$ is, then, to denote propositions; and we may suppose, from the way it is constructed, that it can be understood as denoting any proposition which can be analyzed into two factors, where $(x, y)$ will denote the whole proposition, and $x$ and $y$ two constituents which go together to make it up. Thus $(x, y)$ may denote "$A$ is round," where $x$ corresponds to $A$ and $y$ to 'being round'; or it may denote "Red is a color," where $x$ corresponds to "Red" and $y$ to 'being a color.' In this conception there can, of course, be no preassigned range of values for $x$ and $y$; but we do have something which has a preassigned range, namely $(x, y)$, since it is held to denote any proposition exemplifying its form. Indeed, it is inevitable, in the nature of denoting, that something should have an initially fixed range of variation; and we are simply attempting to suppose that it is the matrix, and not any variable constituent of it, which has such a range. And it must be carefully noted that it is the *whole* matrix, upon which a proposition is constructed, with regard to which we wish to suppose this; for, of course, it is expressions standing for propositions to which significance must be secured; so that, for example, if $(x, y)$ is brought into conjunction with $(y, z)$ in such a way that we have $(x, y) . (y, z)$, it is this latter, and not its constituents, which must have a preassigned range.

Now if, by way of generalizing $x$ and $y$, we write $(x) : (\exists y) . (x, y)$, it may be asked what the range of $x$ is to be, and whether it is possible for a universal generalization to be significant unless some range is fixed in advance. It has been maintained in Chapter IX that a symbol like $(x)$ is really not an integral sign, but is to be understood merely as replacing $\sim(\exists x) . \sim$, in accordance with the view that all universal propositions are negative in force and can only be properly interpreted as denials of particulars; so that we really have $\sim(\exists x) : \sim(\exists y) . (x, y)$, which is to be read "There does not exist a value of $x$ without a value of $y$ such that $(x, y)$ is true." And since $(x, y)$ has a fixed total range of variation, the values that $x$ and $y$ can take will be determined by it. To find a value of $x$, we go to any proposition denoted by $(x, y)$, and take one of the two factors into which it is analyzable for $x$ to correspond to; then, to find the values of $y$ for this determination of $x$, we consider all those values of $(x, y)$ in which this constituent occurs, and take the remaining constituent in each case as an admissible value for $y$. When a new value of $x$ is chosen, a set of admissible values of $y$ will, of course, again be determined, which may or may not be the same as the set in the first case. And the proposition $(x) : (\exists y) . (x, y)$ will mean simply that however $x$ may be chosen, there will always be an admissible value of $y$, for that value of $x$, such that $(x, y)$ will be true. Of course, values must here be assigned to $x$ first, because it has the wider scope; the order of generalization alone determines the order of assignment of values.

It appears, therefore, according to the account here suggested, that we must distinguish between what may be called the 'total range of variation' of a variable and its range within a specified context. In any proposition constructed on $(x, y)$ in which $x$ is generalized first, the values that $y$ can take in conjunction with an assigned value of $x$ will be restricted, but the values that it can take with *some value or other* of $x$ will be as wide as the range of the function $(x, y)$; and this latter defines the 'total variation' of $y$. Let us take another example, in which we have a function of three variables, $(x, y, z)$. This matrix, it is to be supposed, will denote any proposition whatever which can be analyzed into three variable factors, and the restrictions to be placed upon the variables will depend upon the order of generalization, and upon what values are assigned to associated variables. If, for example, we have

$$(\exists x) :. (y) : (\exists z) . (x, y, z),$$

$x$ can be given any value within its total range of variation, and the values of $y$ will be restricted, in any context, by the values assigned to $x$, whereas the values of $z$ will be restricted both by the values assigned to $x$ and by those assigned to $y$. The total variation of $x$, $y$, and $z$, however, will be, in each case, as wide as that of the matrix $(x, y, z)$.

There are two different sorts of substituting that can be carried out by way of deriving logical consequences from a general proposition of the kind here illustrated. Suppose we have a proposition of the form $(x) : (\exists y) . f(x, y)$ and replace $x$ by a value in such a way that the expression takes the form $(\exists y) . f(a, y)$. In such a case, it may be that the value assigned to $x$ carries with it any number of generalizations, and we may have, in consequence, an expression like

$$(\exists y)[(z) : (\exists w) . f'(a, y, z, w)].$$

The variable $x$ will involve in its determination some constant, either material or logical, but it will also carry with it new generalizations, which, however, all fall within the scope of the original prefix $(\exists y)$. A substitution such as this is legitimate because the form of the function $(\exists y) . f(x, y)$ is simply made more determinate, and whatever is true in the more generic case will be true in the more specific one. Moreover, it is to be noted that by successive substitutions we do not necessarily come finally to propositions not containing generalizations; the substitutions may in fact lead to an ever-increasing number.

But, now, there are substitutions which actually alter the form of the function, and these are the ones in which vicious-circle fallacies are likely to arise. Let us take an example of the simplest kind. Suppose we have the function $(\exists y) . f(x, y)$, where $f$ is to be understood as being fixed and $x$ as being a free variable, and where, therefore, we can derive by generalization either of the propositions $(x) : (\exists y) . f(x, y)$ or $(\exists x) : (\exists y) . f(x, y)$, and by specification $(\exists y) . f(a, y)$. It might be that any one of these procedures resulted in a true proposition and that we wished to say so in a general statement. We might then write $(F) : F[(\exists y) . f(x, y)]$, where, when $F$ was determined, we should have, say, $(\exists x) : (\exists y) . f(x, y)$, which would involve putting the prefix $(\exists y)$ of the original expression within the scope of a new one, $(\exists x)$. Again, consider $(z) . f(x, y, z)$ and the number of different propositions that can be derived by generalization and specification. We might write $(F) : F[(z) . f(x, y, z)]$, and take $(x) :. (\exists y) : (z) . f(x, y, z)$ as resulting from the assignment of a value to $F$.

It has already been pointed out that in cases such as these a hierarchy of variables must be introduced, and the only matter now in point is that this hierarchical arrangement occurs only within a single complex proposition. When, for example, we have

$$(x) :. (\exists y) : (z) . f(x, y, z) :. \supset . (\exists F) . F[(z) . f(x, y, z)],$$

where all the factors are purely logical, there must be distinctions of order among the variables. But the antecedent of this proposition, by itself, requires the introduction of no such distinctions. This does not mean, however, that the variables $x$, $y$, $z$ in a function expressed by the antecedent alone will wander over all logical types; for the view we are trying to make plausible is precisely that there is no absolute hierarchy for them to wander over. And it must be noted that this is maintained only with regard to purely logical propositions, which contain no non-logical constituents. It is obvious that as soon as material constants are introduced, absolute hierarchies inevitably result. Thus, take the example about all propositions asserted by A during a given interval of time, which was discussed above. In that case, we have a particular time and person, and typic adjustments based on those factors as fixed points of reference will start a sequence of propositions that is absolute. The point is that purely logical propositions are more generic, and that logical functions can vary over all orders in such a non-logical hierarchy, provided relative adjustments of type are properly made.

There remains, however, in the way of such a view as this, an obstacle which seems at first sight insuperable. Let us consider the theoretical situation as it has been dealt with so far. Mr. Russell's principle about 'illegitimate totalities,' in the sense in which he intended it, must be accepted. And we have tried to get around some of the apparent consequences of this principle by denying what may be held to be an independent assumption, namely, that a variable must determine some totality of values in such a way that any member of that totality can be significantly substituted for the variable in any context. In this sense, it is to be held that a variable may correspond to no single totality at all and still be significant as an item of syntax in a function. But, now, in accepting the principle of illegitimate totalities, as we must, we seem to be driven in effect into an absolute hierarchy. Let us consider, for example, the proposition $(p) \cdot p \vee \sim p$, and ask what the range of the variable $p$ is to be. In consequence of the vicious-circle principle, this proposition itself cannot be a member of that range; so that we shall require a further principle, etc.; and no reference to typic adjustments among the variables in a proposition can cover such a case. There will apparently be an infinite sequence of principles of excluded middle, and every logical proposition we may express (if it is to be true or false) will have to fall under one of these principles and thus fall at some definite place in the hierarchy so determined.

In attempting to meet this point, we shall be led into a somewhat detailed discussion of the nature of a proposition and of the conditions of significant judgment. We shall present in this connection a particular theory, which has to do with the way propositions function in judgment, and what it means to believe or to assert them. It will be a consequence of this theory that no substitution of one purely logical proposition in another can be of the genus-instance kind, but must always be validated by reference to the relation of genus to species. We have seen that all genus-species substitution is, so to speak, horizontal; it does not entail any stepping-up or stepping-down; so that no hierarchy ever gets started in connection with it. We have seen, also, that the substitution of $(p) . p \vee {\sim}p$ in itself can be validated as being of the genus-species kind, where the $p$ in the resulting proposition will be of the same order as the $p$ in the original one. But whether we can get all desired results by this procedure or not, if a genus-instance substitution is significant in this connection (where the $p$ in the resulting proposition will be of a lower order than that in the original one), a hierarchy must exist; and we shall therefore have to hold that no such substitution is ever significant. It may be remarked that a theory of the sort now to be considered is important on its own account and is relevant to any discussion of the logical paradoxes, even if it does not enable us to meet the particular point here in question.

It is generally recognized that every genuine judgment presupposes, on the part of the person who makes it, some knowledge of some sort or other. And it is generally held that this knowledge consists in being acquainted with certain concepts, and with certain conceptual complexes which arise out of observed relationships among these concepts. We are going to suppose that this view is, so far, a correct one, and are going to ask what, in certain respects, the nature of such complexes is and how they function in judgment, with a view to ascertaining under what conditions genuine propositions do or do not arise.[12]

Let us take, as an example to begin with, the proposition "There are men" or "Men exist," and let us suppose a judgment

[12] Views similar in various respects to the one to be suggested are to be found in Wittgenstein's *Tractatus Logico-philosophicus, passim;* Ramsey's *Foundations of Mathematics*, Ch. VI; Whitehead's *Symbolism, Its Meaning and Effect*, Ch. I; Eaton's *Symbolism and Truth*, Chs. II, IV, V; and *Principia Mathematica*, 2d ed., Vol. I, Appendix C. For a closely similar view, see G. F. Stout, *Mind*, XLI (1932), 297.

actually to be expressed by these words. If you make an actual judgment properly expressible by the words "Men exist," you must have before your mind a conceptual complex which these words may be said to stand for or name. And one important thing about this complex is that it is a 'possibility,' which is susceptible of being 'realized.' Clearly, in some sense, the realization or lack of realization of this possibility, which is a conceptual complex, determines the truth or falsity of your judgment. When you judge that there are men, you must be envisaging a possibility which, whether it is realized or not, is, in respect of its own intrinsic nature, susceptible of being realized; and your judgment will be true or false according as the possibility in question is or is not actually realized. This, as has just been said, is one important characteristic of the conceptual complex through which your judgment is effected. But there is another thing that can be said about this conceptual complex which is perhaps even more important, and that is that it is itself a *fact*. The factual character of the complex in question can be brought out by actually stating the analytic possibility which you have before your mind in the words "There *might be* men" or "Men *might* exist." Of course, the entity named by these words, which is an analytic possibility and also an analytic fact, is not what you are judging when you judge that there are men; you are *knowing* this fact, and 'judging through' it. And again, when you believe that there are men, you are, of course, not believing the directly apprehended fact that there might be men; this fact is the medium of your belief, and you may be said to be 'believing through' it. The fact that there might be men can be known *a priori*, and it is only by knowing this *a priori* possibility that you are able significantly to judge or to believe that men exist.

Now, we are going to say, quite simply, that the proposition "Men exist" is literally one and the same with the fact that men might exist. And we shall hold, in general, that all propositions are analytic facts of the kind here in question. We shall say that such facts can 'function propositionally,' and that when they do so, they are called propositions. It is to be noted, however, that we are not saying that all analytic facts are propositions. There will be many such facts (to be expressed by means of statements in intension) which are not capable of functioning propositionally and which are therefore not to be identified with propositions. Intensional facts of this kind will usually contain parts which can function as propositions, so that these facts may be said to be about propositions; it is simply that the whole fact in question in such a case will not itself be a proposition.[13] This matter is important, because the distinction between statements in intension and statements in extension is so obviously necessary in logic that any view which implied that they were logically the same would be hardly worth developing.

It is to be held, however, as has just been said, that so far as any logical entity named is concerned, the words "Men exist" and the words " Men might exist" stand for the same thing; and we must endeavor to remove the paradox involved in this position. As a first approximation, it may be said that the difference here is that between asserting a proposition and merely entertaining it, and that this difference is an extra-logical one, which has to do with the communicative use of words rather than with their logical use. This distinction between the communicative and logical functions of language is an important one, and we can perhaps make it clear by comparing what may be called correct and incorrect beliefs with true and false propositions. If you merely apprehend or entertain a false proposition, you are not, on that account, making a mistake; and if you have such a proposition in mind, and believe that it is false, your belief is a correct one. If, on the other hand, you have in mind a true proposition, and believe it to be false, you are of course making a mistake. In this case, you may more properly be said to be believing the false proposition which is the contradictory of the true one you have in mind; but that is a matter which is not important in the present connection. A proposition will be true or false, and a belief associated with it will be correct or incorrect according as it agrees or disagrees with what happens to be the case. If the attitude is not one of belief, no question of correct-

[13] For the purposes of this discussion, the term 'proposition' is used in a restricted sense to which it is not elsewhere confined.

ness or incorrectness can arise, although there will be some entity apprehended which is in point of fact either true or false.

Now, when any one says "Men exist," he is bound to convey more than his words stand for in respect of their strict logical import. If he is making this assertion as a single proposition, we are led to suppose under ordinary circumstances that he believes the proposition so expressed; and indeed the indicative form of expression is designed to convey precisely this fact. But the speaker can hardly be held to be actually expressing the proposition that he believes men to exist. The way this latter would actually be expressed is, of course, by using the words "I believe that men exist," and this is not what is being said, though it is generally something that is being conveyed. If this latter were what was being expressed, then, in denying what was said, we should be saying that so-and-so did not believe men to exist, and this of course is not at all what we should be expressing if we denied the statement on the part of anybody that men do exist. When, on the other hand, we use the words "Men might exist" and use "might" in its logical sense, as indicative of logical possibility, we direct attention to an analytic fact without suggesting to the hearer that we are 'believing through' this fact. It is true that we do, in such a case, suggest to the hearer that we believe the words "Men might exist" actually to stand for a fact, but we do not indicate to him that we are making a judgment which is mediated by that fact. Perhaps a closer approximation to the purely logical import of these words, without communicative suggestions, is obtained when we simply utter the phrase 'that men *should* exist.'

It will very likely be said, however, that the two statements "Men exist" and "Men might exist" cannot possibly designate the same logical entity because one is obviously a stronger statement than the other; and that if we merely change the example, and take, say, "Ghosts exist" and "Ghosts might exist," the first will be false while the second will be true. Clearly, we shall have to hold that the term 'true' is here used ambiguously; and that when we say that "Ghosts might exist" is true, we mean simply that these words do stand for or designate a fact, but that when we say "Ghosts exist" is true, we mean that this fact, which is a possibility, is 'realized,' i.e., corresponds to some other fact which constitutes its realization. In the first case, we shall be making a judgment about a sentence, to the effect that that sentence does name a fact or, in other words, is significant; in the second case, we shall be making a judgment about a logical possibility, which is a proposition and not a sentence, to the effect that that possibility is fulfilled. It no doubt often happens that the terms 'true' and 'false' are applied to sentences like "Men exist" and "Ghosts exist" as well as to those like "Men might exist" and "Ghosts might exist." If we should say of the sentence "Men exist" that it was true, we should very likely be saying, in effect, that there was an intensional possibility represented by these words and that that possibility was in fact realized. We should likely be saying this because anybody who chose these words to express that possibility would ordinarily be 'believing through' the possibility in question, and would therefore be believing truly. If, however, we said of the sentence "Men might exist" that it was true, we should commonly mean merely that these words did designate a genuine possibility, because anybody who chose the words in question to designate that possibility would ordinarily be merely entertaining the possibility and not 'believing through' it. It follows, of course, that there will be sentences which, as wholes, do not stand for anything at all, although parts of them may do so. Take, for example, the sentence "Ghosts *could not* exist." Here the separate words are meaningful enough; but when we try to apprehend what the sentence as a whole stands for, and try to envisage the situation, not verbally but in terms of genuine ideas, the only entity we come upon is the fact that ghosts *could* exist, for which, of course, the words "Ghosts could not exist" are not a proper expression.

An objection similar to the one just dealt with is that, whatever may be meant by the words "Men exist" and "Men do not exist," these meanings are incompatible, whereas no incompatibility arises between "Men might exist" and "Men might not exist." With regard to this objection, it must be noted that no two entities whatever can be directly—i.e., as between themselves alone—'incompatible.' When we say that two propositions are incompatible, we mean that *if* they were both true, an incompatibility *would* exist; and that therefore they are not in fact both true. But the same thing can be said with regard to the two possibilities "Men might exist" and "Men might not exist": *if* these two possibilities were both realized, an incompatibility *would* exist; and we can know, for this reason, that they are not both realized. It is simply that expressions like "Men might exist" serve to direct attention to analytic possibilities in contexts in which the question of realization or lack of realization does not occur, while expressions like "Men exist" are used where the question of truth or falsity is relevant, since they are used where we wish to indicate that the possibilities designated are accompanied by belief.

Let us try to define more exactly the conditions under which two propositions are to be said to be incompatible. Since we are holding that every proposition, strictly so called, must be an analytic possibility, which is susceptible of being realized, we may raise the question under what conditions two separate propositions will give rise to a third single proposition which is their conjunction. The older logicians used to talk of drawing a conclusion from several distinct propositions as premises, whereas we now say that the premises in such a case are really one compound proposition—on the assumption, of course, that if $p$ and $q$ are two propositions, there will always be one third proposition which is their conjunction. This assumption, however, may be called in question. And it is clear, on the theory we are here explaining, that we shall have to say that two incompatible propositions never do give rise by conjunction to a third proposition, and that this is precisely what it means for two propositions to be incompatible. If we write "Men might exist, and men might not exist," we shall have made a single statement, although we shall not have expressed a single fact, but only two separate facts by means of one compound sentence. There can be no objection to making compound statements of this sort, provided we do not suppose that these statements as wholes necessarily express single facts; and there can be no objection to writing "Men exist, and men do not exist" provided, again, we take the expression to express two propositions and not one. When we try to envisage the unitary meaning of a statement of this kind, we find that this is quite impossible, and that therefore it has no single meaning, but rather one meaning corresponding to one part of the verbal expression, and another to another. If a proposition is something that can mediate a significant judgment, then there can be no single proposition which an expression of this kind can express.

In regard to the separate statements "Men exist" and "Men do not exist," there is a temptation to hold that only one possibility actually occurs; and that "not" in the second statement is simply a sign of an attitude, namely that of disbelief. There would then be only positive possibilities presented, and contradiction would be merely a matter of conflicting convictions, actual or hypothetical. We have not adopted this view, for the reason, among others, that although it seems to work well enough for singly-general propositions, when we try to apply it in interpreting multiply-general propositions, it breaks down altogether. We can say that "Men exist" simply indicates that the speaker is believing through the concept 'men,' and that "Men do not exist" means that he is disbelieving through this same concept; but we cannot interpret a proposition like "Something is larger than everything else" in this way. We shall have only the two ideas $(\exists x)$ and $\sim(\exists x)$, and the proposition here given will be of the form $(\exists x) : \sim(\exists y) . \sim f(x, y)$. It will therefore involve subordinate negations which cannot be removed; and since the proposition is complex but not compound, it cannot be divided into distinct parts toward which separate attitudes corresponding to the several occurrences of $\sim$ can be taken.

Let us turn now to statements expressing 'necessities.' And let us take the two propositions "Men exist" and "Conscious beings exist," and replace the first by $P$ and the second by $Q$, so that we can write $\sim P \vee Q$. What is necessary is of course possible; so that there is no reason why this expression should not express a genuine proposition. And we can see why, according to the theory, the proposition in question will be a necessary one. If we try to construct the contradictory of $\sim P \vee Q$, we shall get, according to the rules, $P . \sim Q$, where both $P$ and $\sim Q$ designate genuine possibilities, but where they are so related that no third possibility, and therefore no third proposition, arises from their conjunction. We may say that a proposition is necessary if and only if, in point of fact, it does not have a contradictory; a proposition is an analytic fact, and when there is no associated fact of the required kind, no contradictory will exist. It is not easy to see what other reason could be assigned why some propositions are 'necessary truths.'

Before going on, we had better call attention to a possible source of misapprehension. We are saying that the expression $P. \sim Q$ does not, as a whole, stand for any single proposition. But it is, nevertheless, easy to read this expression so that it will express one proposition. We may understand it to mean "There is a proposition named by $P$, and another named by $\sim Q$, and the conjunction of the two propositions so named is true." This is a natural reading, and one that is frequently resorted to; but it is not a logical reading, since it is in part about the way certain symbols are, as a matter of fact, conventionally used. It might quite well be true that $P$ and $\sim Q$ were employed to stand for two propositions which, when conjoined, gave rise to a true proposition; this simply does not happen to be so, and the proposition to the effect that it is, is merely a contingent one, which happens to be false. The point is, of course, that $P. \sim Q$ is intended to be about what $P$ and $\sim Q$ stand for; it is intended to mean "Men exist, but conscious beings do not"; so that the fact that such an alternative reading is possible does not constitute an objection to the view that no appropriate unitary meaning for the expression can be found. It is important to call attention to this point, because, in failing to find a primary meaning for $P. \sim Q$, we are inclined to give the expression this secondary interpretation; and if this is not recognized, we are likely to suppose ourselves to have found an interpretation which is strictly logical.

Let us consider now the statement $P \prec Q$, i.e., "Men exist strictly implies that conscious beings exist." This, it will be seen, is a statement about the two propositions $P$ and $Q$, and expresses a relationship in which they stand. It is, moreover, a direct statement of fact; and it is not a proposition. There can be no question of falsehood in such a case, because falsehood can occur only where there is transcendence and mediation by propositions, and we have here to do with the expression of a fact without mediation. This is why such facts are *a priori;* they are simply given to direct apprehension; though, of course, this does not preclude the possibility of confusion regarding whether a given expression does or does not properly express anything at all.

Facts like the one here in question are of a sort which we have not so far considered, since they are not possibilities open to realization and so cannot function propositionally; they are facts about propositions which are not themselves propositions. In the case of $P \prec Q$, however, there is a closely associated fact which can function propositionally, namely, $\sim P \vee Q$. And it will be seen that the first of these expressions is an intensional function of $P$ and $Q$, while the second is an extensional function. We wish to hold, quite generally, that all statements in intension, if they stand as units for anything, state facts about propositions which are not themselves propositions; and that all extensional statements state facts that can function propositionally, if they have any unitary meaning at all. It might seem as if we had made an exception to this in saying that the expressions "Men exist" and "Men might exist" were to be understood as representing the same proposition, the first carrying the suggestion that the speaker is 'believing through' the fact denoted, and the second that he is merely apprehending the fact and directing the attention of the hearer to it; for the second of these expressions might naturally be taken to be tantamount to "$\Diamond$(men exist)," which is an intensional statement. We have said, however, that this second expression is equivalent in logical import to the phrase 'that men should exist'; and this, we may hold, is to be distinguished from "It is possible that men should exist," which is to be understood as a statement of fact about the proposition "Men exist" that cannot itself function propositionally. Thus, functions like $\Diamond p$, $\Diamond(p \vee q)$, and $p \prec q$, which become statements in intension when values are assigned to the variables, will denote facts that are not propositions, in the strict sense in which this term is here being used; whereas functions like $p$, $p \vee q$, and $p \supset q$ will denote facts which are, in this strict sense, propositions; and it will therefore be clear that a logic which includes intensional statements, in addition to extensional ones, is wider than a logic which confines itself to extensional statements.

Now, the fact that, on the view we are considering, many forms of expression must be without unitary significance, and therefore as wholes strictly meaningless, might be taken to be an objection to this view. It is to be noted, however, that nobody would wish to make a statement which had, let us say, the form $p \,.\, {\sim}p$, although it might be desirable to make statements with subordinate constituents of this form. Thus, we might wish to say ${\sim}(p \,.\, {\sim}p)$, and this might seem to be meaningless unless $p \,.\, {\sim}p$ had a unitary meaning. That will depend, however, upon how this expression has been defined in terms of appropriately chosen primitive ideas. For example, ${\sim}(p \,.\, {\sim}p)$ might have been defined to mean ${\sim}p \vee p$, and in that case it would have a unitary significance despite the fact that $p \,.\, {\sim}p$ did not. Again, although $p \,.\, q$ will not express a proposition if $p$ and $q$ are incompatible, ${\sim}\Diamond(p \,.\, q)$ will express a fact, provided it is interpreted as a statement in intension about the two propositions. It may, for instance, be so defined as to mean what is meant by $p \prec {\sim}q$. But even if it were not possible to carry through such an analysis, that circumstance by itself would hardly be a final objection to the present view. It is a well-known phenomenon connected with logistic systems that they may have 'partial' interpretations, and that there may be a good deal of symbolic by-play and notational pantomime which in itself has no meaning whatever. In such a case, some of the expressions will be significant and others not; but it may happen that if we follow the rules of the system, as we pass from significance to non-significance and then back to significance again, no error in the statement of fact will arise; and it may, indeed, be a convenience to have fictitious statements in a system, since the rules of operation may be simplified thereby. It is, however, in following such rules of operation that the logical paradoxes arise; and we may say, therefore, that the existence on the present view of logical expressions having no unitary significance is in general accord with the facts.

We have seen how an expression of the form $p \,.\, q$, where the constituent propositions may or may not be incompatible, can always be given an interpretation which will be, in part, about the symbols, and which will be a merely contingent proposition. As has been said, such an expression may be understood to mean "$p$ and $q$ both stand for propositions; there is a proposition which is their conjunction; and this proposition is true." This point is important in understanding how genuine falsehood in mathematics is possible. Consider, for example, the simple arithmetical proposition $2 + 3 = 5$. We shall have to hold that, in its primary significance, this expression states a fact directly, and that such an expression as $2 + 3 = 6$ is, as a whole, without purely arithmetical significance. Yet mistakes in arithmetic constantly occur which are hardly mere matters of confusion. Suppose we take $7 \times 8 = 63$ and ask what anybody who made this statement could be meaning by it. It is clear that we do not commonly grasp the purely arithmetical meanings of the parts of such an expression, if we ever do. On the contrary, in making this statement we should presumably be asserting something like the following: "The symbols '7' and '8' stand, conventionally, for natural numbers; the product of any two natural numbers is itself a natural number; and the product of the numbers for which '7' and '8' stand is, according to standard conventions, represented by '63.'" This is false in the strict sense of the term; but the parts of it which are false, and which make the whole statement so, are not about the arithmetical properties of numbers, but about certain human conventions.

It should perhaps be mentioned that conceptual complexes often involve data of sense as constituents, where these data are integrated with certain purely conceptual factors, and that such complexes are often possibilities and can therefore function propositionally. This will be true of any conceptual complex which is involved in a judgment of perception in such a way as to be the medium of that judgment. Let us take, for example, a judgment which can be expressed by the words "That is a table." We have seen that the word "That" in such an expression corresponds to a presented sense-datum, and that the import of the whole expression can be rendered in the words "That is an appearance of one and only one table." In a case in which we really have a genuine judgment of perception expressible in these words, there will be a fact that the datum might, so far as the intrinsic nature of the given complex is concerned, be an appearance of a table; and we can therefore express this possibility, which will be a proposition, by saying "That *might be* an appearance of one and only one table." But if we were actually judging through this possibility, as we should be doing if we were making a judgment of perception, we should, in order to indicate that we were so judging, express this same proposition by saying "That *is* an appearance of one and only one table." Suppose, on the other hand, that we have a given datum of sense which, let us say, is red, and suppose we say with regard to this datum simply "This is red." Here there will be no transcending of what is given, and no judging, but merely a direct expression of fact, without the intermediation of any proposition; and the fact so expressed will not be of a sort that can function propositionally. If we said, in such a case, "This is green," where the given datum was in fact red, there would be no significant statement. The statement would have a significant syntax, and parts of it would name genuine entities, but there would be nothing which was the meaning of the whole statement, because there would be nothing which was the synthesis of these different entities.

The foregoing discussion is perhaps detailed enough to give a fairly clear notion of the kind of view we wish to suggest with regard to the nature of propositions; and we may now summarize briefly the main points. Significant sentences stand for or designate conceptual complexes, which are always open to direct apprehension. These conceptual complexes are factual in character, and such facts make up the domain of the *a priori*. The expression of these facts is direct rather than mediated, and therefore propositions are not required as a means of expressing them. A sentence may vary in grammatical structure (in particular, from the indicative mood to the conditional) merely as a means of indicating to the hearer some attitude of the speaker, and without any alteration of the conceptual complex which the sentence represents. Conceptual complexes (which are also called analytic facts, because of their factual character and because they can be known by direct inspection) can sometimes function propositionally; and when they are such that they can, they *are* propositions. In particular, all such complexes as are 'possibilities' open to realization are propositions, and every proposition is such a possibility. The realization of a possibility will consist in the being of some state of affairs external to the proposition which is the possibility; and all significant judgment consists in judging or believing through such possibilities. Some analytic facts, however, are not possibilities, and cannot function propositionally or be realized; they are often such as are 'about' possibilities, and so involve, in a certain way, propositions as constituents. Statements in intension, which are constructed by means of $\prec$ and derivative notions, seem always to express analytic facts which are not propositions, whereas statements in extension, which are constructed by means of $\sim$, $\vee$, and the like, alone, seem always to express propositions.

We should not wish to place much emphasis upon the details of this view. It is plain that, in the present state of our knowledge regarding the points dealt with, nobody can expect to formulate a theory that will turn out to be correct in detail. All that can be hoped is that certain points will be right and that they will contribute toward a finally satisfactory view. And, of course, we have not adopted elsewhere the terms which would be strictly correct if the theory should be a true one. We have used the term 'proposition' to designate any statement whatever, whether, according to the theory, it would merely express a fact directly, or whether it would express a proposition strictly so called, or whether it would be, as a whole, without significance. Any other course would plainly involve overemphasis and misevaluation, and would, in addition, tend to confuse the reader. We are mainly interested, in the present connection, in the bearing of the theory upon the conception of a hierarchy of logical propositions, and we turn now to a consideration of this matter.

Before this digression on the nature of propositions, we were saying that if the function $p \vee \sim p$ could take as values purely logical propositions, then an absolute hierarchy of logical propositions would seem inevitable, because there would then have to be an infinity of principles of excluded middle, with each proposition falling under one and only one of these principles; and what is true of excluded middle will plainly be true of any other logical principle. Such a hierarchy will result, however, only if our substitutions are made on the ground of the relation of genus to instance, because it is only in that kind of substitution that the resulting proposition will be of an order other than that of the proposition from which it is derived. And it follows from the theory we have developed that no substitution of a purely logical proposition in a function like $p \vee \sim p$ can be of the genus-instance kind. This is true because all purely logical propositions are 'necessary' and have no significant contradictories; so that if $p$ is logical, $\sim p$ is without significance, and so is $p \vee \sim p$.

If we replace the $p$ in $p \vee \sim p$ by $(p) . p \vee \sim p$, we shall get, according to the formal rules, $(p) . p \vee \sim p . \vee . (\exists p) . \sim p . p$. But if $\sim p . p$ cannot denote one single proposition, there can be no proposition expressed by $(\exists p) . \sim p . p$. The point is, that if we take an ordinary contingent proposition $P$, it will be satisfied by certain possibilities, and made false by others, which are covered by $\sim P$; so that if we take the disjunction of these two, all possibilities will be covered, and there will be nothing left for $\sim(P \vee \sim P)$ to stand for. Such an expression may appear as a convenient fiction in a statement which, as a whole, has significance; but it cannot so appear if it is to be understood as resulting from genus-instance substitution, because there will be no proposition which is an instance of the function in question.

Consider the matrix $p \vee \sim p . \vee . \sim p . p$, which contains the fictitious alternative $\sim p . p$. It might be convenient if we gave this whole expression meaning by saying that it was to be understood as identical with $p \vee \sim p$; that is, if we simply neglected the non-significant part and read the remainder. We could then write

$$(p) : p \vee \sim p . \vee . \sim p . p,$$

which would mean exactly what was meant by $(p) . p \vee \sim p$; and we could also write

$$(p) : . (\exists q) : p \vee \sim p . \vee . \sim q . q,$$

and then, by purely verbal definition,

$$(p) . p \vee \sim p . \vee . (\exists q) . \sim q . q,$$

which could be read without any reference to the fictitious part $(\exists q) . \sim q . q$.

Let us take the matrix $p . \supset . p \vee q$, and, without regard to justification, substitute $(p) . p \vee \sim p$ for $p$, and $(\exists q) . q$ for $q$, so that we shall have

$$(p) . p \vee \sim p . \supset : (p) . p \vee \sim p . \vee . (\exists q) . q.$$

When $\supset$ is replaced by its definition, it will be seen that we have $(\exists p) . \sim p . p$ as a non-significant antecedent, and inference would appear to be impossible. Consider, however, how the consequent in this case can be validly reached.[14] We have, to begin with,

$$(p) :. (q) : p . \supset . p \vee q,$$

which is equivalent to

$$(p) :. (q) : p \vee \sim p . \vee . q,$$

which implies

$$(p) :. (\exists q) : p \vee \sim p . \vee . q,$$

which is equivalent to

$$(p) . p \vee \sim p . \vee . (\exists q) . q.$$

Of course, in a process such as this, the resulting propositions are of the same kind as those from which they are derived, so that a hierarchy of purely logical propositions does not arise. There must be a hierarchy, or hierarchies, of non-logical propositions, however, as is shown by such examples as that about 'all rules,' or that about all propositions asserted by A during a given interval of time. And there will have to be a relative hierarchy of logical functions, to enable us to make typic adjustments among the variables in a complex logical proposition, and to take as values propositions belonging to an absolute non-logical hierarchy. It is to be held that the variables in a relative hierarchy of functions can, with appropriate typic adjustments, take values beginning at any point in an absolute hierarchy of non-logical propositions. This wandering of a logical function over different non-logical types is possible in virtue of our denial that a variable in a matrix need have a preassigned range of variation.

[14] Cf. *Principia Mathematica*, 2d ed., Vol. I, Appendix A.

# APPENDIX I

## THE USE OF DOTS AS BRACKETS

There are a number of points with regard to the punctuation or bracketing of logical expressions which could not be conveniently explained at any one place in the text, because the symbols of different sorts, in connection with which the use of bracketing dots requires explanation, were not all introduced at once. So, we propose to deal here somewhat in detail with the technique of the use of dots as brackets and to explain in order the several points involved. The scheme that we have adopted is that of *Principia Mathematica*, which, as will be seen, includes some conventions that are essential to any system of bracketing and others that are arbitrary.

Consider, in the first place, an expression like

$$(p \supset p') \vee (q \supset q'),$$

where the use of brackets, or some equivalent scheme of punctuation, is essential. It will be seen, in the case of this particular expression, that we can if we like dispense with the two extreme brackets without incurring ambiguity; we can write

$$p \supset p') \vee (q \supset q'.$$

And then we can replace the remaining brackets by dots:

$$p \supset p' . \vee . q \supset q'.$$

But if this is to be done, one point must be carefully noted: the brackets are asymmetrical, and thus indicate the direction in which they operate, whereas the dots are ambiguous in this respect; so that we must introduce the convention that a dot is always to be understood as operating away from the connective or other symbol beside which it occurs.

Suppose, now, that we have such an expression as

$$[(p \vee p') \supset (q \vee q')] \vee [(r \vee r') \supset (s \vee s')],$$

which involves brackets of two sorts, wider and narrower. It is easy to see that we can write, without ambiguity,

$$p \vee p') \supset (q \vee q')] \vee [(r \vee r') \supset (s \vee s';$$

and if we adopt the convention that a square bracket is to be understood as being stronger than a round one, in the sense that a square bracket can have within its scope a round one, but not conversely, then we can write:

$$p \vee p') \supset (q \vee q'] \vee [r \vee r') \supset (s \vee s'.$$

We can then replace square brackets by double dots and round brackets by single ones:

$$p \vee p' . \supset . q \vee q' : \vee : r \vee r' . \supset . s \vee s'.$$

The scope of a single dot is to be understood as being closed by another single dot, or by two dots, whereas the scope of two dots is not closed by a single one. Thus, in place of

$$(p \supset p') \vee (q \supset q') \vee (r \supset r'),$$

we can write

$$p \supset p' . \vee . q \supset q' . \vee . r \supset r',$$

or

$$p . \supset . p' : \vee : q . \supset . q' : \vee : r . \supset . r'.$$

And these same conventions are to be extended to the use of any number of dots that may be required.

Now, let us take the two expressions:

$$(p) \supset (q \vee r) \text{ and } p \supset (q \vee r),$$

where, of course, brackets around the $p$ in the first expression are not strictly necessary; and let us replace brackets by dots, so that we have

$$p . \supset . q \vee r \text{ and } p \supset . q \vee r.$$

Here, although one of the dots in the first expression is superfluous, we commonly put it in for the sake of symmetry. Again, let us take the three expressions:

$$p \supset [(q \vee r) \supset (q \vee r)],$$
$$[p] \supset [(q \vee r) \supset (q \vee r)],$$
$$(p) \supset [(q \vee r) \supset (q \vee r)],$$

in connection with which, when brackets are replaced by dots, we have

$$p \supset : q \vee r . \supset . q \vee r,$$

$$p : \supset : q \vee r . \supset . q \vee r,$$

$$p . \supset : q \vee r . \supset . q \vee r.$$

In accordance with our conventions, each of these expressions is correct, the first being the most economical in the use of dots. The second has the advantage that coördinate elements in the complex are punctuated alike; but this is really unnecessary, and it is common practice to adopt the third form. Whenever one or more dots are required on one side of a connective, we put one dot on the other side even when it is not necessary to do so.

We have, so far, omitted consideration of expressions involving conjunction, because we also use dots to mean 'and,' so that the conventions in this respect require special discussion. Let us take the expression

$$(p \vee q) . (r \vee s),$$

in which the dot stands only for conjunction. If we here replace brackets by dots, as above, we have

$$p \vee q \;.\;.\;.\; r \vee s,$$

where the middle dot is the sign of conjunction and the outer ones serve as brackets. But it is customary, in such a case, simply to write

$$p \vee q . r \vee s,$$

and thus to allow a single dot to stand for conjunction and do the work of bracketing as well. When this is done, however, it is to be noted that the bracketing dot used, unlike the others we have considered, must be understood as operating in both directions, since it does the work of two dots, one on each side of the sign of conjunction.

Again, consider such an expression as

$$[(p \supset q) . (q \supset p)] \vee [(r \supset s) . (s \supset r)],$$

which, when brackets are replaced by dots in accordance with the conventions so far put down, becomes

$$p \supset q . q \supset p : \vee : r \supset s . s \supset r.$$

Now, it is not customary in such a case to use double dots in connection with $\vee$; we may write

$$p \supset q \,.\, q \supset p \,.\vee.\, r \supset s \,.\, s \supset r$$

and understand the dots which stand also for conjunction as being 'weaker' than those occurring beside a connective—as if some of their force were taken up in meaning 'and.' In place of $(p \,.\, q) \vee r$ we write $p \,.\, q \,.\vee.\, r$ rather than $p \,.\, q :\vee.\, r$; and in place of $p \,.\, [q \supset (r \vee s)]$ we write $p : q \,.\supset.\, r \vee s$. In general, a given number of dots occurring beside a connective will carry over an equal number standing also for conjunction, and a given number standing for conjunction will carry over a lesser number beside a connective. And, of course, a single dot meaning conjunction will carry over a bare connective—as in $p \,.\, q \vee r$, which means $p \,.\, (q \vee r)$.

There is one further matter that must be dealt with regarding the way dots are to be understood as operating in given directions. Consider the expression

$$s \vee [p \vee \{(q \supset r) \supset s\}],$$

which we should write

$$s \,.\vee:.\, p \,.\vee:\, q \supset r \,.\supset.\, s,$$

and note that we here use three dots after the first occurrence of $\vee$ in order to get over the two dots which come after the second occurrence, despite the fact that these latter dots operate in the same direction as the set of three. That is to say, we regard the scope of a set of dots as being closed when another set of equal or greater strength is met, no matter what the direction of operation of the other set. It would be possible to adopt a convention to the effect that the scope of a set of dots could be closed only by dots operating in the opposite direction; and in accordance with such a convention, we could write

$$s \,.\vee:\, p \,.\vee:\, q \supset r \,.\supset.\, s,$$

which would correspond to

$$s \vee \{p \vee \{(q \supset r) \supset s\}\}.$$

But this would make our expressions less easy to read and would effect a very slight compensating economy.

There remains only one other class of dots to be discussed, namely, those which come after prefixes. Consider, for example, the expression

$$(x)[f(x) \,.\, f'(x)],$$

which is to be written

$$(x) \,.\, f(x) \,.\, f'(x).$$

We regard a dot which comes after a prefix as being stronger than one which indicates conjunction. But, on the other hand, we take such a dot to be weaker than one standing beside a connective; so that, for example,

$$p \vee [(x) \,.\, f(x)]$$

may be written

$$p \,.\vee.\, (x) \,.\, f(x),$$

where the single dot after $\vee$ brackets the entire expression to the right of it. We write

$$(x) : (\exists y) \,.\, f(x) \,.\, f'(y)$$

in place of

$$(x)[(\exists y)\{f(x) \,.\, f'(y)\}],$$

and

$$(x) \,.\, f(x) : (\exists y) \,.\, f'(y)$$

in place of

$$[(x)\{f(x)\}] \,.\, [(\exists y)\{f'(y)\}].$$

Now, inasmuch as $\sim$ and $\Diamond$ are prefixes, it might be expected that we should deal with them as we do with $(x)$ and $(\exists x)$; that we should, for example, replace

$$\sim[(\exists x) \,.\, f(x)] \text{ and } \Diamond[(\exists x) \,.\, f(x)]$$

by

$$\sim:(\exists x) \,.\, f(x) \text{ and } \Diamond:(\exists x) \,.\, f(x),$$

and replace

$$\sim(p \vee q \,.\supset.\, p) \text{ and } \Diamond(p \vee q \,.\supset.\, p)$$

by

$$\sim:p \vee q \,.\supset.\, p \text{ and } \Diamond:p \vee q \,.\supset.\, p.$$

This procedure would be quite in accordance with the conventions we have adopted; but, in fact, we dispose of these two cases in other ways. In the first case, we write

$$\sim(\exists x) \,.\, f(x) \quad \text{and} \quad \Diamond(\exists x) \,.\, f(x),$$

without either brackets or dots—as if $\sim(\exists x)$ and $\Diamond(\exists x)$ were single operators, although of course they are not, since the scope of the attached prefix is, in each case, the entire expression $(\exists x) \,.\, f(x)$. In the same way, we write

$$(x) : \sim(\exists y) \,.\, f(x, y) \quad \text{and} \quad (x) : \Diamond(\exists y) \,.\, f(x, y)$$

in place of

$$(x) \,.\, \sim[(\exists y) \,.\, f(x, y)] \quad \text{and} \quad (x) \,.\, \Diamond[(\exists y) \,.\, f(x, y)];$$

and, again,

$$\sim\Diamond(\exists x) \,.\, f(x)$$

in place of

$$\sim[\Diamond\{(\exists x) \,.\, f(x)\}].$$

In the second case, where we have $\sim(p \vee q \,.\supset .\, p)$ and $\Diamond(p \vee q \,.\supset .\, p)$, it is customary simply to retain the brackets, rather than to make use of dots.

It will be observed that nearly all the foregoing examples illustrate the minimum number of dots that may be used in a given case. We must therefore point out that the scheme is more elastic than would appear from these illustrations. It is always possible, in the interest of clarity or of emphasis, to use more dots than are strictly required, provided, of course, that we have due regard for the different degrees of strength of dots of different classes. Thus, $(x) \,.\, f(x) \,.\, g(x)$ and $(x) : f(x) \,.\, g(x)$ mean the same thing, as do $p \,.\supset .\, (\exists x) \,.\, f(x)$ and $p \,.\supset :\, (\exists x) \,.\, f(x)$.

## APPENDIX II

## THE STRUCTURE OF THE SYSTEM OF STRICT IMPLICATION [1]

The System of Strict Implication, as presented in Chapter V of *A Survey of Symbolic Logic* (University of California Press, 1918), contained an error with respect to one postulate. This was pointed out by Dr. E. L. Post, and was corrected by me in the *Journal of Philosophy, Psychology, and Scientific Method* (XVII [1920], 300). The amended postulates (set A below) compare with those of Chapter VI of this book (set B below) as follows:

[1] This appendix is written by Mr. Lewis, but the points demonstrated are, most of them, due to other persons.

Groups II and III, below, were transmitted to Mr. Lewis by Dr. M. Wajsberg, of the University of Warsaw, in 1927. Dr. Wajsberg's letter also contained the first proof ever given that the System of Strict Implication is not reducible to Material Implication, as well as the outline of a system which is equivalent to that deducible from the postulates of Strict Implication with the addition of the postulate later suggested in Becker's paper and cited below as C11. It is to be hoped that this and other important work of Dr. Wajsberg will be published shortly.

Groups I, IV, and V are due to Dr. William T. Parry, who also discovered independently Groups II and III. Groups I, II, and III are contained in his doctoral dissertation, on file in the Harvard University Library. Most of the proofs in this appendix have been given or suggested by Dr. Parry.

It follows from Dr. Wajsberg's work that there is an unlimited number of groups, or systems, of different cardinality, which satisfy the postulates of Strict Implication. Mr. Paul Henle, of Harvard University, later discovered another proof of this same fact. Mr. Henle's proof, which can be more easily indicated in brief space, proceeds by demonstrating that any group which satisfies the Boole-Schröder Algebra will also satisfy the postulates of Strict Implication if $\Diamond p$ be determined as follows:

$$\Diamond p = 1 \text{ when and only when } p \neq 0;$$

$$\Diamond p = 0 \text{ when and only when } p = 0.$$

This establishes the fact that there are as many distinct groups satisfying the postulates as there are powers of 2, since it has been shown by Huntington that there is a group satisfying the postulates of the Boole-Schröder Algebra for every power of 2 ("Sets of Independent Postulates for the Algebra of Logic," *Trans. Amer. Math. Soc.*, V [1904], 309).

The proof of (14), p. 498, is due to Y. T. Shen (Shen Yuting).

| | |
|---|---|
| A1. $p\,q \,.\prec.\, q\,p$ | B1. $p\,q \,.\prec.\, q\,p$ |
| A2. $q\,p \,.\prec.\, p$ | B2. $p\,q \,.\prec.\, p$ |
| A3. $p \,.\prec.\, p\,p$ | B3. $p \,.\prec.\, p\,p$ |
| A4. $p(q\,r) \,.\prec.\, q(p\,r)$ | B4. $(p\,q)r \,.\prec.\, p(q\,r)$ |
| A5. $p \prec \sim(\sim p)$ | B5. $p \prec \sim(\sim p)$ |
| A6. $p \prec q \,.\, q \prec r :\prec.\, p \prec r$ | B6. $p \prec q \,.\, q \prec r :\prec.\, p \prec r$ |
| A7. $\sim\Diamond p \prec \sim p$ | B7. $p \,.\, p \prec q :\prec.\, q$ |
| A8. $p \prec q \,.\prec.\, \sim\Diamond q \prec \sim\Diamond p$ | B8. $\Diamond(p\,q) \prec \Diamond p$ |
| | B9. $(\exists\, p, q) : \sim(p \prec q) \,.\, \sim(p \prec \sim q)$ |

The primitive ideas and definitions are not identical in the two cases; but they form equivalent sets, in connection with the postulates.

Comparison of these two sets of postulates, as well as many other points concerning the structure of Strict Implication, will be facilitated by consideration of the following groups. Each of these is based upon the same matrix for the relation $p\,q$ and the function of negation $\sim p$. (This is a four-valued matrix which satisfies the postulates of the Boole-Schröder Algebra.) The groups differ by their different specification of the function $\Diamond p$. We give the fundamental matrix for $p\,q$ and $\sim p$ in the first case only. The matrix for $p \prec q$, resulting from this and the particular determination of $\Diamond p$, is given for each group:

Group I

| $p\,q$ | $q$: 1 | 2 | 3 | 4 | $\sim p$ | $\Diamond$ | $\prec$ | 1 | 2 | 3 | 4 |
|---|---|---|---|---|---|---|---|---|---|---|---|
| $p$: 1 | 1 | 2 | 3 | 4 | 4 | 1 | 1 | 2 | 4 | 4 | 4 |
| 2 | 2 | 2 | 4 | 4 | 3 | 1 | 2 | 2 | 2 | 4 | 4 |
| 3 | 3 | 4 | 3 | 4 | 2 | 1 | 3 | 2 | 4 | 2 | 4 |
| 4 | 4 | 4 | 4 | 4 | 1 | 3 | 4 | 2 | 2 | 2 | 2 |

Group II

| $\Diamond$ | $\prec$ | 1 | 2 | 3 | 4 |
|---|---|---|---|---|---|
| 1 | 1 | 1 | 4 | 3 | 4 |
| 2 | 2 | 1 | 1 | 3 | 3 |
| 1 | 3 | 1 | 4 | 1 | 4 |
| 4 | 4 | 1 | 1 | 1 | 1 |

Group III

| $\Diamond$ | $\prec$ | 1 | 2 | 3 | 4 |
|---|---|---|---|---|---|
| 1 | 1 | 1 | 4 | 4 | 4 |
| 1 | 2 | 1 | 1 | 4 | 4 |
| 1 | 3 | 1 | 4 | 1 | 4 |
| 4 | 4 | 1 | 1 | 1 | 1 |

GROUP IV

| $\Diamond$ | $\prec$ | 1 | 2 | 3 | 4 |
|---|---|---|---|---|---|
| 2 | 1 | 1 | 3 | 3 | 3 |
| 2 | 2 | 1 | 1 | 3 | 3 |
| 2 | 3 | 1 | 3 | 1 | 3 |
| 4 | 4 | 1 | 1 | 1 | 1 |

GROUP V

| $\Diamond$ | $\prec$ | 1 | 2 | 3 | 4 |
|---|---|---|---|---|---|
| 1 | 1 | 2 | 4 | 3 | 4 |
| 2 | 2 | 2 | 2 | 3 | 3 |
| 1 | 3 | 2 | 4 | 2 | 4 |
| 3 | 4 | 2 | 2 | 2 | 2 |

The 'designated values,' for all five groups, are 1 and 2; that is, the group is to be taken as satisfying any principle whose values, for all combinations of the values of its variables, are confined to 1 and 2. (In Groups II, III, and IV, 1 alone might be taken as the designated value: but in that case it must be remembered that, since

$$(\exists\, p, q) : \sim(p \prec q) \,.\, \sim(p \prec \sim q) :. = :. \sim[(p, q) : p \prec q \,.\vee.\, p \prec \sim q],$$

B9 would be satisfied *unless* $p \prec q \,.\vee.\, p \prec \sim q$ *always* has the value 1. It is simpler to take 1 and 2 both as designated values; in which case B9 is satisfied if and only if $\sim(p \prec q) \,.\, \sim(p \prec \sim q)$ has the value 1 or the value 2 for some combination of the values of $p$ and $q$.)

All of these groups satisfy the operations of 'Adjunction,' 'Inference,' and the substitution of equivalents. If $P$ and $Q$ are functions having a designated value, then $P\,Q$ will have a designated value. If $P$ has a designated value, and $P \prec Q$ has a designated value, then $Q$ will have a designated value. And if $P = Q$—that is, if $P \prec Q \,.\, Q \prec P$ has a designated value—then $P$ and $Q$ will have the same value, and for any function $f$ in the system, $f(P)$ and $f(Q)$ will have the same value.

The following facts may be established by reference to these groups:

(1) The system, as deduced from either set of postulates, is consistent. Group I, Group II, and Group III each satisfy all postulates of either set. For any one of these three groups, B9 is satisfied by the fact that $\sim(p \prec q) \,.\, \sim(p \prec \sim q)$ has a designated value when $p = 1$ and $q = 2$, and when $p = 1$ and $q = 3$.

(2) The system, as deduced from either set, is not reducible to Material Implication. For any one of the five groups,

$\sim(p \sim q) . \prec . p \prec q$ has the value 3 or 4 when $p = 1$ and $q = 2$. None of the 'paradoxes' of Material Implication, such as $p . \supset . q \supset p$ and $\sim p . \supset . p \supset q$, will hold for any of these groups if the sign of material implication, $\supset$, is replaced by $\prec$ throughout.

(3) The Consistency Postulate, B8, is independent of the set (B1–7 and B9) and of the set A1–7. Group V satisfies B1–7, and satisfies $\sim(p \prec q) . \sim(p \prec \sim q)$ for the values $p = 1$, $q = 2$. It also satisfies A1–7. But Group V fails to satisfy B8: B8 has the value 4 when $p = 2$ and $q = 3$, and when $p = 2$ and $q = 4$.

(4) Similarly, A8 is independent of the set A1–7, and of the set (B1–7 and B9). For Group V, A8 has the value 4 when $p = 1$ and $q = 3$, and when $p = 2$ and $q = 3$.

(5) Postulate B7 is independent of the set (B1–6 and B8, 9), and of the set (A1–6 and A8). Group IV satisfies B1–6, B8, and B9, and satisfies A1–6 and A8. But for this group, B7 has the value 3 when $p = 1$ and $q = 2$, and for various other combinations of the values of $p$ and $q$.

(6) Similarly, A7 is independent of the set (A1–6 and A8) and of the set (B1–6 and B8, 9). For Group IV, A7 has the value 3 when $p = 1$ and when $p = 3$.

That the Existence Postulate, B9, is independent of the set B1–8, and of the set A1–8, is proved by the following two-element group, which satisfies B1–8 and A1–8:

| $p\,q$ | 1 | 0 | $\sim p$ |
|---|---|---|---|
| 1 | 1 | 0 | 0 |
| 0 | 0 | 0 | 1 |

| $\Diamond$ | $\prec$ | 1 | 0 |
|---|---|---|---|
| 1 | 1 | 1 | 0 |
| 0 | 0 | 1 | 1 |

(This is, of course, the usual matrix for Material Implication, with the function $\Diamond p$ specified as equivalent to $p$.) For this group, $\sim(p \prec q) . \sim(p \prec \sim q)$ has the value 0 for all combinations of the values of $p$ and $q$.

Dr. Parry has been able to deduce B2 from the set (B1 and B3–9). However, the omission of B2 from the postulate set of Chapter VI would have been incompatible with the order of exposition there adopted, since the Consistency Postulate is required for the derivation of B2. Whether with this exception the members of set B are mutually independent has not been fully determined.

The question naturally arises whether the two sets A1–8 and B1–8 are equivalent. I have discovered no proof but believe that they are not. B1–8 are all deducible from A1–8: and A1–7 are all deducible from B1–8. The question is whether A8 is deducible from B1–8. If it is not, then the system as deduced from the postulate set of Chapter VI, B1–9, is somewhat 'stricter' than as deduced in the *Survey* from set A.

The logically important issue here concerns certain consequences which enter the system when A8 is introduced. Both Dr. Wajsberg and Dr. Parry have proved that the principle

$$p \prec q \,.\prec:\, q \prec r \,.\prec.\, p \prec r$$

is deducible from A1–8. I doubt whether this proposition should be regarded as a valid principle of deduction: it would never lead to any inference $p \prec r$ which would be questionable when $p \prec q$ and $q \prec r$ are given premises; but it gives the inference $q \prec r \,.\prec.\, p \prec r$ whenever $p \prec q$ is a premise. Except as an elliptical statement for "$p \prec q \,.\, q \prec r :\prec.\, p \prec r$ and $p \prec q$ is true," this inference seems dubious.

Now as has been proved under (3) above, the Consistency Postulate, B8, is not deducible from the set (B1–7 and B9). Likewise the principle mentioned in the preceding paragraph is independent of the set (B1–7 and B9): Group V satisfies this set, but for that group the principle in question has the value 4 when $p = 1$, $q = 3$, and $r = 1$, as well as for various other values of $p$, $q$, and $r$. But Group V also fails to satisfy B8, as was pointed out in (3) above. If it should hereafter be discovered that the dubious principle of the preceding paragraph is deducible from the set B1–9, then at least it is not contained in the system deducible from the set (B1–7 and B9); and I should then regard that system—to be referred to hereafter as S1—as the one which coincides in its properties with the strict principles of deductive inference. As the reader will have noted, Chapter VI was so developed that the theorems belonging to this system, S1, are readily distinguishable from those which require the Consistency Postulate, B8.

The system as deduced either from set A or from set B leaves undetermined certain properties of the modal functions, $\Diamond p$, $\sim\Diamond p$, $\Diamond\sim p$, and $\sim\Diamond\sim p$. In view of this fact, Professor Oskar Becker [2] has proposed the following for consideration as further postulates, any one or more of which might be added to either set:

C10. $\sim\Diamond\sim p \prec \sim\Diamond\sim\sim\Diamond\sim p$ $\qquad \sim\Diamond\sim\sim\Diamond\sim p = \sim\Diamond\sim p$

C11. $\Diamond p \prec \sim\Diamond\sim\Diamond p$ $\qquad \Diamond p = \sim\Diamond\sim\Diamond p$

C12. $p \prec \sim\Diamond\sim\Diamond p$

(Becker calls C12 the "Brouwersche Axiom.")

When A1–8, or B1–9, are assumed, the second form in which C10 is given can be derived from the first, since the converse implication, $\sim\Diamond\sim\sim\Diamond\sim p \prec \sim\Diamond\sim p$, is an immediate consequence of the general principle, $\sim\Diamond\sim p \prec p$ (18·42 in Chapter VI). The second form of C11 is similarly deducible from the first.

An alternative and notationally simpler form of C10 would be

C10·1 $\Diamond\Diamond p \prec \Diamond p$ $\qquad \Diamond\Diamond p = \Diamond p$

(As before, the second form of the principle can be derived from the first; since the converse implication, $\Diamond p \prec \Diamond\Diamond p$, is an instance of the general principle $p \prec \Diamond p$, which is 18·4 in Chapter VI, deducible from A1–8, or B1–9.)

Substituting $\sim p$ for $p$, in C10·1, we have

$$\Diamond\Diamond\sim p \prec \Diamond\sim p \qquad \text{(a)}$$

$$\text{(a)} .=. \sim\Diamond\sim p \prec \sim\Diamond\Diamond\sim p .=. \sim\Diamond\sim p \prec \sim\Diamond\sim\sim\Diamond\sim p.$$

And substituting $\sim p$ for $p$ in C10, we have

$$\sim\Diamond\sim(\sim p) \prec \sim\Diamond\sim\sim\Diamond\sim(\sim p) \qquad \text{(b)}$$

$$\text{(b)} .=. \sim\Diamond p \prec \sim\Diamond\sim\sim\Diamond p .=. \sim\Diamond p \prec \sim\Diamond\Diamond p .=. \Diamond\Diamond p \prec \Diamond p.$$

(The principles used in these proofs are 12·3 and 12·44 in Chapter VI.)

For reasons which will appear, we add, to this list of further postulates to be considered, the following:

C13. $\Diamond\Diamond p$

That is, "For every proposition $p$, the statement '$p$ is self-consistent' is a self-consistent statement."

[2] See his paper "Zur Logik der Modalitäten," *Jahrbuch für Philosophie und Phänomenologische Forschung*, XI (1930), 497–548.

Concerning these proposed additional postulates, the following facts may be established by reference to Groups I, II, and III, above, all of which satisfy the set A1–8 and the set B1–9:

(7) C10, C11, and C12 are all consistent with A1–8 and with B1–9 and with each other. Group III satisfies C10, C11, and C12.

(8) C10, C11, and C12 are each independent of the set A1–8 and of the set B1–9. For Group I, C10, C11, and C12 all fail to hold when $p = 3$.

(9) Neither C11 nor C12 is deducible from the set (A1–8 and C10) or from the set (B1–9 and C10). Group II satisfies C10; but C11 fails, for this group, when $p = 2$ or $p = 4$; and C12 fails when $p = 2$.

(10) C13 is consistent with the set A1–8 and with the set B1–9. Group I satisfies C13.

(11) C13 is independent of the set A1–8 and of the set B1–9, and of (A1–8 and C10, C11, and C12) or (B1–9 and C10, C11, and C12). Group III satisfies all these sets; but for this group, C13 fails when $p = 4$.

When A1–8, or B1–9, are assumed, the relations of C10, C11, and C12 to each other are as follows:

(12) C10 is deducible from C11. By C11 and the principle $\sim(\sim p) = p$,

$$\begin{aligned} \sim\Diamond\sim p &= \sim[\Diamond(\sim p)] = \sim[\sim\Diamond \sim\Diamond(\sim p)] = \Diamond[\sim\Diamond(\sim p)] \\ &= \sim\Diamond \sim\Diamond(\sim\Diamond \sim p) = \sim\Diamond[\sim\Diamond \sim\Diamond(\sim p)] \\ &= \sim\Diamond[\Diamond(\sim p)] = \sim\Diamond\{\sim[\sim(\Diamond\sim p)]\} = \sim\Diamond\sim \sim\Diamond\sim p. \end{aligned}$$

(13) C12 also is deducible from C11. By 18·4 in Chapter VI, $p \prec \Diamond p$; and this, together with C11, implies C12, by A6 or by B6.

(14) From C10 and C12 together, C11 is deducible. Substituting $\Diamond p$ for $p$ in C12, we have

$$\Diamond p \prec \sim\Diamond \sim\Diamond \Diamond p. \qquad \text{(a)}$$

And by C10·1, $\sim\Diamond \sim\Diamond \Diamond p = \sim\Diamond \sim\Diamond p$. Hence (a) is equivalent to C11.

From (12), (13), and (14), it follows that as additional postulates to the set A1–8, or the set B1–9, C11 is exactly equivalent to C10 and C12 together. But as was proved in (9), the addition of C10 alone, gives a system in which neither C11 nor C12 is deducible.

Special interest attaches to C10. The set A1–8, or the set B1–9, *without* C10, gives the theorem

$$\sim\Diamond\sim\ \sim\Diamond\sim p\ .\ ⥽\ :\ \sim\Diamond\sim p = p.$$

This is deducible from 19·84 in Chapter VI. It follows from this that if there should be some proposition $p$ such that $\sim\Diamond\sim\ \sim\Diamond\sim p$ is true, then the equivalences

$$p = \sim\Diamond\sim p \qquad \text{and} \qquad \sim\Diamond\sim p = \sim\Diamond\sim\ \sim\Diamond\sim p$$

would hold for that particular proposition. And since, by 19·84 itself, all necessary propositions are equivalent, it follows that if there is *any* proposition $p$ which is necessarily-necessary—such that $\sim\Diamond\sim\ \sim\Diamond\sim p$ is true—then *every* proposition which is necessary is also necessarily-necessary; and the principle stated by C10 holds universally. But as was proved in (8), this principle, $\sim\Diamond\sim p = \sim\Diamond\sim\ \sim\Diamond\sim p$, is not deducible from A1–8 or from B1–9. Hence the two possibilities, with respect to necessary propositions, which the system, as deduced from A1–8 or from B1–9, leaves open are: (a) that there exist propositions which are necessarily-necessary, and that for every proposition $p$, $\sim\Diamond\sim p = \sim\Diamond\sim\ \sim\Diamond\sim p$; and (b) that there exist propositions which are necessary—as 20·21 in Chapter VI requires—but *no* propositions which are *necessarily*-necessary. This last is exactly what is required by C13, $\Diamond\ \Diamond p$. Substituting here $\sim p$ for $p$, we have, as an immediate consequence of C13, $\Diamond\ \Diamond\sim p$. This is equivalent to the theorem "For every proposition $p$, '$p$ is necessarily-necessary' is false": $\Diamond\ \Diamond\sim p = \Diamond\sim\ \sim\Diamond\sim p = \sim(\sim\Diamond\sim\ \sim\Diamond\sim p)$ [by the principle $\sim(\sim p) = p$]. Thus C10 expresses alternative (a) above; and C13 expresses alternative (b). Hence as additional postulates, C10 and C13 are contrary assumptions.

(As deduced from A1–8, the system leaves open the further alternative that there should be no necessary propositions, or that the class of necessary propositions should merely coincide with the class of true propositions; but in that case the system becomes a redundant form of Material Implication.)

From the preceding discussion it becomes evident that there is a group of systems of the general type of Strict Implication and each distinguishable from Material Implication. We shall arrange these in the order of increasing comprehensiveness and decreasing 'strictness' of the implication relation:

S1, deduced from the set B1–7, contains all the theorems of Sections 1–4 in Chapter VI. It contains also all theorems of Section 5, in the form of *T*-principles, but not with omission of the *T*. This system does not contain A8 or the principle

$$p \prec q . \prec : q \prec r . \prec . p \prec r.$$

However, it does contain, in the form of a *T*-principle, any theorem which could be derived by using A8 as a principle of inference: because it contains

$$p \prec q . \sim\Diamond q : \prec . \sim\Diamond p;$$

and hence if (by substitutions) $p \prec q$ becomes an asserted principle, we shall have

$$T . \sim\Diamond q : \prec . \sim\Diamond p.$$

When the Existence Postulate, B9, is added, this system S1 contains those existence theorems which are indicated in Section 6 of Chapter VI as not requiring the Consistency Postulate, B8.

S2, deduced from the set B1–8, contains all the theorems of Sections 1–5 in Chapter VI, any *T*-principle being replaceable by the corresponding theorem without the *T*. When the Existence Postulate, B9, is added, it contains all the existence theorems of Section 6. Whether S2 contains A8 and the principle

$$p \prec q . \prec : q \prec r . \prec . p \prec r$$

remains undetermined. If that should be the case, then it will be equivalent to S3.

S3, deduced from the set A1–8, as in the *Survey*, contains all the theorems of S2 and contains such consequences of A8 as

$$p \prec q . \prec : q \prec r . \prec . p \prec r.$$

If B9 is added, the consequences include all existence theorems of S2.

For each of the preceding systems, S1, S2, and S3, any one of the additional postulates, C10, C11, C12, and C13, is consistent with but independent of the system (but C10 and C13 are mutually incompatible).

S4, deduced from the set (B1–7 and C10), contains all theorems of S3, and in addition the consequences of C10. A8 and B8 are deducible theorems. S4 is incompatible with C13. C11 and C12 are consistent with but independent of S4. If B9 be added, the consequences include all existence theorems of S2.

S5, deduced from the set (B1–7 and C11), or from the set (B1–7, C10, and C12), contains all theorems of S4 and in addition the consequences of C12. If B9 be added, all existence theorems of S2 are included. A8 and B8 are deducible theorems. S5 is incompatible with C13.

Dr. Wajsberg has developed a system mathematically equivalent to S5, and has discovered many important properties of it, notably that it is the limiting member of a certain family of systems. Mr. Henle has proved that S5 is mathematically equivalent to the Boole-Schröder Algebra (*not* the Two-valued Algebra), if that algebra be interpreted for propositions, and the function $\Diamond p$ be determined by:

$$\Diamond p = 1 \text{ when and only when } p \neq 0;$$

$$\Diamond p = 0 \text{ when and only when } p = 0.$$

In my opinion, the principal logical significance of the system S5 consists in the fact that it divides all propositions into two mutually exclusive classes: the intensional or modal, and the extensional or contingent. According to the principles of this system, all intensional or modal propositions are either necessarily true or necessarily false. As a consequence, for any modal proposition—call it $p_m$—

$$\Diamond(p_m) = (p_m) = {\sim}\Diamond{\sim}(p_m),$$

$$\text{and } \Diamond{\sim}(p_m) = {\sim}(p_m) = {\sim}\Diamond(p_m).$$

For extensional or contingent propositions, however, possibility, truth, and necessity remain distinct.

Prevailing good use in logical inference—the practice in mathematical deductions, for example—is not sufficiently precise and self-conscious to determine clearly which of these five systems expresses the acceptable principles of deduction. (The meaning of 'acceptable' here has been discussed in Chapter VIII.) The issues concern principally the nature of the relation of 'implies' which is to be relied upon for inference, and certain subtle questions about the meaning of logical 'necessity,' 'possibility' or 'self-consistency,' etc.—for example, whether C10 is true or false. (Professor Becker has discussed at length a number of such questions, in his paper above referred to.) Those interested in the merely mathematical properties of such systems of symbolic logic tend to prefer the more comprehensive and less 'strict' systems, such as S5 and Material Implication. The interests of logical study would probably be best served by an exactly opposite tendency.

# APPENDIX III

## FINAL NOTE ON SYSTEM $S_2$

January 5, 1959

This Appendix is intended to supplement Chapter VI which presents the calculus of Strict Implication, S2, and Appendix II concerning the series of related systems S1—S5.

An adequate summary of the literature pertinent to these two topics which has appeared since the first publication of this book in 1932 would not be possible within reasonable limits of space here. But inasmuch as what is included in this present edition will stand as the permanent record of Strict Implication there are four items brief account of which should be set down.

J. C. C. McKinsey has shown that the postulate 11•5 in Chapter VI (B5 in Appendix II) is redundant, being deducible from the remainder of the set.[1]

E. V. Huntington contributed additional theorems which are important for understanding the logical import of the Consistency Postulate, 19•01, and for the comparison of Strict Implication with Boolean Algebra, to be mentioned later.[2]

Two basic theorems in Section 5 of Chapter VI—supposedly theorems requiring the Consistency Postulate—can be proved without that assumption and are included in S1.

W. T. Parry has supplied the proof that the systems S2 and S3 are distinct, thus completing proof that all five of the systems S1—S5 are distinct from one another.[3]

The first three of these topics can be covered summarily by proving additional theorems, so numbered that the place where they can be interpolated in the development as given in Chapter VI will be indicated. A few other theorems, omitted in the original edition but helpful for one reason or another, will be included here.

The first group of theorems gives the derivation of 11•5; 12•29 below. The proof as given by McKinsey is here simplified, taking advantage of the fact that, in Chapter VI, no use of 11•5 is made in proof of any theorem prior to 12•3.

[1] J. C. C. McKinsey, "A Reduction in the Number of Postulates for C. I. Lewis' System of Strict Implication," *Bull. Amer. Math. Soc.*, Vol. 40 (1934), pp. 425–427.

[2] E. V. Huntington, "Postulates for Assertion, Conjunction, Negation, and Equality," *Proc. Amer. Acad. of Arts and Sciences*, Vol. 72 (1937), No. 1, pp. 1–44.

[3] W. T. Parry, "The Postulates for 'Strict Implication'," *Mind*, Vol. XLIII, N. S. (1934), No. 169, pp. 78–80.

I am also indebted to Professor Parry for adding to my list of the errata needing correction and other assistance.

**12·27** $\sim\{\sim[\sim(\sim p)]\} \prec p$

$[12{\cdot}25{:}\ \sim(\sim p)/p]\ \sim\{\sim[\sim(\sim p)]\} \prec \sim(\sim p)$ (1)

$[11{\cdot}6]$ (1) . 12·25: $\prec$ Q.E.D.

**12·28** $\sim p = \sim[\sim(\sim p)]$

$[12{\cdot}2{:}\ \sim[\sim(\sim p)]/p;\ p/q]$ 12·27 . = : $\sim p \prec \sim[\sim(\sim p)]$ (1)

$[12{\cdot}25 : \sim p/p]\ \ \sim[\sim(\sim p)] \prec \sim p$ (2)

[11·03] (1) . (2) : = Q.E.D.

**12·29** $p \prec \sim(\sim p)$

$[12{\cdot}1]\ \sim\Diamond(p \sim p) . \prec . \sim\Diamond(p \sim p)$ (1)

[12·28] (1) $\therefore$ = : . $\sim\Diamond(p \sim p) . \prec . \sim\Diamond\{p \sim[\sim(\sim p)]\}$ (2)

[11·02] (2) . = : 12·1 . $\prec$ Q.E.D.

**12·3** $p = \sim(\sim p)$

[11·03] 12·25 . 12·29 : = Q.E.D.

The next group are simple and obvious theorems, omitted in Chapter VI but helpful for the comparison of Strict Implication with Boolean Algebra.

**12·91** $p \sim p . \prec . q$

$[11{\cdot}2 : \sim q/q]\ \ p \sim q . \prec . p$ (1)

[12·3, 12·6] (1) = Q.E.D.

**12·92** $p \sim p . = . q \sim q$

$[12{\cdot}91 : q \sim q/q]\ \ p \sim p . \prec . q \sim q$ (1)

$[12{\cdot}91 : q/p;\ p \sim p/q]\ q \sim q . \prec . p \sim p$ (2)

[11·03] (1) . (2) : = Q.E.D.

**12·93** $\sim\Diamond p . = . p \prec \sim p$

$[12{\cdot}7, 12{\cdot}3]\ \sim\Diamond p . = . \sim\Diamond[p \sim(\sim p)]$ (1)

[11·02] (1) = Q.E.D.

**12·94** $\sim\Diamond\sim p . = . \sim p \prec p$

$[12{\cdot}93 : \sim p/p]\ \ \sim\Diamond\sim p . = : \sim p . \prec . \sim(\sim p)$ (1)

[12·3] (1) = Q.E.D.

**12·95** $\Diamond p . = . \sim(p \prec \sim p)$

$[12{\cdot}11]\ \sim(\sim\Diamond p) . = . \sim(\sim\Diamond p)$ (1)

[12·3, 12·93] (1) = Q.E.D.

**12·96** $\Diamond\sim p . = . \sim(\sim p \prec p)$

[12·95, 12·3]

**13·6** $p \vee \sim p . = . q \vee \sim q$

[12·11, 12·92, 11·01, 12·3]

**13·7** $q . \prec . p \vee \sim p$

$[12{\cdot}91 : \sim p/p;\ \sim q/q]\ \sim p \sim(\sim p) . \prec . \sim q$ (1)

[12·42, 11·01] (1) $\prec$ Q.E.D.

Theorems 19•57 and 19•58 of Section 5 in Chapter VI do not require the Consistency Postulate, 19•01. Proof of them from postulates and theorems of S1 exclusively follows. Two consequences are added.

***16•36*** $p \,.\, q \sim q :=.\, q \sim q$ (See 19•57)

[11•2] $q \sim q \,.\, p : \prec : q \sim q$ (1)

[12•91] $q \sim q \,.\prec .\, p$ (2)

[16•33] (2) $.=:.\, q \sim q \,.\prec : q \sim q \,.\, p$ (3)

[11•03] (1) . (3) $:=: q \sim q \,.\, p :=.\, q \sim q$ (4)

[12•15] (4) = Q.E.D.

***16•37*** $p .=: p \,.\vee.\, q \sim q$ (See 19•58)

[12•91] $q \sim q \,.\prec .\, p$ (1)

[16•34, 13•11] (1) $.=:.\, p \,.\vee.\, q \sim q : \prec .\, p$ (2)

[13•2] $p \,.\prec : p \,.\vee.\, q \sim q$ (3)

[11•03] (2) . (3) : = Q.E.D.

***16•38*** $p .=: p \,.\, q \vee \sim q$

[12•3] $p = \sim(\sim p)$

[16•37] $=: \sim(\sim p \,.\vee.\, q \sim q)$

[11•01, 12•3] $=: \sim(\sim p) \,.\sim(q \sim q)$

[12•3, 11•01] $=: p \,.\sim q \vee q$

[13•11] $=: p \,.\, q \vee \sim q$

***16•39*** $p \vee \sim p .=: p \vee \sim p \,.\vee.\, q$

[12•11] $\sim(p \sim p) .=. \sim(p \sim p)$ (1)

[16•36] (1) $.=: \sim(p \sim p) .=. \sim(p \sim p \,.\sim q)$ (2)

[11•01] (2) $.=:.\sim p \vee p .=:.\sim p \vee p \,.\vee.\, q$ (3)

[13•11] (3) = Q.E.D.

The group of theorems which follows are all of them important in connection with the topic of the 'paradoxes of Strict Implication', to be discussed in conclusion. Proofs of 16•395, 19•86 and 19•87 are due to Huntington, and proofs of the others are to be found in his paper cited above. The first, 16•395, is a theorem in S1; the remainder of the group are theorems in S2.

***16•395*** $p\, q \,.\prec .\, p :=. \sim\Diamond(r \sim r)$

[12•11] $\sim\Diamond(r \sim r) .=. \sim\Diamond(r \sim r)$

[12•92] $=. \sim\Diamond(p \sim p)$

[16•36, 12•15] $=. \sim\Diamond(p \sim p \,.\, q)$

[12•5] $=. \sim\Diamond(p\, q \,.\sim p)$

[11•02] $=: p\, q \,.\prec .\, p$

***19•85*** $\sim\Diamond(p \sim q) \,.\prec . \sim\Diamond(r \sim r)$

[19•01 : $p \sim q/p$] $\Diamond(p \sim q \,.\, q) \,.\prec .\, \Diamond(p \sim q)$ (1)

[12•5, 16•36] (1) $.=: \Diamond(q \sim q) \,.\prec .\, \Diamond(p \sim q)$ (2)

[12•92] (2) $.=: \Diamond(r \sim r) \,.\prec .\, \Diamond(p \sim q)$ (3)

[12•44] (3) = Q.E.D.

***19·86*** $\sim\Diamond p \,.\, ⥽ \,.\, r ⥽ r$

[19·85 : $\sim p/q$] $\sim\Diamond[p \sim(\sim p)] \,.\, ⥽ \,.\, \sim\Diamond(r \sim r)$ (1)

[12·3, 12·7] (1) $. = : \sim\Diamond p \,.\, ⥽ \,.\, \sim\Diamond(r \sim r)$ (2)

[11·02] (2) = Q.E.D.

***19·87*** $p ⥽ q \,.\, ⥽ : p \,.\, = \,.\, p q$

[16·33] 19·85 $. = : . \sim\Diamond(p \sim q) \,.\, ⥽ : \sim(p \sim q) \,.\, \sim\Diamond(r \sim r)$

[11·02] $= : . p ⥽ q \,.\, ⥽ : p ⥽ q \,.\, \sim\Diamond(r \sim r)$

[16·395] $= : : p ⥽ q \,.\, ⥽ : . p ⥽ q : p q \,.\, ⥽ \,.\, p$

[16·33] $= : : p ⥽ q \,.\, ⥽ : .$
$p \,.\, ⥽ \,.\, p q : p q \,.\, ⥽ \,.\, p$

[11·03] = Q.E.D.

***19·88*** $p ⥽ q \,.\, = : p \,.\, = \,.\, p q$

[11·03, 12·1] $p \,.\, = \,.\, p q : ⥽ : p \,.\, ⥽ \,.\, p q : p q \,.\, ⥽ \,.\, p$ (1)

[11·2] $p \,.\, ⥽ \,.\, p q : p q \,.\, ⥽ \,.\, p : . ⥽ : p \,.\, ⥽ \,.\, p q$ (2)

[11·6] (1) . (2) $: ⥽ : . p \,.\, = \,.\, p q : ⥽ : p \,.\, ⥽ \,.\, p q$ (3)

[16·33] (3) $. = : . p \,.\, = \,.\, p q : ⥽ \,.\, p ⥽ q$ (4)

[11·03] (4) . 19·87 : = Q.E.D.

***19·89*** $\sim\Diamond p \,.\, = : p \,.\, = \,.\, q \sim q$

[19·88] $p ⥽ \sim p \,.\, = : p \,.\, = \,.\, p \sim p$ (1)

[12·92] (1) $. = : . p ⥽ \sim p \,.\, = : p \,.\, = \,.\, q \sim q$ (2)

[18·12] (2) = Q.E.D.

***19·891*** $\sim\Diamond\sim p \,.\, = : p \,.\, = \,.\, q \vee \sim q$

[19·89 : $\sim p/p$] $\sim\Diamond\sim p \,.\, = : \sim p \,.\, = \,.\, q \sim q$

[11·03] $= : \sim p \,.\, ⥽ \,.\, q \sim q : q \sim q \,.\, ⥽ \,.\, \sim p$

[12·45, 12·3] $= : \sim(q \sim q) ⥽ p : p ⥽ \sim(q \sim q)$

[11·01, 12·3] $= : q \vee \sim q \,.\, ⥽ p : p \,.\, ⥽ \,.\, q \vee \sim q$

[11·03] $= : p \,.\, = \,.\, q \vee \sim q$

We turn to the fourth item mentioned in our introductory remarks: Parry's proof that the principle

$$p ⥽ q \,.\, ⥽ : q ⥽ r \,.\, ⥽ \,.\, p ⥽ r,$$

deducible from the postulates of S3 (A1—8 in Appendix II) is not deducible from the postulates of S2. On this point, we could not do better than to quote his succinct demonstration in the paper cited above:

"In answer to this question as to the two sets of postulates, it will here be shown that A8, and the consequence of A1—8 referred to by Mr. Lewis, are *independent* of B1—9, *i. e.*, that they cannot be deduced from set B by the admitted operations. This fact can be demonstrated by the matrix method as follows:—

"(1) The eight numbers, 0 to 7, are taken as 'elements'; the numbers 6 and 7 are said to be the 'designated values'.

"(2) The 'primitive ideas' of the System of Strict Implication are given matrix (or extensional) definitions in terms of the elements, as follows:

$\sim p = 7 - p$

| $p$ | $\Diamond p$ |
|---|---|
| 0 | 1 |
| 1 | 5 |
| 2 | 7 |
| 3 | 7 |
| 4 | 7 |
| 5 | 7 |
| 6 | 7 |
| 7 | 7 |

| $p\ q$ | 0 | 1 | 2 | 3 | 4 | 5 | 6 | 7 |
|---|---|---|---|---|---|---|---|---|
| 0 | 0 | 0 | 0 | 0 | 0 | 0 | 0 | 0 |
| 1 | 0 | 1 | 0 | 1 | 0 | 1 | 0 | 1 |
| 2 | 0 | 0 | 2 | 2 | 0 | 0 | 2 | 2 |
| 3 | 0 | 1 | 2 | 3 | 0 | 1 | 2 | 3 |
| 4 | 0 | 0 | 0 | 0 | 4 | 4 | 4 | 4 |
| 5 | 0 | 1 | 0 | 1 | 4 | 5 | 4 | 5 |
| 6 | 0 | 0 | 2 | 2 | 4 | 4 | 6 | 6 |
| 7 | 0 | 1 | 2 | 3 | 4 | 5 | 6 | 7 |

"From these tables, with the definitions 11·02 and 11·03, the tables for $p \dashv q$ and $p = q$ are readily constructed. $(\exists p)\, f(p)$ has a designated value if and only if $f(p)$ has a designated value for some substitution of an element for $p$.

"(3) All the postulates of set B are found to be 'satisfied'; *i. e.*, if we make any substitution of elements for the variables of a postulate, and calculate according to the matrix definitions, the result is a designated value.

"(4) If certain principles are satisfied, any principle derivable from them by means of the operations used for proof is also satisfied.

"(5) Finally, A8 and certain consequences of set A are *not* satisfied, hence are not derivable from set B by the admitted operations. If we substitute 1 for $p$, 0 for $q$, in A8, the result is 0. (Even if we weaken the main relation of A8 to material implication, the principle is not satisfied.) That the principle mentioned above,

$$p \dashv q \,.\, \dashv : q \dashv r \,.\, \dashv \,.\, p \dashv r$$

is not satisfied, is shown by the substitution 1,0,0 for $p,q,r$ respectively."

Let us add, however, that although the above-mentioned principle is not provable in S2, we can derive in S2, from any premise of the form $P \dashv Q$, a corresponding conclusion $Q \dashv R \,.\, \dashv \,.\, P \dashv R$, as Parry has shown by the following proof-schema:

Given $P \dashv Q$; To prove $Q \dashv R \,.\, \dashv \,.\, P \dashv R$ .

[Hypothesis] $P \dashv Q$ (1)
[19·87] (1) $. \dashv : P \,.\!=\!.\, P Q$ (2)
[19·52] $Q \dashv R \,.\, \dashv : P Q \,.\, \dashv \,.\, R$ (3)
[(2)] (3) $. = : Q \dashv R \,.\, \dashv \,.\, P \dashv R$

This completes the proof, otherwise established in Appendix II, that all five of the systems S1—S5 are distinct, and that each later system in the series requires some postulate which is independent of its predecessor system in the series.

In a paper published in 1946, Dr. Ruth C. Barcan Marcus has shown that the system S2 can be extended to first-order propositional functions.[1] Though it happens that I hold certain logical convictions in the light of which I should prefer to approach the logic of propositional functions in a different way, I appreciate this demonstration that there is a calculus of functions which bears to the calculus of Strict Implication a relation similar to that which holds between the calculus of functions in *Principia Mathematica* (*9—*11) and the calculus of propositions (*1—*5) in that work.

For anyone who should be interested in Strict Implication as logic, and not merely in the mathematical and metamathematical structure of it as a system, there are two further topics which I think it is of some importance to consider. First, it may be of historical interest, and it certainly will be of logical interest, to compare both Strict Implication and Material Implication with the Boolean Algebra in the classic form given it by Schröder. Second, it should be the prime desideratum of deductive logic to identify correctly and develop the properties of that logical nexus which holds between a premise $p$ and a consequence $q$ when and only when $q$ is validly deducible from $p$. And in that connection, attention to the 'paradoxes', both of Strict Implication and of Material Implication, will be called for. The first of these two topics can be notably illuminating for any consideration of the second.

Schröder developed the two systems referred to in the early chapters of this book: first, the general Boolean Algebra interpreted by him as the logic of classes; second, the Two-Valued Algebra which he interprets as the logic of propositions. However, it will be more convenient for our purposes to suppose that we have both these systems before us in the form of uninterpreted mathematical systems, defined after the manner made familiar by Huntington; *i. e.*, as "a class K of elements $a, b, c, \ldots$, and an operation o such that;"—the postulates being appended. Also, for simplicity, let us use the notations of the propositional calculus throughout— $\sim p$, $p.q$, $p \vee q$, etc.—whether it is the interpretation for classes or that for propositions which is under consideration at the moment. For brevity, we may refer to the general calculus interpreted for classes as K1, the Two-Valued Algebra as K2.

K2 is derived from the same postulates as K1, with the *addition* of a postulate expressed by Schröder as "$p = (p = 1)$,"

[1] Ruth C. Barcan, "A Functional Calculus of the first order, based on Strict Implication;" *Journal for Symbolic Logic,* Vol. II, No. 1, pp. 1–16.

which is equivalent in force to the assumption, "For any element $p$, either $p = 0$ or $p = 1$." The basic mathematical properties of K1 and K2 both, are determined by the fact that the zero element of the system is the modulus of the operation of (logical) multiplication; the 'and'-relation of elements. For any element $p$,

$$p \sim p = 0. \qquad \text{Hence } p \sim p = q \sim q = r \sim r, \text{ etc.}$$

And the element 1, which is the inverse of 0, is the modulus of the operation of (logical) addition; the 'or'-relation of elements. For any element $p$,

$$p \vee \sim p = 1. \qquad \text{Hence } p \vee \sim p = q \vee \sim q = r \vee \sim r, \text{ etc.}$$

Let us here write that relation which is read, for propositions, as '$p$ implies $q$', and for classes as 'The class $p$ is contained in the class $q$', as $p \rightarrow q$. Both in K1 and in K2, this relation is so defined that it holds when and only when $p \sim q = 0$ and $\sim p \vee q = 1$. Thus, even in the uninterpreted system, $p \rightarrow q$ is a *statement*, equivalent to the equations just mentioned, which holds when and only when, for any element $r$,

$$p \sim q = 0 = r \sim r \quad \text{and} \quad \sim p \vee q = 1 = r \vee \sim r.$$

Let us remember also that, both in K1 and in K2, $0 \rightarrow p$ and $p \rightarrow 1$ for any element $p$; *e. g.*, the null class is contained in every class, and every class is contained in the universal class, 'everything.'

For the propositional interpretation, Schröder interpreted $p = 1$—equivalent to $p = r \vee \sim r$—as '$p$ is true'; and $p = 0$—equivalent to $p = r \sim r$—as '$p$ is false.' On this interpretation, the added postulate of K2 is called for: every proposition is either true or false. But all the postulates of K1 are also consistent with the *contradictory* of this added postulate: "For some element $p$, $p \neq 0$ and $p \neq 1$." (It is false that all classes are either empty or universal).

The properties of the relation $p \supset q$ in the truth-value calculus of Material Implication are correlative throughout with those of $p \rightarrow q$ in K2, since $p \supset q$ is, by reason of its definition, equivalent to $\sim(p \sim q)$—in K2, $p \sim q = 0$. In Boolean Algebra generally (K1 and K2 both) $r = 0$ is equivalent to $\sim r = 1$; and $1 \cdot 1 = 1$, $1 \cdot 0 = 0$, $0 \cdot 1 = 0$, and $0 \cdot 0 = 0$. And all the paradoxes of the truth-value interpretation of $p \rightarrow q$, obliged by the added postulate of K2, are implicit in the fact that when the values of $p$ and $q$ are restricted to 0 and 1, there are only four alternatives:

$p = 1, q = 1: p \supset q, \sim p \supset q, \sim p \supset \sim q; \sim p \supset p, \sim q \supset q$
$p = 0, q = 0: p \supset q, p \supset \sim q, \sim p \supset \sim q; p \supset \sim p, q \supset \sim q$
$p = 0, q = 1: p \supset q, \sim p \supset q, p \supset \sim q; p \supset \sim p, \sim q \supset q$
$p = 1, q = 0: p \supset \sim q, \sim p \supset q, \sim p \supset \sim q; \sim p \supset q, q \supset \sim q$

Also, for any one of these alternatives, either $p \supset q$ or $q \supset p$, either $\sim p \supset q$ or $q \supset \sim p$, and so on. A relation so nearly ubiquitous could not coincide with that which holds when and only when $q$ is deducible from $p$.

However, there is another interpretation of Boolean Algebra which can be imposed on K1 (not K2) for which it becomes a calculus of propositions. All that is necessary in order to assure the possibility of this second interpretation of K1 is to observe that, retaining the same meaning of $\sim p$ as the contradictory of $p$, of $p.q$ as '$p$ and $q$', and of $p \vee q$ as 'either $p$ or $q$', a different meaning can be imposed on the element 0 ($= r \sim r$, for any element $r$) and the element 1 ($= r \vee \sim r$, for any element $r$). For any proposition $r$, '$r$ and $\sim r$' is not only a *false* proposition but also a formal contradiction, necessarily false, self-inconsistent, analytically certifiable as false. And '$r$ or $\sim r$' is not only a *true* statement but a formal tautology, necessarily true, analytic. And taking $p = 1$ to signify '$p$ is analytic', $p = 0$ to signify '$p$ is self-inconsistent, contradictory', it is evident at once that we have another possible reading for all the postulates and theorems of K1. For this second interpretation, $p = 1$ becomes the function $\sim\Diamond\sim p$ of Strict Implication; $p = 0$ becomes $\sim\Diamond p$; $p \neq 0$ becomes $\Diamond p$; and $p \neq 1$ becomes $\Diamond\sim p$. And $p \rightarrowtail q$, equivalent to $p \sim q = 0$, becomes the relation of strict implication, $p \prec q$. And for *this* interpretation of K1, the added postulate of K2, "For every element $p$, either $p = 0$ or $p = 1$," will be false, and its contradictory, "For some element $p$, $p \neq 0$ and $p \neq 1$," will be true. There are contingent propositions, neither analytic and logically necessary nor contradictory and logically impossible. It is interesting to conjecture what might have happened, in the further development of exact logic, if Schröder or Charles S. Peirce had taken thought upon this second possible interpretation of Boolean Algebra as a propositional calculus.

As this will suggest, every postulate and theorem of K2 can, with a suitable dictionary, be translated into a postulate or theorem of Material Implication; and, with a slightly different dictionary, every postulate and theorem of K1 can be translated into a postulate or theorem of Strict Implication. However, this relation of 'mathematical equivalence' is clouded, in both cases, by the fact that our dictionary would have to provide *symbolic* equivalents for some of the English (or German) in K1 or K2. The *presumed* logic and logical relations of any uninterpreted mathematical system are usually not written in symbols but in the vernacular. Incidentally it is this kind of fact which accounts, in part, for the possible distinctness of the systems S1—S5, turning upon such questions as the inclusion or non-inclusion of $\Diamond\Diamond p = \Diamond p$. (See Appendix II). In a Boolean Algebra, $(p \neq 0) \neq 0$ would have no meaning; and if it were given one by declaring it equivalent to $p \neq 0$, the significance of that assumption would be obscure.

As we have said, this comparison with K1 and K2 can throw light upon the paradoxes, both of Material Implication and of Strict Implication. Strict Implication escapes the paradoxes of the truth-value logic of propositions because, by the different interpretation of 0 ($= p \sim p$) and 1 ($= p \vee \sim p$) and by repudiating restriction of propositions to these two values, it also escapes restriction to the four alternatives tabulated above for the relation of material implication. It leaves the 'middle ground' of contingent propositions between the analytic and the self-contradictory.

As a consequence of these facts, the paradoxes of Strict Implication are confined to the implications which are assertable when one or both of the propositions related is contradictory (equivalent, for some $r$, to $r \sim r$) or when one or both is analytic (equivalent, for some $r$, to $r \vee \sim r$). They do not extend to implications assertable as holding between premises and conclusions both of which are contingent propositions, neither analytic and logically necessary nor contradictory and logically impossible. Thus they do not affect what implies what amongst empirically substantiated and factually informational premises and their empirically significant consequences. In contrast to this, the paradoxes of Material Implication affect the implications assertable between any chosen pair of propositions without restriction, because *all* propositions are either *truth-value* equivalent to $r \sim r$ or *truth-value* equivalent to $r \vee \sim r$.

However—and here is a main point of the comparison with the Boolean systems K1 and K2—every theorem of K1 (common to K1 and K2) which is paradoxical on the interpretation of $p = 1$ as '$p$ is true' and $p = 0$ as '$p$ is false', remains paradoxical when $p = 1$ is interpreted as '$p$ is analytic' and $p = 0$ as '$p$ is contradictory'.

In Material Implication, the key paradoxes, implicating all the others, are: A false proposition implies any proposition; A true proposition is implied by any; Any two false propositions are equivalent; Any two true propositions are equivalent. Correspondingly, the key paradoxes of Strict Implication are: A contradictory (self-inconsistent) proposition implies any proposition; An analytic proposition is implied by any; Any two contradictory propositions are equivalent; Any two analytic propositions are equivalent. Other paradoxical theorems of Strict Implication include 16•95, 19•85 and 19•86 above.

Strict Implication, defining $p \prec q$ as a statement which holds when and only when the conjoint statement $p \sim q$, which asserts the premise and denies the conclusion, is self-inconsistent, is put forward with the intent to satisfy the requirement that $p \prec q$ hold when and only when $q$ is a consequence validly deducible from the premise $p$. On acount of the paradoxes, there are many who doubt that it does so satisfy this requirement. And some amongst them have put forward alternative developments of a calculus of propositions designed to eliminate the paradoxes. It is especially regrettable to omit consideration of such proposals. But these have been too numerous and various to allow adequate report and discussion of them here. I shall, however, venture the conviction—recognizing my hazard in so doing—that without sacrifice or plain omission of some intuitively acceptable, analytically certifiable, and time-honored principle of inference, or the introduction of some assumption which fails of accord with such perduring logical principles, the paradoxes of Strict Implication are inescapable. They are unavoidable consequences of indispensable rules of inference.

The manner in which the paradoxes are involved in our logical commonplaces is, of course, a complex matter. But it will do no harm to remind ourselves of a trivial example or two. If the moon is a planet, and is not made of green cheese, then the moon is a planet. But if two premises together imply a conclusion and that conclusion is false while one of the premises is true, then the other premise must be false. So if the moon is a planet and also is not a planet, then the moon is made of green cheese. We need not dally with a suppositious amendment: "Whatever in the premises is non-essential to the conclusion is no part of what implies that conclusion." That dictum would condemn the syllogism, since in every syllogism the premises contain information not contained in the conclusion. So to alter the meaning of 'implies' that all implications would be reducible to the form '$p$ implies $p$', would destroy the usefulness of logic.

That analytic conclusions are implied by any premise, is inescapable once we recognize as valid the procedure by which, our premise being taken, alternatives to be conjoined can be exhaustively specified. In a simple case, use of the principle in question may appear jejune; but in more complex instances we hardly could proceed without it. If today is Monday, then either today is Monday and it is hot or today is Monday and it is not hot. And that implies that either it is hot or it is not hot. This has the appearance of clumsy sleight of hand; and we may say, "In what sense of 'If . . . then' and 'implies'?" It can be answered; "In the sense of 'presupposed'." A presupposition of X is a necessary condition of X. When $p$ implies $q$ and $q$ implies $r$, the truth of $p$ is a *sufficient* condition of the truth of $q$, but it is $r$ the truth of which is a *necessary* condition of the truth of $q$. The analytic principle called the Law of the Excluded Middle is presupposed when we begin to logicize.. When any premise is taken, all statements of the form $p \vee {\sim}p$ are already presumed, whether we think of them or not. Otherwise we could not move forward by an inference: $p$ is true, hence either $p$ and $q$ or $p$ and not-$q$. But $p$ and not-$q$ is not possible; $p$ implies $q$. So $q$.[1]

[1] It would be sufficient here if we substitute "But $p$ and not-$q$ is not the case." But we need to *infer* $q$ only when we do not know, without reference to some premise, whether $q$ is true or not. We infer that it is the case by knowing the *incompatibility* of its falsity with the truth of the premise.

It remains to suggest why these paradoxes of Strict Implication are paradoxical. Let us observe that they concern two questions: What is to be taken as consequence of an assumption which, being self-contradictory, could not possibly be the case; and what is to be taken as sufficient premise for that which, being analytic and self-certifying, could not possibly fail to be the case? That to *infer* in such cases is affected with a sense of paradox, reflects the futility of drawing any inference when the premise is not only known false but is not even rational to suppose; and the gratuitous character of inferring what could be known true without reference to any premise. 'Deducible' and 'inferable' have a normative connotation: they do not concern what we are 'able' to infer in our foolish moments, but what, having taken commitment to our premises, it is rationally warranted to conclude and rationally forbidden to deny. And it becomes paradoxical to say; "From a premise of the form '*p* and not-*p*' any and every conclusion is to be inferred." Such a statement invites the rejoinder; "From such a premise, no conclusion at all should be drawn, because no such premise should ever be asserted; the supposition of it is irrational." Somewhat similarly it has the air of paradox to say; "The Law of the Excluded Middle, and any conclusion reducible to the form 'either *p* or not-*p*,' is to be inferred from any and every premise." This might invite the rejoinder; "Any such conclusion is not to be inferred at all, being self-certifying to any clear and rational mind." But in this case, the rejoinder would have less force. Some rational minds—including those of human logicians and mathematicians—sometimes have a need to deduce something which they recognize will, if deducible, be analytic. They do not yet know whether what they have in mind is analytic or not, or even whether it is true. To deduce it will be to prove it. What manner of procedure is open to them in such cases? They *might* proceed by seeing whether they can reduce this statement which they wish to establish as a theorem to the form '*p* or not-*p*' for some complex expression *p*. Ordinarily, they do not attempt that manner of proof. Instead, they seek to deduce what they have in mind from the postulates, definitions, and other theorems already assumed or proved. But, without knowing whether the hoped-for theorem is analytic or not, what steps of inference are open to them? Plainly, they must confine themselves to deductive steps which are universally justifiable modes of inference, valid whether the conclusion sought is analytic or is contingent on given premises. Perhaps this is so obvious as to be banal. It comes to the same thing to say: "That what is analytic is deducible from any and every premise, warrants the presumption that a particular statement, *p*, is deducible from any and every premise, only on the *additional* premise that *p* is analytic." The sense in which what is *known* to be reducible to the form '*r* or not-*r*' is thereby known to be deducible from any and every premise, has already been illustrated. The point is that such a paradigm as $p . \prec . q \vee \sim q$, though it is a true and analytic statement about what is deducible from what, is incapable of any use as a rule for deducing any conclusion which is not already known with certainty. That is the paradox.

Thus none of the paradoxical paradigms, either those which indicate what is deducible from the logically impossible, or those which formulate sufficient conditions of the logically necessary, are capable of any use for the characteristic purpose of inferring—for establishing the truth or increasing the credibility of something by reference to premises which imply it. This holds, for paradigms of the former sort, for the double reason that the contradictory premise is not assertable, and that being deducible from such a premise adds no scintilla of credibility to the consequence of it. And it holds for paradigms of the latter type because the paradigms cannot be applied unless the conclusion is known with analytic certainty in advance.

In the light of these considerations affecting the paradoxes, we may observe the possibility of drawing a somewhat fine distinction between 'deducibility' and 'inferability'. (I do not propose this distinction.) We might say that no inference is to be drawn from anything the assertion of which is rationally contraindicated. And for that the acceptance of which is rationally dictated—the analytic—no premise is to be taken as a condition of assertion: the sense in which it is to be 'inferred' is extralogical. If we should be minded so to limit the sense of 'infer', we could then say that the paradoxes of Strict Implication are unexceptionable paradigms of deduction, but are not relevant to logically valid inference.

C. I. LEWIS

# INDEX

# Catalog of DOVER BOOKS

## BOOKS EXPLAINING SCIENCE

(Note: The books listed under this category are general introductions, surveys, reviews, and non-technical expositions of science for the interested layman or scientist who wishes to brush up. Dover also publishes the largest list of inexpensive reprints of books on intermediate and higher mathematics, mathematical physics, engineering, chemistry, astronomy, etc., for the professional mathematician or scientist. For our complete Science Catalog, write Dept. catrr., Dover Publications, Inc., 180 Varick Street, New York 14, N. Y.)

**CONCERNING THE NATURE OF THINGS, Sir William Bragg.** Royal Institute Christmas Lectures by Nobel Laureate. Excellent plain-language introduction to gases, molecules, crystal structure, etc. explains "building blocks" of universe, basic properties of matter, with simplest, clearest examples, demonstrations. 32pp. of photos; 57 figures. 244pp. 5⅜ x 8.
T31 Paperbound **$1.35**

**MATTER AND LIGHT, THE NEW PHYSICS, Louis de Broglie.** Non-technical explanations by a Nobel Laureate of electro-magnetic theory, relativity, wave mechanics, quantum physics, philosophies of science, etc. Simple, yet accurate introduction to work of Planck, Bohr, Einstein, other modern physicists. Only 2 of 12 chapters require mathematics. 300pp. 5⅜ x 8.
T35 Paperbound **$1.60**

**THE COMMON SENSE OF THE EXACT SCIENCES, W. K. Clifford.** For 70 years, Clifford's work has been acclaimed as one of the clearest, yet most precise introductions to mathematical symbolism, measurement, surface boundaries, position, space, motion, mass and force, etc. Prefaces by Bertrand Russell and Karl Pearson. Introduction by James Newman. 130 figures. 249pp. 5⅜ x 8.
T61 Paperbound **$1.60**

**THE NATURE OF LIGHT AND COLOUR IN THE OPEN AIR, M. Minnaert.** What causes mirages? haloes? "multiple" suns and moons? Professor Minnaert explains these and hundreds of other fascinating natural optical phenomena in simple terms, tells how to observe them, suggests hundreds of experiments. 200 illus; 42 photos. xvi + 362pp.
T196 Paperbound **$1.95**

**SPINNING TOPS AND GYROSCOPIC MOTION, John Perry.** Classic elementary text on dynamics of rotation treats gyroscopes, tops, how quasi-rigidity is induced in paper disks, smoke rings, chains, etc, by rapid motion, precession, earth's motion, etc. Contains many easy-to-perform experiments. Appendix on practical uses of gyroscopes. 62 figures. 128pp.
T416 Paperbound **$1.00**

**A CONCISE HISTORY OF MATHEMATICS, D. Struik.** This lucid, easily followed history of mathematics from the Ancient Near East to modern times requires no mathematical background itself, yet introduces both mathematicians and laymen to basic concepts and discoveries and the men who made them. Contains a collection of 31 portraits of eminent mathematicians. Bibliography. xix + 299pp. 5⅜ x 8.
T255 Paperbound **$1.75**

**THE RESTLESS UNIVERSE, Max Born.** A remarkably clear, thorougn exposition of gases, electrons, ions, waves and particles, electronic structure of the atom, nuclear physics, written for the layman by a Nobel Laureate. "Much more thorough and deep than most attempts . . . easy and delightful," CHEMICAL AND ENGINEERING NEWS. Includes 7 animated sequences showing motion of molecules, alpha particles, etc. 11 full-page plates of photographs. Total of nearly 600 illus. 315pp. 6⅛ x 9¼.
T412 Paperbound **$2.00**

**WHAT IS SCIENCE?, N. Campbell.** The role of experiment, the function of mathematics, the nature of scientific laws, the limitations of science, and many other provocative topics are explored without technicalities by an eminent scientist. "Still an excellent introduction to scientific philosophy," H. Margenau in PHYSICS TODAY. 192pp. 5⅜ x 8.
S43 Paperbound **$1.25**

TRADE.

**FADS AND FALLACIES IN THE NAME OF SCIENCE, Martin Gardner.** The standard account of the various cults, quack systems and delusions which have recently masqueraded as science: hollow earth theory, Atlantis, dianetics, Reich's orgone theory, flying saucers, Bridey Murphy, psionics, irridiagnosis, many other fascinating fallacies that deluded tens of thousands. "Should be read by everyone, scientist and non-scientist alike," R. T. Birge, Prof. Emeritus, Univ. of California; Former President, American Physical Society. Formerly titled, "In the Name of Science." Revised and enlarged edition. x + 365pp. 5⅜ x 8.
T394 Paperbound **$1.50**

**THE STUDY OF THE HISTORY OF MATHEMATICS, THE STUDY OF THE HISTORY OF SCIENCE, G. Sarton.** Two books bound as one. Both volumes are standard introductions to their fields by an eminent science historian. They discuss problems of historical research, teaching, pitfalls, other matters of interest to the historically oriented writer, teacher, or student. Both have extensive bibliographies. 10 illustrations. 188pp. 5⅜ x 8. T240 Paperbound **$1.25**

**THE PRINCIPLES OF SCIENCE, W. S. Jevons.** Unabridged reprinting of a milestone in the development of symbolic logic and other subjects concerning scientific methodology, probability, inferential validity, etc. Also describes Jevons' "logic machine," an early precursor of modern electronic calculators. Preface by E. Nagel. 839pp. 5⅜ x 8. S446 Paperbound **$2.98**

**SCIENCE THEORY AND MAN, Erwin Schroedinger.** Complete, unabridged reprinting of "Science and the Human Temperament" plus an additional essay "What is an Elementary Particle?" Nobel Laureate Schroedinger discusses many aspects of modern physics from novel points of view which provide unusual insights for both laymen and physicists. 192 pp. 5⅜ x 8.
T428 Paperbound **$1.35**

**BRIDGES AND THEIR BUILDERS, D. B. Steinman & S. R. Watson.** Information about ancient, medieval, modern bridges; how they were built; who built them; the structural principles employed; the materials they are built of; etc. Written by one of the world's leading authorities on bridge design and construction. New, revised, expanded edition. 23 photos; 26 line drawings, xvii + 401pp. 5⅜ x 8. T431 Paperbound **$1.95**

**HISTORY OF MATHEMATICS, D. E. Smith.** Most comprehensive non-technical history of math in English. In two volumes. Vol. I: A chronological examination of the growth of mathematics from primitive concepts up to 1900. Vol. II: The development of ideas in specific fields and areas, up through elementary calculus. The lives and works of over a thousand mathematicians are covered; thousands of specific historical problems and their solutions are clearly explained. Total of 510 illustrations, 1355pp. 5⅜ x 8. Set boxed in attractive container. T429, T430 Paperbound, the set **$5.00**

**PHILOSOPHY AND THE PHYSICISTS, L. S. Stebbing.** A philosopher examines the philosophical implications of modern science by posing a lively critical attack on the popular science expositions of Sir James Jeans and Arthur Eddington. xvi + 295pp. 5⅜ x 8.
T480 Paperbound **$1.65**

**ON MATHEMATICS AND MATHEMATICIANS, R. E. Moritz.** The first collection of quotations by and about mathematicians in English. 1140 anecdotes, aphorisms, definitions, speculations, etc. give both mathematicians and layman stimulating new insights into what mathematics is, and into the personalities of the great mathematicians from Archimedes to Euler, Gauss, Klein, Weierstrass. Invaluable to teachers, writers. Extensive cross index. 410pp. 5⅜ x 8.
T489 Paperbound **$1.95**

# NATURAL SCIENCE, BIOLOGY, GEOLOGY, TRAVEL

**A SHORT HISTORY OF ANATOMY AND PHYSIOLOGY FROM THE GREEKS TO HARVEY, C. Singer.** A great medical historian's fascinating intermediate account of the slow advance of anatomical and physiological knowledge from pre-scientific times to Vesalius, Harvey. 139 unusually interesting illustrations. 221pp. 5⅜ x 8. T389 Paperbound **$1.75**

**THE BEHAVIOUR AND SOCIAL LIFE OF HONEYBEES, Ronald Ribbands.** The most comprehensive, lucid and authoritative book on bee habits, communication, duties, cell life, motivations, etc. "A MUST for every scientist, experimenter, and educator, and a happy and valuable selection for all interested in the honeybee," AMERICAN BEE JOURNAL. 690-item bibliography. 127 illus.; 11 photographic plates. 352pp. 5⅜ x 8⅜. S410 Clothbound **$4.50**

**TRAVELS OF WILLIAM BARTRAM,** edited by **Mark Van Doren.** One of the 18th century's most delightful books, and one of the few first-hand sources of information about American geography, natural history, and anthropology of American Indian tribes of the time. "The mind of a scientist with the soul of a poet," John Livingston Lowes. 13 original illustrations, maps. Introduction by Mark Van Doren. 448pp. 5⅜ x 8. T326 Paperbound **$2.00**

**STUDIES ON THE STRUCTURE AND DEVELOPMENT OF VERTEBRATES, Edwin Goodrich.** The definitive study of the skeleton, fins and limbs, head region, divisions of the body cavity, vascular, respiratory, excretory systems, etc., of vertebrates from fish to higher mammals, by the greatest comparative anatomist of recent times. "The standard textbook," JOURNAL OF ANATOMY. 754 illus. 69-page biographical study. 1186-item bibliography. 2 vols. Total of 906pp. 5⅜ x 8. Vol. I: S449 Paperbound **$2.50**
Vol. II: S450 Paperbound **$2.50**

# LITERATURE

**WORLD DRAMA, B. H. Clark.** 46 plays from Ancient Greece, Rome, to India, China, Japan. Plays by Aeschylus, Sophocles, Euripides, Aristophanes, Plautus, Marlowe, Jonson, Farquhar, Goldsmith, Cervantes, Molière, Dumas, Goethe, Schiller, Ibsen, many others. One of the most comprehensive collections of important plays from all literature available in English. Over 1/3 of this material is unavailable in any other current edition. Reading lists. 2 volumes. Total of 1364pp. 5 3/8 x 8. Vol. I, T57 Paperbound **$2.00**
Vol. II, T59 Paperbound **$2.00**

**MASTERS OF THE DRAMA, John Gassner.** The most comprehensive history of the drama in print. Covers more than 800 dramatists and over 2000 plays from the Greeks to modern Western, Near Eastern, Oriental drama. Plot summaries, theatre history, etc. "Best of its kind in English," NEW REPUBLIC. 35 pages of bibliography. 77 photos and drawings. Deluxe edition. xxii + 890pp. 5 3/8 x 8. T100 Clothbound **$5.95**

**THE DRAMA OF LUIGI PIRANDELLO, D. Vittorini.** All 38 of Pirandello's plays (to 1935) summarized and analyzed in terms of symbolic techniques, plot structure, etc. The only authorized work. Foreword by Pirandello. Biography. Bibliography. xiii + 350pp. 5 3/8 x 8.
T435 Paperbound **$1.98**

**ARISTOTLE'S THEORY OF POETRY AND THE FINE ARTS, S. H. Butcher,** ed. The celebrated "Butcher translation" faced page by page with the Greek text; Butcher's 300-page introduction to Greek poetic, dramatic thought. Modern Aristotelian criticism discussed by John Gassner. lxxvi + 421pp. 5 3/8 x 8.
T42 Paperbound **$2.00**

**EUGENE O'NEILL: THE MAN AND HIS PLAYS, B. H. Clark.** The first published source-book on O'Neill's life and work. Analyzes each play from the early THE WEB up to THE ICEMAN COMETH. Supplies much information about environmental and dramatic influences. ix + 182pp. 5 3/8 x 8. T379 Paperbound **$1.25**

**INTRODUCTION TO ENGLISH LITERATURE, B. Dobrée,** ed. Most compendious literary aid in its price range. Extensive, categorized bibliography (with entries up to 1949) of more than 5,000 poets, dramatists, novelists, as well as historians, philosophers, economists, religious writers, travellers, and scientists of literary stature. Information about manuscripts, important biographical data. Critical, historical, background works not simply listed, but evaluated. Each volume also contains a long introduction to the period it covers.

Vol. I: **THE BEGINNINGS OF ENGLISH LITERATURE TO SKELTON, 1509, W. L. Renwick. H. Orton.** 450pp. 5 1/8 x 7 1/8. T75 Clothbound **$3.50**

Vol. II: **THE ENGLISH RENAISSANCE, 1510-1688, V. de Sola Pinto.** 381pp. 5 1/8 x 7 1/8.
T76 Clothbound **$3.50**

Vol. III: **THE AUGUSTANS AND ROMANTICS, 1689-1830, H. Dyson, J. Butt.** 320pp. 5 1/8 x 7 1/8.
T77 Clothbound **$3.50**

Vol. IV: **THE VICTORIANS AND AFTER, 1830-1914, E. Batho, B. Dobrée.** 360pp. 5 1/8 x 7 1/8.
T78 Clothbound **$3.50**

**EPIC AND ROMANCE, W. P. Ker.** The standard survey of Medieval epic and romance by a foremost authority on Medieval literature. Covers historical background, plot, literary analysis, significance of Teutonic epics, Icelandic sagas, Beowulf, French chansons de geste, the Niebelungenlied, Arthurian romances, much more. 422pp. 5 3/8 x 8. T355 Paperbound **$1.95**

**THE HEART OF EMERSON'S JOURNALS, Bliss Perry,** ed. Emerson's most intimate thoughts, impressions, records of conversations with Channing, Hawthorne, Thoreau, etc., carefully chosen from the 10 volumes of The Journals. "The essays do not reveal the power of Emerson's mind . . .as do these hasty and informal writings," N. Y. TIMES. Preface by B. Perry. 370pp. 5 3/8 x 8. T447 Paperbound **$1.85**

**A SOURCE BOOK IN THEATRICAL HISTORY, A. M. Nagler.** (Formerly, "Sources of Theatrical History.") Over 300 selected passages by contemporary observers tell about styles of acting, direction, make-up, scene designing, etc., in the theatre's great periods from ancient Greece to the Théâtre Libre. "Indispensable complement to the study of drama," EDUCATIONAL THEATRE JOURNAL. Prof. Nagler, Yale Univ. School of Drama, also supplies notes, references. 85 illustrations. 611pp. 5 3/8 x 8. T515 Paperbound **$2.75**

**THE ART OF THE STORY-TELLER, M. L. Shedlock.** Regarded as the finest, most helpful book on telling stories to children, by a great story-teller. How to catch, hold, recapture attention; how to choose material; many other aspects. Also includes: a 99-page selection of Miss Shedlock's most successful stories; extensive bibliography of other stories. xxi + 320pp. 5 3/8 x 8. T245 Clothbound **$3.50**

**THE DEVIL'S DICTIONARY, Ambrose Bierce.** Over 1000 short, ironic definitions in alphabetical order, by America's greatest satirist in the classical tradition. "Some of the most gorgeous witticisms in the English language," H. L. Mencken. 144pp. 5 3/8 x 8. T487 Paperbound **$1.00**

# MUSIC

**A DICTIONARY OF HYMNOLOGY, John Julian.** More than 30,000 entries on individual hymns, their authorship, textual variations, location of texts, dates and circumstances of composition, denominational and ritual usages, the biographies of more than 9,000 hymn writers, essays on important topics such as children's hymns and Christmas carols, and hundreds of thousands of other important facts about hymns which are virtually impossible to find anywhere else. Convenient alphabetical listing, and a 200-page double-columned index of first lines enable you to track down virtually any hymn ever written. Total of 1786pp. 6¼ x 9¼. 2 volumes. T133. The Set, Clothbound **$15.00**

**STRUCTURAL HEARING, TONAL COHERENCE IN MUSIC, Felix Salzer.** Extends the well-known Schenker approach to include modern music, music of the middle ages, and Renaissance music. Explores the phenomenon of tonal organization by discussing more than 500 compositions, and offers unusual new insights into the theory of composition and musical relationships. "The foundation on which all teaching in music theory has been based at this college," Leopold Mannes, President, The Mannes College of Music. Total of 658pp. 6½ x 9¼. 2 volumes. S418 The set, Clothbound **$8.00**

**A GENERAL HISTORY OF MUSIC, Charles Burney.** The complete history of music from the Greeks up to 1789 by the 18th century musical historian who personally knew the great Baroque composers. Covers sacred and secular, vocal and instrumental, operatic and symphonic music; treats theory, notation, forms, instruments; discusses composers, performers, important works. Invaluable as a source of information on the period for students, historians, musicians. "Surprisingly few of Burney's statements have been invalidated by modern research . . . still of great value," NEW YORK TIMES. Edited and corrected by Frank Mercer. 35 figures. 1915pp. 5½ x 8½. 2 volumes. T36 The set, Clothbound **$12.50**

**JOHANN SEBASTIAN BACH, Phillip Spitta.** Recognized as one of the greatest accomplishments of musical scholarship and far and away the definitive coverage of Bach's works. Hundreds of individual pieces are analyzed. Major works, such as the B Minor Mass and the St. Matthew Passion are examined in minute detail. Spitta also deals with the works of Buxtehude, Pachelbel, and others of the period. Can be read with profit even by those without a knowledge of the technicalities of musical composition. "Unchallenged as the last word on one of the supreme geniuses of music," John Barkham, SATURDAY REVIEW SYNDICATE. Total of 1819pp. 5⅜ x 8. 2 volumes. T252 The set, Clothbound **$10.00**

# HISTORY

**THE IDEA OF PROGRESS, J. B. Bury.** Prof. Bury traces the evolution of a central concept of Western civilization in Greek, Roman, Medieval, and Renaissance thought to its flowering in the 17th and 18th centuries. Introduction by Charles Beard. xl + 357pp. 5⅜ x 8.
T39 Clothbound **$3.95**
T40 Paperbound **$1.95**

**THE ANCIENT GREEK HISTORIANS, J. B. Bury.** Greek historians such as Herodotus, Thucydides, Xenophon; Roman historians such as Tacitus, Caesar, Livy; scores of others fully analyzed in terms of sources, concepts, influences, etc., by a great scholar and historian. 291pp. 5⅜ x 8. T397 Paperbound **$1.50**

**HISTORY OF THE LATER ROMAN EMPIRE, J. B. Bury.** The standard work on the Byzantine Empire from 395 A.D. to the death of Justinian in 565 A.D., by the leading Byzantine scholar of our time. Covers political, social, cultural, theological, military history. Quotes contemporary documents extensively. "Most unlikely that it will ever be superseded," Glanville Downey, Dumbarton Oaks Research Library. Genealogical tables. 5 maps. Bibliography. 2 vols. Total of 965pp. 5⅜ x 8. T398, T399 Paperbound, the set **$4.00**

**GARDNER'S PHOTOGRAPHIC SKETCH BOOK OF THE CIVIL WAR, Alexander Gardner.** One of the rarest and most valuable Civil War photographic collections exactly reproduced for the first time since 1866. Scenes of Manassas, Bull Run, Harper's Ferry, Appomattox, Mechanicsville, Fredericksburg, Gettysburg, etc.; battle ruins, prisons, arsenals, a slave pen, fortifications; Lincoln on the field, officers, men, corpses. By one of the most famous pioneers in documentary photography. Original copies of the "Sketch Book" sold for $425 in 1952. Introduction by E. Bleiler. 100 full-page 7 x 10 photographs (original size). 244pp. 10¾ x 8½
T476 Clothbound **$6.00**

**THE WORLD'S GREAT SPEECHES, L. Copeland and L. Lamm,** eds. 255 speeches from Pericles to Churchill, Dylan Thomas. Invaluable as a guide to speakers; fascinating as history past and present; a source of much difficult-to-find material. Includes an extensive section of informal and humorous speeches. 3 indices: Topic, Author, Nation. xx + 745pp. 5⅜ x 8.
T468 Paperbound **$2.49**

**FOUNDERS OF THE MIDDLE AGES, E. K. Rand.** The best non-technical discussion of the transformation of Latin paganism into medieval civilization. Tertullian, Gregory, Jerome, Boethius, Augustine, the Neoplatonists, other crucial figures, philosophies examined. Excellent for the intelligent non-specialist. "Extraordinarily accurate," Richard McKeon, THE NATION. ix + 365pp. 5⅜ x 8. T369 Paperbound **$1.85**

**THE POLITICAL THOUGHT OF PLATO AND ARISTOTLE, Ernest Barker**. The standard, comprehensive exposition of Greek political thought. Covers every aspect of the "Republic" and the "Politics" as well as minor writings, other philosophers, theorists of the period, and the later history of Greek political thought. Unabridged edition. 584pp. 5⅜ x 8.
T521 Paperbound **$1.85**

# PHILOSOPHY

**THE GIFT OF LANGUAGE, M. Schlauch.** (Formerly, "The Gift of Tongues.") A sound, middle-level treatment of linguistic families, word histories, grammatical processes, semantics, language taboos, word-coining of Joyce, Cummings, Stein, etc. 232 bibliographical notes. 350pp. 5⅜ x 8.
T243 Paperbound **$1.85**

**THE PHILOSOPHY OF HEGEL, W. T. Stace.** The first work in English to give a complete and connected view of Hegel's entire system. Especially valuable to those who do not have time to study the highly complicated original texts, yet want an accurate presentation by a most reputable scholar of one of the most influential 19th century thinkers. Includes a 14 x 20 fold-out chart of Hegelian system. 536pp. 5⅜ x 8.
T254 Paperbound **$2.00**

**ARISTOTLE, A. E. Taylor.** A lucid, non-technical account of Aristotle written by a foremost Platonist. Covers life and works; thought on matter, form, causes, logic, God, physics, metaphysics, etc. Bibliography. New index compiled for this edition. 128pp. 5⅜ x 8.
T280 Paperbound **$1.00**

**GUIDE TO PHILOSOPHY, C. E. M. Joad.** This basic work describes the major philosophic problems and evaluates the answers propounded by great philosophers from the Greeks to Whitehead, Russell. "The finest introduction," BOSTON TRANSCRIPT. Bibliography, 592pp. 5⅜ x 8.
T297 Paperbound **$2.00**

**LANGUAGE AND MYTH, E. Cassirer.** Cassirer's brilliant demonstration that beneath both language and myth lies an unconscious "grammar" of experience whose categories and canons are not those of logical thought. Introduction and translation by Susanne Langer. Index. x + 103pp. 5⅜ x 8.
T51 Paperbound **$1.25**

**SUBSTANCE AND FUNCTION, EINSTEIN'S THEORY OF RELATIVITY, E. Cassirer.** This double volume contains the German philosopher's profound philosophical formulation of the differences between traditional logic and the new logic of science. Number, space, energy, relativity, many other topics are treated in detail. Authorized translation by W. C. and M. C. Swabey. xii + 465pp. 5⅜ x 8.
T50 Paperbound **$2.00**

**THE PHILOSOPHICAL WORKS OF DESCARTES.** The definitive English edition, in two volumes, of all major philosophical works and letters of René Descartes, father of modern philosophy of knowledge and science. Translated by E. S. Haldane and G. Ross. Introductory notes. Total of 842pp. 5⅜ x 8.
T71 Vol. 1, Paperbound **$2.00**
T72 Vol. 2, Paperbound **$2.00**

**ESSAYS IN EXPERIMENTAL LOGIC, J. Dewey.** Based upon Dewey's theory that knowledge implies a judgment which in turn implies an inquiry, these papers consider such topics as the thought of Bertrand Russell, pragmatism, the logic of values, antecedents of thought, data and meanings. 452pp. 5⅜ x 8.
T73 Paperbound **$1.95**

**THE PHILOSOPHY OF HISTORY, G. W. F. Hegel.** This classic of Western thought is Hegel's detailed formulation of the thesis that history is not chance but a rational process, the realization of the Spirit of Freedom. Translated and introduced by J. Sibree. Introduction by C. Hegel. Special introduction for this edition by Prof. Carl Friedrich, Harvard University. xxxix + 447pp. 5⅜ x 8.
T112 Paperbound **$1.85**

**THE WILL TO BELIEVE** and **HUMAN IMMORTALITY, W. James.** Two of James's most profound investigations of human belief in God and immortality, bound as one volume. Both are powerful expressions of James's views on chance vs. determinism, pluralism vs. monism, will and intellect, arguments for survival after death, etc. Two prefaces. 429pp. 5⅜ x 8.
T294 Clothbound **$3.75**
T291 Paperbound **$1.65**

**INTRODUCTION TO SYMBOLIC LOGIC, S. Langer.** A lucid, general introduction to modern logic, covering forms, classes, the use of symbols, the calculus of propositions, the Boole-Schroeder and the Russell-Whitehead systems, etc. "One of the clearest and simplest introductions," MATHEMATICS GAZETTE. Second, enlarged, revised edition. 368pp. 5⅜ x 8.
S164 Paperbound **$1.75**

**MIND AND THE WORLD-ORDER, C. I. Lewis.** Building upon the work of Peirce, James, and Dewey, Professor Lewis outlines a theory of knowledge in terms of "conceptual pragmatism," and demonstrates why the traditional understanding of the a priori must be abandoned. Appendices. xiv + 446pp. 5⅜ x 8.
T359 Paperbound **$1.95**

**THE GUIDE FOR THE PERPLEXED, M. Maimonides** One of the great philosophical works of all time, Maimonides' formulation of the meeting-ground between Old Testament and Aristotelian thought is essential to anyone interested in Jewish, Christian, and Moslem thought in the Middle Ages. 2nd revised edition of the Friedlander translation. Extensive introduction. lix + 414pp. 5⅜ x 8.
T351 Paperbound **$1.85**

# ORIENTALIA AND RELIGION

**THE MYSTERIES OF MITHRA, F. Cumont.** The great Belgian scholar's definitive study of the Persian mystery religion that almost vanquished Christianity in the ideological struggle for the Roman Empire. A masterpiece of scholarly detection that reconstructs secret doctrines, organization, rites. Mithraic art is discussed and analyzed. 70 illus. 239pp. 5⅜ x 8.
T323 Paperbound **$1.85**

**CHRISTIAN AND ORIENTAL PHILOSOPHY OF ART. A. K. Coomaraswamy.** The late art historian and orientalist discusses artistic symbolism, the role of traditional culture in enriching art, medieval art, folklore, philosophy of art, other similar topics. Bibliography. 148pp. 5⅜ x 8.
T378 Paperbound **$1.25**

**TRANSFORMATION OF NATURE IN ART, A. K. Coomaraswamy.** A basic work on Asiatic religious art. Includes discussions of religious art in Asia and Medieval Europe (exemplified by Meister Eckhart), the origin and use of images in Indian art, Indian Medieval aesthetic manuals, and other fascinating, little known topics. Glossaries of Sanskrit and Chinese terms. Bibliography. 41pp. of notes. 245pp. 5⅜ x 8. T368 Paperbound **$1.75**

**ORIENTAL RELIGIONS IN ROMAN PAGANISM, F. Cumont.** This well-known study treats the ecstatic cults of Syria and Phrygia (Cybele, Attis, Adonis, their orgies and mutilatory rites); the mysteries of Egypt (Serapis, Isis, Osiris); Persian dualism; Mithraic cults; Hermes Trismegistus, Ishtar, Astarte, etc. and their influence on the religious thought of the Roman Empire. Introduction. 55pp. of notes; extensive bibliography. xxiv + 298pp. 5⅜ x 8.
T321 Paperbound **$1.75**

# ANTHROPOLOGY, SOCIOLOGY, AND PSYCHOLOGY

**PRIMITIVE MAN AS PHILOSOPHER, P. Radin.** A standard anthropological work based on Radin's investigations of the Winnebago, Maori, Batak, Zuni, other primitive tribes. Describes primitive thought on the purpose of life, marital relations, death, personality, gods, etc. Extensive selections of original primitive documents. Bibliography. xviii + 420pp. 5⅜ x 8.
T392 Paperbound **$2.00**

**PRIMITIVE RELIGION, P. Radin.** Radin's thoroughgoing treatment of supernatural beliefs, shamanism, initiations, religious expression, etc. in primitive societies. Arunta, Ashanti, Aztec, Bushman, Crow, Fijian, many other tribes examined. "Excellent," NATURE. New preface by the author. Bibliographic notes. x + 322pp. 5⅜ x 8. T393 Paperbound **$1.85**

**SEX IN PSYCHO-ANALYSIS, S. Ferenczi.** (Formerly, "Contributions to Psycho-analysis.") 14 selected papers on impotence, transference, analysis and children, dreams, obscene words, homosexuality, paranoia, etc. by an associate of Freud. Also included: THE DEVELOPMENT OF PSYCHO-ANALYSIS, by Ferenczi and Otto Rank. Two books bound as one. Total of 406pp. 5⅜ x 8. T324 Paperbound **$1.85**

**THE PRINCIPLES OF PSYCHOLOGY, William James.** The complete text of the famous "long course," one of the great books of Western thought. An almost incredible amount of information about psychological processes, the stream of consciousness, habit, time perception, memory, emotions, reason, consciousness of self, abnormal phenomena, and similar topics. Based on James's own discoveries integrated with the work of Descartes, Locke, Hume, Royce, Wundt, Berkeley, Lotse, Herbart, scores of others. "A classic of interpretation," PSYCHIATRIC QUARTERLY. 94 illus. 1408pp. 2 volumes. 5⅜ x 8.
T381 Vol. 1, Paperbound **$2.50**
T382 Vol. 2, Paperbound **$2.50**

**THE POLISH PEASANT IN EUROPE AND AMERICA, W. I. Thomas, F. Znaniecki.** Monumental sociological study of peasant primary groups (family and community) and the disruptions produced by a new industrial system and emigration to America, by two of the foremost sociologists of recent times. One of the most important works in sociological thought. Includes hundreds of pages of primary documentation; point by point analysis of causes of social decay, breakdown of morality, crime, drunkenness, prostitution, etc. 2nd revised edition. 2 volumes. Total of 2250pp. 6 x 9. T478 2 volume set, Clothbound **$12.50**

**FOLKWAYS, W. G. Sumner.** The great Yale sociologist's detailed exposition of thousands of social, sexual, and religious customs in hundreds of cultures from ancient Greece to Modern Western societies. Preface by A. G. Keller. Introduction by William Lyon Phelps. 705pp. 5⅜ x 8. S508 Paperbound **$2.49**

**BEYOND PSYCHOLOGY, Otto Rank.** The author, an early associate of Freud, uses psychoanalytic techniques of myth-analysis to explore ultimates of human existence. Treats love, immortality, the soul, sexual identity, kingship, sources of state power, many other topics which illuminate the irrational basis of human existence. 291pp. 5⅜ x 8. T485 Paperbound **$1.75**

**ILLUSIONS AND DELUSIONS OF THE SUPERNATURAL AND THE OCCULT, D. H. Rawcliffe.** A rational, scientific examination of crystal gazing, automatic writing, table turning, stigmata, the Indian rope trick, dowsing, telepathy, clairvoyance, ghosts, ESP, PK, thousands of other supposedly occult phenomena. Originally titled "The Psychology of the Occult." 14 illustrations. 551pp. 5⅜ x 8. T503 Paperbound **$2.00**

**YOGA: A SCIENTIFIC EVALUATION, Kovoor T. Behanan.** A scientific study of the physiological and psychological effects of Yoga discipline, written under the auspices of the Yale University Institute of Human Relations. Foreword by W. A. Miles, Yale Univ. 17 photographs. 290pp. 5⅜ x 8. T505 Paperbound **$1.65**

**HOAXES, C. D. MacDougall.** Delightful, entertaining, yet scholarly exposition of how hoaxes start, why they succeed, documented with stories of hundreds of the most famous hoaxes. "A stupendous collection . . . and shrewd analysis, "NEW YORKER. New, revised edition. 54 photographs. 320pp. 5⅜ x 8. T465 Paperbound **$1.75**

**CREATIVE POWER: THE EDUCATION OF YOUTH IN THE CREATIVE ARTS, Hughes Mearns.** Named by the National Education Association as one of the 20 foremost books on education in recent times. Tells how to help children express themselves in drama, poetry, music, art, develop latent creative power. Should be read by every parent, teacher. New, enlarged, revised edition. Introduction. 272pp. 5⅜ x 8. T490 Paperbound **$1.50**

## LANGUAGES

**NEW RUSSIAN-ENGLISH, ENGLISH-RUSSIAN DICTIONARY, M. A. O'Brien.** Over 70,000 entries in new orthography! Idiomatic usages, colloquialisms. One of the few dictionaries that indicate accent changes in conjugation and declension. "One of the best," Prof. E. J. Simmons, Cornell. First names, geographical terms, bibliography, many other features. 738pp. 4½ x 6¼. T208 Paperbound **$2.00**

**MONEY CONVERTER AND TIPPING GUIDE FOR EUROPEAN TRAVEL, C. Vomacka.** Invaluable, handy source of currency regulations, conversion tables, tipping rules, postal rates, much other travel information for every European country plus Israel, Egypt and Turkey. 128pp. 3½ x 5¼. T260 Paperbound **60¢**

**MONEY CONVERTER AND TIPPING GUIDE FOR TRAVEL IN THE AMERICAS** (including the United States and Canada), **C. Vomacka.** The information you need for informed and confident travel in the Americas: money conversion tables, tipping guide, postal, telephone rates, etc. 128pp. 3½ x 5¼. T261 Paperbound **65¢**

**DUTCH-ENGLISH, ENGLISH-DUTCH DICTIONARY, F. G. Renier.** The most convenient, practical Dutch-English dictionary on the market. New orthography. More than 60,000 entries: idioms, compounds, technical terms, etc. Gender of nouns indicated. xviii + 571pp. 5½ x 6¼. T224 Clothbound **$2.50**

**LEARN DUTCH!, F. G. Renier.** The most satisfactory and easily-used grammar of modern Dutch. Used and recommended by the Fulbright Committee in the Netherlands. Over 1200 simple exercises lead to mastery of spoken and written Dutch. Dutch-English, English-Dutch vocabularies. 181pp. 4¼ x 7¼. T441 Clothbound **$1.75**

**PHRASE AND SENTENCE DICTIONARY OF SPOKEN RUSSIAN,** English-Russian, Russian-English. Based on phrases and complete sentences, rather than isolated words; recognized as one of the best methods of learning the idiomatic speech of a country. Over 11,500 entries, indexed by single words, with more than 32,000 English and Russian sentences and phrases, in immediately usable form. Probably the largest list ever published. Shows accent changes in conjugation and declension; irregular forms listed in both alphabetical place and under main form of word. 15,000 word introduction covering Russian sounds, writing, grammar, syntax. 15-page appendix of geographical names, money, important signs, given names, foods, special Soviet terms, etc. Travellers, businessmen, students, government employees have found this their best source for Russian expressions. Originally published as U.S. Government Technical Manual TM 30-944. iv + 573pp. 5⅝ x 8⅜. T496 Paperbound **$2.75**

**PHRASE AND SENTENCE DICTIONARY OF SPOKEN SPANISH,** Spanish-English, English-Spanish. Compiled from spoken Spanish, emphasizing idiom and colloquial usage in both Castilian and Latin-American. More than 16,000 entries containing over 25,000 idioms—the largest list of idiomatic constructions ever published. Complete sentences given, indexed under single words —language in immediately usable form, for travellers, businessmen, students, etc. 25-page introduction provides rapid survey of sounds, grammar, syntax, with full consideration of irregular verbs. Especially apt in modern treatment of phrases and structure. 17-page glossary gives translations of geographical names, money values, numbers, national holidays, important street signs, useful expressions of high frequency, plus unique 7-page glossary of Spanish and Spanish-American foods and dishes. Originally published as U.S. Government Technical Manual TM 30-900. iv + 513pp. 5⅝ x 8⅜. T495 Paperbound **$1.75**

# SAY IT language phrase books

"SAY IT" in the foreign language of your choice! We have sold over ½ million copies of these popular, useful language books. They will not make you an expert linguist overnight, but they do cover most practical matters of everyday life abroad.

**Over 1000 useful phrases,** expressions, with additional variants, substitutions.

**Modern! Useful!** Hundreds of phrases not available in other texts: "Nylon," "air-conditioned," etc.

The ONLY inexpensive phrase book **completely indexed.** Everything is available at a flip of your finger, ready for use.

Prepared by native linguists, travel experts.

Based on years of travel experience abroad.

This handy phrase book may be used by itself, or it may supplement any other text or course; it provides a living element. Used by many colleges and institutions: Hunter College; Barnard College; Army Ordnance School, Aberdeen; and many others.

Available, 1 book per language:

**Danish** (T818) 75¢
**Dutch** T(817) 75¢
**English** (for German-speaking people) (T801) 60¢
**English** (for Italian-speaking people) (T816) 60¢
**English** (for Spanish-speaking people) (T802) 60¢
**Esperanto** (T820) 75¢
**French** (T803) 60¢
**German** (T804) 60¢
**Modern Greek** (T813) 75¢
**Hebrew** (T805) 60¢
**Italian** (T806) 60¢
**Japanese** (T807) 60¢
**Norwegian** (T814) 75¢
**Russian** (T810) 75¢
**Spanish** (T811) 60¢
**Turkish** (T821) 75¢
**Yiddish** (T815) 75¢
**Swedish** (T812) 75¢
**Polish** (T808) 75¢
**Portuguese** (T809) 75¢

# LISTEN & LEARN language record sets

**LISTEN & LEARN** is the only language record course designed especially to meet your travel needs, or help you learn essential foreign language quickly by yourself, or in conjunction with any school course, by means of the automatic association method. Each set contains three 33⅓ rpm long- playing records — 1½ hours of recorded speech by eminent native speakers who are professors at Columbia, N.Y.U., Queens College and other leading universities. The sets are priced far below other sets of similar quality, yet they contain many special features not found in other record sets:

* Over 800 selected phrases and sentences, a basic vocabulary of over 3200 words.
* Both English and foreign language recorded; with a pause for your repetition.
* Designed for persons with limited time; no time wasted on material you cannot use immediately.
* Living, modern expressions that answer modern needs: drugstore items, "air-conditioned," etc.
* 128-196 page manuals contain everything on the records, plus simple pronunciation guides.
* Manual is fully indexed; find the phrase you want instantly.
* High fidelity recording—equal to any records costing up to $6 each.

The phrases on these records cover 41 different categories useful to the traveller or student interested in learning the living, spoken language: greetings, introductions, making yourself understood, passing customs, planes, trains, boats, buses, taxis, nightclubs, restaurants, menu items, sports, concerts, cameras, automobile travel, repairs, drugstores, doctors, dentists, medicines, barber shops, beauty parlors, laundries, many, many more.

"Excellent . . . among the very best on the market," Prof. Mario Pei, Dept. of Romance Languages, Columbia University. "Inexpensive and well-done . . . an ideal present," CHICAGO SUNDAY TRIBUNE. "More genuinely helpful than anything of its kind which I have previously encountered," Sidney Clark, well-known author of "ALL THE BEST" travel books. Each set contains 3 33⅓ rpm pure vinyl records, 128- 196 page with full record text, and album. One language per set. LISTEN & LEARN record sets are now available in—

| | | | |
|---|---|---|---|
| **FRENCH** | the set $4.95 | **GERMAN** | the set $4.95 |
| **ITALIAN** | the set $4.95 | **SPANISH** | the set $4.95 |
| **RUSSIAN** | the set $5.95 | **JAPANESE** * | the set $5.95 |

* Available Sept. 1, 1959

UNCONDITIONAL GUARANTEE: Dover Publications stands behind every Listen and Learn record set. If you are dissatisfied with these sets for any reason whatever, return them within 10 days and your money will be refunded in full.

# ART HISTORY

**STICKS AND STONES, Lewis Mumford.** An examination of forces influencing American architecture: the medieval tradition in early New England, the classical influence in Jefferson's time, the Brown Decades, the imperial facade, the machine age, etc. "A truly remarkable book," SAT. REV. OF LITERATURE. 2nd revised edition. 21 illus. xvii + 228pp. 5⅜ x 8.
T202 Paperbound **$1.60**

**THE AUTOBIOGRAPHY OF AN IDEA, Louis Sullivan.** The architect whom Frank Lloyd Wright called "the master," records the development of the theories that revolutionized America's skyline. 34 full-page plates of Sullivan's finest work. New introduction by R. M. Line. xiv + 335pp. 5⅜ x 8. T281 Paperbound **$1.85**

**THE MATERIALS AND TECHNIQUES OF MEDIEVAL PAINTING, D. V. Thompson.** An invaluable study of carriers and grounds, binding media, pigments, metals used in painting, al fresco and al secco techniques, burnishing, etc. used by the medieval masters. Preface by Bernard Berenson. 239pp. 5⅜ x 8. T327 Paperbound **$1.85**

**PRINCIPLES OF ART HISTORY, H. Wölfflin.** This remarkably instructive work demonstrates the tremendous change in artistic conception from the 14th to the 18th centuries, by analyzing 164 works by Botticelli, Dürer, Hobbema, Holbein, Hals, Titian, Rembrandt, Vermeer, etc., and pointing out exactly what is meant by "baroque," "classic," "primitive," "picturesque," and other basic terms of art history and criticism. "A remarkable lesson in the art of seeing," SAT. REV. OF LITERATURE. Translated from the 7th German edition. 150 illus. 254pp. 6⅛ x 9¼. T276 Paperbound **$2.00**

**FOUNDATIONS OF MODERN ART, A. Ozenfant.** Stimulating discussion of human creativity from paleolithic cave painting to modern painting, architecture, decorative arts. Fully illustrated with works of Gris, Lipchitz, Léger, Picasso, primitive, modern artifacts, architecture, industrial art, much more. 226 illustrations. 368pp. 6⅛ x 9¼. T215 Paperbound **$1.95**

# HANDICRAFTS, APPLIED ART, ART SOURCES, ETC.

**WILD FOWL DECOYS, J. Barber.** The standard work on this fascinating branch of folk art, ranging from Indian mud and grass devices to realistic wooden decoys. Discusses styles, types, periods; gives full information on how to make decoys. 140 illustrations (including 14 new plates) show decoys and provide full sets of plans for handicrafters, artists, hunters, and students of folk art. 281pp. 7⅞ x 10¾. Deluxe edition. T11 Clothbound **$8.50**

**METALWORK AND ENAMELLING, H. Maryon.** Probably the best book ever written on the subject. Tells everything necessary for the home manufacture of jewelry, rings, ear pendants, bowls, etc. Covers materials, tools, soldering, filigree, setting stones, raising patterns, repoussé work, damascening, niello, cloisonné, polishing, assaying, casting, and dozens of other techniques. The best substitute for apprenticeship to a master metalworker. 363 photos and figures. 374pp. 5½ x 8½. T183 Clothbound **$7.50**

**SHAKER FURNITURE, E. D. and F. Andrews.** The most illuminating study of Shaker furniture ever written. Covers chronology, craftsmanship, houses, shops, etc. Includes over 200 photographs of chairs, tables, clocks, beds, benches, etc. "Mr. & Mrs. Andrews know all there is to know about Shaker furniture," Mark Van Doren, NATION. 48 full-page plates. 192pp. Deluxe cloth binding. 7⅞ x 10¾. T7 Clothbound **$6.00**

**PRIMITIVE ART, Franz Boas.** A great American anthropologist covers theory, technical virtuosity, styles, symbolism, patterns, etc. of primitive art. The more than 900 illustrations will interest artists, designers, craftworkers. Over 900 illustrations. 376pp. 5⅜ x 8.
T25 Paperbound **$1.95**

**ON THE LAWS OF JAPANESE PAINTING, H. Bowie.** The best possible substitute for lessons from an oriental master. Treats both spirit and technique; exercises for control of the brush; inks, brushes, colors; use of dots, lines to express whole moods, etc. 220 illus. 132pp. 6⅛ x 9¼. T30 Paperbound **$1.95**

**HANDBOOK OF ORNAMENT, F. S. Meyer.** One of the largest collections of copyright-free traditional art: over 3300 line cuts of Greek, Roman, Medieval, Renaissance, Baroque, 18th and 19th century art motifs (tracery, geometric elements, flower and animal motifs, etc.) and decorated objects (chairs, thrones, weapons, vases, jewelry, armor, etc.). Full text. 3300 illustrations. 562pp. 5⅜ x 8. T302 Paperbound **$2.00**

**THREE CLASSICS OF ITALIAN CALLIGRAPHY. Oscar Ogg,** ed. Exact reproductions of three famous Renaissance calligraphic works: Arrighi's OPERINA and IL MODO, Tagliente's LO PRESENTE LIBRO, and Palatino's LIBRO NUOVO. More than 200 complete alphabets, thousands of lettered specimens, in Papal Chancery and other beautiful, ornate handwriting. Introduction. 245 plates. 282pp. 6⅛ x 9¼. T212 Paperbound **$1.95**

**THE HISTORY AND TECHNIQUES OF LETTERING, A. Nesbitt.** A thorough history of lettering from the ancient Egyptians to the present, and a 65-page course in lettering for artists. Every major development in lettering history is illustrated by a complete alphabet. Fully analyzes such masters as Caslon, Koch, Garamont, Jenson, and many more. 89 alphabets, 165 other specimens. 317pp. 5⅜ x 8. T427 Paperbound **$2.00**

**LETTERING AND ALPHABETS, J. A. Cavanagh.** An unabridged reissue of "Lettering," containing the full discussion, analysis, illustration of 89 basic hand lettering tyles based on Caslon, Bodoni, Gothic, many other types. Hundreds of technical hints on construction, strokes, pens, brushes, etc. 89 alphabets, 72 lettered specimens, which may be reproduced permission-free. 121pp. 9¾ x 8. T53 Paperbound **$1.25**

**THE HUMAN FIGURE IN MOTION, Eadweard Muybridge.** The largest collection in print of Muybridge's famous high-speed action photos. 4789 photographs in more than 500 action-strip-sequences (at shutter speeds up to 1/6000th of a second) illustrate men, women, children—mostly undraped—performing such actions as walking, running, getting up, lying down, carrying objects, throwing, etc. "An unparalleled dictionary of action for all artists," AMERICAN ARTIST. 390 full-page plates, with 4789 photographs. Heavy glossy stock, reinforced binding with headbands. 7⅞ x 10¾. T204 Clothbound **$10.00**

**ANIMALS IN MOTION, Eadweard Muybridge.** The largest collection of animal action photos in print. 34 different animals (horses, mules, oxen, goats, camels, pigs, cats, lions, gnus, deer, monkeys, eagles—and 22 others) in 132 characteristic actions. All 3919 photographs are taken in series at speeds up to 1/1600th of a second, offering artists, biologists, cartoonists a remarkable opportunity to see exactly how an ostrich's head bobs when running, how a lion puts his foot down, how an elephant's knee bends, how a bird flaps his wings, thousands of other hard-to-catch details. "A really marvelous series of plates," NATURE. 380 full-pages of plates. Heavy glossy stock, reinforced binding with headbands. 7⅞ x 10¾. T203 Clothbound **$10.00**

**THE BOOK OF SIGNS, R. Koch.** 493 symbols—crosses, monograms, astrological, biological symbols, runes, etc.—from ancient manuscripts, cathedrals, coins, catacombs, pottery. May be reproduced permission-free. 493 illustrations by Fritz Kredel. 104pp. 6⅛ x 9¼. T162 Paperbound **$1.00**

**A HANDBOOK OF EARLY ADVERTISING ART, C. P. Hornung.** The largest collection of copyright-free early advertising art ever compiled. Vol. I: 2,000 illustrations of animals, old automobiles, buildings, allegorical figures, fire engines, Indians, ships, trains, more than 33 other categories! Vol II: Over 4,000 typographical specimens; 600 Roman, Gothic, Barnum, Old English faces; 630 ornamental type faces; hundreds of scrolls, initials, flourishes, etc. "A remarkable collection," PRINTERS' INK.

Vol. I: Pictorial Volume. Over 2000 illustrations. 256pp. 9 x 12. T122 Clothbound **$10.00**

Vol. II: Typographical Volume. Over 4000 speciments. 319pp. 9 x 12. T123 Clothbound **$10.00**
Two volume set, Clothbound, only **$18.50**

**DESIGN FOR ARTISTS AND CRAFTSMEN, L. Wolchonok.** The most thorough course on the creation of art motifs and designs. Shows you step-by-step, with hundreds of examples and 113 detailed exercises, how to create original designs from geometric patterns, plants, birds, animals, humans, and man-made objects. "A great contribution to the field of design and crafts," N. Y. SOCIETY OF CRAFTSMEN. More than 1300 entirely new illustrations. xv + 207pp. 7⅞ x 10¾. T274 Clothbound **$4.95**

**HANDBOOK OF DESIGNS AND DEVICES, C. P. Hornung.** A remarkable working collection of 1836 basic designs and variations, all copyright-free. Variations of circle, line, cross, diamond, swastika, star, scroll, shield, many more. Notes on symbolism. "A necessity to every designer who would be original without having to labor heavily," ARTIST and ADVERTISER. 204 plates. 240pp. 5⅜ x 8. T125 Paperbound **$1.90**

**THE UNIVERSAL PENMAN, George Bickham.** Exact reproduction of beautiful 18th century book of handwriting. 22 complete alphabets in finest English roundhand, other scripts, over 2000 elaborate flourishes, 122 calligraphic illustrations, etc. Material is copyright-free. "An essential part of any art library, and a book of permanent value," AMERICAN ARTIST. 212 plates. 224pp. 9 x 13¾. T20 Clothbound **$10.00**

**AN ATLAS OF ANATOMY FOR ARTISTS, F. Schider.** This standard work contains 189 full-page plates, more than 647 illustrations of all aspects of the human skeleton, musculature, cutaway portions of the body, each part of the anatomy, hand forms, eyelids, breasts, location of muscles under the flesh, etc. 59 plates illustrate how Michelangelo, da Vinci, Goya, 15 others, drew human anatomy. New 3rd edition enlarged by 52 new illustrations by Cloquet, Barcsay. "The standard reference tool," AMERICAN LIBRARY ASSOCIATION. "Excellent," AMERICAN ARTIST. 189 plates, 647 illustrations. xxvi + 192pp. 7⅞ x 10⅝. T241 Clothbound **$6.00**

**AN ATLAS OF ANIMAL ANATOMY FOR ARTISTS, W. Ellenberger, H. Baum, H. Dittrich.** The largest, richest animal anatomy for artists in English. Form, musculature, tendons, bone structure, expression, detailed cross sections of head, other features, of the horse, lion, dog, cat, deer, seal, kangaroo, cow, bull, goat, monkey, hare, many other animals. "Highly recommended," DESIGN. Second, revised, enlarged edition with new plates from Cuvier, Stubbs, etc. 288 illustrations. 153pp. 11⅜ x 9. T82 Clothbound **$6.00**

**ANIMAL DRAWING: ANATOMY AND ACTION FOR ARTISTS, C. R. Knight.** 158 studies, with full accompanying text, of such animals as the gorilla, bear, bison, dromedary, camel, vulture, pelican, iguana, shark, etc., by one of the greatest modern masters of animal drawing. Innumerable tips on how to get life expression into your work. "An excellent reference work,' SAN FRANCISCO CHRONICLE. 158 illustrations. 156pp. 10½ x 8½. T426 Paperbound **$2.00**

**THE CRAFTSMAN'S HANDBOOK, Cennino Cennini.** The finest English translation of IL LIBRO DELL' ARTE, the 15th century introduction to art technique that is both a mirror of Quattrocento life and a source of many useful but nearly forgotten facets of the painter's art. 4 illustrations. xxvii + 142pp. D. V. Thompson, translator. 6⅛ x 9¼. T54 Paperbound **$1.50**

**THE BROWN DECADES, Lewis Mumford.** A picture of the "buried renaissance" of the post-Civil War period, and the founding of modern architecture (Sullivan, Richardson, Root, Roebling), landscape development (Marsh, Olmstead, Eliot), and the graphic arts (Homer, Eakins, Ryder). 2nd revised, enlarged edition. Bibliography. 12 illustrations. xiv + 266 pp. 5⅜ x 8. T200 Paperbound **$1.65**

**STIEGEL GLASS, F. W. Hunter.** The story of the most highly esteemed early American glassware, fully illustrated. How a German adventurer, "Baron" Stiegel, founded a glass empire; detailed accounts of individual glasswork. "This pioneer work is reprinted in an edition even more beautiful than the original," ANTIQUES DEALER. New introduction by Helen McKearin. 171 illustrations, 12 in full color. xxii + 338pp. 7⅞ x 10¾. T128 Clothbound **$10.00**

**THE HUMAN FIGURE, J. H. Vanderpoel.** Not just a picture book, but a complete course by a famous figure artist. Extensive text, illustrated by 430 pencil and charcoal drawings of both male and female anatomy. 2nd enlarged edition. Foreword. 430 illus. 143pp. 6⅛ x 9¼. T432 Paperbound **$1.45**

**PINE FURNITURE OF EARLY NEW ENGLAND, R. H. Kettell.** Over 400 illustrations, over 50 working drawings of early New England chairs, benches, beds cupboards, mirrors, shelves, tables, other furniture esteemed for simple beauty and character. "Rich store of illustrations . . . emphasizes the individuality and varied design," ANTIQUES. 413 illustrations, 55 working drawings. 475pp. 8 x 10¾. T145 Clothbound **$10.00**

**BASIC BOOKBINDING, A. W. Lewis.** Enables both beginners and experts to rebind old books or bind paperbacks in hard covers. Treats materials, tools; gives step-by-step instruction in how to collate a book, sew it, back it, make boards, etc. 261 illus. Appendices. 155pp. 5⅜ x 8. T169 Paperbound **$1.35**

**DESIGN MOTIFS OF ANCIENT MEXICO, J. Enciso.** Nearly 90% of these 766 superb designs from Aztec, Olmec, Totonac, Maya, and Toltec origins are unobtainable elsewhere! Contains plumed serpents, wind gods, animals, demons, dancers, monsters, etc. Excellent applied design source. Originally $17.50. 766 illustrations, thousands of motifs. 192pp. 6⅛ x 9¼. T84 Paperbound **$1.85**

**AFRICAN SCULPTURE, Ladislas Segy.** 163 full-page plates illustrating masks, fertility figures, ceremonial objects, etc., of 50 West and Central African tribes—95% never before illustrated. 34-page introduction to African sculpture. "Mr. Segy is one of its top authorities," NEW YORKER. 164 full-page photographic plates. Introduction. Bibliography. 244pp. 6⅛ x 9¼. T396 Paperbound **$2.00**

**THE PROCESSES OF GRAPHIC REPRODUCTION IN PRINTING, H. Curwen.** A thorough and practical survey of wood, linoleum, and rubber engraving; copper engraving; drypoint, mezzotint, etching, aquatint, steel engraving, die sinking, stencilling, lithography (extensively); photographic reproduction utilizing line, continuous tone, photoengravure, collotype; every other process in general use. Note on color reproduction. Section on bookbinding. Over 200 illustrations, 25 in color. 143pp. 5½ x 8½. T512 Clothbound **$4.00**

**CALLIGRAPHY, J. G. Schwandner.** First reprinting in 200 years of this legendary book of beautiful handwriting. Over 300 ornamental initials, 12 complete calligraphic alphabets, over 150 ornate frames and panels, 75 calligraphic pictures of cherubs, stags, lions, etc., thousands of flourishes, scrolls, etc., by the greatest 18th century masters. All material can be copied or adapted without permission. Historical introduction. 158 full-page plates. 368pp. 9 x 13. T475 Clothbound **$10.00**

* * *

**A DIDEROT PICTORIAL ENCYCLOPEDIA OF TRADES AND INDUSTRY,** Manufacturing and the Technical Arts in Plates Selected from "L'Encyclopédie ou Dictionnaire Raisonné des Sciences, des Arts, et des Métiers," of Denis Diderot, edited with text by C. Gillispie. Over 2000 illustrations on 485 full-page plates. Magnificent 18th century engravings of men, women, and children working at such trades as milling flour, cheesemaking, charcoal burning, mining, silverplating, shoeing horses, making fine glass, printing, hundreds more, showing details of machinery, different steps in sequence, etc. A remarkable art work, but also the largest collection of working figures in print, copyright-free, for art directors, designers, etc. Two vols. 920pp. 9 x 12. Heavy library cloth. T421 Two volume set **$18.50**

* * *

**SILK SCREEN TECHNIQUES, J. Biegeleisen, M. Cohn.** A practical step-by-step home course in one of the most versatile, least expensive graphic arts processes. How to build an inexpensive silk screen, prepare stencils, print, achieve special textures, use color, etc. Every step explained, diagrammed. 149 illustrations, 8 in color. 201pp. 6⅛ x 9¼. T433 Paperbound **$1.45**

# *CATALOG OF*

# PUZZLES, GAMES, AND ENTERTAINMENTS

**MATHEMATICS, MAGIC AND MYSTERY, Martin Gardner.** Astonishing feats of mind reading, mystifying "magic" tricks, are often based on mathematical principles anyone can learn. This book shows you how to perform scores of tricks with cards, dice, coins, knots, numbers, etc., by using simple principles from set theory, theory of numbers, topology, other areas of mathematics, fascinating in themselves. No special knowledge required. 135 illus. 186pp. 5⅜ x 8.
T335 Paperbound **$1.00**

**MATHEMATICAL PUZZLES FOR BEGINNERS AND ENTHUSIASTS, G. Mott-Smoth.** Test your problem-solving techniques and powers of inference on 188 challenging, amusing puzzles based on algebra, dissection of plane figures, permutations, probabilities, etc. Appendix of primes, square roots, etc. 135 illus. 2nd revised edition. 248pp. 5⅜ x 8.
T198 Paperbound **$1.00**

**LEARN CHESS FROM THE MASTERS, F. Reinfeld.** Play 10 games against Marshall, Bronstein, Najdorf, other masters, and grade yourself on each move. Detailed annotations reveal principles of play, strategy, etc. as you proceed. An excellent way to get a real insight into the game. Formerly titled, "Chess by Yourself." 91 diagrams. vii + 144pp. 5⅜ x 8.
T362 Paperbound **$1.00**

**REINFELD ON THE END GAME IN CHESS, F. Reinfeld.** 62 end games of Alekhine, Tarrasch, Morphy, other masters, are carefully analyzed with emphasis on transition from middle game to end play. Tempo moves, queen endings, weak squares, other basic principles clearly illustrated. Excellent for understanding why some moves are weak or incorrect, how to avoid errors. Formerly titled, "Practical End-game Play." 62 diagrams. vi + 177pp. 5⅜ x 8.
T417 Paperbound **$1.25**

**101 PUZZLES IN THOUGHT AND LOGIC, C. R. Wylie, Jr.** Brand new puzzles you need no special knowledge to solve! Each one is a gem of ingenuity that will really challenge your problem-solving technique. Introduction with simplified explanation of scientic puzzle solving. 128pp. 5⅜ x 8.
T167 Paperbound **$1.00**

**THE COMPLETE NONSENSE OF EDWARD LEAR.** The only complete edition of this master of gentle madness at a popular price. The Dong with the Luminous Nose, The Jumblies, The Owl and the Pussycat, hundreds of other bits of wonderful nonsense. 214 limericks, 3 sets of Nonsense Botany, 5 Nonsense Alphabets, 546 fantastic drawings, much more. 320pp. 5⅜ x 8.
T167 Paperbound **$1.00**

**28 SCIENCE FICTION STORIES OF H. G. WELLS.** Two complete novels, "Men Like Gods" and "Star Begotten," plus 26 short stories by the master science-fiction writer of all time. Stories of space, time, future adventure that are among the all-time classics of science fiction. 928pp. 5⅜ x 8.
T265 Clothbound **$3.95**

**SEVEN SCIENCE FICTION NOVELS, H. G. Wells.** Unabridged texts of "The Time Machine," "The Island of Dr. Moreau," "First Men in the Moon," "The Invisible Man," "The War of the Worlds," "The Food of the Gods," "In the Days of the Comet." "One will have to go far to match this for entertainment, excitement, and sheer pleasure," N. Y. TIMES. 1015pp. 5⅜ x 8.
T264 Clothbound **$3.95**

**MATHEMAGIC, MAGIC PUZZLES, AND GAMES WITH NUMBERS, R. V. Heath.** More than 60 new puzzles and stunts based on number properties: multiplying large numbers mentally, finding the date of any day in the year, etc. Edited by J. S. Meyer. 76 illus. 129pp. 5⅜ x 8.
T110 Paperbound **$1.00**

**FIVE ADVENTURE NOVELS OF H. RIDER HAGGARD.** The master story-teller's five best tales of mystery and adventure set against authentic African backgrounds: "She," "King Solomon's Mines," "Allan Quatermain," "Allan's Wife," "Maiwa's Revenge." 821pp. 5⅜ x 8.
T108 Clothbound **$3.95**

**WIN AT CHECKERS, M. Hopper.** (Formerly "Checkers.") The former World's Unrestricted Checker Champion gives you valuable lessons in openings, traps, end games, ways to draw when you are behind, etc. More than 100 questions and answers anticipate your problems. Appendix. 75 problems diagrammed, solved. 79 figures. xi + 107pp. 5⅜ x 8.
T363 Paperbound **$1.00**

**CRYPTOGRAPHY, L. D. Smith.** Excellent introductory work on ciphers and their solution, history of secret writing, techniques, etc. Appendices on Japanese methods, the Baconian cipher, frequency tables. Bibliography. Over 150 problems, solutions. 160pp. 5⅜ x 8.
T247 Paperbound **$1.00**

**CRYPTANALYSIS, H. F. Gaines.** (Formerly, "Elementary Cryptanalysis.") The best book available on cryptograms and how to solve them. Contains all major techniques: substitution, transposition, mixed alphabets, multafid, Kasiski and Vignere methods, etc. Word frequency appendix. 167 problems, solutions. 173 figures. 236pp. 5⅜ x 8.
T97 Paperbound **$1.95**

**FLATLAND, E. A. Abbot.** The science-fiction classic of life in a 2-dimensional world that is considered a first-rate introduction to relativity and hyperspace, as well as a scathing satire on society, politics and religion. 7th edition. 16 illus. 128pp. 5⅜ x 8.
T1 Paperbound **$1.00**